TH REAL ALE PUB GUIDE

2000

GRAHAM TITCOMBE
& NICOLAS ANDREWS

foulsham
LONDON • NEW YORK • TORONTO • SYDNEY

foulsham

The Publishing House, Bennetts Close,
Cippenham, Berkshire, SL1 5AP, England.

While every effort has been made to ensure the accuracy of all the information contained within this book, neither the authors nor the publisher can be liable for any errors. The publisher would welcome letters of correction and further information.

ISBN 0-572-02555-6

Printed in Great Britain by St. Edmundsbury Press, Bury St. Edmunds, Suffolk.

CONTENTS

CONTENTS

Cans, kegs and widgets, sparklers, gases – even a slice of lime. The multi-national conglomerates that still dictate much of the British beer-drinking market will stop at nothing in their determined drive to make their latest product appear new, exciting and the ultimate accessory for the sophisticated drinker. Presentation and image are all: huge sums are spent on advertising and packaging; film stars and stand-up comedians are employed to try and make you, the consumer, believe that whatever they finally force down your neck really is the last word in state-of-the-art British brewing. It ain't what you drink, it's who sees you drinking it.

As the trends move relentlessly on, from Third-World imports to ice beers to can-conditioned creamy confections that in one case, apparently, doubles up as moisturiser, the shallowness of all this image control becomes increasingly clear. Alcoholic lemonade is all very well, but will they be encouraging you to drink it in 12 months time? And if not, why not?

Fortunately, at the same time, there is an ever-increasing band of independent micro-brewers and discerning drinkers who have discovered that the best way to move forward is in fact to take a step back. Modern methods and the latest in brewing expertise can be successfully allied to a product that has served us well for centuries. The problems associated with producing *real* real ale, which the big drinks companies were so keen to exaggerate 30 years ago, can be and have been overcome. The best beers in Britain are now brewed, transported and then served to perfection. They need no advance advertising or heavy promotion for these are products that speak for themselves.

The exclusive world of truly traditional brewing is closer to that of the makers of fine wines than of fine television commercials. Once tasted, these beers will hook you forever and draw you in. All other ales will be exposed as the pale and unsophisticated imitations that they really are.

The Real Ale Pub Guide is a celebration of these brews and of the brewers for whom quality, not quantity, is all that matters. Other guides do an admirable job in listing those pubs with handpumps or by telling you about the impressive architecture, decor and food to be found at inns around the country. In this book, it is quite simply the beer that counts – and not just any old beer at that. Use this guide and lose yourself in an exhilarating world of exceptional craftsmen and exquisite tastes. Timeless techniques and sufficient attention to detail ensure that never again need you be disappointed by the product in your glass.

We tell you where to go to find beers of the finest character and complexity, served by enthusiasts who really care about what you are drinking. We explain why the way it is stored and served is as important as the contents of the barrel itself. And we invite you to help us to put the very best beers in Britain, and the brewers and barmen responsible for them, on the map so that, having travelled to the pubs we list, hopefully, that first sip from the first pint will tell you that you have truly arrived.

THE HISTORY OF BEER

Possibly discovered as a result of airborne wild yeast infecting open food, the art of brewing originated in Mesopotamia, between 8000 and 6000 BC. Slowly, the secret spread to Greece, Egypt and eventually to Rome. It was Caesar's invading army that brought beer to Britain in 55 AD.

Roman aristocracy still preferred to drink wine but, over the centuries, beer became an important source of nutrition for the native Britons and was often safer to drink than water. Beer continued to thrive long after the Romans had gone, and more than 40 breweries were listed in the Domesday Book of 1086.

Hops, which impart flavour and aroma, and act as a preservative, were initially introduced from Scandinavia in the middle of the tenth century, but they were not widely used until the fifteenth century, when growing became widespread in Kent.

Brewing took place in monasteries and the monks improved brewing techniques and introduced better varieties of barley. But, during Henry VIII's break with Rome in the 1530s, the monasteries were abolished and their land and assets seized by the Crown. The noble art passed into the hands of farmers and owners of landed estates, who installed private brewhouses which provided beer for farm workers and staff. These were the forerunners of the breweries we have today.

Commercial breweries began to set up in business during the latter part of the sixteenth century, growing steadily in number until around 30,000 breweries were registered in Great Britain in the 1870s, when beer drinking per head of the population was at its peak. Breweries were then found serving local communities throughout the British Isles. Even small towns could support such establishments. The Beer Act of 1830 permitted any householder to obtain a licence from the excise authorities allowing them to brew and sell beer on the premises. But, gradually, home-brewing went into decline. New taxes were levied on malt and hops which accelerated this demise until, by the end of the nineteenth century, the market was dominated by commercial brewers.

Many of these, too, have now gone, either bought up and closed down by large national breweries or, unable to survive in an increasingly competitive market, have simply faded away. A considerable number of excellent breweries have been lost with them and only 55 of the independent breweries that were in operation at the turn of the century still brew today.

Of these, Shepherd Neame Ltd at Faversham in Kent is believed to be the oldest. Beer has been produced on the same site without interruption since the brewery's official foundation in 1698. Britain's oldest surviving brewpub is believed to be the Blue Anchor at Helston in Cornwall. It first became a pub around the middle of the sixteenth century, although it seems certain that monks were already brewing beer on the premises long before then.

The title of the oldest pub in Britain probably belongs to the Trip to Jerusalem in Nottingham, part of which is cut into the rock of the castle and dates from 1189. This was once the malthouse for the castle brewery.

Although brewing technology may have progressed over the centuries, the process and basic ingredients have changed very little. Today, real ales still arrive at the pub with live yeast and fermentable sugars present in the brew, allowing the final stages of fermentation to take place in the cellar. This produces a fresh, pert, rounded flavour and natural effervescence. This is beer at its very best, and part of the proud tradition which spans the centuries.

Happily, new breweries are again setting up across the land and total around 400, a considerable improvement on the situation of just 20 years ago. The real ale cause is a rare triumph for quality and tradition in an age of all-consuming commercialism.

WHAT WENT WRONG?

Many pubs originally brewed their own beer in an outbuilding or similar adjacent place, often drawing water from a spring or well beneath. Frequently it was the lady of the house who did the brewing while her husband worked elsewhere.

But cask-conditioned beers tended to be unreliable and were too often not properly looked after in the cellar. To overcome this problem, the larger brewers turned to bottles and keg beers which, though bland and characterless by comparison, were consistent and had a much longer shelf life. They were easy to transport and easy to look after. Huge investments were made in kegs, equipment and advertising and, by the middle of the 1960s, real ale had all but disappeared from the British pub. Watneys Red Barrel, Worthington E and Double Diamond became the order of the day.

Just four of the once ubiquitous brewpubs remained and, as recently as 1985, there were fewer than 150 independent breweries in operation. Lager, too, although a poor imitation of some of the excellent continental brews, became increasingly successful in Britain, due largely to massive advertising campaigns which targeted the trend-conscious younger drinker. The national breweries had imposed their corporate will to increase profits at the expense of quality. Real ale sales continued to decline to the verge of extinction.

Though consistent, keg beer is a disappointing substitute for the natural product. It starts life as real ale but, prior to filling into containers, the beer is filtered, pasteurised and chilled. This process destroys and removes the yeast, preventing any further fermentation, and ensures that the beer is clear and bright in the keg.

But the beer is now dead. It produces no natural carbon dioxide and lacks the depth of character that cask-conditioned beers offer. In an effort to overcome this problem, it is now frequently served using a mixture of nitrogen and carbon dioxide, which gives the beer a tighter, creamy head in the glass while reducing the overall fizziness associated with carbon dioxide. The result can be compared with drinking cappuccino, which often uses the cheapest coffee beans available but becomes acceptable when frothed.

Additionally, no work is required in the pub cellar to bring keg beer into condition. It can be dispensed upon receipt and will remain servable, under the layer of gas used to dispense it, for many weeks. Consequently, no skill is required of the cellarman and very few keg beers are unfit to be served, necessitating their return to the brewery.

Little wonder that the national brewers, and some publicans too, would prefer it if cask-conditioned beers quietly faded away.

THE REAL ALE REVIVAL

Over the past 20 years, due to the dedication of a number of small brewery owners and the campaigning efforts of CAMRA (Campaign for Real Ale), the country's excellent real ales have gradually been rediscovered and Britain's great heritage of independent breweries is now thriving once more.

A change in the law known as The Beer Orders has helped, too, permitting pubs previously tied to one brewery for all beer supplies to take one guest beer from elsewhere. This has increased considerably the potential market for the smaller independent suppliers.

While some would argue that the tied pub system works against the smaller breweries which are unable to supply beer at sufficiently competitive prices, if at all, there is a strongly held view among larger independents and regional brewers that complete abolition of the system could result in the closure of some breweries which would no longer be able to rely on the necessary guaranteed outlets for their brews.

Meanwhile, new micro-breweries are springing up all over the country. These operate on a much smaller scale, so costs and overheads are much smaller. The micro-brewers concentrate, at least initially, on supplying a limited range of pubs. Some brewpubs produce beer on the premises that is not available anywhere else.

Not to be outdone, most existing brewers are adding new beers to their portfolios too. Today, there are approximately 400 independent breweries in Britain providing well over 1000 beers of widely varying styles and character, plus a plethora of one-off special or occasional brews. Wheat, tandoori, garlic, vanilla, melon, coriander, lemon, orange, strawberry and liquorice are just a few of the flavours on offer, in addition to the whole raft of more traditional beers.

Fortunately, more and more enterprising publicans are now offering these delightful brews and the revived interest in cask-conditioned beers has produced a new breed of drinker, the 'Scooper' or 'Ticker', who will often travel many miles just to find a new beer.

The market should easily be able to support the current crop of independents, and those that produce good brews of consistent quality and possess sufficient marketing and distribution skills should continue to thrive. But the national brewers have not gone to sleep. Keg beer, dispensed using mixed gases in an effort to mimic the character of real ale, is gaining ground on the back of multi-million pound marketing campaigns. But why drink a substitute when the real thing is available from the independent breweries in so many pubs throughout Britain?

If you take the trouble to search those pubs out, you will undoubtedly enjoy the best beer that Britain has to offer and help to prevent a return to the dark days of the 1960s and 70s.

THE BREWING PROCESS

The brewing process is a delicate one and most brewers inevitably experience occasional problems. The very nature of ale makes it impossible to produce a consistently uniform product, barrel after barrel, month after month. Also, brewers will be constantly striving to improve and refine the quality of the beer they produce.

Of course, this is part of the attraction for the real ale drinker. There is nothing like the experience of discovering new tastes and drinking sensations, and it places a premium on the skills and experience of both the brewer and the publican. But this inconsistency is something that the makers of bland, uniform keg beers are also keen to emphasise.

The slightest variation in established practice or, more commonly, yeast infections, equipment failures, changes in water or ingredient sources can upset the brewing process and affect the resulting beer. Often, a combination of these elements causes problems. No matter how much care is taken, it is simply not feasible to expect every new brew to taste and behave just the same as it did the last time. But each one must be of a similar high standard and as consistent as possible.

Even renowned, award-winning beers are sometimes unacceptably inconsistent in quality and flavour. Increased demand during the summer months can lead to beer being sent out 'green' or too soon. Some may even be contract-brewed and lose subtle, but important, characteristics.

Barley, which the Mesopotamians were lucky enough to have growing wild, is still an important ingredient for beer making today. It is soaked in water, then spread over the floor of the malthouse and gently heated to promote germination. This releases sugars, which are vital for fermentation. The barley is constantly raked to ensure even germination throughout. Once the grains start to produce rootlets, they are roasted to prevent further germination. The higher the temperature, the darker the malt will be, and the beer produced from it will be darker, with a more roasted flavour. Pale malt will impart a sweeter, more delicate flavour to the brew.

MALT MILL
At the brewery, the malt is passed through rollers in the malt mill, which crushes the grains releasing the soluble starch.

MASH TUN
The malt is passed from the malt mill into the mash tun where it is mixed with hot water or 'liquor'. This is known as 'mashing' and converts the soluble starches into fermentable and non-fermentable sugars. Depending on the type of beer required a mix of malts may be used.

Water used in the brewing process is usually treated in order to remove any unwanted characteristics, and to emulate water found in other areas, which is considered most suitable to the style of beer required.

The 'mash' is thoroughly stirred, then allowed to stand until it becomes clear, when it is known as 'wort'.

THE COPPER
The wort is then run into the copper, where it is boiled and hops are added. At this stage, various 'adjuncts' may be added to the wort, such as invert sugar, to increase fermentability, but any additive is considered by many to be an insult to the brewer's art.

Depending on the variety used, hops impart bitterness of flavour or aroma and help to prevent infection in the wort. A mixture of hops may be used.

But they were not always popular with everyone. Henry VIII objected to this foreign habit of putting hops into beer and suggested that it should be outlawed. Fortunately, the noble hop survived.

Of the many varieties available, those most commonly used in Britain are still the

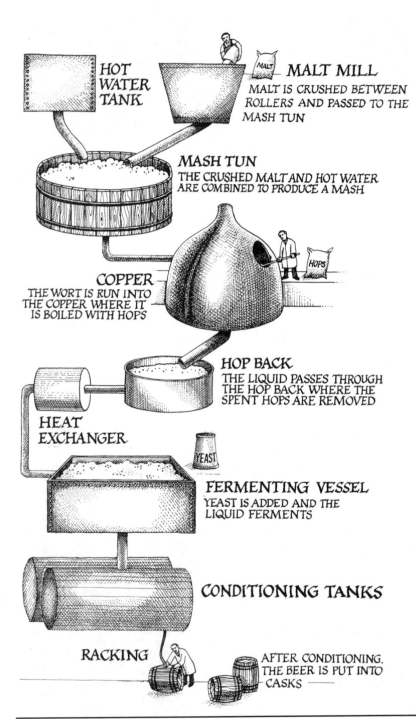

HOT WATER TANK

MALT MILL
MALT IS CRUSHED BETWEEN ROLLERS AND PASSED TO THE MASH TUN

MASH TUN
THE CRUSHED MALT AND HOT WATER ARE COMBINED TO PRODUCE A MASH

COPPER
THE WORT IS RUN INTO THE COPPER WHERE IT IS BOILED WITH HOPS

HOP BACK
THE LIQUID PASSES THROUGH THE HOP BACK WHERE THE SPENT HOPS ARE REMOVED

HEAT EXCHANGER

FERMENTING VESSEL
YEAST IS ADDED AND THE LIQUID FERMENTS

CONDITIONING TANKS

RACKING
AFTER CONDITIONING, THE BEER IS PUT INTO CASKS

Golding and the Fuggle, although other types are rapidly finding favour.

Unfortunately, some brewers substitute hop oils but it is widely felt that this has a detrimental effect on the flavour of the finished brew. Perhaps we should learn from some of our continental friends where this practice would contravene purity laws.

The wort will remain in the copper for one to two hours.

HOP BACK
From the copper the wort is then passed through the hop back where the spent hops are removed.

HEAT EXCHANGER
On its way to the fermenting vessel, the wort is passed through a heat exchanger, where its temperature is reduced to 20°C. This is important for producing ideal conditions for the yeast. Extremes of temperature will either kill the yeast or result in a sluggish fermentation.

FERMENTING VESSEL
The wort is now 'pitched' or has yeast added. It will remain here for around five days, the yeast feeding on the fermentable sugars, while excreting alcohol and producing carbon dioxide.

A thick creamy head of yeast builds up in the fermentation vessel, and this is skimmed and retained for further use. But, as the yeast in the brew becomes tired and much of the sugar has been converted to alcohol, the process slows down. The primary fermentation is now over, and it is at this point that beer produced for the keg will go its separate way.

CONDITIONING TANKS
At this stage, beer is said to be 'green' and the flavour is harsh. It is passed into conditioning tanks, where it will remain for several days, and much of the remaining sugar will ferment out to produce a more rounded flavour.

RACKING
At last, the beer is ready to be put into the cask, or 'racked'. By now, any harsh or undesirable flavours will have disappeared, but the brew will be crisp and fresh.

Finings, which draw the dying yeast cells to the bottom of the cask, are added allowing the beer to 'drop bright' or clear down.

Some fermentable sugars and living yeast cells remain, so the beer continues to ferment in the cask. Sometimes, priming sugar will be added to assist this secondary fermentation. Hops may also be added to impart a hoppy aroma to the brew.

Once in the pub cellar, the beer will continue to ferment, producing carbon dioxide, which gives real ale its natural vitality.

The finings will clear the beer down until it is bright, and the cask will then be tapped, in preparation for use. This final stage, which is known as cask-conditioning, typically takes two or three days and brings the beer naturally to perfection. It should now be served as soon as possible.

TRAVELLING BEER
Assuming that a beer is in the proper condition when it leaves the brewery, plenty of damage can still be done during distribution. Most beers will 'travel' providing that they are properly handled.

The brew within the cask is a living product that must be treated with respect if it is ultimately to be served at its best. Every time a cask is rolled, the finings, which draw all the solid matter to the bottom of the cask, are activated and these will work effectively for approximately five cask rollings.

Better quality finings are available which will allow far more cask rollings, but they are significantly more expensive and many, shortsighted, brewers still fail to understand the full implications of their cost cutting.

Therefore, a cask from a brewer in Scotland arriving at a pub in Cornwall may well have been moved between wholesalers and rolled a number of times. It may also have been in transit too long, having been left in various stores en route, and so be nearing the end of its life even before it arrives. The result will almost certainly be a lifeless, dull brew lacking in any subtlety of flavour.

Extremes of temperature can also prevent a brew from getting into condition properly and dropping clear and bright. Casks may be left in very hot or cold conditions, in warehouses, garages or on the back of vehicles where there is no temperature control equipment. This, too, may result in a brew being damaged before it arrives at the pub and, unfortunately, the publican will not know about this until it is too late.

Co-operation is the answer. Regional and larger independent brewers have, for some time, also offered beers from other breweries and an increasing number of the smaller independents are now offering their product wholesale in an effort to improve turnover and distribution. Delivering beers to a brewery in another part of the country, while collecting that brewery's beer for sale with one's own, is obviously of great benefit to both parties. These beers are likely to be subjected to a minimum amount of movement and a shorter transit time, resulting in beer reaching the pub in a much better condition than if it had been shipped from wholesaler to wholesaler.

So, it is very much in a publican's interest to deal directly with the breweries wherever possible and to avoid brews from wholesalers which may arrive via a devious route. It is important, too, to boycott any source of supply if it proves necessary to return more than the occasional cask. Having said that, there are some excellent real ale wholesalers operating in Britain. The key is to find them and then deal with them only, even if this ultimately limits the range of beers on offer.

IN THE CELLAR

During the hot summer of 1995, pubs were on the receiving end of an unusually high proportion of brews that were sour or, more usually, that would not 'drop bright'. With limited cellar capacity, this can cause problems. Many publicans pursuing a more adventurous guest beer policy found it necessary to restrict the range of beers on offer in order to maintain quality and availability at the bar.

Unlike keg beer, cask-conditioned brews are alive and have not finished fermenting when they are delivered to the pub. The final stages of the conditioning process take place in the cellar before the beer is served. Temperature control and cleanliness are therefore vital if the beer is to drop clear and bright and without infection. Additionally, good stock control and rapid turnover combined with regular beer line cleaning are essential if each pint is to be served in peak condition.

A small amount of beer is inevitably lost when spilling and tapping each cask and, no matter how carefully it may be stooped, some beer will always be unservable. For this reason, many licensees prefer to buy larger casks in order to minimise wastage, but this often results in casks remaining on-line in the cellar for too long. Once a beer has worked into condition, it will remain at its best for a relatively short period of time. Every pint pulled draws more air into the cask, increasing the rate of oxidisation. If a beer remains on-line for four or five days, not unusual in some pubs, although still drinkable, it will be well past its best.

Controversially, in order to prevent air being taken into the cask, some cellarmen use a cask breather system, which maintains a blanket of carbon dioxide on top of the beer. The gas is at a much lower pressure than that used for the dispensing of keg beer, so there is relatively little absorbence, although it is often detectable as a pint is served.

Some drinkers also believe that the flavour of the beer is impaired by this, although blind tasting tests have not proved that this is so. While it is certainly better than serving a beer that is out of condition, this process inevitably offends the purist and so it is surely preferable to use smaller containers that allow the beer to be served naturally and at its best.

The method of dispensing beer has also become a very contentious issue and there are few hard and fast rules. Many people object to long 'swan necks' or multi-holed

sparklers on the end of a handpump, although some beers are brewed specifically to be served in this way. Some beer is at its best served through the conventional slit-type sparkler and short neck, although some brews lose much of their condition and hoppiness if served through any form of sparkler at all. In such cases, the beer should be served straight from the barrel if all its subtleties of flavour are to be enjoyed to the full.

Different beers are at their best served in different ways. To insist that all sparklers are an abomination, or that all beer is at its best straight from the wood, is to misunderstand the nature of cask-conditioned beers.

SMALL IS BEAUTIFUL

So many things can go wrong between the start of the brewing process and the presentation of the pint at the bar, and inconsistency, for whatever reason, inevitably plays right into the hands of the big, national brewers. They have the ability to undercut smaller breweries on price and to capitalise on first-class marketing and distribution expertise.

The introduction of nitro-keg products to the market has proved a great success. Keg beer is served using a mixture of carbon dioxide and nitrogen to give it a tighter, creamier head. The beer itself may be bland, but such products are very popular. With all the investment tied up in kegs and plant, national and larger independent brewers will understandably continue to look for new ways to utilise existing equipment.

Most so-called freehouses still retain some type of trading agreement with a particular brewery and many emerging brewers have difficulty finding regular outlets for their beers. Frequently unable to raise money to buy a pub, a publican will borrow additional funds from a national brewer. Conditions will obviously be attached to such loans, usually in the form of stipulated barrelage figures. A pub will be required to serve a certain amount of a particular well-known beer.

Such a policy leaves the publican with little room for manoeuvre. A guest beer may prove more popular than the permanent offering and it will then be difficult to honour the commitment to the national brewer, resulting in stiff financial penalties. National brewers have also been know to offer financial inducements to a publican to drop a guest beer not supplied by them if it becomes too popular. Additionally, most trading agreements provide discounts, which may be substantial in certain cases.

A publican operating a true freehouse, free of all ties and agreements, and providing a constantly changing range of unusual guest beers, will probably not deal with any one source in sufficient volume to receive much, if any, discount. Even by reducing profit margins to significantly below the accepted norm, the publican may struggle to sell beers at a competitive rate. Only by then increasing the volume of beer sold can they hope to survive.

Little wonder then that most publicans are not prepared to take such risks and so stick to a regular range of guest beers upon which good discounts are available. In areas where beer is traditionally cheaper, or where there are high levels of unemployment, these discounts can be critical to a pub's survival and so few publicans are likely to risk their livelihood by pursuing an adventurous guest beer policy.

THE NEXT 1000 YEARS

One priceless commodity that the small, independent brewer can use in their favour is the British drinking public's insatiable curiosity. The pub remains an integral part of our way of life, just as it has done for several hundred years, and the national brewers know only too well that there will always be a market for something new and exciting.

So, the brewer who puts the quality of the product first will always find a market of potential pub-goers eager to try something different and something which represents good value for money. Seasonal ales and celebration brews are an excellent way to revive flagging interest.

Even for those drinkers who believe they already know what they like, a degree of variety remains the key. And once the pub-goer knows that a particular publican can be trusted, whether they know the beer in question or not, a bond is established that can be nurtured and strengthened.

When it comes to real ale, you cannot have too much of a good thing, so

independent pub chains that can afford to are rapidly adding new sites to their estates. Many large towns and cities now boast a number of group-owned pubs offering a good range of brews from the independent breweries. Their purchasing power allows them to be very competitive, although they are usually still subject to some trading agreements which can limit the range of beers available.

One day, perhaps, everyone will get the message, but it can still prove frustratingly difficult to find good-quality beers from the smaller and new independent breweries even when visiting the area in which they are produced. Independent brewers today still supply less than 15 per cent of the beer found in Britain's pubs and clubs.

Fortunately, there are true freehouses, some with an interesting range of tried and tested beers and others serving a constantly changing range of guest beers from across the British Isles, including those from the smallest and newest breweries.

The pubs that you will find in the pages that follow vary in character from the basic back-street boozer to the idyllic country inn, but all offer beer well worth searching out. So, while we enjoy British beer at its best, let us spare a thought for brews unlucky enough to be sent to the keg. Cold, devoid of character and flavour and dependent on a gas cylinder for life ... a sad existence indeed.

Even today's commercial giants have been unable to substitute their lifeless, pale imitations for the real thing. Instinctively, one recognises the genuine article, regardless of hype and advertising. Britain's independent brewers have been producing traditional ales for 1000 years. They have withstood the test of time, even through adversity, with banners held high. Let us drink to them, and the next 1000 years.

Most regular drinkers still appreciate a first-class pint that they may have tried before more than an indifferent brew, no matter how new or exotic. But fortunately, there are pubs where both of these needs can be satisfied. For an increasing number of publicans serving beer in peak condition, an interesting guest beer policy remains paramount, and so it is possible to find beers from Orkney in Cornwall, and brews from Jersey in Cumbria.

We all have our favourite real ales but, given the amazing variety of characters and flavours that are produced from such a limited number of ingredients, these obviously vary from individual to individual.

Lighter, paler brews are generally more popular during the summer months, while porters come into their own when the weather is colder. There are, however, certain brews that, regardless of style and time of year, prove to be most popular.

Graham Titcombe, who currently owns the Bell Inn at Pensax, Worcestershire serves a constantly changing range of brews from the independent breweries. From records kept of almost 3000 different beers served there and at his previous pub, over a seven-year period, it has been possible to compile a list of drinkers' favourite 100 brews.

The picture is constantly changing, with many new beers and breweries appearing, so although many of the beers displayed here are familiar favourites, there are a number of welcome newcomers.

1 ARCHERS: GOLDEN BITTER
WILTSHIRE

2 OTTER: BRIGHT
DEVON

3 BATHAMS: BEST BITTER
WEST MIDLANDS

4 WOODFORDE'S: WHERRY
NORFOLK

5 ENVILLE: ALE
WEST MIDLANDS

6 RCH: PITCHFORK
SOMERSET

7 FULLER'S: LONDON PRIDE
LONDON

8 MOORHOUSE'S: PENDLE WITCHES BREW
LANCASHIRE

9 CALEDONIAN: R & D DEUCHARS IPA
SCOTLAND

10 HARVIESTOUN: SCHIEHALLION
SCOTLAND

11 HOP BACK: SUMMER LIGHTNING
WILTSHIRE

12 EXMOOR: GOLD
SOMERSET

13 HOBSONS: TOWN CRIER
HEREFORD & WORCESTER

14 BURNTISLAND: DOCKYARD RIVETS
SCOTLAND

15 BLACK SHEEP: SPECIAL BITTER
YORKSHIRE

16 BULLMASTIFF: SON OF A BITCH
WALES

17 SKINNER'S: CORNISH KNOCKER
CORNWALL

18 TIMOTHY TAYLOR: LANDLORD
YORKSHIRE

19 HOOK NORTON: OLD HOOKY
OXFORDSHIRE

20 ENVILLE: WHITE
WEST MIDLANDS

21 WOOD'S:
SHROPSHIRE LAD
SHROPSHIRE

22 WADWORTH: 6X
WILTSHIRE

23 SARAH HUGHES:
DARK RUBY MILD
WEST MIDLANDS

24 ADNAMS: BITTER
SUFFOLK

25 MAULDONS:
WHITE ADDER
SUFFOLK

26 HOLDEN'S:
SPECIAL BITTER
WEST MIDLANDS

27 DARK HORSE:
FALLEN ANGEL
HERTFORDSHIRE

28 CHERITON:
POTS ALE
HAMPSHIRE

29 FULLER'S:
RED FOX
LONDON

30 RINGWOOD:
FORTYNINER
HAMPSHIRE

31 KELHAM ISLAND:
PALE RIDER
YORKSHIRE

 ENVILLE:
PHOENIX
WEST MIDLANDS

33 **HARDY & HANSONS:**
KIMBERLEY CLASSIC
NOTTINGHAMSHIRE

34 **COTLEIGH:**
HARRIER
SOMERSET

 BRAKSPEAR:
SPECIAL
OXFORDSHIRE

36 **ADNAMS:**
EXTRA
SUFFOLK

37 **WADWORTH:**
FARMERS GLORY
WILTSHIRE

 MORRELLS:
VARSITY
OXFORDSHIRE

 BATEMAN'S:
VICTORY ALE
LINCOLNSHIRE

 MORDUE:
WORKIE TICKET
TYNE & WEAR

 MARSTON'S:
LITTLE LAMBSWICK
STAFFORDSHIRE

42 **ADNAMS:**
BROADSIDE
SUFFOLK

43 **EXMOOR: ALE**
SOMERSET

44 CHERITON:
DIGGERS GOLD
HAMPSHIRE

45 BERROW:
TOPSY TURVY
SOMERSET

46 PALMERS:
TALLY HO!
DORSET

47 RINGWOOD:
XXXX PORTER
HAMPSHIRE

48 WYE VALLEY:
HPA
HEREFORD & WORCESTER

49 BUNCES:
DANISH DYNAMITE
WILTSHIRE

50 BARNSLEY:
BITTER
YORKSHIRE

51 GOFF'S:
JOUSTER
GLOUCESTERSHIRE

52 LEATHERBRITCHES:
ASHBOURNE ALE
DERBYSHIRE

53 RIDLEYS:
RUMPUS
ESSEX

54 CHARLES WELLS:
BOMBARDIER
BEDFORDSHIRE

55 WOODBURY:
WHITE GOOSE
HEREFORD & WORCESTER

56 JOLLYBOAT:
PLUNDER
DEVON

57 GODDARDS:
FUGGLE DEE DUM
ISLE OF WIGHT

58 EVERARDS:
TIGER
LEICESTERSHIRE

59 OTTER:
BITTER
DEVON

60 WOODFORDE'S:
BALDRIC
NORFOLK

61 WYRE PIDDLE:
PIDDLE IN THE WIND
HEREFORD & WORCESTER

62 CONCERTINA:
BENGAL TIGER
YORKSHIRE

63 ECCLESHALL:
SLATERS SUPREME
STAFFORDSHIRE

64 ARKELL'S:
KINGSDOWN
WILTSHIRE

65 ORKNEY:
DARK ISLAND
SCOTLAND

66 SARAH HUGHES:
SEDGLEY SURPRISE
WEST MIDLANDS

67 YATES:
PREMIUM
CUMBRIA

68 KING & BARNES:
FESTIVE
SUFFOLK

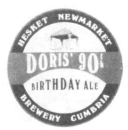

69 HESKET NEWMARKET:
DORIS' 90TH BIRTHDAY
CUMBRIA

70 MOORHOUSE'S:
OWD ALE
LANCASHIRE

71 ICENI:
GOLD
NORFOLK

72 CANNON ROYALL:
BUCKSHOT
HEREFORD & WORCESTER

73 HOGS BACK:
HOP GARDEN GOLD
SURREY

74 SHARP'S:
CORNISH COASTER
CORNWALL

75 RINGWOOD:
OLD THUMPER
HAMPSHIRE

76 BALLARD'S:
TROTTON
HAMPSHIRE

77 GREENE KING:
ABBOT ALE
SUFFOLK

78 CHURCH END:
WHAT THE FOX'S HAT
WARWICKSHIRE

79 FERNANDES:
WAKEFIELD PRIDE
YORKSHIRE

80 ABBEY:
BELLRINGER
SOMERSET

81 BRAKSPEAR:
BEE STING
OXFORDSHIRE

82 FROG ISLAND:
BEST BITTER
NORTHAMPTONSHIRE

83 MITCHELL'S:
LANCASTER BOMBER
LANCASHIRE

84 DENT:
T'OWD TUP
CUMBRIA

85 BATH:
BARNSTORMER
SOMERSET

86 BALLARD'S:
WASSAIL
HAMPSHIRE

87 SARAH HUGHES:
SNOWFLAKE
WEST MIDLANDS

88 MALVERN HILLS:
BLACK PEAR
HEREFORD & WORCESTER

89 BIGFOOT:
GAINSBOROUGH GOLD
LINCOLNSHIRE

90 VALE:
EDGAR'S GOLDEN ALE
BUCKINGHAMSHIRE

91 WOLF:
GRANNY WOULDN'T LIKE IT
NORFOLK

92 OAKHAM:
JHB
LEICESTERSHIRE

93 FENLAND:
SPARKLING WIT
CAMBRIDGESHIRE

94 ECCLESHALL:
TOP TOTTY
STAFFORDSHIRE

95 MORLAND:
OLD SPECKLED HEN
OXFORDSHIRE

96 TRAQUAIR:
BEAR ALE
SCOTLAND

97 TEME VALLEY:
T'OTHER
HEREFORD & WORCESTER

98 BURTONWOOD:
JAMES FORSHAW'S BITTER
CHESHIRE

99 SWALE:
GOLDING WIT
KENT

100 BEARTOWN:
AMBEARDEXTROUS
CHESHIRE

The Real Ale Pub Guide is a celebration of the rejuvenated art of brewing in Great Britain. Our concern, deliberately, is not with the often bland and certainly mass-produced market leaders, but simply with the smaller, independent makers of what we consider to be the *real* real ales. For this reason, we do not tell you about the big, multi-national brewers and their products, good or bad. Nor do we tell you about the pubs whose reputation owes more to their impressive location, their excellent cooking or their extensive range of malt whiskies, although we may mention their claim in passing. This is a book about beer and is aimed squarely at those who love drinking it, who want to know more about it and who want to know where to find it at its best. The entries within England are arranged alphabetically by county, taking into account the boundary changes that came into force in 1996. Since plenty of people never got used to the last round of boundary changes this will envitably cause some confusion.

For example, Avon, Cleveland and Humberside now no longer exist. Parts of these counties have been swallowed up by their recent neighbours and towns have returned to what many have always considered to be their spiritual homes. Elsewhere a large number of new unitary authorities have been established. Bristol, for example, is no longer at the heart of Avon, but nor has it returned to its Gloucestershire roots. Leicester has an authority of its own, despite being located in the middle of the county of Leicestershire.

We have attempted to adopt a logical approach (incorporating Bristol within Gloucestershire and Leicester within Leicestershire, etc.) to minimise this confusion. Some border towns and villages may still surprise you, however. The postal address may be in one county whereas the actual place is over the boundary. We have tried to place all entries in the counties to which they actully belong (and not where the post office may indicate that they should be), so be prepared for a bit of county-hopping along the borders.

The brewery entries come first, at the beginning of the county, followed by the pubs and brewpubs, organised alphabetically by town or village. We have attempted to give as full an address as possible and a telephone number in most cases. Brief directions may also be found within the entry itself but, if you do get lost and there is no one available to ask, a call ahead should keep the inconvenience to a minimum.

Our primary aim is to make this guide as useful to people looking for a place to drink real ale as possible. The criteria, therefore, is that a selection of real ales in proportion to the number of beers sold in total is always available. Tied houses, even those tied to national breweries, are included if they meet this criteria. However, because cask ales are the focus of our project we have usually excluded details of the keg beers available.

Where possible, we have sought to include the licensee's name for we believe that the character and quality of a pub owes much to the person who runs it. Inevitably, these people move on and many enjoy the challenge of taking on a new pub and establishing its place on the map. While every acknowledgement should be made of the nation's finest innkeepers, this is more than just a chance for publicans to see their names in print. We hope that readers will recognise the people who run particularly successful pubs and, as they move, need no other recommendations to visit than that person's name.

Because we believe the beers are the most important thing to be found in a pub, we have sought to give an indication of the names and numbers of ales that you are likely to find when you walk through the door. Of course, there are few hard and fast rules. Availability varies and, on some days, the choice will probably be wider than on others. Nevertheless, a pub that says it has 12 beers on tap should come reasonably close to doing just that. If you discover this is not the case, then we want to know.

There is a short description of the type of pub to be found with each entry, intended to give you an idea of what to expect. If they have told us they specialise in a certain type of food, or have accommodation or other features then we have sought to pass that on. However, as this is not the purpose of our guide we have kept the details to a minimum.

Opening hours are another feature that will inevitably vary, particularly as the Government relaxes the licensing laws. An increasing number of pubs are opening for longer and later than was the case just a few years ago. However, we suggest that, if you are proposing to visit in the middle of the afternoon, for instance, a telephone call ahead will ensure that you are not disappointed.

Unfortunately, for a number of reasons it has not been possible to include an entry for every real ale pub in the country. Similarly, there are many pubs about which we have heard favourable reports but which we have been unable to verify first hand. A selection of those pubs appears at the end of each county under the heading 'You Tell Us'. Perhaps if you visit them you can let us know your findings by returning one of the questionnaires at the back of the book. Similarly, if you find a pub does not live up to your expectations or you know of a good pub which is not included, we'd love to hear from you. Send us your completed questionnaire, or visit our web site at www.foulsham.com and leave us your comments.

Graham Titcombe and Nicolas Andrews

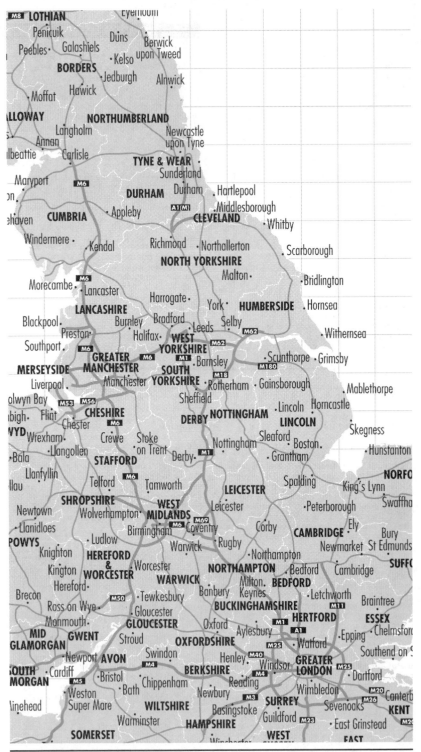

Lowestoft

Norwich

Swaffham

King's Lynn

Spalding

Felixstowe

Ipswich

Eye

SUFFOLK

Bury St Edmunds

Newmarket

Cambridge

Braintree

Chelmsford

ESSEX

Southend on Sea

Dover

Canterbury

Hastings

Eastbourne

KENT

M20

Dartford

Epping

M11

HERTFORD

Letchworth

Watford

GREATER LONDON

M25

Wimbledon

Sevenoaks

East Grinstead

EAST SUSSEX

Brighton

Bognor Regis

WEST SUSSEX

SURREY

Guildford

M23

Windsor

Reading

Basingstoke

Winchester

Portsmouth

Sandown

Peterborough

Ely

CAMBRIDGE

Bedford

BEDFORD

Corby

Northampton

Milton Keynes

NORTHAMPTON

Banbury

Aylesbury

BUCKINGHAMSHIRE

Oxford

M40

Henley

Newbury

BERKSHIRE

HAMPSHIRE

Southampton

M27

Bournemouth

Poole

Swindon

OXFORDSHIRE

Chippenham

WILTSHIRE

Warminster

Weymouth

DORSET

Yeovil

Lyme Regis

SOMERSET

Bath

Bristol

AVON

Weston Super Mare

Taunton

Honiton

Exmouth

Leicester

LEICESTER

Rugby

Coventry

M6

Warwick

WARWICK

WEST MIDLANDS

Birmingham

Tamworth

Worcester

Tewkesbury

Gloucester

Stroud

GLOUCESTER

M5

HEREFORD & WORCESTER

M50

Newport

GWENT

Monmouth

Ross on Wye

Hereford

Cardiff

SOUTH GLAMORGAN

MID GLAMORGAN

Porthcawl

Brecon

Minehead

Ilfracombe

Barnstaple

Bideford

Bude

CORNWALL

Padstow

Newquay

St Ives

Penzance

Helston

Truro

Falmouth

Bodmin

Liskeard

Plymouth

Okehampton

Tavistock

DEVON

M5

Exeter

Torquay

Dartmouth

Swansea

WEST GLAMORGAN

M4

Llandovery

Lampeter

DYFED

Aberayron

New Quay

Cardigan

Fishguard

Haverfordwest

Pembroke

Knighton

Kington

Llanidloes

Newtown

POWYS

Aberystwyth

Towyn

Barmouth

Dolgellau

Telford

Wolverhampton

SHROPSHIRE

Ludlow

M54

Telford

KENT M20

M20

M25

M4

M3

M20

M23

M11

M1

Places Featured:

Bedford
Biggleswade
Dunstable
Great Barford
Leighton Buzzard
Luton

Millbrook Village
Ridgmont
Shefford
Stotfold
Studham
Wingfield

THE BREWERIES

B & T BREWERY LTD

The Brewery, Shefford SG17 5DZ
☎ *01462 815080*

SHEFFORD BITTER 3.8% ABV
Golden and hoppy with dry hop finish.
SHEFFORD DARK MILD 3.8% ABV
Rich, mellow, dry and hoppy dark mild.
DRAGONSLAYER 4.5% ABV
Sharp, light and golden with good body.
SHEFFORD PALE ALE 4.5% ABV
Hoppy with balancing malt and dry finish.
EDWIN TAYLOR'S EXTRA STOUT 4.5% ABV
Creamy and full-bodied.
SHEFFORD OLD DARK 5.0% ABV
Deep red, sweet caramel and malt flavour.
SHEFFORD OLD STRONG 5.0% ABV
Hoppy with bitter malty flavour.
BLACK BAT 6.0% ABV
Ruby black, malt and fruit flavour.
2XS 6.0% ABV
Golden, rich aroma and fruit undertones.
OLD BAT 7.0% ABV
Dry, pale, refreshing barley wine.
Plus occasional beers

CHARLES WELLS LTD

The Eagle Brewery, Havelock Street, Bedford MK40 4LU
☎ *01234 272766*

EAGLE 3.6% ABV
Balanced, dry, full-flavoured IPA.
BOMBARDIER 4.3% ABV
Hoppy, well-balanced with dry finish.
FARGO 5.0% ABV
Bittersweet, fruity flavour with dryness in the finish.

POTTON BREWING CO.

10 Shannon Place, Potton, Sandy SG19 2PZ
☎ *01767 261042*

PHOENIX 3.8% ABV
SHAMBLES 4.3% ABV
VILLAGE BIKE 4.3% ABV

THE PUBS

BEDFORD

The Castle

17 Newnham Street, Bedford MK40 3JR
☎ *(01234) 353295* Michael Holmes

A Charles Wells tenancy. Four guest beers available from a range of 12 per year including Morland Old Speckled Hen, Marston's Pedigree, Young's Special, Brains Bitter and Badger Tanglefoot.

A two-bar public house with country pub atmosphere. Bar food available at lunchtime and evenings. Thai menu Mon–Thurs. Car park, accommodation. Children allowed at lunchtime only.

12–3pm and 5.30–11pm Mon–Thurs and Sun; all day Fri–Sat.

De Parys Hotel

45 De Parys Avenue, Bedford MK40 2UA
☎ *(01234) 352121* John Latimer

A freehouse with Castle Eden, Potton Brewery and Fenland Brewery ales regularly available plus Fuller's London Pride. Beers changed weekly with emphasis on smaller breweries.

Hotel with bar, garden, 100-seater restaurant and 20 rooms. Situated near the park. Food available at lunchtimes and evenings Mon–Sat, and all day Sun. Children allowed.

All day, every day.

BIGGLESWADE

The Brown Bear

29 Hitchin Street, Biggleswade SG18 8BE
☎ *(01767) 316161* Mary Hamilton

Seven hand pumps serving a constantly changing range of real ales (approx. 40 per month) from micro and other small breweries. Recent examples include beers from Maypole, Cottage, Bank Top, Salopian, Teignworthy and Eccleshall.

A two-bar, open-plan pub with a small non-smoking eating area. Two annual beer festivals and a mini festival on the second weekend of every month. Homemade food available all day. Located on the main street, off the market square.

12–3pm and 5–11pm Mon–Wed; 11am–11pm Thurs–Sat; 12–3pm and 7–10.30pm Sun.

DUNSTABLE

The Victoria

69 West Street, Dunstable LU6 1ST
☎ *(01582) 662682* Ian Mackay

Five hand pumps regularly serving a house beer (Victoria Ale) from the Tring Brewery, plus a range of guest beers (approx. 200 per year) from independent breweries such as Fuller's, Vale, Mauldons, Cottage, Wye Valley, York and Fernandes.

A traditional pub just outside the town centre. Bar food is served at lunchtimes only (12–2.30pm), with roasts on Sundays. Well-behaved children allowed. The landlord's policy is to have a session, a premium and a mind-blowing beer always on sale! Regular beer festivals are held in the barn at the rear of the pub.

All day, every day.

GREAT BARFORD

The Golden Cross

2–4 Bedford Road, Great Barford MK44 3JD
☎ *(01234) 870439* Mr Older

Greene King IPA permanently available, plus four guest beers changed weekly including Hop Back Summer Lightning and brews from Charles Wells, Bateman, Shepherd Neame, Morland and Wadworth, among others.

A traditional pub on the main road with an unconventional twist as the rear houses a Chinese restaurant. There is only Chinese food available. Children allowed in restaurant.

12.30–2.30pm and 5–11pm Mon–Fri; 11am–11pm Sat; 12–10.30pm Sun.

LEIGHTON BUZZARD

The Stag

1 Heath Road, Leighton Buzzard LU7 8AB
☎ *(01525) 372710* Bob Patrick

Serves the full range of Fuller's beers, including seasonal specials such as Honey Dew, Summer Ale, Red Fox and Old Winter Ale.

A traditional town pub with food served Mon–Sat lunchtimes (12–2pm) and evenings (6–9.30pm). Children not allowed.

12–2.30pm and 6–11pm.

LUTON

The Two Brewers
43 Dumfries Street, Luton LU1 5AY
☎ *(01582) 616008* Andy Gill

Four B&T brews always available (Shefford Bitter, Dragonslayer, Edwin Taylor's Extra Stout and Shefford Old Strong), plus three changing guest ales perhaps including Timothy Taylor Landlord or brews from Adnams, Titanic, Tisbury, Wye Valley, Marlow, Woods, Hoskins, Nethergate, Mansfield or Everards.

A welcoming, old-style, back-street pub just two minutes from the town centre. No food. Children allowed.

12–11pm Mon–Sat; (10.30pm Sun).

MILLBROOK VILLAGE

The Chequers
Millbrook Village MK45 2JB
☎ *(01525) 403835* Mr G Polti

Fuller's London Pride and Hook Norton Old Hooky are regulars, others appear occasionally.

An Italian family-run pub specialising in pasta and chargrilled food, which is available every day (12–3pm and 6.30–11pm) except Sunday. Children allowed in the restaurant. Located off A507 from Ridgmont, opposite the Vauxhall proving ground.

11.30am–3pm and 6.30–11pm Mon–Sat (10.30pm Sun).

RIDGMONT

The Rose & Crown
89 High Street, Ridgmont MK43 0TY
☎ *(01525) 280245* Neil McGregor

Adnams Broadside and Mansfield Riding Bitter are regularly available, while other guests may include Morland's Old Speckled Hen or a Young's brew.

A traditional, rural pub with food available (12–2pm and 7–9pm). Children allowed.

10.30am–2.30pm and 6–11pm Mon–Sat (10.30pm Sun).

SHEFFORD

Brewery Tap
14 North Bridge Street, Shefford SG17 5DH
☎ *(01462) 628448* David Mortimer

B&T's Shefford Bitter, Dragonslayer and Dark Mild are always available plus two guests, which change every week, but might include brews from Dent, Crouch Vale, Leatherbritches, Yorkshire or Burton Bridge.

A traditional alehouse and, as the name suggests, the B&T brewery tap. Snacks available, but no bar food. Small children's room and garden.

11am–11pm Mon–Sat; 12–10.30pm Sun.

STOTFOLD

The Stag Inn
Brook Street, Stotfold SG5 4LA
☎ *(01462) 730261* Ray Rudzki

Home of Abel Brown's Brewery, which was launched in 1995 and is named after the first publican of The Stag. Full range of home beers brewed and sold on the premises plus various guests, three or four served at any one time (250 per year), to include ales from Titanic and Hop Back.

B uilt in 1920, the pub is set in a rural location. Thai and Indian food is available in evenings. Accommodation. Children allowed. One mile from A1 junction 10.

JACK OF HEARTS 4.0%
A premium bitter with dry finish.
LITTLE BILLY 4.0%
A light, pale ale.
POCOLOCO 5.0%
PLOUGHMAN'S PICKLE 5.0%
A strong, brown ale

12–2.30pm and 5–11pm Mon–Thurs; all day Fri–Sat; 12–10.30pm Sun.

STUDHAM

The Red Lion at Studham
Church Road, Studham LU6 2QA
☎ *(01582) 872530* Philip Potts

Five real ales available, perhaps including Timothy Taylor Landlord, Greene King Abbot Ale, Fuller's London Pride, Wadworth 6X and Farmers Glory, plus Black Sheep Bitter and Thwaites or Marston brews. The selection changes on a weekly basis.

T raditional country pub with food at lunchtimes and evenings (12–2.30pm and 7–9.30pm). Children allowed at lunchtimes only.

11.30am–3pm and 5.30–11pm Mon–Fri; 11am–11pm Sat; 12–10.30pm Sun.

WINGFIELD

The Plough Inn

Tebworth Road, Wingfield, Leighton Buzzard LU7 9QH

☎ *(01525) 873077* Mr and Mrs Worsley

Six beers permanently available including B&T Shefford Bitter, Fuller's London Pride, Brakspear Special and a Hook Norton brew. Also a large number of guests per year including B&T Black Bat, Vale Notley Bitter and many more.

A thatched olde-English pub. CAMRA South Bedfordshire Pub of the Year 1993 and 1994. Bar and restaurant food available at lunchtimes and evenings. Garden with children's play area. From M1 junction 12, follow the A5120 through Toddington to Houghton Regis. Turn off to Wingfield.

OPEN *11am–3pm and 5.30–11pm Mon–Fri; 11am–11pm Sat; 12–10.30pm Sun.*

YOU TELL US

★ *The Bricklayer's Arms,* 14–16 Hightown Road, Luton
★ *The Cock,* 23 High Street, Broom
★ *The Countryman,* Shefford
★ *The Engineer's Arms,* 66 High Street, Henlow
★ *The Old Bell,* Church Road, Totternhoe
★ *The Queen's Head,* The Lane, Tebworth
★ *The Swan with Two Necks,* High Street, Sharnbrook
★ *The Wheatsheaf,* 5 Lawrence Road, Biggleswade
★ *The White Hart,* Mill Lane, Campton

Places Featured:

Aldworth	Reading
Caversham	Shinfield
Chieveley	Slough
Cookham	Sonning
Eton	Stanford Dingley
Frilsham	Sunninghill
Littlewick Green	Tidmarsh
Lower Inkpen	Twyford
Maidenhead	White Waltham
Newbury	Winterbourne

THE BREWERIES

BUTTS BREWERY LTD

Unit 6a, Northfield Farm, Wantage Road, Great Shefford, Hungerford RG17 7BY
☎ *01488 648133*

 JESTER 3.5% ABV
Light, easy-drinking.
BITTER 4.0% ABV
Golden and fruity.
BLACKGUARD 4.5% ABV
Smooth chocolate malt flavour.
BARBUS BARBUS 4.6% ABV
Hoppy throughout.
Plus occasional brews

THE WEST BERKSHIRE BREWERY CO

Pot Kiln Lane, Frilsham, Yattendon, Newbury RG18 0XX
☎ *01635 202638*

 SKIFF 3.6% ABV
Refreshing session beer.
GOOD OLD BOY 4.0% ABV
Hop flavours throughout.
BRICK KILN BITTER 4.0% ABV
Fruity. Only brewed for the Pot Kiln.
OLD TYLER 4.0% ABV
Brewed for The Bell at Aldworth.
DR HEXTER'S WEDDING 4.1% ABV
Golden and refreshing.
GRAFT BITTER 4.3% ABV
Hoppy, with bitterness in the finish.
GOLDSTAR 5.0% ABV
Brewed with honey.
DR HEXTER'S HEALER 5.0% ABV
Pale and fruity.
Plus occasional brews

THE PUBS

ALDWORTH

The Bell

Aldworth, Nr Reading RG8 9SE
☎ *(01635) 578272* Mr and Mrs IJ Macaulay

 Arkell's 3B and Kingsdown Ale, West Berkshire's Old Tyler and Magnificent Mild plus Crouch Vale Best always available.

A small, unaltered inn dating from 1340 in good walking country. Bar food available at lunchtimes and evenings. Well-behaved children allowed in the tap room. Country garden with adjacent cricket ground. Two miles from Streatley on B4009 to Newbury.

OPEN *Closed all day Mon (except bank holidays). 11am–3pm and 6–11pm Tue–Sat; 12–3pm and 7–10.30pm Sun.*

CAVERSHAM

Baron Cadogan

22–4 Prospect Street, Caversham, Reading RG4 8JG
☎ *(0118) 947 0626* John Williamson

Fuller's London Pride permanently available, plus two guests rotating weekly including, perhaps, Shepherd Neame Spitfire, Archers Golden, Hogs Back TEA among many others.

A modern town freehouse with food available all day. No children.

OPEN *All day, every day.*

CHIEVELEY

Olde Red Lion
Green Lane, Chieveley RG20 8XB
☎ *(01635) 248379* David Eccles

 Arkell's 3B and Kingsdown Ale always available plus other, seasonal Arkell's brews.

A traditional pub with bar food available (12–2.30pm and 6.30–9.30pm). Children allowed. Located off M4 J13, near the services.

🍺 *11am–3pm and 6–11pm Mon–Sat (10.30pm Sun).*

COOKHAM

Cookham Tavern
Lower Road, Cookham SL6 9HJ
☎ *(01628) 529519* Marilyn Rothwell

A Whitbread tied house. Up to six cask ales including Brakspear's Bitter, Greene King Abbot Ale, Marston's Pedigree and Young's ales. Changed monthly.

A traditional, community local with food available (12–2.30pm and 6–9.30pm). Children allowed. Near Cookham station.

🍺 *11.30am–2.30pm and 5.30–11pm Mon–Thur; 11.30am–11pm Fri–Sat; 12–10.30pm Sun.*

ETON

Waterman's Arms
Brocas Street, Eton SL4 6BW
☎ *(01753) 861001* Mr Collibee

Greene King IPA, Wadworth 6X, Charles Wells Bombardier and a Brakspear brew always available, plus guests from Bateman, Gales and Felinfoel.

An old English-style pub with food served in a separate restaurant at lunchtimes and evenings. Children allowed.

🍺 *11am–2.30pm and 6–11pm Mon–Fri; all day Sat–Sun.*

FRILSHAM

Pot Kiln
Yattendon, Frilsham RG18 0XX
☎ *(01635) 201366* Philip Gent

West Berkshire Brick Kiln Bitter only available here, plus Morland Original, Arkell's 3B and others. Seasonal brews and specials, usually from West Berkshire brewery.

A traditional pub with the West Berkshire micro-brewery in an out-building at the back. Food available (12–1.45pm and 7–9.30pm). Children allowed. From Newbury take B4009 into Hermitage. Turn right at The Fox, follow Yattendon sign. Turn right and continue for a mile. Pub on the right.

🍺 *12–2.30pm (except Tues) and 6.30–11pm Mon–Sat; 12–3pm and 7–10.30pm Sun.*

LITTLEWICK GREEN

The Cricketers
Coronation Road, Littlewick Green SL6 3RA
☎ *(01628) 822888* Mr Carter

Timothy Taylor Landlord plus seasonal Fuller's and Brakspear ales. Other brews rotating regularly may include Shepheard Neame Spitfire, Wadworth 6X and Morland Old Speckled Hen.

A traditional village pub close to the old Bath Road (A4). Food available (12–2pm and 7–9pm). Children allowed.

🍺 *11am–11pm Mon–Sat; 12–10.30pm Sun.*

LOWER INKPEN

Swan Inn
Lower Inkpen, Hungerford RG17 9DX
☎ *(01488) 668326* Mr Harris

Hook Norton Bitter and Mild and Butts Brewery's Traditional and Blackguard regularly available, plus Adnams beers served on a guest basis.

A traditional village hotel with 'free house' bar. Ten bedrooms and a restaurant. Bar food also available. Children allowed.

🍺 *All day, every day.*

MAIDENHEAD

The Hobgoblin
High Street, Maidenhead SL6 1QE
☎*(01628) 636510* D Dean (Manager)

A Wychwood tied house with at least two seasonal Wychwood ales always available, plus three guests changing weekly, such as Fuller's London Pride, Rebellion ales, Hooray Henley, or Ow'sthat (a cricket celebration ale).

A lively town pub with a young clientele, particularly at weekends. One bar, beer garden. Food available 12–2pm. Children allowed in the garden only.

🍺 *12–11pm Mon–Sat; 3–10.30pm Sun.*

The Hobgoblin

Bartholomew Street, Newbury RG14 5HB
☎ *(01635) 47336* Gay Diss

A Wychwood special always available, plus up to five guest ales such as Wadworth 6X, Brakspear Special or other Wychwood brew. Beers changed every fortnight.

A traditional town pub with one bar, beams and wooden floors. Food available at lunchtime only. Children allowed.

OPEN *12–11pm (10.30pm Sun).*

The Monument

57 Northbrook Street, Newbury RG14 1AN
☎ *(01635) 41964* Simon Owens

Eight real ales available, usually including Tap & Spile Premium, Gales HSB and brews from Jennings, Adnams, Bateman, Nethergate, Four Rivers and Titanic.

This 350-year-old pub is the oldest in Newbury. Until recently, it was owned by the Tap & Spile chain and has only just changed back to its original name. Food available all day. Children and dogs very welcome.

OPEN *11am–11pm Mon–Sat; 12–10.30pm Sun.*

3B's Bar

Old Town Hall, Blagrave Street, Reading RG1 1QH
☎ *(0118) 939 9803* Stefano Buratta

Four real ales at any one time often including Bunces Old Smokey and Pigswill, and Timothy Taylor Landlord. Guests changed weekly from breweries such as Ash Vine, Ushers, Greene King and others.

A friendly café bar right next to the station. Families welcome. Food available all day.

OPEN *11am–11pm Mon–Sat; 12–10.30pm Sun.*

Back of Beyond

104–8 Kings Road, Reading RG4 8DT
☎ *(0118) 959 5906* Sean Pickering

Fuller's London Pride is among the beers always available. Regular guests include Archers Golden and Hogs Back Traditional English Ale plus others from independent breweries such as Cains, Caledonian, Cotleigh, Exmoor, Hardys & Hansons, Smiles, Wychwood and Timothy Taylor.

A traditional JD Wetherspoon's pub with garden, located five minutes from the railway station. Food available all day. No children.

OPEN *10am–11pm Mon–Sat; 12–10.30pm Sun.*

The Hobgoblin

2 Broad Street, Reading RG1 2BH
☎ *(01734) 508119* Duncan Ward

Wychwood beers always available plus up to 700 guests per year exclusively from small independent brewers. No national products are stocked. Also real cider, perry and genuine German lager.

Small, friendly town-centre pub. No jukebox, but background R&B etc. Occasional live music, traditional pub games. Bar food at lunchtimes. Supervised children allowed up to 7pm.

OPEN *All permitted hours.*

The Hop Leaf

163–5 Southampton Street, Reading RG1 2QZ
☎ *(0118) 931 4700*

The full range of Hop Back ales brewed and served on the premises.

This formerly derelict pub on the edge of the town centre was taken over and revitalised as a brewpub by the Hop Back Brewery. A late Victorian building, recently refurbished. Parking can be difficult.

MILD 3.0% ABV
GFB 3.5% ABV
HOP LEAF 4.0% ABV
EXTRA STOUT 4.0% ABV
SUMMER LIGHTNING 5.0% ABV
RYE BEER 5.0% ABV
WHEAT BEER 5.0% ABV

OPEN *All permitted hours.*

Sweeney & Todd

10 Castle Street, Reading RG1 7RD
☎ *(0118) 958 6466* Catherine J Hayward

Wadworth 6X usually available, plus one guest such as Eldridge Pope Royal Oak, Adnams Best and brews from Butts, Itchen Valley, Brakspear, Gales, Greene King and Young's.

A traditional 'pie and pint' pub. A huge range of pies is served all day in the dedicated restaurant. Children allowed in the restaurant.

OPEN *11am–11pm Mon–Sat; 12–10.30pm Sun.*

Wheelwright's Arms

Davis Way, St Nicholas Hurst, Reading RG10 0TR
☎ *(0118) 934 4100* Kevin Morley

Four Wadworth brews always available, plus four guests perhaps including Adnams Extra, Badger Tanglefoot and others. Guests are changed monthly.

A traditional pub on the Twyford Road with low beams and a real fire. Food available 12–2pm and 6.30–9pm. Children allowed in restaurant only.

OPEN *11.30am–2.30pm and 5.30–11pm Mon–Fri; 11am–11pm Sat; 12–10.30pm Sun.*

Bell & Bottle

School Green, Shinfield, Reading RG2 9EE
☎ *(0118) 988 3563* Fran Jane

Nine cask ales available, regularly featuring beers from Beckett's, Cottage, Wychwood, Butts, Smiles, plus Marston's Pedigree, Archers Village and Golden, Rebellion Mild and Wadworth 6X from time to time. Beers rotated weekly.

A traditional pub with food available. Children and dogs welcome.

OPEN *11.30am–11.30pm Mon–Sat; 12–10.30pm Sun.*

Moon & Spoon

86–88 High Street, Slough SL1 1EL
☎ *(01753) 531650*
Alan Martin and Nyki Haylett

Fuller's London Pride and Brakspear Special available, plus up to five guests changed every three months.

A themed JD Wetherspoon's pub with a lively, young clientele. Food served all day, every day. Children not allowed. At the end of the High Street, opposite the library.

OPEN *11am–11pm Mon–Sat; 12–10.30pm Sun.*

The Bull

High Street, Sonning, Reading RG4 6UP
☎ *(0118) 969 3901*
Christine and Dennis Mason

A George Gale tied house, permanently serving Gales HSB, Best and Butser, plus Gales seasonal specials. Marston's Pedigree often available as a guest.

A n old country pub with log fires. Food available lunchtimes and evenings. Children allowed.

OPEN *11am–3pm and 5.30–11pm Mon–Fri; all day Sat–Sun.*

The Boot

Stanford Dingley, Reading RG7 6LT
☎ *(0118) 974 4292* John Haley

Real ales rotated fortnightly usually from Smiles, Archers or West Berkshire breweries.

A traditional, olde-worlde freehouse. Bar food available (12–2.15pm and 7–9.15pm). Children welcome.

OPEN *11am–3pm and 6–11pm Mon–Sat; (7–10pm Sun).*

The Bull

Stanford Dingley, Reading RG7 6LS
☎ *(0118) 974 4409* Pat Langdon

West Berkshire's Good Old Boy, Skiff and Gold Star plus Brakspear Bitter regularly available. Also West Berkshire specials as and when available.

A traditional freehouse with food available (12–2.30pm and 7.30–10pm). Well-behaved children allowed in the saloon bar at lunchtimes and early evenings. Six miles from J12 of M4.

OPEN *12–3pm and 7–11pm (10.30pm Sun); closed Mon lunchtime except bank holidays.*

The Dukes Head

Upper Village Road, Sunninghill SL5 7AG
☎ *(01344) 626949* Philip Durrant

Marston's Pedigree and Greene King Abbot permanently available, plus Greene King seasonal ales as and when available.

A traditional village pub specialising in Thai food (12–2pm and 7–10pm). Owned by Greene King. Well-behaved children allowed. Upper Village Road runs parallel to the High Street. A beer festival is held once a year.

OPEN *11am–11pm Mon–Sat; 12–10.30pm Sun.*

Greyhound

The Street, Tidmarsh RG8 8ER
☎ *(0118) 984 3557* Martin Ford

Five real ales including Fuller's London Pride and others rotated monthly from Shepherd Neame, Rebellion, West Berkshire, Morland, Coniston, Wadworth and other breweries.

A traditional, twelfth-century village pub serving food at lunchtimes. Children allowed. On the main A340.

OPEN *11am–3pm and 5.30–11pm Mon–Fri; 11am–11pm Sat; 12–10.30pm Sun.*

The Golden Cross

38 Waltham Road, Twyford, Reading RG10 9EG
☎ *(0118) 934 0180* Duncan Campbell

Brakspear brews and Fuller's London Pride permanently available, plus guests regularly including Greene King IPA, Marston's Pedigree, and Wadworth 6X.

A locals' pub with restaurant area and beer garden. Food served every lunchtime and Tues–Sat evenings. Children allowed in the garden and restaurant only.

OPEN *All day, every day.*

WHITE WALTHAM

The Beehive
Waltham Road, White Waltham SL6 3SH
☎ *(01628) 822877* Guy Martin

🍺 A Whitbread tied house with Brakspear bitters permanently available, plus twice-weekly changing guests such as Fuller's ESB and brews from the Cottage Brewery, Hampshire Brewery and Rebellion.

A rural pub under new management. Garden, separate restaurant and large children's area. Food available at lunchtimes and evenings. Children allowed.

OPEN *All day, every day.*

WINTERBOURNE

The Winterbourne Arms
Winterbourne, Newbury RG20 8BB
☎ *(01635) 248200* Alan Hodge

🍺 West Berkshire Brewery's Good Old Boy and Brakspear brews regularly available, with three weekly changing guests from breweries such as Cottage, Moles, Shepherd Neame or Morrells.

A one-bar freehouse with restaurant and attractive garden. Food available every lunchtime and Tues–Sat evenings. Children allowed in the restaurant area. Located off the B4494.

OPEN *11am–3pm and 6–11pm every day (10.30pm Sun).*

YOU TELL US

★ *The Belgian Arms*, Holyport Street, Holyport, Nr Maidenhead
★ *The Brewery Tap* (brewpub), 27 Castle Street, Reading
★ *The Cooper's Arms*, 39 Bartholomew Street, Newbury
★ *The Cricketers*, Cricketer's Lane, Warfield
★ *The Crooked Billet*, Honey Hill, Wokingham
★ *The Dew Drop Inn*, Batt Green, Honey Lane, Hurley
★ *The Flower Pot Hotel*, Ferry Lane, Aston
★ *The Horse & Jockey*, 120 Castle Street, Reading
★ *The Nag's Head*, 28 High Street, Sunningdale
★ *Stocks Inn*, Beenham, Reading
★ *The Three Horseshoes*, Brimpton Lane, Brimpton
★ *The Vansittart Arms*, 105 Vansittart Road, Windsor

Places Featured:
Ashenden
Asheridge
Beaconsfield
Bradwell Common
Chesham
Cublington
Haddenham
Hedgerley
Ibstone
Little Marlow
Little Missenden
Littleworth Common

Loudwater
Marlow
New Bradwell
Newport Pagnell
North Crawley
Prestwood
Stoke Poges
Tatling End
The Lee
Thornborough
Wheeler End

THE BREWERIES

THE CHILTERN BREWERY
Nash Lee Road, Terrick, Aylesbury HP17 0TQ
☎ *(01296) 613647*

CHILTERN ALE 3.7% ABV
Pale, smooth and refreshing clean finish.
BEECHWOOD BITTER 4.3% ABV
Well-rounded, with nut flavours and a long finish.
THREE HUNDREDS OLD ALE 5.0% ABV
Dark, good body and long finish.

REBELLION BEER CO.
Bencombe Farm, Marlow Bottom Road,
Marlow SL7 3LT
☎ *(01628) 476594*

IPA 3.7% ABV
Balanced easy quaffer.
SMUGGLER 4.1% ABV
Well-rounded and full-flavoured.
MUTINY 4.5% ABV
Smooth and hoppy.
Plus seasonal and monthly brews.

SAM TRUEMAN'S BREWERY
The Little Brewery, Henley House, School Lane,
Medmenham SL7 2HJ
☎ *(01491) 576100*

BEST 3.5% ABV
TIPPLE 4.2% ABV
GOLD 5.0% ABV

VALE BREWERY CO. LTD
Thame Road, Haddenham HP17 8BY
☎ *(01844) 290008*

NOTLEY ALE 3.3% ABV
Bitter and refreshing.
WYCHERT ALE 3.9% ABV
Smooth and mellow flavours.
HADDA'S SUMMER GLORY 4.0% ABV
EDGAR'S GOLDEN ALE 4.3% ABV
Pale and hoppy.
HADDA'S AUTUMN ALE 4.5% ABV
HADDA'S SPRING GOLD 5.0% ABV
GOOD KING SENSELESS 5.2% ABV

THE PUBS

ASHENDEN

Gatehangers
Lower End, Ashenden HP18 0HE
☎ *(01296) 651296*

Wadworth IPA and 6X, Adnams Best and a Badger brew always available plus a guest beer (up to 30 per year) from breweries such as Mole's, Elgood's, Hook Norton, Felinfoel, Everard's, Bateman's, Smiles, or Marston's.

A 300-year-old country pub with traditional atmosphere. Beamed in part with open fires and large L-shaped bar. Bar food at lunchtime and evenings. Car park and garden. Children allowed. Twenty minutes to Oxford. Between the A41 and A418 west of Aylesbury, near the church.

OPEN *12–2.30pm and 7–11pm.*

ASHERIDGE

The Blue Ball
Asheridge, Chesham, HP5 2UX
☎ *(01494) 758263 Peter George*

A freehouse, whose June beer festival offers at least 32 real ales. Greene King IPA and Fuller's London Pride are always available plus two guest beers, changed weekly, which may come from Adnams, Brakspear, Cottage, Orkney, Rebellion or Arundel breweries.

A traditional pub built in 1851, two miles north of Chesham, with a mixed clientele. Non-smoking function room, big garden. Food served at lunchtime and evenings. Children allowed in dining area.

OPEN *12–2.30pm and 5.30–11pm Mon–Thur; 11am–11pm Fri–Sat; 12–10.30pm Sun.*

BEACONSFIELD

The Greyhound
33 Windsor End, Beaconsfield HP9 2JN
☎ *(01494) 673823 Jamie Godrich*

A freehouse, with Fuller's London Pride and Wadworth 6X always on sale. Two guest beers are also available, one changed weekly, one monthly, which may include Brakspear Special, Timothy Taylor Landlord, O'Hanlon's Spring Gold or something from the Vale or Cottage breweries.

A traditional public house with separate dining area. Food served at lunchtime and evenings. Children not admitted.

OPEN *11am–3pm and 5.30–11pm.*

BRADWELL COMMON

The Countryman
Bradwell Boulevard, Bradwell Common, Milton Keynes MK13 8EZ
☎ *(01908) 676346 Dave Keating*

A freehouse with eight cask ale pumps. Marston's Pedigree is among the regular brews served.

A one-bar pub built in 1986 in the middle of the estate. Popular with families. Food available. Children's room. Bradwell Boulevard is the main road through Bradwell Common.

OPEN *11am–11pm Mon–Sat; 12–10.30pm Sun.*

CHESHAM

The Black Horse
The Vale, Chesham, Bucks HP5 3MS
☎ *(01494) 784656 Lyn Hawkes*

Tied to Benskins (Carlsberg-Tetley), with four real ales. Regulars include Morland Old Speckled Hen, Black Stallion (5%, brewed specially by Tring Brewery) and Adnams Best Bitter.

A fourteenth-century coaching inn just outside Chesham (with certified ghosts!), mainly operating as a restaurant. Large garden. Children allowed in bar area.

OPEN *12–3pm and 6–11pm Mon–Sat (sometimes all day during summer); 12–10.30pm Sun.*

The Queens Head
120 Church Street, Old Chesham, Bucks HP5 1JD
☎ *(01494) 783773 Mr Shippey*

A freehouse offering five real ales. Brakspear's Bitter and Coniston Bluebird are regulars; other guests may include seasonal Brakspear brews and Fuller's London Pride.

A traditional family pub, offering English and Thai food in the bar, and a Thai restaurant. Children allowed.

OPEN *11am–2.30pm and 5–11pm Mon–Fri; 11am–3pm and 5–11pm Sat; 12–3pm and 7–10.30pm Sun.*

CUBLINGTON

The Unicorn

High Street, Cublington
☎ *(01296) 681261* Mr and Mrs Ibbotson

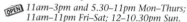 Five beers always available including brews from Morland plus Jennings Bitter and Shepherd Neame Spitfire Ale. Approx 100 guests per year including Vale Wychert Ale and Greene King Abbot.

A country pub dating from 1600 with open fires and low beams in the main bar. Bar and restaurant food served at lunchtime and evenings during the week. Car park and garden. Children allowed in the restaurant.

OPEN *12–3pm and 5.30–11pm.*

HADDENHAM

The Rising Sun

9 Thame Road, Haddenham HP17 8EN
☎ *(01844) 291744* Michael Mock

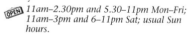 A freehouse with Charles Wells Eagle and IPA always on sale. Guest beers, including Badger Tanglefoot, Wadworth 6X and Morland Old Speckled Hen, change on a daily basis.

A village pub, on the main road from Thame to Aylesbury. Very much a drinker's pub, with bar snacks only. Children allowed until 7.30pm.

OPEN *11am–3pm and 5.30–11pm Mon–Thurs; 11am–11pm Fri–Sat; 12–10.30pm Sun.*

HEDGERLEY

The White Horse

Village Lane, Hedgerley, Slough SL2 3UY
☎ (01753) 643225 Mr and Mrs Hobbs

Seven or eight beers always available and dispensed by gravity including brews from Charles Wells and Greene King. Also dozens of guest beers from small breweries only.

B eer festival held every year. No machines, no music, no straight glasses. Bar food at weekends. Car park, garden. Bird sanctuary nearby.

OPEN *11am–2.30pm and 5.30–11pm Mon–Fri; 11am–3pm and 6–11pm Sat; usual Sun hours.*

IBSTONE

The Fox

The Common, Ibstone, Nr High Wycombe HP14 3GG
☎ *(01491) 638722* Mrs Banks

Brakspear ales always available plus three guests in summer, two in winter, serving a range of real ales such as Fuller's London Pride or Rebellion. Stocks beers from local breweries whenever possible.

A 300-year-old traditional country inn. Bar and restaurant food available lunchtimes and evenings. Accommodation. Children allowed.

OPEN *12–3pm and 6–11pm daily (10.30pm Sun).*

LITTLE MARLOW

The King's Head

Church Road, Little Marlow, Bucks SL7 3RZ
☎ *(01628) 484407* Tim Pegrum

Tied to Whitbread with up to six real ales. Fuller's London Pride, Timothy Taylor Landlord and something from Brakspear always on sale. Others, changed every three to four weeks, include Wadworth 6X, Greene King Abbot Ale, Marston's Pedigree and beers from Rebellion, Vale and Eccleshall breweries.

S ituated between Marlow and Bourne End, the pub has one large, comfortable bar, a non-smoking dining room, and a function room for 50–80 people. Food is served at lunchtime and evenings. Children welcome.

OPEN *11am–3pm and 5–11pm Mon–Fri; 11am–11pm Sat; 12–10.30pm Sun.*

LITTLE MISSENDEN

The Crown
Little Missenden HP7 0RD
☎ *(01494) 862571 Mr How*

A freehouse with four beers on pumps and occasionally one from the wood. Marston's Pedigree, Hook Norton Best and Bateman's brews are always on offer. Other guests, changed twice weekly, include Mordue Workie Ticket or something from Greene King, Brakspear, King and Barnes, Adnams, Rebellion or Vale breweries.

A country pub off the A413 coming from Amersham towards Aylesbury, with one bar and two real fires. Mixed clientele, no juke box or machines. Large garden. Food served at lunchtime only. Children allowed, but not in bar area.

11am–2.30pm and 6–11pm Mon–Sat; 12–3pm and 7–10.30pm Sun.

LITTLEWORTH COMMON

The Jolly Woodman
Littleworth Common, Burnham SL1 8PF
☎ *(01753) 644350 Debbie Akehurst*

A Whitbread-managed house with no restrictions on the guest beer policy so a good selection is maintained. Brakspear Bitter always available, plus four beers changed twice-weekly, including Rebellion Mutiny and Smuggler, Smiles March Hare, Caledonian Deuchars IPA, Timothy Taylor Landlord, Morland Old Speckled Hen, Wadworth 6X, Marston's Pedigree, Greene King Abbot Ale and seasonal beers.

A traditional seventeenth-century pub in the middle of Burnham Beeches. Lovely walks all around. Beer garden. Food available at lunchtime and evenings. Children allowed, but not at the bar.

11am–11pm Mon–Sat; 12–10.30pm Sun.

LOUDWATER

Derehams Inn
5 Derehams Lane, Loudwater HP14 3ND
☎ *(01494) 530965*
Graham and Margaret Sturgess

Eight beers always available including Fuller's London Pride, Young's Bitter, Brakspear Bitter, Timothy Taylor Landlord and two guest beers rotating constantly.

Small and cosy local freehouse. Bar food on weekdays at lunchtime. Car park, garden. Children allowed in the restaurant area. Less than a mile from M40 junction 3.

11.30am–3pm and 5.30–11pm.

MARLOW

The Prince of Wales
1 Mill Road, Marlow SL7 1PX
☎ *(01628) 482970 Mr WS Sarrell*

Tied to Whitbread, with Fuller's London Pride, Brakspear Bitter and Greene King IPA always served. A guest beer changes every three weeks. Brakspear Special, Wadworth 6X, Greene King Abbot and brews from Rebellion, Vale and Hook Norton are regular favourites.

A traditional pub just off the high street, with no juke box, pool, darts or alcopops. Food served at lunchtime and evenings. Separate dining area. Children allowed.

11am–11pm Mon–Sat; 12–10.30pm Sun.

NEW BRADWELL

The New Inn
2 Bradwell Road, New Bradwell, Milton Keynes MK13 0EN
☎ *(01908) 312094 Mr Fulker*

A Charles Wells tenanted house. Four real ales always available (Adnams Broadside, Morland Old Speckled Hen, Charles Wells Eagle and Bombardier) plus a guest beer, changed at least once a month.

Canalside, family-run traditional pub, with juke box, pool table and beer garden, between Newport Pagnell and Wolverton. Food available in a separate 70-seater restaurant. Children allowed. No restrictions on guests.

11.30am–11pm Mon–Sat; 12–10.30pm Sun.

NEWPORT PAGNELL

The Bull Inn
33 Tickford Street, Newport Pagnell MK16 9AE
☎ *(01908) 610325 Paul Hobbins*

A freehouse serving up to eight cask ales at any one time, with a minimum of two changed each week. Favourites include Hook Norton Best, Fuller's London Pride, Wadworth 6X and Ridleys Rumpus. Others might be Shepherd Neame Spitfire, Hampshire Pride of Romsey, Jennings Sneck Lifter, Burton Bridge Top Dog Stout and Ridleys ESX Best, to name but a few.

An old-fashioned coaching inn, just like pubs used to be! No music in lounge. Food at lunchtime and evenings. Children allowed. Take M1, junction 14; pub next door to the Aston Martin Lagonda factory.

11.30am–2.30pm and 5–11pm Mon–Fri; 11am–2.30pm and 6–11pm Sat; 12–3pm and 7–10.30pm Sun.

NORTH CRAWLEY

The Cock Inn

16 High Street, North Crawley, Newport Pagnell MK16 9LH
☎ *(01234) 391222* Mr Evans

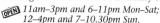 Tied to Charles Wells, serving four real ales at any one time. Adnams Broadside, Charles Wells Eagle and Morland Old Speckled Hen always available, plus a guest, changed every couple of months, from somewhere like Everards, Wadworth or Young's.

A very old, oak-beamed pub, built around 1460, next to the church in the village square. A broad cross-section of customers. Two bars and a family room. Food served at lunchtime and evenings, except Sunday evening. Children allowed in family room.

OPEN *11am–3pm and 6–11pm Mon–Sat; 12–4pm and 7–10.30pm Sun.*

PRESTWOOD

The King's Head

188 Wycombe Road, Prestwood HP16 0HJ
☎ *(01494) 868101* Simon Wiles

Marston's ales always available, including Pedigree and Owd Roger. The head brewer's choice changes every fortnight, providing 26 different beers through the year.

An old pub tastefully refurbished, offering a full range of meals from 12–10pm daily. Friendly service to tables or at the bar. Large car park. Children tolerated. Garden and barbecue. Take the A4128 from High Wycombe.

OPEN *11am–11pm Mon–Sat; 12–10.30pm Sun.*

STOKE POGES

Rose & Crown

Hollybush Hill, Stoke Poges SL2 4PW
☎ *(01753) 662148* Mr Holloran

A Morland tied house serving the Morland beers plus Adnams Broadside.

A traditional village pub with food served at lunchtimes. Well-behaved children allowed.

OPEN *11am–3pm and 5.30–11pm daily (10.30pm Sun).*

TATLING END

The Tatling Arms

Oxford Road, Tatling End SL9 7AT
☎ *(01753) 883100* Joe Cullan

A freehouse off the old A40 Oxford Road, formerly called The Stag and Griffin. Four real ales on offer, two (Fuller's London Pride and Rebellion IPA) always available, two as guests, changed monthly. Brakspear and Rebellion are favoured breweries.

A small 300-year-old listed building with a mixed clientele. Vehicles in the car park range from Rolls Royces to Transits. Food served all day. Children allowed.

OPEN *11am–11pm Mon–Sat; 12–10.30pm Sun.*

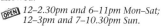
THE LEE

The Cock & Rabbit

The Lee, Great Missenden HP16 9LZ
☎ *(01494) 837540*

A freehouse, with four to five real ales always available. Permanent fixtures are Cock and Rabbit Bitter (brewed by Morland), Fuller's London Pride and Morland Old Speckled Hen. Other guests are changed seasonally.

A classic English pub with an Italian flavour. Restaurant, dining area and garden lounge. Food served lunchtimes and evenings, seven days a week. Children allowed.

OPEN *12–2.30pm and 6–11pm Mon–Sat; 12–3pm and 7–10.30pm Sun.*

The Old Swan

Swan Lane, Swan Bottom, The Lee, Great Missenden HP16 9NU
☎ *(01494) 837239* Sean Michaelson-Yeats

A freehouse, with Fuller's London Pride and something from Adnams and Brakspear always available.

A traditional sixteenth-century inn in the Chiltern Hills. Off the beaten track, it lies between Tring, Chesham, Great Missenden and Wendover. Food served at lunchtime and evenings. Restaurant area. Children allowed.

OPEN *12–3pm and 6–11pm; closed Mon except bank holidays.*

THORNBOROUGH

The Lone Tree

Bletchley Road, Thornborough MK18 2DZ
☎ *(01280) 812334* PB Taverner

Five beers available (over 850 served so far) produced by breweries stretching from Orkney to Cornwall, Norfolk to Wales. Plus one real cider.

S mall roadside pub with a large choice of food available at lunchtime and evenings. Car park and garden. Children allowed in the restaurant.

11.30am–3pm and 6–11pm Mon–Sat; 12–3pm and 6.30–10.30pm Sun.

WHEELER END

The Chequers

Bullocks Farm Lane, Wheeler End, High Wycombe HP14 3NH
☎ *(01494) 883070* Mr and Mrs Robinson

A freehouse with Brakspear Bitter, Fuller's London Pride, Greene King IPA and Adnams Broadside always on sale. Another guest beer is rotated, often from the local Vale Brewery.

A very old, beer pub. Beamed, inglenook fireplace, beer garden. Food served at lunchtime only. Supervised children allowed. Live music every Tuesday evening.

11am–2.30pm and 5.30–11pm Mon–Fri; 11am–11pm Sat; 12–10.30pm Sun.

YOU TELL US

★ *The Cock Inn*, High Street, Wing
★ *The Grapes*, 36 Market Square, Aylesbury
★ *The Green Man*, 92 Silver Street, Newport Pagnell
★ *The Greyhound*, West Edge, Marsh Gibbon
★ *The King's Arms*, 1 King Street, Chesham
★ *Prince Albert*, Moors End, Frieth
★ *The Red Lion*, Chenies
★ *The Rose & Crown*, Desborough Road, High Wycombe
★ *The Rose & Crown*, Vicarage Lane, Ivinghoe
★ *The Stag & Griffin*, Oxford Road, Tatling End
★ *Vaults Bar at The Bull Hotel*, 64 High Street, Stony Stratford

Places Featured:

Boxworth
Cambridge
Castle Camps
Deeping St James
Ely
Glinton
Graveley
Hinxton
Holywell
Huntingdon
Leighton Bromswold
March

Milton
Needingworth
Newton
Old Weston
Peterborough
St Ives
Stow cum Quay
Thriplow
Whittlesey
Wisbech
Woodston

THE BREWERIES

CITY OF CAMBRIDGE BREWERY LTD

19 Cheddars Lane, Cambridge CB5 8LD
☎ *(01223) 353939*

 JET BLACK 3.7% ABV
Smooth and dark.
BOAT HOUSE BITTER 3.8% ABV
Refreshing.
HOBSON'S CHOICE 4.1% ABV
Pale and hoppy.
ATOMSPLITTER 4.7% ABV
Full-bodied and hoppy.
PARKER'S PORTER 5.3% ABV
Good fruity hoppiness.
BRAMLING TRADITIONAL 5.5% ABV
Fruity.

ELGOOD AND SONS LTD

North Brink Brewery, Wisbech PE13 1LN
☎ *(01945) 583160*

 BLACK DOG MILD 3.6% ABV
Malty, dark mild with good balance.
CAMBRIDGE BITTER 3.8% ABV
Malt fruit flavours with dry finish.
PAGEANT ALE 4.3% ABV
Rounded and balanced with a bittersweet flavour.
GOLDEN NEWT 4.6% ABV
Dry and hoppy.
GREYHOUND STRONG BITTER 5.2% ABV
Bittersweet flavour.
Plus seasonal brews.

THE FENLAND BREWERY

Unit 4, Prospect Way, Chatteris PE16 6TY
☎ *(01354) 696776*

 FBB 4.0% ABV
SPARKLING WIT 4.5% ABV
DOCTOR'S ORDERS 5.0% ABV
RUDOLPH'S ROCKET FUEL 5.5% ABV

OAKHAM ALES

80 Westgate, Peterborough PE1 1RD
☎ *(01733) 358300*

 JEFFREY HUDSON BITTER 3.8% ABV
WHITE DWARF 4.3% ABV
BISHOP'S FAREWELL 4.6% ABV
MOMPESSONS GOLD 5.0% ABV
Plus seasonal brews.

ROCKINGHAM ALES

25 Wansford Road, Elton PE8 6RZ
☎ *(01832) 280722*

FINESHADE 3.8% ABV
ELTON PALE ALE 3.9% ABV
FOREST GOLD 3.9% ABV
A1 AMBER ALE 4.0% ABV
FRUITS OF THE FOREST 4.1% ABV
Plus seasonal and occasional brews.

BOXWORTH

The Golden Ball

High Street, Boxworth CB3 8LY
☎ *(01954) 267397* Mr and Mrs Arliss

 Beers available may include Hop Back Summer Lightning, Greene King IPA and Abbot, Everards Tiger and Nethergate Old Growler.

Typical country pub in good walking area. Bar and restaurant food at lunchtime and evenings. Meeting room, car park, disabled entrance and toilets. Large garden with separate entrance. Children allowed. Ten miles from Cambridge, six miles from St Ives.

OPEN *11.30am–2.30pm and 6.30–11pm.*

CAMBRIDGE

Ancient Druids

Napier Street, Cambridge CB1 1HR
☎ *(01223) 576324*

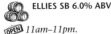 There are plans to expand the range of beers brewed here. They have recently begun producing a dark mild of about 3.3%. Plus a range of guest beers.

There is a history of brewing on the premises. Charles Wells originally set up business here and the present managers took over and restarted production in 1993. This big, bright pub enjoys a laid-back atmosphere, with a wide variety of customers including students and shoppers. Background music. Bar food available all day until 10pm. Children allowed.

🛢 **ELLIES SB 6.0% ABV**

OPEN *11am–11pm.*

Cambridge Blue

85–7 Gwydir Street, Cambridge CB1 2LG
☎ *(01223) 361382*
Mandy and Nick Winnington

Six beers at a time including Nethergate Bitter, IPA and Old Growler. Approx 140 guest beers per year with an avowed policy of trying as many new brews as possible.

Terraced side-street pub with large garden and two bars (one non-smoking). Healthy bar food at lunchtimes. Children allowed in conservatory area until 9pm. Off Mill Road on the city side of railway bridge.

OPEN *12–2.30pm (3.30pm Sat) and 6–11pm.*

The Elm Tree

42 Orchard Street, Cambridge, CB1 1JT
☎ *(01223) 363005* John Simons

A Charles Wells tenancy with Bombardier and Eagle IPA always on offer. Two guest beers, such as Adnams Best or Marston's Pedigree, are changed regularly.

A traditional one-bar pub off the city centre, near Grafton shopping centre, with large-screen TV and lots of table games (including chess). Rolls only served. No children allowed.

OPEN *12–2.30pm and 4 or 5–11.30pm Mon–Thurs; 11am–11pm Fri–Sat; 12–10.30pm Sun.*

Live and Let Live

40 Mawson Road, Cambridge CB1 2EA
☎ *(01223) 460261* Margaret Holliday

Seven beers available. The landlord deals mainly with Everards but also Adnams and B&T. The guest list (20 per year) includes Exmoor Stag, Felinfoel Double Dragon, Morland Old Speckled Hen, Shepherd Neame Bishops Finger, Badger Tanglefoot, Bateman Lincolnshire Yellow Belly and Victory Ale.

Situated in central Cambridge, off Mill Road, popular with students and business people alike. Wooden furniture and walls plus real gas lighting. Bar food available at lunchtime and evenings. Street parking. Children allowed in restaurant section.

OPEN *12–2.30pm and 6–11pm.*

St Radegund

129 King Street, Cambridge CB1 1LD
☎ *(01223) 311794* Terry Kavanagh

Four beers available, but nothing stronger than 4.7% ABV. Fuller's London Pride and Nethergate Bitter plus a selection (20 per year) from Timothy Taylor Landlord, Bateman XB, Badger Best, Mauldon's Best, Shepherd Neame Spitfire, Iceni Deirdre of Sorrows etc.

The smallest pub in Cambridge. CAMRA Pub of the Year 1993–94. No juke box, no games machines. Background jazz music. Filled rolls only. Children not allowed. Opposite the Wesley church in King Street.

OPEN *12–2.30pm and 5.30–11pm Mon–Fri; 12–11pm Sat; 6.30–10.30pm Sun.*

Tap & Spile
14 Mill Lane, Cambridge CB2 1RX
☎ *(01223) 357026* Peter Snellgrover

Approx 300 beers per year (nine at any one time) including brews from Adnams, Bateman, Black Sheep, Hadrian, Thwaites, Ushers, Nethergate and many other independent breweries.

Traditional alehouse with oak floors and exposed brickwork in picturesque setting right next to the river (perhaps the biggest beer garden in England?). Punting station nearby. Bar food at lunchtime.

OPEN *11am–11pm Mon–Sat; 12–3pm and 7–10.30pm Sun.*

Wrestlers
337 Newmarket Road, Cambridge CB5 8JE
☎ *(01223) 566553* Tom Goode

A house tied to Charles Wells, with Eagle IPA and Bombardier always served, plus two guest beers changed fortnightly. Favoured breweries include Lees, Archers, Morland, Caledonian and Adnams.

The pub specialises in Thai food. Children allowed.

OPEN *12–3pm and 5–11pm Mon–Sat; closed Sun.*

CASTLE CAMPS

The Cock Inn
High Street, Castle Camps, Cambridge CB1 6SN
☎ *(01799) 584207* Mr Puell

A freehouse always serving Greene King IPA plus a guest beer, which may be Fuller's London Pride, something from Nethergate or Shepherd Neame Spitfire. Changed weekly.

An olde-worlde drinkers' pub. Snacks available. Children allowed.

OPEN *12–2pm and 7–11pm Sun–Fri; 11am–11pm Sat.*

DEEPING ST JAMES

The Goat
155 Spalding Road, Frognall, Deeping St James, Nr Peterborough PE6 8SA
☎ *(01778) 347629* Peter Wilkins

Adnams Bitter plus up to five guest beers from micro-breweries and brewpubs. Over the past five years, more than 1,200 different guests have been served, from more than 280 breweries.

A country pub dating from 1640. Bar and restaurant food at lunchtime and evenings. Functions catered for. Car park, large beer garden with play equipment and children's room. On the old A16 between Market Deeping and Spalding.

OPEN *11am–2.30pm (3pm Sat) and 6–11pm Mon–Sat; 12–3pm and 6–10.30pm Sun.*

ELY

The Fountain
1 Silver Street, Ely CB7 4JF
☎ *(01353) 663122* John Borland

A freehouse with Adnams Best and Broadside plus Fuller's London Pride as permanent fixtures. A guest beer, changed frequently, could well be Charles Wells Bombardier.

A modern, one-bar pub. No food. Children allowed until 9pm.

OPEN *5–11.30pm Mon–Fri; 12–2pm and 6–11.30pm Sat; 12–2pm and 7–11pm Sun.*

GLINTON

The Blue Bell
10 High Street, Glinton, Peterborough PE6 7LS
☎ *(01733) 252285* Mr Mills

Tied to Greene King brewery and permanently serving IPA and Abbot Ale. Other guests from various breweries available.

A village pub with separate dining area. Food served at lunchtime and evenings. Children allowed.

OPEN *12–3pm Mon–Thurs; 11am–11pm Fri–Sat; 12–10.30pm Sun.*

GRAVELEY

The Three Horseshoes
23 High Street, Graveley, Huntingdon PE18 9PL
☎ *(01480) 830992* Mr Moss

A freehouse with three pumps serving a variety of guest beers, which change weekly, mainly from independent breweries such as Fenland, Judges and others.

A very old country inn, with no juke box or pool tables. Non-smoking eating area. Food at lunchtime and evening. Children allowed.

OPEN *11am–3pm and 6–11pm Mon–Sat; 12–3pm and 7–10.30pm Sun.*

HINXTON

The Red Lion
32 High Street, Hinxton, Cambridge CB10 1QX
☎ *(01799) 530601* Linda Crawford

A freehouse with Adnams Best and Woodforde's Wherry Best always on sale. There is also one guest.

A sixteenth-century pub half a mile south of junction 9 off the M11, with one bar and a non-smoking restaurant. Food served at lunchtime and evenings. Children allowed.

OPEN *11am–2.30pm and 6–11pm Mon–Sat; 12–2.30pm and 7–10.30pm Sun.*

The Ferryboat Inn
Holywell PE17 3TG
☎ *(01480) 463227* Joules Bonnett

Tied to Greene King, with IPA always available plus Marston's Pedigree. The four guests might include Fuller's London Pride, Timothy Taylor Landlord, Morland Old Speckled Hen or Greene King Abbot.

A remote pub in a rural setting down a country lane and overlooking a river. Ring for directions, if needed! With four small rooms for eating, plus a large function room. Emphasis on food, which is served at lunchtime and in evenings. Children allowed.

OPEN *12–3pm and 6–11pm Mon–Fri; 11am to 11pm Sat; 12–10.30pm Sun.*

The Old Bridge Hotel
1 High Street, Huntingdon PE18 6TQ
☎ *(01480) 452681* Mick Steiger

Adnams Best and City of Cambridge Hobson's Choice are always available, along with three guest beers.

A country-style, family-run pub on the ring road and easy to find. Food at lunchtime and in the evenings. Afternoon tea also served. Children and animals allowed. Live entertainment (including jazz) on the first Friday of each month.

OPEN *11am–11pm Mon–Sat; 12–10.30pm Sun.*

The Green Man
37 The Avenue, Leighton Bromswold, Nr Huntingdon PE18 0SH
☎ *(01480) 890238* Mr Hanagan

Timothy Taylor Landlord, Nethergate Bitter, Badger Tanglefoot and Fuller's London Pride always available plus two guest beers (150 per year) perhaps from Wadworth, Adnams, Nene Valley, Young's, Robinson's, Everards or Goddards breweries.

S eventeenth-century, detached public house with a collection of water jugs and memorabilia. Bar food available at lunchtime and evenings. Car park, garden, children's room. One mile off the A14.

OPEN *12–3pm and 7–11pm; closed Mon.*

The Rose & Crown
41 St Peters Road, March PE15 9NA
☎ *(01354) 652879* Mr D Evans

Up to six beers from a menu that changes on a daily basis. Caledonian Deuchars IPA and Marston's Pedigree are usually popular.

O lde-worlde pub. Non-smoking lounge bar. Bar snacks Thurs–Sat. No children.

OPEN *12–2.30pm and 7–11pm Mon–Fri (closed Wed lunchtime); 12–3pm and 7–11pm Sat–Sun.*

The Waggon & Horses
39 High Street, Milton CB4 6DF
☎ *(01223) 860313* Mr McDonald

More than 2,000 different beers have been served in this freehouse over the past three years. Bateman XB is permanently on offer, along with five others. Regular favourites include Cottage Champflower and Isle of Skye Avalanche.

A mock-Tudor building with separate dining area. Food at lunchtime and evenings. Children allowed with adult supervision.

OPEN *12–2.30pm and 5–11pm Mon–Fri; 11am–11pm Sat; 12–10.30pm Sun.*

The Queen's Head
30 High Street, Needingworth, Nr Huntingdon PE17 2SA
☎ *(01480) 463946* Mr and Mrs Vann

Six beers always available including Smiles Best, Woodforde's Wherry Best and Hop Back Summer Lightning. Approximately 100 guests per year including Nene Valley Old Black Bob, the Reindeer range, Timothy Taylor Landlord, Parish Somerby Premium, Butterknowle Conciliation, Hook Norton Best, Chiltern Beechwood, Sarah Hughes Dark Ruby Mild and brews from Wild's brewery.

F riendly pub. Bar snacks served 12–8pm. Car park and garden. Children allowed in lounge bar. Close to St Ives.

OPEN *12–11pm.*

NEWTON
Queen's Head
Newton, Nr Cambridge CB2 5PG
☎ *(01223) 870436* Mr David Short

 Has specialised in Adnams beers for the past 30 years. Best Bitter and Broadside always available plus Old Ale in winter and Tally Ho at Christmas.

A typical early eighteenth-century pub beside the village green. Bar food at lunchtime and evenings. Bar games. Children's room, various bar games. Three miles from M11 junction 10; less than two miles off the A10 at Harston.

11.30am–2.30pm and 6–11pm Mon–Sat; 12–2.30pm and 7–10.30pm Sun.

OLD WESTON
The Swan
Main Road, Old Weston, Huntingdon PE17 5LL
☎ *(01832) 293400* Jim Taylor

Greene King Abbot, Adnams Best and Broadside are always available in this free house, along with two guest beers each week. Hook Norton Old Hooky is regularly featured.

A restaurant/pub, with a fish and chip night each Wednesday. Children allowed.

6.30–11.30pm Mon–Fri; 11am–11pm Sat; 12–10.30pm Sun.

PETERBOROUGH
Bogart's Bar and Grill
17 North Street, Peterborough PE1 2RA
☎ *(01733) 349995*

A house beer brewed by Eldridge Pope plus six guest beers always available from a varied selection (300+ per year) usually ranging in strength from a mild at 3.0% to 5.5% ABV. The pub hosts a regional beer festival at the start of each month, featuring brewers from a specific part of the United Kingdom. Real cider also available.

B ogart's was built at the turn of the century and now has a wide-ranging clientele of all ages. The horseshoe-shaped bar is decorated with film posters and Humphrey Bogart features prominently. There is background music but no juke box or pool table. Bar food available at lunchtime. Car park opposite and beer garden. Children not allowed. Located off the main Lincoln Road.

11am–11pm Mon–Sat; closed Sun.

Charters Cafe Bar
Town Bridge, Peterborough PE1 1DG
☎ *(01733) 315700* Paul Hook

Oakham JHB plus Fuller's London Pride and Everards Tiger always available. Also up to eight (400 per year) guest beers from every independent brewery possible.

A floating connected Dutch barge moored in the centre of town. CAMRA Pub of the Year 1994. Bar and restaurant food available at lunchtime and evenings. Parking and garden. Children allowed. Town Bridge crosses the River Nene in central Peterborough.

12–11pm.

ST IVES
The Royal Oak
13 Crown Street, St Ives PE17 4EB
☎ *(01480) 462586* Miss M Pilson

A freehouse with Marston's Pedigree always on sale. Five guests, changed weekly might include something from breweries such as Smiles or Maclays.

A n old-style pub with one bar. Food served from 12–2pm. Children allowed until 7pm.

11am–11pm Mon–Sat; 12–10.30pm Sun.

STOW CUM QUY
Prince Albert
Newmarket Road, Stow cum Quy CB5 9AQ
☎ *(01223) 811294* Mr and Mrs Henderson

Five beers always available including Greene King IPA. Guests might include Ash Vine Bitter, Stormforce Ten, Worzel Wallop and Shardlow Reverend Eaton's Ale.

L ively roadside pub built in 1830. Bar and restaurant food served at lunchtime and weekend evenings. Private functions catered for. Car park and garden. Children allowed. Just off A14 on the Newmarket road (A1303).

11am–3.30pm and 5–11pm Mon–Fri; all day Sat–Sun.

White Swan
Main Street, Stow cum Quy CB5 9AB
☎ *(01223) 811821* Mr A Cocker

Among those beers always available are Greene King IPA, Adnams Best, Shepherd Neame Spitfire and Woodforde's Wherry Best plus a guest beer changed fortnightly. Regulars include Everards Tiger, Fuller's London Pride and something from Charles Wells.

A freehouse and restaurant with one small public bar. No smoking. Food served at lunchtime and Tue–Sun evenings. Children allowed but no facilities for them.

11am–3pm and 6–11pm Tue–Sat; 12–3pm and 7–10.30pm Sun.

THRIPLOW

The Green Man
2 Lower Street, Thriplow SG8 7RJ
☎ *(01763) 208855* DS and RJ Ward

 Adnams Best Bitter, Hook Norton Best and Timothy Taylor Landlord always available plus two or three guests beers (30 per year) from Felinfoel, Nethergate, Bateman, Black Sheep or Morland breweries.

Open-plan, two-bar pub by the village green with small non-smoking dining area. Formerly Charles Wells. Bar and restaurant food available at lunchtime and evenings (not Sunday). Car park and garden. Children not allowed. Turn off the A505 near the Imperial War Museum, Duxford.

OPEN *12–3pm Mon–Sat; 12–3pm and 7–10.30pm Sun.*

WHITTLESEY

The Boat Inn
2 Ramsey Road, Whittlesey, Nr Peterborough PE7 1DR
☎ *(01733) 202488*

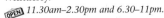 Elgood's Cambridge Bitter and Pageant Ale always available plus Black Dog Mild in May. Guest beers (12 per year) have included Morrells Graduate, Crouch Vale Millennium Gold and Mitchell's Lancaster Bomber.

A seventeenth-century pub on a site mentioned in the Domesday Book. Large informal bar, plus small restaurant featuring the bow of a boat as the bar. Resident ghost! Bar and restaurant food at lunchtime and evenings. Car park and garden. Children allowed. Ask for directions on reaching Whittlesey.

OPEN *11.30am–2.30pm and 6.30–11pm.*

WISBECH

The Rose Tavern
53 North Brink, Wisbech PE13 1JX
☎ *(01945) 588335*

 Everards Beacon and Morrells ales always available, plus guest beers.

A 200-year-old listed building forming a comfortable, one-roomed pub on the banks of the river. The closest pub to Elgood's Brewery. Outdoor area, wheelchair access, traditional pub games, accommodation.

OPEN *12–3pm and 5.30–11pm.*

WOODSTON

Palmerston Arms
82 Oundle Road, Woodston, Peterborough PE2 9PA
☎ *(01733) 565865* Mrs P Patterson

 A freehouse always offering Hop Back Summer Lightning and Batemans XB, with regular guest beers including Shepherd Neame Spitfire, Church End Vicar's Ruin and RCH Pitchfork.

A traditional pub with lounge and public bar. All beers straight from the barrel, gravity from cellar. No food. No children.

OPEN *11am–11pm Mon–Sat; 12–10.30pm Sun. Closed bank holidays.*

YOU TELL US

★ *The Blue Bell*, Welland Road, Dogsthorpe, Peterborough
★ *Chequers*, 71 Main Road, Little Gransden
★ *The Golden Pheasant*, 1 Main Street, Etton
★ *The Green Man*, London Road, Six Mile Bottom
★ *Hand & Heart*, 12 Highbury Street, Peterborough
★ *The Hardwicke Arms*, Ermine Way, Arrington
★ *Millstone*, Millstone Lane, Barnack
★ *Pig & Abbot*, High Street, Abingdon Piggots
★ *The Plough*, St Peters Street, Duxford
★ *The Ship*, Brandon Creak

Places Featured:

Appleton Thorn
Aston
Chester
Frodsham
Great Sutton
Heaton Norris
Langley

Macclesfield
Mobberley
Nantwich
Stalybridge
Strines
Tushingham
Warrington

THE BREWERIES

BEARTOWN BREWERY
Unit 9, Varey Road, Eaton Bank Industrial Estate, Congleton, CW12 1UW
☎ *(01260) 299964*

KODIAK BEAR 4.0% ABV
BEAR ASS 4.0% ABV
BEARSKINFUL 4.2% ABV

BURTONWOOD BREWERY PLC
Bold Lane, Burtonwood, Warrington WA5 4PJ
☎ *(01925) 225131*

MILD 3.0% ABV
Dark and mellow with malt.
BITTER 3.7% ABV
Rich, smooth malt flavour. Hoppy aroma.
JAMES FORSHAW BITTER 4.0% ABV
Distinctive, full-bodied malt flavour.
TOP HAT 4.8% ABV
Rich flavour with dry hop character
BUCCANEER 5.2% ABV
Smooth and complex, with a light colour.

COACH HOUSE BREWING CO. LTD
Wharf Street, Howley, Warrington WA1 2DQ
☎ *(01925) 232800*

COACHMAN'S BEST BITTER 3.7% ABV
Smooth, rich malt flavour, with some fruit.
GUNPOWDER STRONG MILD 3.8% ABV
Full flavour, with slight bitter aftertaste.
OSTLERS SUMMER PALE ALE 4.0% ABV
SQUIRES GOLD SPRING ALE 4.2% ABV
DICK TURPIN 4.2% ABV
Golden and smooth with good hoppiness.
INNKEEPER'S SPECIAL RESERVE 4.5% ABV
Crisp and malty with balancing hops.
POSTHORN PREMIUM 5.0% ABV
Rich, smooth and complex.
TAVERNERS AUTUMN ALE 5.0% ABV

FREDERIC ROBINSON LTD
Unicorn Brewery, Stockport SK1 1JJ
☎ *(0161) 480 6571*

HATTERS MILD 3.3% ABV
Fresh, with malt throughout.
OLD STOCKPORT BITTER 3.5% ABV
Golden, with a hoppy flavour.
XB 4.0% ABV
Malt flavour with hoppy bitterness.
BEST BITTER 4.2% ABV
Light in colour with a bitter hop taste and aroma.
FREDERIC'S 5.0% ABV
Smooth and well-balanced, gold in colour.
OLD TOM 8.5% ABV
Superb, mellow winter warmer.

STORM BREWING CO.
15 Larkhill Crescent, Macclesfield
☎ *(0161) 908 5032*

 ALE FORCE 4.2% ABV

WEETWOOD ALES LTD
The Brewery, Weetwood, Tarporley CW6 0NQ
☎ *(01829) 752377*

BEST BITTER 3.8% ABV
Sharp with a hoppy finish.
EASTGATE ALE 4.2% ABV
Golden, with fruity hoppiness.
OLD DOG BITTER 4.5% ABV
Deep colour, smooth and rich.
OASTHOUSE GOLD 5.0% ABV
Pale and hoppy with a dry finish.

THE PUBS

APPLETON THORN

Appleton Thorn Village Hall

*Stretton Road, Appleton Thorn, Nr Warrington
WA4 4RT*
☎ *(01925) 261187* Mr and Mrs P White

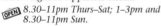 Coach House brews always available plus five guest beers (500 per year) and real cider.

A charitable village club operated voluntarily by local residents. 1994 CAMRA club of the year. Car park, garden and children's room. Boule, pool and darts. From M6 junction 20 or M56 junction 10, follow signs to Appleton Thorn.

OPEN *8.30–11pm Thurs–Sat; 1–3pm and
8.30–11pm Sun.*

ASTON

Bhurtpore Inn

Wrenbury Road, Aston, Nr Nantwich CW5 8DQ
☎ *(01270) 780917* Simon and Nicky George

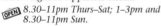 Hanby Drawwell always available plus nine guest beers (over 800 per year) which may include a brew from Tomlinson's, Burton Bridge, Weetwood, Adnams, Slaters (Eccleshall), Bateman, Black Sheep and Rudgate. Also real cider and 180 bottled Belgian beers plus three Belgian beers on draught.

T he family has been connected with this comfortable, traditional, award-winning pub since 1849. Fresh bar and restaurant food at lunchtime and evenings. Car park, garden. Children allowed in pub at lunchtime and in early evening. Located just west of the A530, midway between Nantwich and Whitchurch.

OPEN *12–2.30pm and 6.30–11pm Mon–Sat;
12–3pm and 7–10.30pm Sun.*

CHESTER

The George & Dragon Hotel

Liverpool Road, Chester CH2 1AA
☎ *(01244) 380714* Tony Chester

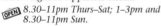 A huge range of real ales always available in this freehouse. Castle Eden Ale, Flowers IPA and Original plus Boddingtons Mild are permanent fixtures. Regular guests, changed weekly, include Wadworth 6X, Titanic White Star, Timothy Taylor Landlord, Morland Old Speckled Hen, Fuller's London Pride and Greene King Abbot Ale.

A pub with a traditional atmosphere. Separate dining area and background music. Hotel accommodation. Food served at lunchtime and evenings. Children not allowed.

OPEN *11am–11pm Mon–Sat; 12–10.30pm Sun.*

The Mill Hotel

Milton Street, Chester CH1 3NF
☎ *(01244) 350035*

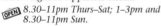 CAMRA Pub of the Year 1996 offering up to 15 real ales. Five permanent beers come from the Coach House brewery plus ten guests that change on a daily basis including one mild. An average of at least 800 different ales from all over the country are served each year.

H otel bar and restaurant on the site of a working mill, which is visible behind glass walls. Bar and restaurant food available at lunchtime and evenings. Canalside patio, restaurant boat lunch and dinner cruises. Accommodation available, families most welcome and ample car parking.

OPEN *11am–11pm Mon–Sat; 12–10.30pm Sun.*

The Union Vaults

44 Egerton Street, Chester CH1 3ND
☎ *(01244) 322170* Miss Lee

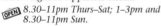 Former Greenalls pub offering Plassey Bitter from Wrexham and Greenalls Bitter plus two guests, which are changed weekly.

A little local alehouse, five minutes from Chester train station, this is a drinker's pub with one bar. No food. Children allowed.

OPEN *11am–11pm Mon–Sat; 12–10.30pm Sun.*

Netherton Hall
Chester Road, Frodsham WA6 6UL
☎ *(01928) 732342 Mr Rowland*

A freehouse with a Jennings brew a permanent fixture plus four guest beers rotated every other day. Regulars include beers from Weetwood, Burtonwood, Phoenix and Hanby.

A typical Cheshire country pub on the main road, with one large bar, half of which is smoking and half non-smoking. Food served at lunchtime and evenings, and all day Friday and Saturday. Well-behaved children allowed.

OPEN *11am–11pm Mon–Sat; 12–10.30pm Sun.*

Rowland's Bar
31 Church Street, Frodsham WA6 6PN
☎ *(01928) 733361 Matt and Nick Rowland*

Weetwood Best Bitter always available plus four from around 250 guest beers per year, mostly from independent breweries such as Oak, Coach House, Cains, Hanby and Dyffryn Clwyd.

One-room public bar with restaurant above. Bar and restaurant food at lunchtime and evenings. Restaurant closed Saturday lunchtime and all day Sunday. Parking. Children allowed in restaurant. In the main shopping area, close to British Rail station.

OPEN *11am–11pm.*

The White Swan Inn
Old Chester Road, Great Sutton CH66 3NZ
☎ *(0151) 339 9284 Denise Hardy*

Tied to the Burtonwood Brewery, offering five different brews a week, the Burtonwood range plus guests such as Shepherd Neame Bishops Finger and Jennings Sneck Lifter.

A community local, off the main road (not signposted), with Sky TV and pub grub served at lunchtime and evenings. No children allowed.

OPEN *11am–11pm Mon–Sat; 12–10.30pm Sun.*

The Crown Inn
154 Heaton Lane, Heaton Norris, Stockport SK4 1AR
☎ *(0161) 429 8646 Steven James*

JW Lees beers always available, plus a wide range of guest beers, hundreds each year and up to ten at any one time. Examples include Phoenix Thirsty Moon, Kelham Island Bitter and Golden Eagle, and Princetown Jail Ale.

Cosy five-roomed pub with small bar and cobbled beer garden. Cheap and cheerful bar food at lunchtime. Car park 50 yards away. Non-smoking room. Children allowed. Underneath the viaduct.

OPEN *12–11.30pm Mon–Sat; 12–3.30pm and 7–10.30pm Sun.*

Leathers Smithy
Langley, Nr Macclesfield SK11 0NE
☎ *(01260) 252313*

Morland Old Speckled Hen and Timothy Taylor Landlord always available, plus alternating guests.

A former smithy (originally run by William Leather), built in the sixteenth century in beautiful surroundings on the edge of Macclesfield Forest overlooking the Ridge Gate Reservoir (fishing possible). Food available at lunchtime and evenings. Also 80 different whiskies. Car park, garden, family/function room.

OPEN *12–3pm and 7–11pm Mon–Thurs and Sat; 12–3pm and 5.30–11pm Fri; 12–10.30pm Sun.*

Waters Green Tavern
96 Waters Green, Macclesfield SK11 6LH
☎ *(01625) 422653 Mr MacDermott*

Up to four beers available. Regular guests might come from Exmoor, Whim and Lloyds breweries.

A traditional pub with food served at lunchtime only. Children not allowed.

OPEN *11.30am–3pm and 5.30–11pm Mon–Sat; 7–11pm Sun.*

MOBBERLEY

The Roebuck Inn
Mill Lane, Mobberley WA16 7XH
☎ *(01565) 872757* Dave Robinson

A freehouse with regular guests, changed weekly, that may include Hydes' Anvil Bitter, Shepherd Neame Spitfire or Elgood's Pageant Ale.

An old-fashioned country inn, formerly a coach house. Food served at lunchtime and evenings. Children allowed.

OPEN *11am–11pm Mon–Sat; 12–10.30pm Sun.*

NANTWICH

The Black Lion
29 Welsh Row, Nantwich CW5 5ED
☎ *(01270) 628711* Jill Llewellyn

A three-pump freehouse with Weetwood Old Dog and Best Bitter plus Titanic Premium always available.

A traditional two-bar pub. Food at lunchtime and evenings. No children.

OPEN *11am–11pm Mon–Sat; 12–10.30pm Sun.*

Wilbraham Arms
58 Welsh Row, Nantwich CW5 5EJ
☎ *(01270) 626419*

Marston's Pedigree and Banks' Best Bitter always available.

Close to the town centre, near canal, with traditional Georgian frontage, bar and dining area. Bar food available at lunchtime and evenings. Small car park, accommodation. Children allowed in dining room.

OPEN *12–11pm Mon–Sat; 12–10.30pm Sun.*

STALYBRIDGE

The Buffet Bar
Stalybridge Railway Station, Stalybridge SK15 1RF
☎ *(0161) 303 0007*

Seven or eight real ales available. Wadworth 6X is a permanent fixture plus a constantly changing range of guest beers from independent breweries.

A unique and authentic buffet bar built in 1855 with a real fire, real ale, and real people! Bar food available at most times. Parking. Children allowed. On platform one at Stalybridge railway station.

OPEN *11am–11pm Mon–Sat; 12–10.30pm Sun.*

Q Inn
3 Market Street, Stalybridge SK15 2AL
☎ *(0161) 303 9157* David Conner

Beers from Marston and Thwaites always available. Guest beers (200 per year) from Gibbs Mew, Phoenix, Hull, Hart, Bateman, Fuller's, Wadworth and Exmoor breweries also served.

The pub with the shortest name in Britain forms part of the Stalybridge Eight – eight pubs in the town offering 37 different beers. Brick walls and a flagstone floor. Quiz night on Monday, Cocktail bar on Friday. No food. Next to the railway station.

OPEN *5–11pm Mon–Sat; 12–3pm and 7–10.30pm Sun.*

The White House
1 Water Street, Stalybridge SK15 2AG
☎ *(0161) 303 2288* Mr Connor

A freehouse with a good range of real ales always available. Exmoor Gold, Greene King Abbot, a Marston's brew and a Timothy Taylor brew are permanent fixtures, plus four guests such as Morland Old Speckled Hen or Moorhouses Pendle Witches Brew.

A traditional town-centre working-man's pub. Snacks only. Children allowed until 8pm.

OPEN *All day, every day.*

STRINES

The Sportsman's Arms

105 Strines Road, Strines SK12 3AE
☎ *(0161) 427 2888*

Cain's Mild and Bitter always available, plus a weekly alternating guest from any independent brewery.

An old, two-roomed pub with a lounge/dining room. Home-cooked food is available at lunchtime and evenings. Car park, garden. On the B6101.

12–3pm and 5.15–11pm Mon–Fri; all day Sat and Sun.

TUSHINGHAM

The Blue Bell Inn

Tushingham, Nr Whitchurch
☎ *(01948) 662172* Patrick and Lydia Gage

Hanby Drawwell Bitter always available plus one or two others (20 per year), perhaps including beers from Plassey, Joule, Hadrian, Cains and Felinfoel breweries.

Dating from 1667, this claims to be Cheshire's oldest pub, with an American landlord and Russian landlady. Friendly and welcoming. No games machines or loud music. Sunday papers and comfortable settee. Bar and restaurant food available at lunchtime and evenings. Car park and garden. Children and dogs always very welcome. Four miles north of Whitchurch on the A41 Chester road.

12–3pm and 6–11pm Mon–Sat; 7–11pm Sun.

WARRINGTON

The Old Town House

Buttermarket Street, Warrington WA1 2NL
☎ *(01925) 242787* Roy Baxter

A five-pump freehouse, always serving Marston's Pedigree and Morland Old Speckled Hen.

A country town pub with one bar, situated in the main street leading into the town centre. Food served at lunchtime only. Children allowed.

11am–11pm Mon–Sat; 12–10.30pm Sun.

YOU TELL US

★ *The Albion*, 1 Pedley Street, Crewe
★ *The Ferry Tavern*, Station Road, Great Sankey, Warrington
★ *George & the Dragon*, 61 Rainbow Road, Higher Hurdsfield, Macclesfield
★ *The Lion & Railway Hotel*, Station Road, Nantwich
★ *The Railway*, Station Road, Handforth
★ *The Royal Oak*, 41 Sandbach Road, Rode Heath
★ *The Swan*, 2 Swan Street, Wilmslow
★ *Willey Moor Lock*, Taporley Road, Willey Moor

Places Featured:

Altarnun
Blisland
Crackington Haven
Charlestown
Crantock
Edmonton
Falmouth
Golant
Gunnislake
Hayle
Helston
Lerryn
Lostwithiel
Nancenoy

Penzance
Polperro
Porthallow
Porthleven
Quintrell Downs
St Cleer
Stratton
Trebarwith Strand
Tregrehan
Tresparrett
Truro
Widemouth Bay
Zelah

BREWERIES

ST AUSTELL BREWERY CO. LTD
63 Trevarthian Road, St Austell PL25 4BY
☎ *(01726) 74444*

BOSUN'S BITTER 3.1% ABV
Well-balanced, sweeter light flavour.
XXXX MILD 3.6% ABV
Dark and distinctive, with malt flavour.
TINNERS ALE 3.7% ABV
Well-balanced hops and malt throughout.
TRELAWNY'S PRIDE 4.4% ABV
Pale golden, malty. Smooth hoppy finish.
HICKS SPECIAL DRAUGHT 5.0% ABV
Powerful and distinctive.
WINTER WARMER 6.0% ABV
Full-flavoured, with malt throughout.

SHARP'S BREWERY
Rock, Wadebridge PL27 6NU
☎ *(01208) 862121*

CORNISH COASTER 3.6% ABV
DOOM BAR BITTER 4.0% ABV
OWN 4.4% ABV
SPECIAL ALE 5.2% ABV

SKINNER'S BREWING CO.
Riverside View, Newham, Truro TR1 2SU
☎ *(01872) 271885*

SPRIGGAN ALE 3.8% ABV
Quenching, with flavour of hops.
BETTY STOGS BITTER 4.0% ABV
Light-coloured, with hops throughout.
CORNISH KNOCKER 4.5% ABV
Gold in colour and refreshing.
FIGGY'S BREW 4.5% ABV
Rich and well-rounded.
SKILLIWIDDEN ALE 5.1% ABV
Malty with good balancing hoppiness.

VENTONWYN BREWING CO. LTD
Unit 2b, Grampound Road, Truro TR2
☎ *(01726) 884367*

LEVANT GOLDEN 4.0% ABV
OLD PENDEEN 4.0% ABV
CORNISH GLORY 4.2% ABV

THE PUBS

ALTARNUN

The Rising Sun

Altarnun, Nr Launceston PL15 7SN
☎ *(01566) 86332* Mr and Mrs Manson

Up to six beers available, including brews from Sharp's, Hoskins & Oldfield, Cotleigh, Skinner's, Butcombe, Otter and Exe Valley. Continually changing.

Sixteenth-century, single-bar pub with open fires and slate/hardwood floor. Bar food available at lunchtime and evenings. Ample parking. Children allowed. One mile off the A30, seven miles west of Launceston.

OPEN *11am–3pm and 5.30–11pm Mon–Fri; 11am–11pm Sat; 12–10.30pm Sun. Open all day, every day, during summer season.*

BLISLAND

Blisland Inn

The Green, Blisland, nr Bodmin PL30 4JF
☎ *(01208) 850739* Mr Marshall

Six pumps with guests changing every couple of days. Skinner's Cornish Ales are regulars.

Country-style freehouse, with lounge, public bar and family room. Separate dining area for bar food served at lunchtime and evenings. Children allowed in family room.

OPEN *11.30am–3.30pm and 6–11pm Mon–Thurs; 11am–11pm Fri–Sat; 12–10.30pm Sun.*

CRACKINGTON HAVEN

Coombe Barton Inn

Crackington Haven, Bude EX23 0JG
☎ *(01840) 230345* Mr Cooper

A freehouse offering eight beers including four guests. Sharp's Doom Bar and Dartmoor Best are always available. Regular guests come from St Austell and Sharp's breweries.

A seaside family-run pub on the sea front, with separate dining area and family room. Six rooms available for bed and breakfast. Food at lunchtime and evenings. Children allowed in family room.

OPEN *Summer: 11am–11pm Mon–Sat; 12–10.30pm Sun; winter: 11am–3pm and 6–11pm.*

CHARLESTOWN

Rashleigh Arms

Charlestown Road, Charlestown, St Austell PL25 3NJ
☎ *(01726) 73635* Glen Price

A 14-pump freehouse, Wadworth 6X and Sharp's Doom Bar among those always available. Two guests are changed twice a week. Skinner's ales are often featured.

A country pub with family room, TV and juke box, plus entertainment in winter. Food served at lunchtimes and evenings. Children allowed.

OPEN *11am–11pm Mon–Sat; 12–10.30pm Sun.*

CRANTOCK

Old Albion

Langurroc Road, Crantock, Newquay TR8 5RB
☎ *(01637) 830243*
Mr Andrew Brown and Miss S. Moses

Sharp's and St Austell beers always available. Three guests, changed frequently, might include Cotleigh brews, Morland Old Speckled Hen, Exmoor Gold and Fuller's London Pride.

A country pub, which used to be used for smuggling beer, situated next to the church in Crantock. Homemade food served at lunchtime and evenings in bar area. Children allowed in family room.

OPEN *12–11pm.*

EDMONTON

The Quarryman

Edmonton, Wadebridge PL27 7JA
☎ *(01208) 816444* Terrence de-Villiers Kuun

A four-pump freehouse, with guest beers changed every two or three days. Favourites include Skinner's and Sharp's brews plus Cottage Golden Arrow.

An old Cornish inn with separate restaurant and bar food. Food served at lunchtime and evenings. Well-behaved children allowed.

OPEN *11am–11pm Mon–Sat; 12–10.30pm Sun.*

The Quayside Inn

41 Arwenack Street, Falmouth TR11 3JQ
☎ *(01326) 312113* Mr and Mrs Keir

Up to 15 beers always available, including Sharp's Cornish Coaster. More than 500 guest beers per year from Fuller's, Young's, Bateman, Smiles, Exmoor, Cotleigh, Gibbs Mew, Shepherd Neame, Hook Norton, Hop Back, Summerskills and other independent breweries from around the country.

T wice-yearly beer festivals at this waterside pub with two bars – comfy upstairs lounge and downstairs real ale bar with free peanuts. Bar food at lunchtime and evenings with local fresh fish. Also sells 200 whiskies including 179 single malts. Parking and garden. Children allowed. On Custom House Quay, overlooking Falmouth harbour.

Both bars all day in summer. Ale house all day in winter.

The Fisherman's Arms

Fore Street, Golant, Fowey PL23 1LN
☎ *(01726) 832453* Michael Moran

An Ushers pub with Best and Founders Ale always served.

A village pub on the banks of the River Fowey. Food at lunchtime and evening. Children allowed.

12–3pm and 6–11pm Mon–Fri; 11am–11pm Sat; 12–10.30am Sun.

Rising Sun Inn

Calstock Road, Gunnislake PL18 9BX
☎ *(01822) 832201* Mr Steve Jefferies

A freehouse with Sharp's Cornish Coaster as a permanent fixture. Four guests may include Sharp's Own, Everards Tiger and Otter Bright.

A very olde-worlde pub on the outskirts of Gunnislake (not on the main road; signposts are coming!). Food at lunchtime and evenings. Well-behaved children allowed.

12–2.30pm and 5–11pm Mon–Sat; 12–3pm and 7–10.30pm Sun.

Bird in Hand

Trelissick Road, Hayle TR27 4HY
☎ *(01736) 753974* Mr Miller

A freehouse and brewpub serving a range of own brews, plus two guest beers, perhaps including Greene King Abbot or Shepherd Neame Spitfire.

A n old coach house with one bar. Live music. Food at lunchtime and evenings (summer only). Children allowed.

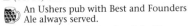 **PARADISE 3.8–4.0% ABV**
A light session bitter.
MILLER'S 4.2–4.4% ABV
A medium light bitter.
SPECKLED PARROT 5.5–6.5% ABV
A dark ale.

11am–11pm Mon–Sat; 12–10.30pm Sun.

The Blue Anchor

50 Coinagehall Street, Helston TR13 8EX
☎ *(01326) 562821*

One of only four pubs in Britain which has brewed continuously for centuries and still produces its famous Spingo ales, from a Victorian word for strong beer.

T his thatched town pub was originally a monks' rest home in the fifteenth century. Brewing continued on the premises after the Reformation and the Blue Anchor is now believed to be the oldest brewpub in Britain. Bar snacks and meals are available at lunchtime. Garden, children's room, skittle alley, function room.

MIDDLE 5.0% ABV
BEST 5.3% ABV
SPECIAL 6.6% ABV
CHRISTMAS AND EASTER SPECIAL 7.6% ABV

11am–11pm Mon–Sat; 12–10.30pm Sun.

The Ship

Lerryn, Nr Lostwithiel PL22 0PT
☎ *(01208) 872374* Mr Packer

Four beers available including Sharp's brews and guests such as Exmoor Gold, Morland Old Speckled Hen, Fuller's London Pride and Otter Ale.

A pub since the early 1600s, with a wood burner in the bar and slate floors. Bar and restaurant food available at lunchtime and evenings. Set in a quiet riverside village three miles south of Lostwithiel. Car park, garden, accommodation. Children allowed.

11.30am–3pm and 6–11pm Mon–Sat; 12–3pm and 7–10.30pm Sun.

The Royal Oak Inn

Duke Street, Lostwithiel PL22 0AG
☎ *(01208) 872552* Mr and Mrs Hine

Marston's Pedigree, Sharp's Own and Fuller's London Pride always available. Orkney Skullsplitter, the Blue Anchor Spingos, Woodforde's Headcracker, Exmoor Gold, Ash Vine Bitter, Badger Tanglefoot and Best are among the guest beers (50 per year).

A popular thirteenth-century inn catering for all tastes. Bar and restaurant food at lunchtime and evenings. Car park, garden, children's room. Spacious accommodation. Located just off the A390 going into Lostwithiel.

11am–11pm.

Trengilly Wartha Inn

Nancenoy, Constantine, Nr Falmouth TR11 5RP
☎ *(01326) 340332*
Nigel Logan and Michael MacGuire

Sharp's Cornish Coaster always available, plus a couple of constantly rotating guests which may include brews from Skinner's, Keltek, St Austell or Exmoor.

A country freehouse and restaurant in six acres of valley gardens and meadows. Bar and restaurant food at lunchtime and evenings. Car park, garden and children's room. Eight bedrooms. Just south of Constantine – follow the signs.

11am–2.30pm and 6.30–11pm.

Globe & Ale House

Queen Street, Penzance TR18 4BJ
☎ *(01736) 364098* Jenny Flewitt

Tied to Greenalls, Skinner's Cornish Knocker and Sharp's Own always available. The three guest beers may be from Bateman or Titanic. Four real ales are straight from the barrel.

An alehouse with live music once a week and quiz nights. Food served lunchtimes and evenings, but no separate dining area. No children.

11am–11pm Mon–Sat; 12–10.30pm Sun.

The Blue Peter Inn

The Quay, Polperro, Nr Looe PL13 2QZ
☎ *(01503) 272743* Terry Bicknell

St Austell's HSD and Tinners Ale, plus Sharp's Doom Bar Bitter always available. Also guest beers (up to 100 per year) changing almost daily, with the emphasis on minor breweries from all over the country. Plus draught local scrumpy.

S mall, atmospheric, traditional pub with beamed ceilings and log fires. No games machines or juke box – the house plays the music; primarily blues and jazz. Live music on Saturday nights and Sunday afternoons. No food, so bring your own rolls and sandwiches. Family room. Children not allowed in the bar. At the end of the fish quay.

11am–11pm Mon–Sat; 12–10.30pm Sun all year.

The Five Pilchards

Porthallow, St Keverne, Helston TR12 6PP
☎ *(01326) 280256* Brandon Flynn

A four-pump freehouse with Greene King Abbot Ale and Sharp's Own always available. Two guests, changed fortnightly, might include favourites Skinner's or Sharp's.

A n old Cornish seafaring pub with separate dining area. Food served lunchtimes and evenings. Children allowed.

12–2.30pm and 6–11pm Mon–Sun.

Atlantic Inn

Peverell Terrace, Porthleven, Helston TR13 9DZ
☎ *(01326) 562439* Valerie Moore

A freehouse with Skinner's Figgy's Brew always available. Guest beers include Wadworth 6X.

A traditional seaside pub in a village location (signposted), with live entertainment every Saturday. Food served lunchtimes and evenings in lounge bar. Children allowed.

11am–11pm Mon–Sat; 12–10.30pm Sun.

QUINTRELL DOWNS

The Two Clomes

East Road, Quintrell Downs, Nr Newquay
TR8 4PD
☎ *(01637) 871163* Frank and Lynn Cheshire

Approx 100 guest beers per year, three or four at any one time. Beers from Exmoor, Otter, St Austell, Fuller's, Cains and Hadrian breweries all favoured.

A converted and extended old miner's cottage built from Cornish stone with a beer garden and 48-seater restaurant. Open log fires in winter. Bar food available at lunchtime and evenings. Car park. Take the A392 from Newquay to Quintrell Downs, straight on at the roundabout, then second right.

OPEN *12–3pm and 7–11pm Mon–Sat; 12–3pm and 7–10.30pm Sun.*

ST CLEER

The Stag Inn

Fore Street, St Cleer, Liskeard PL14 5DA
☎ *(01579) 342305* Alann Eberlein

A seven-pump freehouse, Sharp's Doom Bar and Special plus Greene King Abbot always available. A guest beer, changed weekly, might well be Skinner's Betty Stogs.

An old pub with TV and non-smoking dining area. Food at lunchtime and evenings. Well-behaved children allowed.

OPEN *11am–11pm Mon–Sat; 12–10.30pm Sun.*

STRATTON

King's Arms

Howell's Road, Stratton, Bude EX23 9BX
☎ *(01288) 352396* Steven Peake

A freehouse with four pumps, two serving guest beers. Permanently available are Sharp's Own, Doom Bar Bitter and Exmoor Ale. Favourite guests, changed weekly, include Shepherd Neame Spitfire, Everards Beacon Bitter and Exmoor Gold.

A traditional pub with TV and sports coverage. Food at lunchtime and evenings. Children allowed.

OPEN *12–2pm and 6.30–11pm Mon–Thurs; 11am–11pm Fri–Sat; 12–10.30pm Sun.*

TREBARWITH STRAND

Mill House

Trebarwith Strand, Nr Tintagel, PL34 0HD
☎ *(01840) 770932* Roy and Jenny Vickers

Seven beers available including Sharp's Cornish Coaster, Doom Bar Bitter and Own. Also St Austell Tinners Ale and HSD plus a guest beer changed each month.

A seventeenth-century mill with seven acres of woodland and a trout stream. Bar and restaurant food available at lunchtime and evenings. Car park, garden and patio, accommodation. Children welcome. Head for Trebarwith from Tintagel.

OPEN *11am–11pm.*

TREGREHAN

The Britannia Inn

Tregrehan Par, Tregrehan PL24 2SL
☎ *(01726) 812889* Richard Rogers

This seven-pump freehouse serves Sharp's Own, Fuller's London Pride, Morland Old Speckled Hen and Greene Abbot Ale. A guest beer is changed twice weekly. Regulars include Marston's Pedigree and Fuller's ESB.

An eating house with two separate bars; one tends towards the young, the other towards eating. Food served at lunchtime and evenings. Children allowed in the dining area

OPEN *11am–11pm Mon–Sat; 12–10.30pm Sun.*

TRESPARRETT

The Horseshoe Inn

Tresparrett, Camelford, Cornwall, PL32 9ST
☎ *(01840) 261240* Mr Kirby

Sutton's Knickerdroppa Glory and Hospice (brewed especially for The Horseshoe Inn by Sutton Brewery) always available, plus up to four more including others from Sutton's.

A one-bar country pub situated in walking country. Separate dining area, outside seating, food served lunchtime and evening. Six darts teams and two pool teams. Children allowed. Located off the A39

OPEN *12–3pm and 6.30–11pm (10.30pm Sun).*

TRURO

The Old Ale House

7 Quay Street, Truro
☎ *(01872) 271122* Ray Gascoigne

 Sharp's Doom Bar Bitter is one of 11 beers available straight from the barrel, plus 250 guests per year including Badger Tanglefoot, Exmoor Stag and Gold, Cotleigh Tawny and Old Buzzard, Fuller's London Pride and Shepherd Neame Spitfire.

A n olde-worlde pub in the town centre with old furniture and free peanuts. Bar food available at lunchtime and evenings. Live music twice a week. Parking. Children allowed.

OPEN *11am–11pm Mon–Sat; 12–3pm and 7–10.30pm Sun.*

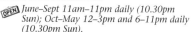

WIDEMOUTH BAY

The Bayview Inn

Marine Drive, Widemouth Bay, Bude EX23 0AW ☎ *(01288) 361273* M Gooder (Manager)

A freehouse with Sharp's Special, Doom Bar and Kitcher's Klassic permanently available, plus one guest ale, changing frequently, on one pump.

A traditional old-style seaside pub decorated with the pump clips of beers past! Two bars, garden, children's play area, large car park and disabled access. Food available at lunchtimes from 12–2.30pm and evenings from 6–9.30pm. Dining and family room. Children allowed.

OPEN *June–Sept 11am–11pm daily (10.30pm Sun); Oct–May 12–3pm and 6–11pm daily (10.30pm Sun).*

ZELAH

Hawkins Arms

High Road, Zelah, Truro TR4 9HU
☎ *(01872) 540339* Mrs Eyre

A freehouse with seven pumps. Guests change regularly.

A one-bar country-style pub. Food served at lunchtime and evenings. Children allowed.

OPEN *11am–3pm and 6–11pm Mon–Sat; 12–3pm and 7–10.30pm Sun.*

YOU TELL US

★ *The Barley Sheaf*, Gorran, Churchtown
★ *Cobweb*, The Bridge, Boscastle
★ *Llawaroc Inn*, Shute Lane, Gorran Haven
★ *London Inn*, Kilkhampton, Bude
★ *Mounts Bay Inn*, Promenade, Penzance
★ *The Old Mill House Hotel*, Mill Hill, Polperro
★ *The Smuggler's Den*, Trebellan

Places Featured:

Allonby	Holmes Green
Ambleside	Ings
Appleby	Ireby
Broughton in Furness	Kendal
Carlisle	Kirkby Lonsdale
Cartmel	Kirksanton
Cockermouth	Lanercost
Coniston	Nether Wasdale
Dent	Newby
Elterwater	Strawberry Bank
Grasmere	Tirril
Great Corby	Troutbeck
Great Langdale	Wasdale Head
Hayton	Winton
Hesket Newmarket	

THE BREWERIES

DENT BREWERY

Hollins, Cowgill, Dent LA10 5DQ
☎ *(01539) 625326*

 BITTER 3.7% ABV
Lightly hopped, and slightly sweet.
AVIATOR 4.0% ABV
Full, rounded hop flavour.
RAMSBOTTOM STRONG ALE 4.5% ABV
Medium-dark, caramel flavour, hop balance.
KAMIKAZE 5.0% ABV
Very pale, good hop flavour and creamy maltiness.
T'OWD TUP 6.0% ABV
Powerful stout. Roast barley, bite and softness.

DERWENT BREWERY

*Station Road Industrial Estate, Carlisle
CA5 4AG*
☎ *(01697) 331522*

 BITTER 3.6% ABV
MUTINEER 4.1% ABV
HANSEY'S OCTOBER FEST 4.2% ABV
TEACHERS PET 4.3% ABV
DOZEY BREW 4.4% ABV
BILL MONK 4.5% ABV
OLD COCKER 5.0% ABV

HESKET NEWMARKET BREWERY

Old Crown Barn, Hesket Newmarket CA7 8JG
☎ *(01697) 478066*

 GREAT COCKUP PORTER 2.8% ABV
Dark, smooth and malty.
BLENCATHRA BITTER 3.1% ABV
Ruby-coloured and hoppy.
SKIDDAW SPECIAL BITTER 3.7% ABV
Gold-coloured and full-flavoured.
DORIS'S 90TH BIRTHDAY ALE 4.3% ABV
Full-flavoured, with fruit throughout.
CATBELLS PALE ALE 5.1% ABV
Refreshing, easy quaffing brew.
OLD CARROCK STRONG ALE 5.6% ABV
Rich, smooth and strong.
Plus seasonal and occasional brews.

JENNINGS BROS PLC

The Castle Brewery, Cockermouth CA13 9NE
☎ *(01900) 823214*

 DARK MILD 3.1% ABV
Sweetness, with malt flavour.
BITTER 3.6% ABV
Dark bitter. Nutty and mellow, with malt.
CUMBERLAND ALE 4.0% ABV
Gold-coloured, rich and smooth.
COCKER HOOP 4.8% ABV
A well-hopped premium bitter.
SNECK LIFTER 5.1% ABV
Strong, slightly sweet and warming.

LAKELAND BREWING CO.

Sepulchre Lane, Kendal LA9 4NJ
☎ *(01539) 734528*

LAKELAND TERRIER 3.8% ABV
AMAZON 4.0% ABV
GREAT NORTHERN 5.0% ABV
Winter brew.
DAMSON ALE 5.5% ABV

ALLONBY

Ship Hotel
Main Street, Allonby CA15 6PZ
☎ *(01900) 881017* Peter and Carole Yates

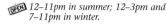 Yates Bitter and Premium always available plus guests changed each week including Orkney Dark Island.

O verlooking Solway Firth, a 300-year-old hotel with considerable history. Bar and restaurant food served at lunchtime and evenings. Car park, accommodation. Dogs welcome.

OPEN *12–11pm in summer; 12–3pm and 7–11pm in winter.*

AMBLESIDE

The Queen's Hotel
Market Place, Ambleside LA22 9BU
☎ *(01539) 432206* Mr Bessey

A free house with Jennings Bitter always available. Two guests, changed twice a week, from a mixture of nationals and independents, with Coniston Bluebird and Black Sheep Best regularly offered.

A centrally situated, Victorian-style pub, with two traditional bars. Food served in the restaurant at lunchtime and evenings. Children allowed.

OPEN *11am–11pm Mon–Sat; 12–10.30pm Sun.*

APPLEBY

The Royal Oak Inn
Bongate, Appleby CA16 6UB
☎ *(017683) 51463* Philippa Borthwick

Yates Bitter is among those beers permanently available plus up to seven guests (50 per year) including Holt's Bitter and ales from Maclay, Harviestoun, Wadworth, Hexhamshire, Hesket Newmarket, Timothy Taylor and Black Sheep breweries.

A long white-washed building, roughly 400 years old with lots of character. Bar and restaurant food available at lunchtime and evenings. Two dining rooms, one non-smoking. Parking and terrace. Children allowed. Accommodation. CAMRA Cumbria Pub of the Year 1993. On entering Appleby from Brough on the A66, the inn is at the foot of a hill, on the right.

OPEN *11am–1am Mon–Sat; 12–10.30pm Sun.*

BROUGHTON IN FURNESS

The Manor Arms
The Square, Broughton in Furness LA20 6HY
☎ *(01229) 716286* David Varty

Seven well-kept real ales available including 160 guest beers per year from small breweries. New brews, winter warmers – you name it, they have served it!

E ighteenth-century traditional family-run freehouse with a welcoming atmosphere. Regular CAMRA pub of the year award-winner. Bar snacks available all day. Parking and outside seats overlooking a picturesque market square. Luxurious accommodation. Children allowed.

OPEN *12–11pm Mon–Sat; 12–10.30pm Sun.*

CARLISLE

Caledonian Inn
17 Botchergate, Carlisle CA1 1QS
☎ *(01228) 530460* Mr Calvert

A Whitbread pub with Wadworth 6X and Castle Eden always available. Three guests, changed weekly, often include Fuller's London Pride, Morland Old Speckled Hen, Bateman XXXB and Burtonwood Top Hat, with others from the Dent Brewery.

A traditional local pub near the train station, with one large bar, pool, darts and big-screen TV. Food served from 12–5pm. Children allowed.

OPEN *11am–11pm Mon–Sat; 12–10.30pm Sun.*

Fox & Pheasant
Armathwaite, Carlisle CA4 9PY
☎ *(01697) 472400* Mrs Starkie

A maximum of four real ales are offered in this freehouse, two in winter and one rotating. Something from Hesket Newmarket (usually Doris' 90th Birthday Ale) is always available. Regular guests, changed weekly, include Ridleys Nobody's Fool and Jennings Cumberland, with a varied selection of others, mostly from local Cumbrian breweries.

A seventeenth-century coaching inn, overlooking the River Eden, in a small village. Log fires, eight bedrooms, outside seating. Food served at lunchtime and evenings in a separate dining area. Children allowed.

OPEN *11am–11pm Mon–Sat; 12–10.30pm Sun.*

CARTMEL

Cavendish Arms

Cavendish Street, Cartmel LA11 6QA
☎ *(01539) 536240* Tom Murray

Four beers always available from a range of more than 300 per year. Favourite guest beers include Timothy Taylor Landlord, Banner Bitter, Hop Back Summer Lightning, Fuller's ESB and Shepherd Neame Spitfire.

A coaching inn, 500 years old, offering bar and restaurant food at lunchtime and evenings. Car park, dining room, non-smoking room, accommodation. Children allowed until 8.30pm.

OPEN *11am–11pm Mon–Sat; 12–10pm Sun.*

COCKERMOUTH

The Bitter End

15 Kirkgate, Cockermouth CA13 9PJ
☎ *(01900) 828993* Susan Askey

Bitter End Cockersnoot is always available in this freehouse and brewpub, along with four guests, changed weekly, which often include Yates Bitter, Coniston Bluebird, Isle of Skye Red Cuillin or Hesket Newmarket Doris' 90th Birthday Ale. Other home brews when available.

A very traditional pub with background music, non-smoking area at lunchtimes. Food served at lunchtime and evenings. Children allowed.

COCKERSNOOT 3.8% ABV
A golden, clean, refreshing beer.
CUDDY LUGS 4.3% ABV
Strong hop aroma with a dry aftertaste.
SKINNER'S OLD STRONG 5.5%
A rich amber beer, sweet and fruity.

OPEN *11.30am–2.30pm and 6–11pm Mon–Thurs; 11.30am–3pm and 6–11pm Fri–Sat; 11.30am–3pm and 7–10.30pm Sun.*

The Bush

Main Street, Cockermouth CA13 9JS
☎ *(01900) 822064* Maureen Williamson

A Jennings house with 12 hand pumps. The full Jennings range is always on offer. Two or three guests, changed weekly, include a wide selection of beers, bought through Flying Firkin.

A very homely pub with open fires. Food served at lunchtime only. Children allowed.

OPEN *11am–11pm Mon–Sat; 12–10.30pm Sun.*

CONISTON

The Black Bull

Yewdale Road, Coniston LA21 8DU
☎ *(01539) 441335* Ronald Edward Bradley

A seven-pump freehouse and brewpub, with the Coniston Brewery at the rear of the pub. Always available are Coniston Bluebird and Old Man Ale. Specials include Coniston Opium and Blacksmith's Ale. Guests are rotated on two pumps and changed fortnightly: regulars are Moorhouse's Black Cat, also Saxons Scrumpy Cider. Other guests are all from small independent and micro-breweries.

A sixteenth-century coaching inn in the centre of Coniston, with oak beams and log fire. No juke box or fruit machines. Outside seating area. Separate restaurant. Food served all day. Children allowed.

BLUEBIRD BITTER 3.6% ABV
A session ale. Champion Best Bitter 1998. Also available as bottle-conditioned at 4.0%.
OPIUM 4.0%
A seasonal autumn brew. Dark amber, malty ale.
OLD MAN ALE 4.4% ABV
Dark and ruby-coloured.
BLACKSMITH'S ALE 5.0% ABV
A seasonal Christmas brew. Winter warmer.

OPEN *11am–11pm Mon–Sat; 12–10.30pm Sun.*

DENT

The George & Dragon

Main Street, Dent LA10 5QL
☎ *(01539) 625256* Mrs Dorothy Goad

Owned by Dent Brewery, with Dent beers always available.

A country-style pub, with one bar and nine bedrooms. Food served lunchtimes and evenings, separate dining area. Children and dogs allowed. Ten miles from junction 37 of the M6.

OPEN *Summer: 11am–11pm; closed afternoons in winter.*

The Sun Inn

Main Street, Dent LA10 5QL
☎ *(01539) 625208* Martin Stafford

Owned by Dent Brewery. Three Dent brews always available.

An old, traditional country pub in the cobbled main street. Friendly, sociable atmosphere, one bar, large beer garden, pool room, non-smoking dining area. Food served lunchtimes throughout the year and evenings (summertime only). Children allowed till 9pm.

OPEN *Winter: 12–2pm and 7–11pm Mon–Fri; 11am–11pm Sat; 12–10.30pm Sun. Summer: 11am–11pm Mon–Sat; 12–10.30pm Sun.*

ELTERWATER

Britannia Inn

Elterwater, Ambleside LA22 9HP
☎ *(01539) 437210* Mrs Fry

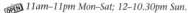 A freehouse with Jennings Bitter, Coniston Bluebird and Dent Aviator always on the menu, plus two guests changed frequently.

A country inn with one main bar. Quiz night on Sunday. Food served lunchtimes and evenings. Separate dining area. Children allowed.

🍺 *11am–11pm Mon–Sat; 12–10.30pm Sun.*

GRASMERE

The Travellers Rest Inn

Grasmere, LA22 9RR
☎ *(01539) 435604* Graham Sweeney

 A pub owned by a family of dedicated beer sellers, with five real ales offered at any one time. Always available are Jennings House Bitter, Snecklifter and Mild. Regular guests, changed every six weeks, include Cumberland and Pedigree.

A sixteenth-century inn. One bar, beer garden, bed and breakfast (ensuite accommodation). Food served from 12–3pm and 6–9pm (winter); 12–9pm (summer). Smoking dining area and non-smoking restaurant. Children allowed. Half a mile north of Grasmere village.

🍺 *11am–11pm Mon–Sat; 12–10.30pm Sun.*

GREAT CORBY

The Corby Bridge Inn

Great Corby, Carlisle CA4 8LL
☎ *(01228) 560221* Barbara Griffiths

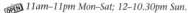 Thwaites Bitter and Mild always available plus a rotating guest, changed once or twice a week, often including Nethergate Old Growler, Charles Wells Bombardier, Fuller's London Pride, Timothy Taylor Landlord, Badger Tanglefoot or a Wychwood brew.

A freehouse built in 1838. Originally a railway hotel. Grade II listed. Approximately four miles from junction 43 of M6. Three rooms, one bar. Large garden, games area, accommodation. Food served all day. Well-behaved children allowed.

🍺 *11am–11pm Mon–Sat; 12–10.30pm Sun.*

GREAT LANGDALE

Old Dungeon Ghyll Hotel

Great Langdale, Ambleside LA22 9JY
☎ *(01539) 437272* Neil and Jane Walmsley

 Seven real ales and scrumpy available in this freehouse. Yates Bitter and Jennings Cumberland Ale always present. Three guests are changed regularly, one barrel at a time. Black Sheep Special is popular.

An interesting National Trust-owned, listed building with real fire. Food served at lunchtime (12–2pm) and evenings (6–9pm). Children allowed.

🍺 *11am–11pm Mon–Sat; 12–10.30pm Sun.*

HAYTON

Stone Inn

Hayton, Nr Carlisle CA4 9HR
☎ *(01228) 70498* Mr and Mrs Tranter

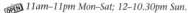 Four beers from Jennings, Buchanan's and Thwaites permanently available plus the occasional guest beer, perhaps from Maclay's.

A traditional village pub serving bar food at lunchtime and evenings. Car park and garden. Children allowed in restaurant, but catering is for parties only (from six to 36). Seven minutes east of M6 junction 43, just off the A69.

🍺 *11am–3pm and 5.30–11pm.*

HESKET NEWMARKET

The Old Crown

Hesket Newmarket, Caldbeck, Wigton CA7 8JG
☎ *(01697) 478288* Kim Matthews

 A freehouse, but concentrating on the Hesket Newmarket brews, with the brewery situated close by Old Carrock Strong Ale, Skiddaw Special, Catbells Pale Ale, Doris' 90th Birthday Ale, Pigs Might Fly, Kern Knott's Crack(ing) Stout, Blencathra Bitter and Great Cockup Porter are always on the menu. A guest is changed once a month. Regulars include Coniston Bluebird and Timothy Taylor Landlord.

A small, old-fashioned pub, with two bars. Food served at lunchtime and evenings. Children allowed. On the edge of the Lake District National Park, the only pub in the village.

🍺 *5.30–11pm Mon; 12–2.30pm and 5.30–11pm Tues–Sat; 12–2.30pm and 7–10.30pm Sun.*

HOLMES GREEN

Black Dog Inn
Broughton Road, Holmes Green, Dalton-in-Furness LA15 8JP
☎ *(01229) 462561* Jack Taylor

A freehouse with Coniston Bluebird and Butterknowle Bitter always available. Five guests might include favourites such as Wye Valley Hereford Pale Ale or York Yorkshire Terrier.

A n old country inn half a mile from South Lakes Wildlife Park. Dining area. Food served all day. Children allowed.

OPEN *11am–11pm Mon–Sat; 12–10.30pm Sun.*

INGS

The Watermill Inn
Ings, Nr Staveley, Kendal LA8 9PY
☎ *(01539) 821309* AF and B Coulthwaite

JW Lees Moonraker is among those beers always available. Also perhaps a dozen guest beers (500 per year) which may come from the Hop Back, Cotleigh, Ridleys, Shepherd Neame, Exmoor, Ash Vine, Summerskills, Black Sheep, Coach House, Yates and Wadworth breweries.

F ormerly a wood mill, now a traditional, family-run pub full of character with log fires, brasses and beams. Two bars. No juke box or games machines. Relaxing atmosphere. Bar food at lunchtime and evenings. Car park, garden, seats and tables by the river. Disabled toilets. Children allowed. Accommodation. From the M6, junction 36, follow the A591 towards Windermere. One mile past the second turning for Staveley. Turn left after the garage, before the church.

OPEN *12–2.30pm and 6–11pm Mon–Sat; 12–3pm and 7–10.30pm Sun.*

IREBY

Paddy's Bar
The Square, Ireby, Carlisle CA5 1EA
☎ *(01697) 371460* Peter Bolton

A four-pump freehouse offering Jennings Bitter and Timothy Taylor Landlord. Plus two guests, changed twice weekly, which might include something from Titanic, Black Sheep or Hesket Newmarket.

T his freehouse was the area's first Irish pub in the late 1980s. Café bar, with traditional oak panels, open fire and wooden floor. Also acts as village post office and shop. Food served at lunchtime and evenings. Children allowed.

OPEN *11am–11pm Mon–Sat; 12–10.30pm Sun.*

KENDAL

Ring o' Bells
39 Kirkland, Kendal LA9 5AF
☎ *(01539) 720326* Tony Bibby

Vaux Samson and Ward's Best always available plus a guest beer (36 per year) such as Marston's Pedigree, Charles Wells Bombardier, Everards Tiger, Fuller's London Pride, Adnams Broadside or Morland Old Speckled Hen.

A n unspoilt seventeenth-century pub in the grounds of the parish church. Bar food available at lunchtime and evenings. Parking. Children allowed. Accommodation. Take M6 junction 36, then follow the A590 and A591 to the A6 in Kendal.

OPEN *12–3pm and 6–11pm Mon–Sat; usual hours Sun.*

KIRKBY LONSDALE

The Snooty Fox
Main Street, Kirkby Lonsdale LA6 2AH
☎ *(01524) 271308* Kim Bileta

A freehouse, with Timothy Taylor Landlord and Hartleys XB (Robinsons) always available. Other real ales expected shortly.

A seventeenth-century inn, with two bars, stonework and beams. Food at lunchtime and evenings. Children allowed.

OPEN *11am–11pm Mon–Sat; 12–10.30pm Sun.*

KIRKSANTON

King William IV
Kirksanton, Nr Millom LA18 4NN
☎ *(01229) 772009*
Roger and Sandra Singleton

A freehouse with Jennings Cumberland Ale (@ £1.50) always available. Up to four guests are changed weekly. Regulars include Marston's Pedigree, Fuller's London Pride, the Slaters ales (Eccleshall) or something from Wye Valley, Coniston or Rooster's breweries.

A 200-year-old country pub with oak beams and real fires. Four letting rooms available for bed and breakfast. Non-smoking dining area. Food at lunchtime and evenings. Children allowed. On the main road from Millom to Whitehaven.

OPEN *12–3pm and 7–11pm.*

LANERCOST

Abbey Bridge Inn
Lanercost, Brampton CA8 2HG
☎ *(016977) 2224* Phillip Sayers

 Yates Bitter always available plus a couple of guests (100+ per year) including Wadworth 6X, Bateman XXXB, Shepherd Neame, Greene King, Fuller's, Burton Bridge, Black Sheep, Charles Wells, Jennings and Exmoor ales.

F amily-run country hotel and bar in a converted seventeenth-century forge retaining original beams and character. Bar and restaurant food available at lunchtime and evenings. Car park, garden, children allowed. Accommodation. CAMRA Cumbria Pub of the Year 1992 plus merit award 1995. Situated close to Lanercost Priory on the riverbank.

12–2.30pm and 7–11pm.

NETHER WASDALE

The Screes Hotel
Nether Wasdale, Seascale CA20 1ET
☎ *(01946) 726262* DH Simpson

 A freehouse, with Yates, Jennings and Black Sheep brews always available. Four guests, changed weekly, come from independents such as Dent.

A n eighteenth-century pub with split-level bar, separate dining area, small function room and five letting rooms. Magnificent views of the fells. Food served at lunchtime and evenings. Children allowed. Can be tricky to find. Ring for directions, if necessary.

May–Sept: 11am–11pm Mon–Sat; 12–10.30pm Sun. Winter: 12–3pm and 6–11pm.

NEWBY

The Newby Hall Hotel
Newby Hall, Newby, Penrith CA10 3EX
☎ *(01931)714456* Mike Hewitt

Award-winning freehouse with a Jennings brew always available. Two guests may change on a daily basis. One is a local brew, such as Coniston Bluebird, Dent Ramsbottom, Yates Best Bitter or Black Sheep Bitter.

A seventeenth-century manor house with oak beams and inglenook fireplace, in a very small village off the A6 and A66. Five bedrooms and 34-seat restaurant. Food served at weekend and bank holiday lunchtimes, and every evening. Children allowed until 9pm.

7–11pm Mon–Fri; 12–4pm and 7–11pm Sat–Sun and bank holidays.

STRAWBERRY BANK

The Mason's Arms
Strawberry Bank, Cartmel Fell LA11 6NW
☎ *(01539) 568486* Mrs Stevenson

 A brewpub, home of The Strawberry Bank Brewery. Five real ales always available, including Barnsley and Four Seasons (Mansfield) brews, Nethergate's Umbel Ale, Tomintoul's Cailie and other guests. The Strawberry Bank Brewery's one home brew is a bottle-conditioned beer which is always on offer.

A rural freehouse set in the middle of nowhere! Slate floor and open fires. Terrace with 12 tables overlooking the valley. Self-catering studio apartments available. Homemade food served at lunchtime and evenings, with a good vegetarian selection. Children allowed.

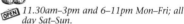 **DAMSON BEER 7% ABV**

11.30am–3pm and 6–11pm Mon–Fri; all day Sat–Sun.

TIRRIL

The Queen's Head
Tirril CA10 2JS
☎ *(01768) 863219* Chris Thomlinson

Black Sheep Best and Jennings Cumberland always available. One guest, changed weekly, might be Dent Aviator or Hesket Newmarket Doris's 90th Birthday Ale.

A 300-year-old pub, situated on the B5320, with stone walls and beams. Two bars. Once owned by William Wordsworth. Food served at lunchtime and evenings, with a separate dining area available. Children allowed.

12–3pm and 6–11pm Mon–Fri; 12–11pm Sat; 12–10.30pm Sun.

TROUTBECK

The Queen's Head Hotel
Troutbeck LA23 1PW
☎ *(01539) 432174* Mark Stewerdson

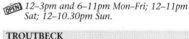 A freehouse with four guests, which change every few days, and which might include Coniston Bluebird, Old Man Ale, Burton Bridge Amazon or Great Northern.

A food-oriented pub and hotel, with nine rooms and seating area outside. Food served at lunchtime and evenings. Children allowed.

11am–11pm Mon–Sat; 11am–10.30pm Sun.

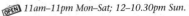

Wasdale Head Inn

Wasdale Head, Nr Gosforth CA20 1EX
☎ *(01946) 726229* Howard Christie

Jennings Cumberland and Cocker Hoop are always on offer in this freehouse, plus 50 guest beers per year served straight from the barrel. These might include Orkney Skullsplitter, Coniston Bluebird and Hesket Newmarket Doris' 90th Birthday Ale.

A traditional pub with a beer garden, set in the Lake District National Park. Food served at lunchtime and evenings. Children allowed (if on a lead!).

OPEN *11am–11pm Mon–Sat; 12–10.30pm Sun.*

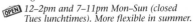

The Bay Horse Inn

Winton, Kirkby Stephen CA17 4HS
☎ *(01768) 371451* Derek Parvin

A freehouse offering four real ales, two rotated, and all hand-pulled from the cask. Youngers Scotch and Black Sheep Bitter are always on offer. Varied guests, changed twice weekly, may include Coniston Bluebird or a Harviestoun brew.

A pub dating from the late 1600s, off the A685, two miles north of Kirkby Stephen. Lounge bar, panelled walls, beams, two open fires, flag floors. Public and lounge bars with central servery. Modern 50-seater dining area. Food served at lunchtime and evenings. Children allowed.

OPEN *12–2pm and 7–11pm Mon–Sun (closed Tues lunchtimes). More flexible in summer.*

YOU TELL US

★ *The Drunken Duck*, Barngates, Ambleside
★ *The Prince of Wales* (brewpub), Foxfield, Broughton in Furness
★ *The Slip Inn*, Barras, Kirkby Stephen

Places Featured:

Bradwell
Buxworth
Chesterfield
Cromford
Dale Abbey
Derby
Fenny Bentley
Horsley Woodhouse
Ilkeston
Kniveton
Makeney
Melbourne

Old Tupton
Over Haddon
Rowarth
Shardlow
Smalley
Staveley
Ticknall
Tideswell
Wardlow Mires
Whaley
Whitehough
Woolley Moor

THE BREWERIES

LEATHERBRITCHES BREWERY

Bently Brook Inn, Fenny Bentley, Ashbourne DE6 1LF
☎ *(01335) 350278*

 BELTER 4.0% ABV
Light, golden with flowery hoppiness.
ASHBOURNE ALE 4.5% ABV
Fruity hints and well-balanced sweet finish.
BESPOKE 5.0% ABV
Ruby-coloured and smooth.
Plus occasional and seasonal brews.

TOWNES BREWERY

Speedwell Inn, Lowgates, Chesterfield S43 3TT
☎ *(01246) 472252*

SUNSHINE 3.6% ABV
Pale and spicy with full-flavoured finish.
GOLDEN BUD 3.8% ABV
BEST LOCKOFORD BITTER 4.0% ABV
SPEEDWELL 4.0% ABV
GMT 4.0% ABV
IPA 4.4% ABV
Hoppy and malty, with a clean finish.
Plus occasional brews.

WHIM ALES

Whim Farm, Hartington, Buxton SK17 0AX
☎ *(01298) 84991*

ARBOR LIGHT 3.6% ABV
Pale and easy drinking.
MAGIC MUSHROOM MILD 3.8% ABV
Very dark and flavoursome.
HARTINGTON BITTER 4.0% ABV
Pale and refreshing.
HARTINGTON IPA 4.0% ABV
Light and well-balanced.

THE PUBS

BRADWELL

Valley Lodge
Church Street, Bradwell, Hope Valley S33 9HJ
☎ *(01433) 620427* Angela Davies

A freehouse serving up to eight brews. Stones Best always available plus guests changed weekly which may include Ruddles Best (Morland), Barnsley Bitter, Robinson's Best and Hartley XB, Smiles Best or Heritage.

A large village pub in walking country with three bar areas and a games room. Outside seating. Food served at lunchtime and evenings. Children allowed.

OPEN *7–11pm Mon–Fri; 12–3pm and 7–11pm Sat; 12–3pm and 7–10.30pm Sun.*

BUXWORTH

Navigation Inn
Buxworth Canal Basin, Buxworth, High Peak SK23 7NE
☎ *(01663) 732072* Alan Hall

A freehouse with Timothy Taylor Landlord, Webster's Yorkshire Bitter and Marston's Pedigree always on the menu. A guest beer changes weekly. Ruddles County (Morland), Shepherd Neame Spitfire, Greene King Abbot, Abbeydale Moonshine and York Yorkshire Terrier are regularly featured.

A canalside pub with one bar, big-screen TV, separate restaurant and children's playground area. Bar snacks available at lunchtime and evenings. Off the A6, on the B6062.

OPEN *11am–11pm Mon–Sat; 12–10.30pm Sun.*

CHESTERFIELD

The Derby Tup
4 Sheffield Road, Wittington Moor, Chesterfield S41 8LS
☎ *(01246) 454316* Mr Williams

Ten beers always available with Kelham Island Fat Cat and Marston's Pedigree among them. Guests come from Cotleigh, Robinson's, Timothy Taylor, Exmoor, Batemans etc.

Old and original, beamed with three rooms and open fires. Bar food available at lunchtime and evenings. Parking nearby, children allowed.

OPEN *11.30am–3pm and 5–11pm Mon–Sat; 12–4pm and 7–10.30pm Sun.*

The Market
95 New Square, Chesterfield S40 1AH
☎ *(01246) 273641* Keith Toone

Tied to Allied Domecq, with Marston's Pedigree and Greene King Abbot always available. Five guests may include Black Sheep Special, Hop Back Summer Lightning or Ushers Founders Ale.

A one-bar, market pub, with dining area in bar. Food served at lunchtime only. No children.

OPEN *11am–11pm Mon–Sat; 12–3pm and 7–10.30pm Sun*

The Royal Oak
43 Chatsworth Road, Brampton, Chesterfield S40 2AH
☎ *(01246) 277854* Mr Younger

Everards Tiger always available, plus several guests (500 per year) including at least two brews from Townes and one from Batham. Other popular brews include Elgood's Black Dog Mild, Charles Wells Bombardier, Leatherbritches Belt 'n' Braces, Morland Old Speckled Hen, Wadworth Old Timer.

A traditional local pub with timbers and open fire. Live music, table football and darts. Beer festivals. No food. Car park and patio. No children.

OPEN *11am–11pm Mon–Sat; 12–10.30pm Sun.*

The Rutland Arms
23 Stephenson Place, Chesterfield S40 1XL
☎ *(01246) 205857* Paul Young

Tied to Whitbread, serving four ales straight from the barrel and five on pumps. Castle Eden, Marston's Pedigree and Greene King Abbot are always on offer plus guests, changed every ten days, which often include Morland Old Speckled Hen, Bateman XXXB or Black Sheep Best.

Predominantly wooden interior, close to Chesterfield's famous crooked spire church. Non-smoking dining area away from the bar. Food served evenings only. No children.

OPEN *11am–11pm Mon–Sat; 12–10.30pm Sun.*

CROMFORD

The Boat Inn
Scarthin, Cromford, Matlock DE4 3QF
☎ *(01629) 823282* Mr Gridley

A freehouse with Mansfield Bitter and Marston's Pedigree always available plus all sorts of guests from a good mix of national and independent brewers. Charles Wells Bombardier and Shepherd Neame Spitfire are regularly featured.

A village pub built about 1772, near the market square. Two bars, log fires, beer garden. Bar snacks at lunchtime and evenings plus Sunday lunches. Children allowed.

11.30am–3pm and 6–11pm.

DALE ABBEY

The Carpenters Arms
Dale Abbey, Ilkeston DE7 4PP
☎ *(0115) 932 5277* John Heraty

Tied to Allied Domecq, with Marston's Pedigree and Ansells Bitter always on the menu. Two guests, changed weekly, may include Wadworth 6X, Greene King Abbot, Morland Old Speckled Hen or Ruddles County (Morland).

A village pub in picturesque walking country, with children's play area, family room and large car park. Food served at lunchtimes and evenings. Children not allowed in bar. Three miles from junction 25 of the M1.

12–3pm and 6–11pm (10.30pm Sun).

DERBY

The Alexandra Hotel
203 Siddals Road, Derby DE1 2QE
☎ *(01332) 293993* Mark Robins

Bateman Mild and XB and Marston's Pedigree always available plus six guest beers (600 per year) with the emphasis firmly on new and rare micro-breweries. Also traditional cider.

B uilt as a coffee and chop house in 1865. Now trading as a comfortable award-winning pub decorated with a railway and brewery theme. Bar food at lunchtime. Car park and garden. Located three minutes' walk from Derby Midland Railway Station.

11am–2.30pm and 4.30–11pm Mon–Fri and Sun; 11am–2.30pm and 6–11pm Sat.

The Brunswick Inn
1 Railway Terrace, Derby DE1 2RU
☎ *(01332) 290677*

Fourteen pumps serve beer from all around the country, notably Marston's Pedigree and Timothy Taylor Landlord, as well as five or six ales from the on-site brewery.

B uilt in 1841–2 as the first purpose-built railwaymen's pub in the world. The birthplace of the Railway Institute, an educational establishment for railway workers. It fell into dereliction in the early 1970s and trading ceased in April 1974. The Derbyshire Historic Buildings Trust started restoration work in 1981. The trust sold it to Trevor Harris, a local businessman, in May 1987. The pub reopened in October 1987 and the installation of the brewing plant followed in 1991. The first beer was produced on June 11 that year. Bar and restaurant food is available at lunchtime and on request in the evening. Parking, garden, children's room, non-smoking room, function room.

RECESSION ALE 3.3% ABV
MILD 3.7% ABV
TRIPLE HOP 4.0% ABV
SECOND BREW 4.2% ABV
RAILWAY PORTER 4.3% ABV
OLD ACCIDENTAL 5.0% ABV

11am–11pm Mon–Sat; 12–10.30pm Sun.

The Crompton Tavern
46 Crompton Street, Derby DE1 1NX
☎ *(01332) 733629* Mr and Mrs Bailey

Marston's Pedigree and Timothy Taylor Landlord always available plus four guest beers (200 per year) perhaps from Fuller's, Coach House, Kelham Island, Banks & Taylor or Burton Bridge breweries. A porter or stout is normally available.

A small pub just outside the city centre. Popular with locals and students. Cobs and sandwiches available daily. Car park and garden. Children now allowed.

11am–11pm Mon–Sat; 12–10.30pm Sun.

The Flowerpot
25 King Street, Derby DE1 3DZ
☎ *(012332) 204955* John Evans

Marston's Pedigree and Timothy Taylor Landlord always available plus at least seven guest beers (500+ per year) from all over the United Kingdom.

A traditional friendly town pub with no music or games machines, but lots of regulars aged 18 to 95. Bar food is available at lunchtime and evenings. Car park 30 yards away. Garden and children's room. Function suite available for up to 250 people. Situated on the A6 just inside the inner ring road, 300 yards north of the cathedral.

11am–11pm Mon–Sat; 12–3pm and 7–10.30pm Sun.

The Friargate
113 Friargate, Derby DE1 1EX
☎ *(01332) 297065* Amanda Rogers

A freehouse serving Marston's Pedigree straight from the barrel plus up to eight others. Regulars come from Rooster's, Hook Norton and Hop Back breweries.

A quiet town pub with one main bar. Acoustic music on Wednesdays. Food served at lunchtime (not Sun). No children.

OPEN *11am–11pm Mon–Sat; 7–11pm Sun.*

The Rowditch Inn
246 Uttoxeter New Road, Derby DE22 3LL
☎ *(01332) 343123* Mr Birkin

A freehouse with six real ales available including Mansfield Riding Bitter, Old Bailey and Marston's Pedigree. Three rotating guests change on a daily basis.

A traditional beer house with one bar, non-smoking area, snug and beer garden. No food, no children. On the main road.

OPEN *7–11pm Mon–Sun and most lunchtimes (not Weds).*

The Smithfield
Meadow Road, Derby DE45 1NN
☎ *(01332) 370429* Mr Stevenson

A freehouse with Whim Arbor Light, Oakham JHB and Bishops Farewell always available. Six guest beers, changed two or three times a week, might include Whim IPA and Marston's Pedigree.

Traditional, friendly atmosphere. Lounge with open fire and pub games plus a family room. Food served 12–2pm only. Children allowed. Ring for directions.

OPEN *11am–11pm Mon–Sat; 12–10.30pm Sun.*

The Coach & Horses
Fenny Bentley DE6 1LB
☎ *(01335) 350246* John Dawson

A freehouse with Mansfield Riding Bitter always available plus three guests, changed weekly, which may include favourites such as Greene King Abbot, Morland Old Speckled Hen or Timothy Taylor Landlord.

A traditional country pub with background music and beer garden. Food at lunchtime and evenings. Children allowed.

OPEN *11am–3pm and 5–11pm Mon–Fri; 11am–11pm Sat; 12–10.30pm Sun.*

Old Oak Inn
176 Main Street, Horsley Woodhouse, Ilkeston DE7 6AW
☎ *(01332) 780672* Mr Hyde

A freehouse with Marston's Pedigree and something from Mansfield always available. Two or three guest beers are offered each week (300 to date). Favourites include Everards Tiger and Morland Old Speckled Hen.

A village pub with background music and beer garden. No food. Children allowed.

OPEN *5.30–11pm Mon–Fri; 11am–11pm Sat; 12–10.30pm Sun.*

Spring Cottage
1 Fulwood Street, Ilkeston DE7 8AZ
☎ *(0115) 932 3153* Mr Wootton

Tied to Punch Taverns, with two guests changed daily, that may include Wadworth 6X, Morland Old Speckled Hen, Marston's Pedigree, Greene King Abbot Ale or Shepherd Neame Spitfire.

A traditional town pub with two bars and background music. Children's room. The lounge doubles as a dining area. Food at lunchtime and evenings. Children allowed. Near the main shopping area on one-way system.

OPEN *11am–3pm and 6–11pm Mon–Thur; 11am–4pm and 6–11pm Fri; 11am–5pm and 7–11pm Sat; 12–3pm and 7–10.30pm Sun.*

The Red Lion
Winksworth Road, Kniveton, Ashbourne DE6 1JH
☎ *(01335) 345554* Angela Tegram

This freehouse always has something from Burton Bridge and Blanchfield Black Bull on the menu. A guest beer, changed every few days, is also offered. Black Sheep Special is popular.

A small village pub with separate dining area. Background music only. Food served at lunchtime and evenings. Children allowed.

OPEN *12–2pm and 7–11pm Mon–Fri; 11am–11pm Sat; 12–10.30pm Sun*

MAKENEY

The Holly Bush Inn

Holly Bush Lane, Makeney, Milford
☎ *(01332) 841729* JJK Bilbie

Marston's Pedigree and Ruddles County (Morland) always available plus four (200+ per year) guests that may include Morland Old Speckled Hen, Exmoor Gold, Fuller's ESB, Marston's Owd Roger, Greene King Abbot, Timothy Taylor Landlord and brews from Bateman. Also scrumpy cider.

A Grade II listed twelfth-century coaching inn with flagstone floors and open fires. Bar food at lunchtime, barbecues in summer. Car park and children's room. Private parties welcome. Just off the main A6 at Milford, opposite the Makeney Hotel.

12–3pm and 6–11pm Mon–Fri; 12–11pm Sat–Sun.

MELBOURNE

The Railway Hotel

222 Station Road, Melbourne DE73 1BQ
☎ *(01332) 862566* Lucy Kelly

A freehouse with two rotating guest beers, changed weekly. Favourites include Marston's Pedigree.

A small pub within a family-run hotel with seven bedrooms and a restaurant. Food served at lunchtime and evenings. Children allowed.

12–3pm and 6–11pm Mon–Thurs; 11am–11pm Fri–Sat; 12–10.30am Sun.

OLD TUPTON

The Royal Oak Inn

Derby Road, Old Tupton, Chesterfield S42 6LA
☎ *(01246) 862180* John Angus

Morland Old Speckled Hen always available plus four guests, changed weekly, often including Ruddles County (Morland), Ushers Founders Ale or Tomintoul Witches Cauldron.

A 100-year-old pub with three rooms. Food at lunchtime and evenings. No children.

12–3pm and 5–11pm Mon–Thur; 11am–11pm Fri–Sat; 12–3pm and 7–10.30pm Sun.

OVER HADDON

Lathkil Hotel

Over Hadden DE45 1JE
☎ *(01629) 812501* Robert Brigrigor-Taylor

A freehouse featuring Ward's and Whim brews plus guests, changed weekly, which may include Timothy Taylor Landlord or Black Sheep Bitter.

A pub with stunning views over the Dales. Occasional TV for sporting events. Food at lunchtime and evenings. Dining area evenings only. Children allowed lunchtimes only.

11.30am–3pm and 6.30–11.30pm Mon–Fri; 11am–11pm Sat; 12–10.30pm Sun.

ROWARTH

Little Mill Inn

Rowarth, High Peak SK22 1EB
☎ *(01663) 743178* Mr Barnes

A freehouse always offering Banks's Bitter, Marston's Pedigree, Camerons Strongarm and Hardys and Hansons Kimberley Best. A guest beer, changed weekly, may well be Hartleys SB (Robinson's).

An old-style pub in the middle of nowhere with a waterwheel at the side. Twelve bars, live music twice a week, quiz and bingo nights. Upstairs restaurant area. Food served all day. Children allowed. Isolated, but fully signposted.

11am–1pm Mon–Sat; 12–10.30pm Sun.

SHARDLOW

The Old Crown

Cavendish Bridge, Nr Shardlow DE72 2HL
☎ *(01332) 792392* PM Horton and GR Morton Harrison

Marston's Pedigree always available plus three guest beers (400 per year) which may include Bateman XXXB, Otter Ale, something from the Shardlow brewery, Eldridge Pope Royal Oak, Shepherd Neame Spitfire or Brewery on Sea Black Rock.

A small inn by the River Trent serving bar food at lunchtime. Car park and garden. Children allowed in the bar at lunchtime for food. Accommodation. Turn left on the A6 before the river bridge, before Shardlow from the M1.

11.30am–3pm and 5–11pm Mon–Sat; 12–3pm and 7–10.30pm Sun.

SMALLEY

The Bell Inn
Main Road, Smalley, Ilkeston DE7 6EF
☎ *(01332) 880635* Mr Burrows

A freehouse often featuring Mallard brews, Marston's Pedigree and Ruddles County (Morland). Guests, changed every two to three weeks, may include something from Rooster's brewery.

A two-roomed, Victorian-style pub. Food at lunchtime and evenings. No children.

11.30am–2.30pm and 6–11pm (10.30pm Sun).

STAVELEY

Speedwell Inn
Lowgate, Staveley, Chesterfield S43 3TT
☎ *(01246) 472252* Alan Wood

A freehouse whose owners run the Townes Brewery but no brewing actually takes place in the pub itself. Townes brews such as Sunshine and Golden Bud always available plus one guest, perhaps from Abbeydale, Glentworth or Durham breweries.

A traditional pub with occasional live music. No food. No children.

5–11pm Mon–Fri; 11am–11pm Sat; 12–10.30pm Sun.

TICKNALL

The Staff of Life
7 High Street, Ticknall DE73 1JH
☎ *(01332) 862479* Bruce Petford

Marston's Pedigree, Everards Tiger, Mill's Old Original, Timothy Taylor Landlord and Fuller's ESB available plus five guests (200 per year) which may include Exmoor Gold, Hook Norton Old Hooky, Hop Back Summer Lightning, Mauldons Black Adder, Ringwood Old Thumper, Uley Old Spot and Temperance Relief.

A fifteenth-century beamed former bakehouse. Bar and restaurant food at lunchtime and evenings. Car park, garden and children's room. At the south end of the village and the intersection between the Ashby-de-la-Zouch and Swadlincote roads.

11.30am–2.30pm and 6–11pm Mon–Sat; 12–2.30pm and 7–10.20pm Sun.

TIDESWELL

The George Hotel
Commercial Road, Tideswell, Buxton SK17 8NU
☎ *(01298) 871382* Mr Norris

A pub tied to Hardys & Hansons' Kimberley Brewery, so with Kimberley Best and Classic always available. Also four guest beers, changed every six to eight weeks, including Hardys and Hansons seasonal ales.

A coaching house dating back to 1730, with separate dining area. Food served at lunchtime and evenings. Children allowed.

11am–3pm and 7–11pm Mon–Sat; 12–3pm and 7–10.30pm Sun.

WARDLOW MIRES

Three Stags' Heads
Wardlow Mires, Tideswell SK17 8RW
☎ *(01298) 872268* Mr and Mrs Fuller

Springhead Bitter, Kelham Island Fat Cat Pale Ale and Pale Rider plus Hoskins & Oldfield Old Navigation Ale always available. Also a guest (ten per year) such as Springhead Leveller, Uley Old Spot, Hoskins & Oldfield Ginger Tom, Christmas Noggin or Wheat Beer. Also farmhouse cider and a selection of bottled beers.

A small seventeenth-century Peak District farmhouse pub with stone-flagged bar and its own pottery workshop. Unspoilt, with no frills, no piped muzak, no games machines. Live folk/Irish music at weekends. Bar food at lunchtime and evenings. Car park. Children allowed. On the A623 at the junction with the B6465.

7–11pm Mon–Fri; 12–11pm Sat–Sun and bank holidays.

WHALEY

Shepherd's Arms
7 Old Road, Whaley, High Peak SK23 7HR
☎ *(01663) 732384* Mr Hollingsworth

A Marston's tenancy, where Banks's Mild, Marston's Bitter and Pedigree are always available. Two guest beers, changed twice a week.

Old-fashioned, traditional, family-orientated pub, with large beer garden. No food. Children allowed. Families and dogs welcome.

Summer: 11am–11pm Mon–Sat; 12–10.30pm Sun. Winter: 11am–11pm Mon–Fri; 11.30am–4pm and 7–11pm Sat–Sun.

The Oddfellows Arms

Whitehead Lane, Whitehough, Chinley, High Peak SK23 6EJ

☎ *(01663) 750306* Changed hands May 1999.

 Tied to Marston's, so always offers Marston's Bitter and Pedigree.

A one-bar country pub. Food at weekends only. Children allowed.

OPEN *5–11pm Mon–Fri; all day Sat–Sun.*

The White Horse Inn

Badger Lane, Woolley Moor, Alfreton DE55 6FG

☎ *(01246) 590319* Bill and Jill Taylor

 A freehouse with four guests which often include Everards Beacon, Bateman Salem Porter and Shepherd Neame Spitfire.

A two-bar pub with non-smoking areas in main lounge, and conservatory for dining. Adventure playground, football goalposts, outside seating on two patios with 25 tables. Barbecue in summer. Food served at lunchtime and evenings. Children allowed.

OPEN *11.30am–3pm and 6–11pm Mon–Fri; 11am–11pm Sat; 12–10.30pm Sun.*

★ *The Barley Mow*, Main Street, Kirk Ireton
★ *Bentley Brook Inn* (brewpub), Fenny Bentley
★ *The Bull's Head Inn*, Foolow
★ *The Dewdrop Inn*, Station Street, Ilkeston
★ *The George Inn*, 46 Lightwood Road, Marsh Lane
★ *The Grouse Inn*, Longshaw
★ *John Thompson Inn*, Ingleby
★ *The Thorn Tree*, 48 Jackson Road, Matlock

Places Featured:

Barnstaple	Iddlesleigh
Blackawton	Kingsbridge
Branscombe	Lapford
Broadhempston	Newton Abbot
Buckfastleigh	Newton St Cyres
Chittlehampton	North Tawton
Coleford	Okehampton
Combeinteignhead	Plymouth
Coombe Martin	Plymstock
Crediton	Princetown
Dartmouth	Ringmore
Doddiscombsleigh	Shaldon
Egg Buckland	Silverton
Exeter	Slapton
Exmouth	Tavistock
Georgeham	Teignmouth
Halwell	Topsham
Hatherleigh	Torquay
Holbeton	Tuckenhay
Horndon	Wimple
Horsebridge	Yarde Down

THE BREWERIES

BLACKAWTON BREWERY

Washbourne, Totnes TQ9 7UF
☎ *(01803) 732339*

 BITTER 3.8% ABV
Well-hopped. A popular session beer.
DEVON GOLD 4.1% ABV
Summer brew. European style. Light and fresh.
44 SPECIAL 4.5% ABV
Full-bodied with rich nutty flavour.
EXHIBITION 4.7% ABV
Pale, soft and fruity.
HEADSTRONG 5.2% ABV
Rich and powerful with fruit flavour. Deceptively smooth.
Plus occasional brews.

THE BRANSCOMBE VALE BREWERY

Great Seaside Farm, Branscombe EX12 3DP
☎ *(01297) 680511*

 BRANOC 3.8% ABV
Golden and malty with a light hop finish.
BVB 4.6% ABV
Mellow and malty.
SUMMA THAT 5.0% ABV
Golden, light and hoppy throughout.
Plus occasional brews.

CLEARWATER BREWERY

2 Devon Units, Hatchmoor Industrial Estate, Torrington EX38 7HP
☎ *(01805) 625242*

SEA TROUT 4.0% ABV
BRONZE BREAM 4.2% ABV
CARP RIPPLE 4.5% ABV
TIGER PERCH 4.8% ABV
RUSSIAN STURGEON 5.2% ABV
Plus occasional brews.

COUNTRY LIFE BREWERY

West Pusehill, Westward Ho!, Bideford EX39 5AH
☎ *(01237) 477615*

OLD APPLEDORE 3.7% ABV
Golden, refreshing session beer.
GOLDEN PIG 4.7% ABV
Golden, smooth and distinctive.
COUNTRY BUMPKIN 5.7% ABV
Dark, with sweeter roast malt flavour.

THE JOLLYBOAT BREWERY
4 Buttgarden Street, Bideford EX39 2AU
☎ *(01237) 424343*

 BUCCANNEER 3.7% ABV
Nut-brown colour and hoppy
throughout.
MAINBRACE BITTER 4.2% ABV
Light chestnut colour, late hopped for aroma.
Plus occasional brews.

OTTER BREWERY
Mathayes Farm, Luppit, Honiton EX14 0SA
☎ *(01404) 891285*

 BITTER 3.6% ABV
Pale brown. Hoppy, fruity aroma.
BRIGHT 4.3% ABV
Light and delicate with long malty finish.
ALE 4.5% ABV
Well-balanced. Malty and well-hopped.
OTTER CLAUS 5.0% ABV
Christmas beer.
HEAD 5.8% ABV
Smooth, strong and malty.

PRINCETOWN BREWERIES LTD
Tavistock Road, Princetown PL20 6QF
☎ *(01822) 890789*

 DARTMOOR IPA/ BEST 4.0% ABV
Pale, refreshing and hoppy.
JAIL ALE 4.8% ABV
Plus occasional brews.

SCATTER ROCK BREWERY
Unit 5, Gidley's Meadow, Christow, Exeter EX6 7QB
☎ *(01647) 252120*

SUMMER TIME 4.0% ABV
TEIGN VALLEY TIPPLE 4.2% ABV
GIDLEY'S BITTER 4.4% ABV
SPINDLE BERRY 4.6% ABV
SCATTERBRAIN 5.0% ABV
MOONSHADOW 5.2% ABV
Plus occasional brews.

SUMMERSKILLS BREWERY
Unit 15, Pomphlett Farm Industrial Estate, Broxton Drive, Billacombe, Plymouth PL9 7BG
☎ *(01752) 481283*

 CELLAR V 3.7% ABV
Well-balanced.
HOPSCOTCH 4.1% ABV
Red-coloured and hoppy.
BEST BITTER 4.3% ABV
Pale, with malty flavour and honey hints.
TAMAR BEST BITTER 4.3% ABV
Hoppy throughout.
MENACING DENNIS 4.5% ABV
Occasional. Robust and clean flavour.
WHISTLEBELLY VENGEANCE 4.7% ABV
Dark ruby colour. Hop, dark malt and liquorice flavour.
NINJABEER 5.0% ABV
Winter ale. Rich and golden, with soft malt, hops and toffee flavour.
TURKEY'S DELIGHT 5.1% ABV
Christmas ale.
INDIANA'S BONES 5.6% ABV
Rich, dark winter warmer.

TEIGNWORTHY BREWERY,
The Maltings, Teign Road, Newton Abbot TQ12 4AA
☎ *(01626) 332066*

 REEL ALE 4.0% ABV
Hoppy, dry session beer.
SPRING TIDE 4.3% ABV
Sweeter, darker brew, with hops throughout.
BEACHCOMBER 4.5% ABV
Thirst-quenching and well-balanced.
Plus occasional brews.

THE PUBS

BARNSTAPLE

The Corner House
108 Boutport Street, Barnstaple EX31 1SY
☎ *(01271) 343528* Christine Billett

 A freehouse with two guests, changed every two days, often include Greene King Abbot, Young's Special or something from Wye Valley.

An old-fashioned drinking pub in the town centre, with separate lounge room. Rolls only. Children allowed in the separate lounge room.

OPEN *11am–3pm and 5–11pm Mon–Thurs; 11am–11pm Fri–Sat; 11am–3pm and 5–10.30pm Sun.*

BLACKAWTON

The George Inn
Main Street, Blackawton, Totnes TQ9 7BG
☎ *(01803) 712342* Mr O'Dowell

Princetown Dartmoor IPA is always on sale in this freehouse. Guest beers change every two days, and often include Orkney Dark Island, Teignworthy's Strawberry and Cream, something from Scatter Rock, or Ash Vine Black Bess Porter.

An old village pub with eating area in the lounge bar. Four en-suite bed and breakfast rooms. Live bands every so often. Food at lunchtime and evenings (summer); evenings only (winter). Children allowed.

OPEN *11am–11pm Mon–Sat; 12–10.30pm Sun.*

BRANSCOMBE

The Fountain Head
Branscombe EX12 3AG
☎ *(01297) 680359* Mrs Luxton

Branscombe Vale Branoc, Olde Stoker and Summa That often available. Guests (60 per year) include Hook Norton Old Hooky, Crouch Vale Millennium Gold and Freeminer Speculation Ale.

A fourteenth-century pub at the top of the village with flagstone floors, log fires and wood panelling. The lounge bar was formerly the village blacksmith's. Food at lunchtime and evenings. Car park, outside seating, non-smoking area and children's room. Self-catering accommodation.

OPEN *11.30am–2.30pm and 6.30–11pm Mon–Sat; 12–2.30pm and 7–10.30pm Sun.*

BROADHEMPSTON

Coppa Dolla Inn
Broadhempston, Totnes TQ9 6BD
☎ *(01803) 812455* Robert Burke

A freehouse with Marston's Pedigree, Wadworth 6X, Dartmoor Best and Morland Old Speckled Hen always on sale.

A country pub with restaurant area. Food at lunchtime and evenings. Children allowed. Easy to find, once you're in Broadhempston.

OPEN *11.30am–3pm and 6.30–11pm (10.30pm Sun).*

BUCKFASTLEIGH

The White Hart
2 Plymouth Road, Buckfastleigh TQ11 0DA
☎ *(01364) 642337* Louise Mann

A freehouse with Teignworthy Beachcomber and a house ale always on the menu. One guest, changed every two days, might well be Greene King Abbot.

An olde-worlde pub, Grade II listed, with flagstone floors and log fires. One bar, background music. Partitioned dining area and family room. Food served at lunchtime and evenings. Children allowed.

OPEN *11am–11pm Mon–Sat; 12–10.30pm Sun (closes 6pm Mon).*

CHITTLEHAMPTON

The Bell Inn
The Square, Chittlehampton, Umberleigh EX37 9QL
☎ *(01769) 540368* Mark Jones

 A freehouse serving a range of real ales. Fuller's London Pride, Badger Tanglefoot and Best, Wadworth 6X and Young's Special often feature as guests.

A traditional, one-bar local opposite the church, with live music and juke box. Food lunchtimes and evenings. Children allowed.

OPEN *11am–3pm and 6–11pm Mon–Fri and Sun; 11am–11pm Sat.*

COLEFORD

New Inn
Coleford, Crediton EX17 5BZ
☎ *(01363) 84242* Mr PS Butt

A freehouse with Otter Ale permanently available, plus one guest, which may include regulars Badger Best or Wadworth 6X.

A thirteenth-century thatched pub, with lots of oak beams. Open-plan dining area. Food served lunchtimes and evenings. Well-behaved children allowed.

OPEN *12–2.30pm and 6–11pm Mon–Sat; 7–10.30pm Sun.*

The Wild Goose
Combeinteignhead, Newton Abbot TQ12 4RA
☎ *(01626) 872241* Mr Honeywill

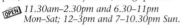 A freehouse offering 30 different real ales a month. Regularly featured are Otter Bright, Princetown Jail Ale, Teignworthy Springtide, Branscombe Vale Branoc, Skinner's Betty Stogs and Exe Valley Devon Glory.

A n old, traditional, country village pub with dining area. Jazz every Monday. Food at lunchtime and evenings. Well-behaved children only (not really a children's pub). Down country lanes, is signposted.

🍺 *11.30am–2.30pm and 6.30–11pm Mon–Sat; 12–3pm and 7–10.30pm Sun.*

The Castle Inn
High Street, Coombe Martin EX34 0HS
☎ *(01271) 883706* Chris Franks

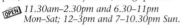 Up to four real ales are available at this freehouse, from a list of more than 500 guests.

A village pub, with one bar and a big-screen TV. A restaurant opened May 1999. Food served at lunchtime and evenings. Children allowed.

🍺 *11am–11pm Mon–Sat; 12–10.30pm Sun.*

The Crediton Inn
20A Mill Street, Crediton EX17 1EZ
☎ *(01363) 772882* Diane Heggadon

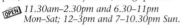 A freehouse with two guests, changed every couple of days. Examples may include Sharp's Doom Bar Bitter or Butcombe Gold or ales from other independents.

A small, friendly local, with skittle alley and function room. Snacks only. No children.

🍺 *11am–11pm Mon–Sat; 12–3pm and 7–10.30pm Sun.*

The Cherub Inn
12 Higher Street, Dartmouth TQ6 9RB
☎ *(01803) 832571* Alan Jones

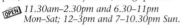 A freehouse with Wadworth 6X and Old Cherub Real Ale among the beers always offered. One guest, changed once a month, might be Everards Beacon or something from Cains, Jennings or Brains.

A 600-year-old pub, very small with beams and open fire. Air-conditioned cellar. Bar food at lunchtime, à la carte restaurant in the evenings. Over-10s only in the restaurant, no under-14s in the bar.

🍺 *11am–11pm Mon–Sat; 12–10.30pm Sun.*

The Nobody Inn
Doddiscombsleigh, Nr Exeter EX6 7DS
☎ *(01647) 252394* Nick Borst-Smith

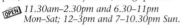 Nobody's House Ale always available plus two guest beers (40 per year) which may include Ballard's Wassail, Titanic Anniversary, Rebellion Mutiny, Exmoor Stag and Exe Valley Devon Glory.

A sixteenth-century inn with beams and inglenook fireplaces. Bar and restaurant food available at lunchtime and evenings. Speciality cheeses. Car park and garden. Children allowed in the restaurant. Accommodation unsuitable for children under 14. Three miles southwest of Exeter racecourse.

🍺 *12–2.30pm and 6–11pm.*

Prince Maurice
3 Church Hill, Egg Buckland, Plymouth PL6 5RJ
☎ *(01752) 771515* Rick and Anne Dodds

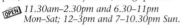 Ten real ales always available, including Badger Tanglefoot, Summerskills Best and Indiana's Bones, plus many various guest beers.

S mall, seventeenth-century freehouse with two bars and log fires. CAMRA Pub of the Year 1994 and 1995. Weekday lunchtime bar snacks. Car park, patio.

🍺 *11am–3pm and 7–11pm Mon–Thurs (6–11pm Fri); all day Sat; 12–3pm and 7–10.30pm Sun.*

Double Locks Hotel
Canal Bank, Exeter EX2 6LT
☎ *(01392) 256947* Tony Stearman

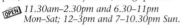 Smiles Golden, Best and Heritage, Adnams Broadside, Everards Old Original, Branscombe Branoc, Greene King Abbot Ale plus up to six guest beers.

R ecently acquired by Smiles, the pub is located in a 250-year-old building situated by twin locks on the oldest ship canal in the country. Bar food is available all day. Car park, large garden, volleyball, barbecue in summer and children's room. Located on the south-west edge of the city, through the Marsh Barton Trading Estate.

🍺 *11am–11pm Mon–Sat; 12–10.30pm Sun.*

Great Western Hotel
St David's Station Approach, Exeter EX4 4NU
☎ *(01392) 274039* Trevor Crouchen

Fuller's London Pride and Hancock HB are always available. Guest beers, changed weekly, may include favourites such as Orkney Dark Island and Morland Old Speckled Hen.

A traditional freehouse within a hotel. Staff pride themselves on looking after their customers. Thirty bedrooms with en-suite facilities. Background music. Live music on bank holidays. Food served all day. Children allowed.

OPEN *11am–11pm Mon–Sat; 12–10.30pm Sun.*

The Hole Inn the Wall
Little Castle Street, Exeter EX14 3PX
☎ *(01392) 273341* Mr Kerrigan

A pub tied to Eldridge Pope, in a back street near the law courts, with five pumps serving real ale. Hardy Country and Royal Oak always on offer.

A two-storey pub with eight pool tables, pub bar at very top. Quiz night on Tuesday. Food at lunchtime only (12–2pm). No children; over-18s only.

OPEN *11am–11pm Mon–Sat; 7–10.30pm Sun and bank holidays.*

The Well House Tavern
Cathedral Yard, Exeter EX1 1HB
☎ *(01392) 495365*
Tracy Cherry and Ian Scanes

Five guest beers available which may include Morland Old Speckled Hen, Guernsey Sunbeam Bitter and Oakhill Best.

There is live music and a quiz night at this popular pub on alternate Sundays. Bar food is available at lunchtime and evenings. Facing Exeter Cathedral, with a Roman cellar.

OPEN *11am–11pm Mon–Sat; 7–11pm Sun.*

The Grove
The Esplanade, Exmouth EX15 2AZ
☎ *(01395) 272101* Mr Doble

A freehouse with Fuller's London Pride always available. A guest beer is changed monthly. Regulars include Otter Ale and Morland Old Speckled Hen.

A quiet, family-run pub with one bar. Live bands on Fridays. Food at lunchtime and evenings. Children allowed.

OPEN *11am–11pm Mon–Sat; 12–10.30pm Sun.*

The Rock Inn
Rock Hill, Georgeham EX33 1JW
☎ *(01271) 890322* Mr and Mrs Scutts

Ruddles, Ushers and Wadworth brews always available plus Morland Old Speckled Hen. Also a couple of guest beers often including ales from Cotleigh, St Austell and Fuller's breweries.

A 400-year-old inn one mile from the sea. CAMRA North Devon Pub of the Year 1994–96. Bar food available at lunchtime and evenings. Car park, garden and children's room. Accommodation.

OPEN *11am–3pm; all day Sat–Sun when possible.*

Old Inn
Halwell, nr Totnes TQ9 7JA
☎ *(01803) 712329* Mr Crowther

A freehouse with RCH East Street Cream always on offer. There is also one guest, changed weekly.

A food and beer pub, with dining area and background music. Food at lunchtime and evenings. Children allowed.

OPEN *11am–3pm and 6–11pm Mon–Sat; 12–3pm and 6–10.30pm Sun.*

Tally Ho Country Inn
14 Market Street, Hatherleigh EX20 3JN
☎ *(01837) 810306*

Offers a range of six popular brews which are produced in the micro-brewery on the premises.

Although the present brewery only started brewing in 1990, its history goes back over 200 years. Records show that it was producing ales in 1790, when it was known as The New Inn Brewery. It was destroyed by fire in 1806 but was brewing again in 1824. The brewery finally closed down in the early 1900s, when it could no longer compete with the larger breweries of the time. The new brewery is situated at the back of The Tally Ho Country Inn in what used to be the town bakery and can produce 260 gallons of real ale a week. The pub itself has a TV and background music. Bar and restaurant food available at lunchtime and evenings. Car park, garden, accommodation. Children allowed.

POT BOILER'S BREW 3.5% ABV
TARKA'S TIPPLE 4.0% ABV
NUTTERS ALE 4.6% ABV
THURGIA 6.0% ABV
Plus seasonal ales such as Master Jack's Mild (3.5% ABV) and Jollop (6.6% ABV).

OPEN *11am–2.30pm and 6–11pm.*

HOLBETON

Mildmay Colours
Holbeton, Plymouth PL8 1NA
☎ *(01752) 830248* Louise Price

Mildmay Colours Best and SP (Skinner's) always on the menu in this freehouse. Two guests, changed fortnightly, may include Skinner's Cornish Knocker or Bunces Danish Dynamite.

A traditional country pub with upstairs dining and bar area. Occasional rock and jazz bands. Food at lunchtime and evenings. Children allowed.

11am–11pm Mon–Sat; 12–10.30pm Sun.

HORNDON

The Elephant's Nest
Horndon, Nr Mary Tavy, PL19 9NQ
☎ *(01822) 810273* Nick Hamer

Palmer's IPA and St Austell HSD always available plus two guest beers (150 per year) including those from Exe Valley, Wye Valley, Cotleigh, Exmoor, Hook Norton, Summerskills and Ash Vine breweries. Also draught cider.

T his sixteenth-century Dartmoor inn with a large garden and log fires has a collection of 'Elephant's Nests' written in different languages on the beams in chalk. Bar food at lunchtime and evenings. Car park and children's room. The garden is home to rabbits, ducks and chickens. Travel along the A386 into Mary Tavy. Take the road signposted Horndon for just under two miles.

11.30am–2.30pm and 6.30–11pm Mon–Sat; 12–2.30pm and 7–10.30pm Sun.

HORSEBRIDGE

The Royal Inn
Horsebridge TL19 8PJ
☎ *(01822) 870214* Catherine Eaton

A freehouse with Wadworth 6X and a Sharp's brew always available. Two guests also offered.

A n old pub with open fires, patio and beer garden. Food at lunchtime and evenings. Children allowed at lunchtime only.

12–3pm and 7–11pm (10.30pm Sun).

IDDESLEIGH

Duke of York
Iddesleigh EX19 8BG
☎ *(01837) 810253* J Stewart

A freehouse, with all real ales served straight from the barrel; no pumps used. Adnams Broadside and Cotleigh Tawny are always available, plus numerous guest beers which change daily. Wye Valley brews are a favourite.

A pub in a rural setting (ring for directions!). No TV, occasional live music. Separate dining area. Food served all day. Children allowed.

11am–11pm Mon–Sat; 12–10.30pm Sun.

KINGSBRIDGE

The Ship & Plough
The Promenade, Kingsbridge TQ7 1JD
☎ *(01548) 852485* Jackie Blewitt

A brewpub, home of Blewitts Brewery with the full range of own brews always available, plus Wadworth 6X. Plans to start a cask-conditioned lager.

A large pub, with beams and open fires, situated in the Sorley Tunnel. The tunnel itself is open to the public (admission charge) and has a children's play area, shop, restaurant and a workshop in which pottery and metalwork are demonstrated. There is also a glass viewing area in which people can watch the brewing process. The pub itself has live music on Thursdays. Food available. Children allowed in family room.

BLEWITTS BEST 4.0% ABV Fruity.
BLEWITTS WAGES 4.5% ABV
Made with barley and maize.
BLEWITTS HEAD OFF 5.0% ABV
A fruity, sweet flavour

11am–11pm Mon–Sat; 12–10.30pm Sun.

LAPFORD

The Old Malt Scoop Inn
Lapford, Nr Crediton EX17 6PZ
☎ *(01363) 83330* John and Pam Berry

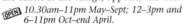 Adnams Broadside and Marston's Pedigree always available, plus 52 guest beers each year, to include Sharp's Doom Bar, Vaux Waggle Dance, Shepherd Neame Spitfire, Charles Wells Bombadier and many more. Also traditional cider.

T his sixteenth-century freehouse is open for morning coffee, bar snacks, meals and cream teas. There are inglenook fireplaces, beamed ceiling, panelled walls, skittle alley, beer garden, patio areas and car park. Children are allowed in the sun lounge and one of the bars. Lapford is on the A377 between Crediton and Barnstaple. Follow brown tourist signs near village. The inn is at the centre of the village, opposite the church.

OPEN *10.30am–11pm May–Sept; 12–3pm and 6–11pm Oct–end April.*

NEWTON ABBOT

Dartmouth Inn
63 East Street, Newton Abbot TQ12 2JP
☎ *(01626) 353451* Malcolm and Brenda Charles

Guest beers (300 per year) may include RCH East Street Cream, Hughes Dark Ruby Mild, Teignworthy Springtide and Sutton Knickerdroppa Glory.

T his 450-year-old pub is reputed to be the oldest inn in Newton Abbot. Beautiful beer garden, a previous Bloom of Britain winner. The pub has also won the regional CAMRA Pub of the Year award on several occasions. Five minutes' walk from the station.

OPEN *11am–11pm Mon–Sat; 12–10.30pm Sun.*

The Golden Lion
4 Market Street, Newton Abbot EX39 1PW
☎ *(01626) 367062* Ali Snell

A freehouse always offering Teignworthy Reel Ale. Two guests may include favourites such as Badger Tanglefoot, Fuller's London Pride or something from Scatter Rock.

A n olde-worlde one-bar pub, with juke box. Food at lunchtime only. No children. In a back alley, can be hard to find.

OPEN *11am–2.30pm and 5.30–11pm Mon–Fri; 11am–4pm and 6–11pm Sat; 11am–3pm and 7–10.30pm Sun.*

NEWTON ST CYRES

The Beer Engine
Sweetham, Newton St Cyres, Nr Exeter EX5 5AX
☎ *(01392) 851282*

Three beers brewed on the premises always available.

T he brewery was established along with a cellar bar in the basement of a former station hotel in 1983. It has now expanded to produce three brews and 65 barrels per month, and supplies a couple of local pubs and wholesalers. Food available at lunchtime and evenings. Car park, garden, accommodation. Children allowed.

RETURN TICKET 3.4% ABV
An occasional beer.
RAIL ALE 3.8% ABV
Amber-coloured, malty nose and flavour of fruit.
PISTON BITTER 4.3% ABV
Sweetness throughout, with some bitterness in the finish.
GOLDEN ARROW 4.6% ABV
An occasional beer.
Porter 4.7% ABV
An occasional beer.
Sleeper Heavy 5.4% ABV
Red, with fruit, sweetness and some bitterness.
Whistlemas 6.7% ABV
A Christmas brew.

OPEN *11.30am–2.30pm and 6–11pm Mon–Fri (12pm Sat); 12–3pm and 7–10.30pm Sun.*

NORTH TAWTON

Fountain Inn
Exeter Street, North Tawton EX20 2HB
☎ *(01837) 82551* Lesley Whitehouse

A freehouse, recently taken over. Shepherd Neame Spitfire, St Austell Hicks and Tinners always available.

A large, lively and friendly pub. Separate dining area. Food at lunchtime and evenings. Well-behaved children allowed.

OPEN *11.30am–2.30pm and 5.30–11pm Mon–Fri (closed Mon lunch); 11.30am–4pm and 6–11pm Sat; 12–4pm and 7–10.30pm Sun.*

Railway Inn
Whiddon Down Road, North Tawton EX20 2BE
☎ *(01837) 82789* Claire Speak

A freehouse with Wadworth 6X always available. Regular guests include Jollyboat Mainbrace, Teignworthy Beachcomber and Reel Ale, Adnams Broadside and Badger Best.

A n old country inn, on the main road but slightly hidden, with one bar and dining area. Bar snacks and evening meals. Children allowed.

OPEN *12–3pm (not Mon) and 6–11pm Mon–Sat; 12–3pm and 7–10.30pm Sun.*

OKEHAMPTON

Plymouth Inn
26 West Street, Okehampton EX20 1HH
☎ *(01837) 53633* Geoff Hoather

A freehouse, with four beers served straight from the barrel. Sharp's Own, Doom Bar and Special are often featured.

A country-style town pub with restaurant, beer garden and function room. Mini beer festivals and occasional folk bands. Food at lunchtime and evenings. Children allowed; function room doubles as children's room.

OPEN *12–3pm and 7–11pm Mon–Fri; 11am–11pm Sat and bank holidays; 12–10.30pm Sun.*

PLYMOUTH

The Clifton
35 Clifton Street, Greenbank, Plymouth PL4 8JB
☎ *(01752) 266563* Mr Rosevear

A freehouse with Clifton Classic (house beer) and Summerskills Indiana's Bones always on offer. Two guests are changed weekly; regulars include Badger Tanglefoot, Greene King Abbot and Timothy Taylor Landlord.

A locals' pub, with one bar and Sky TV for football. No food. No children. Not far from the railway station.

OPEN *5–11pm Mon–Thurs; 11am–11pm Fri–Sat; 12–10.30pm Sun.*

The Library
15 Wyndham Street East, Plymouth EX17 6AL
☎ *(01752) 266042* Douglas Russell

A freehouse with Cornish Rebellion and Sutton XSB always available. Two guest beers may include Vaux Moonlight Mouse.

A student-style pub, juke box (free on Student Night – Tuesday), one long bar. Big-screen TV/Sky. Live acts or karaoke Wednesdays. Pool room. Food: burgers, hot dogs, chips. No children after 7pm.

OPEN *11am–11pm Mon and Wed–Sat; 12–5pm and 7–11pm Tues; 12–10.30pm Sun.*

The Tap & Spile
20 Looe Street, Plymouth PL4 0DA
☎ *(01752) 662485* Jackie Grey

Tied to Century Inns and offering eight real ales, changed every two or three days. Morland Old Speckled Hen, Coach House Dick Turpin and St George's Ale plus Greene King Abbot regularly featured.

A town-centre pub with exposed brickwork and lots of bric-a-brac. Background music. Raised area at top of pub for eating. Food served at lunchtimes. Children allowed.

OPEN *11am–3pm and 5–11.30pm Mon–Fri; 11am–11pm Sat; 12–10.30pm Sun.*

Thistle Park Tavern
32 Commercial Road, Plymouth PL4 0LE
☎ *(01752) 204890*

Next door to the Sutton Brewery, so serves the full range of Sutton brews.

B rewing began in November 1993. Polished wooden floors, maritime relics and oil paintings by a local artist. Bar food and a range of South African cuisine served at lunchtime and evenings. Parking, patio. Further information available on website: www.quintin@xsb42.force9.co.uk.

DARTMOOR PRIDE 3.8% ABV
XSB 4.2% ABV
HOPNOSIS 4.5% ABV
EDDYSTONE LIGHT 5.0% ABV
KNICKADROPPA GLORY 5.5% ABV

OPEN *11am–11pm Mon–Sat; 12–10.30pm Sun.*

PLYMSTOCK

The Boringdon Arms
13 Boringdon Terrace, Turnchapel, Nr Plymstock PL9 9TQ
☎ *(01752) 402053*

Butcombe Bitter, RCH Pitchfork and Summerskills Best among the beers always available plus up to five guests beers (250 per year) from Orkney (north), Burts (south), Sharp's (west), Scott's (east) and all points in between.

A n ex-quarrymaster's house with a good atmosphere. No juke box. Live music on Saturday nights. CAMRA's first Plymouth Pub of the Year. Bar food available at lunchtime and evenings. Car park, conservatory and beer garden in the old quarry to the rear of the pub. Accommodation. Located at the centre of the village, four miles south-east of Plymouth. Signposted from the A379.

OPEN *11am–11pm Mon–Sat; 12–3pm and 7–10.30pm Sun.*

PRINCETOWN

The Two Bridges Hotel

Two Bridges, Princetown, Yelverton PL20 6SW
☎ *(01822) 890581* Philip Davis

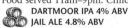 A freehouse and brewery home of the Princetown Brewery, with home brews always on offer plus seasonal specials.

A sixteenth-century country house hotel. Piano player three times a week, occasional jazz band. Restaurant seats 70. Food served 11am–9pm. Children allowed.

DARTMOOR IPA 4% ABV
JAIL ALE 4.8% ABV

(OPEN) *11am–11pm Mon–Sat; 12–10.30pm Sun.*

RINGMORE

The Journey's End

Ringmore, Nr Kingsbridge TQ7 4HL
☎ *(01548) 810205*

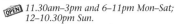 Up to ten brews available including Exmoor Ale and Otter Ale, Badger Tanglefoot, Shepherd Neame Spitfire, Adnams Broadside and Crown Buckley Reverend James Original. Also guests (50 per year) changed weekly including Archers Golden, Greene King Abbot and brews from Fuller's, Cains and Wye Valley.

An eleventh-century thatched inn with flagstone floors and open fires. Bar and restaurant food served at lunchtime and evenings. Conservatory, car park, garden, non-smoking dining room. Accommodation. No children in the bar.

(OPEN) *11.30am–3pm and 6–11pm Mon–Sat; 12–10.30pm Sun.*

SHALDON

The Clifford Arms

34 Fore Street, Shaldon, Teignmouth TQ14 0DE
☎ *(01626) 872311* Mr Balster

 A freehouse with Blackawton Headstrong and Greene King Abbot always on sale. Regular guests include Fuller's London Pride and Shepherd Neame Spitfire.

A one-bar pub with garden, juke box and live music. Food at lunchtime and evenings. Children allowed in certain areas.

(OPEN) *11am–2.30pm and 5–11pm Mon–Fri; 11am–11pm Sat; 11am–2.30pm and 5–11pm Sun.*

SILVERTON

Silverton Inn

Fore Street, Silverton, Nr Exeter EX5 4HP
☎ *(01392) 860196*

Fuller's London Pride always available plus many guests including local beers from the village brewery, Orkney Dark Island, Sutton Hypnosis and Knickerdroppa Glory, Blewitts Head Off, Wychwood Dr Thirsty's Draught, Hop Back Summer Lightning and Ringwood Fortyniner.

Traditional, cosy wooden pub between Exeter and Tiverton with easy access to sea coasts and shopping towns. Separate upstairs restaurant. Food available at lunchtime and evenings. Recently converted luxury rooms available. Nearby parking, beer garden. Children allowed in restaurant.

(OPEN) *11.30am–3pm and 5.30–11pm.*

SLAPTON

The Tower Inn

Slapton, Nr Kingsbridge TQ7 2PN
☎ *(01548) 580216* Mr and Mrs Dickman

Dartmoor Best, Exmoor Ale and Badger Tanglefoot always available plus three or four guests (20+ per year) which may include Gibbs Mew Bishop's Tipple, Blackawton Headstrong, Palmers IPA, Timothy Taylor Landlord and Eldridge Pope Royal Oak.

A fourteenth-century inn offering accommodation and a superb garden. Bar and restaurant food available at lunchtime and evenings. Car park and children's room. Hidden in the centre of the village at the foot of the old ruined tower.

(OPEN) *12–3pm and 6–11pm.*

TAVISTOCK

The Halfway House

Grenofen, Tavistock PL19 9ER
☎ *(01822) 612960* Mr Jones

A freehouse with Princetown Jail Ale always available. Two guests are changed weekly and may include Morland Old Speckled Hen, Smiles Best, Badger Tanglefoot, Greene King Abbot, Fuller's London Pride or Wadworth 6X.

A country inn on the A386. Public bar. Background music. Separate dining and lounge bar. Food at lunchtime and evenings. Children allowed.

(OPEN) *11am–3pm and 5–11pm Mon–Sat; 12–4pm and 6–10.30pm Sun.*

TEIGNMOUTH

The Blue Anchor
Teign Street, Teignmouth TQ14 8EG
☎ *(01626) 72741* Paul Fellows

A freehouse serving Adnams Broadside, Marston's Pedigree and Teignworthy Reel Ale. Three guests, changed two or three times a week, include favourites such as Greene King Abbot, Fuller's ESB or something from Bateman or Branscombe Vale.

A small, very boozy, locals' pub. Old, with log fire. Rolls only. No children.

🍺 *11am–11pm Mon–Sat; 12–10.30pm Sun.*

The Golden Lion
85 Bitton Park Road, Teignmouth TQ14 9BY
☎ *(01626) 776442*

At least two guest beers (approx 50 per year) usually available from regional brewers such as Blackawton, Teignworthy, Exe Valley and Oak Hill.

This is a locals' pub on the main road just out of the town with a public and lounge bar. Darts and pool are played. Bar food is available at lunchtime and evenings. Small car park. Children not allowed.

🍺 *12–4pm and 6–11pm (10.30pm Sun).*

TOPSHAM

Bridge Inn
Bridge Hill, Topsham, Nr Exeter EX3 0QQ
☎ *(01392) 873862*
Mr and Mrs C Cheffers-Heard

Nine real ales always available, including Branscombe Vale's Yo Ho Ho, Hells Belles, Anniversary Ale and Branoc, Moor's Old Freddy Walker, Exe Valley's Winter Glow and Mr Sheppard's Crook, Badger Tanglefoot and Adnams Broadside.

This sixteenth-century pub overlooking the River Clyst has been in the same family since 1897 through four generations. Simple bar food at lunchtime. Car park and children's room. Two miles from M5 junction 30. Topsham is signposted from the exit. In Topsham, follow the yellow signpost (A376) to Exmouth. For further information visit the website at www.cheffers.co.uk.

🍺 *12–2pm and 6–10.30pm (11pm Fri–Sat).*

TORQUAY

Chelston Manor Hotel
Old Mill Road, Torquay, Devon, TQ2 6HW
☎ *(01803) 605142* Simon Breed

A freehouse with Wadworth 6X always available, plus guest beers such as Marston's Pedigree and Morland Old Speckled Hen, Fuller's London Pride, Young's Special, Fuggles IPA, Brains IPA and brews from Brakspear.

Olde-worlde converted manor house with accommodation. Large bar with three separate areas, pool table, children's room, large beer garden. Food served at lunchtime and evenings in the bar, or in the à la carte restaurant

🍺 *12–3pm and 6–11pm (10.30pm Sun).*

Crown & Sceptre
2 Petitor Road, St Marychurch, Torquay TQ1 4QA
☎ *(01803) 328290* Mr R Wheeler

Marston's Pedigree and Ruddles County always on sale. A guest beer, changed weekly, might come from a local brewery such as Teignworthy.

A traditional pub with two bars, children's room and garden. Live music. Food at lunchtimes only. Children allowed.

🍺 *11am–3pm and 5.30–11pm Mon–Fri;*
11am–4pm and 6.30–11pm Sat;
12–3pm and 7–10.30pm Sun.

TUCKENHAY

Maltsters Arms
Bow Creek, Tuckenhay TQ9 7EQ
☎ *(01803) 832350*
Quentin and Denise Thwaites

A freehouse with Blackawton beers and Princetown Dartmoor IPA always available. One or two guests, changed every two days, may include Otter Ale or something from Wye Valley or Thwaites.

A traditional country pub with separate eating area overlooking the river. Bed and breakfast. Barbecues on the river bank. Regular live music. Food at lunchtime and evenings. Children allowed in certain areas. In the middle of nowhere. If you manage to find Tuckenhay, you'll find the pub.

🍺 *All day every day during summer holidays.*
11am–3pm and 6–11pm Mon–Fri;
11am–11pm Sat; 12–10.30pm Sun at
other times.

WHIMPLE

New Fountain Inn

Church Road, Whimple, Exeter EX5 2TA
☎ *(01404) 822350* Paul Mallett

 A free house with Teignworthy beers, Oakhill Bitter and Branscombe Vale Branoc usually on the menu. Guest beers (one from the barrel) come from Exe Valley and elsewhere. Shepherd Neame Spitfire is popular.

A traditional village inn split into two tiers, the top one used for eating. Food served at lunchtime and evenings. Children allowed.

OPEN *12–2.30pm and 6–11pm Mon–Sat; 12–2.30pm and 7–11pm Sun.*

YARDE DOWN

Poltimore Arms

Yarde Down, South Molton EX36 3HA
☎ *(01598) 710381* Richard Austen

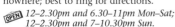 A freehouse with real ales served straight from the barrel. Cotleigh Tawny Ale is always available, and guests, changed weekly, may include Marston's Pedigree, Morland Old Speckled Hen or Greene King Abbot Ale.

Dates back to 1600. Has its own generator for electricity. Food served; a very large menu. Children allowed. In the middle of nowhere; best to ring for directions.

OPEN *12–2.30pm and 6.30–11pm Mon–Sat; 12–2.30pm and 7–10.30pm Sun.*

YOU TELL US

★ *The Check Inn*, 14 Castle Street, Barnstaple
★ *The Chichester Arms*, Mortehoe, Woolacombe
★ *The Crown*, The Square, West Down
★ *The King's Arms*, Fore Street, Winkleigh
★ *The Little Mutton Monster*, 240 James Street, Plymouth
★ *The London Hotel*, West Street, Ashburton
★ *The Manor Inn*, Lower Ashton
★ *The Mill*, Ossaborough
★ *Nog Inn*, Sidmouth Junction, Feniton
★ *The Prince of Wales*, Tavistock Road, Princetown, Yelverton
★ *The Reform Inn* (brewpub), Pilton, Barnstaple
★ *The Rockford Inn*, Brendon
★ *The Royal Inn*, Horsebridge
★ *The Tradesman's Arms*, Stokenham, Kingsbridge
★ *The Welcome Inn*, Haven Banks, Exeter

Places Featured:

Benville
Bournemouth
Burton Bradstock
Cattistock
Chetnole
Child Okeford
Corfe Mullen
Hinton St Mary
Hurn
Lyme Regis
North Wootton
Parkstone

Plush
Poole
Pulham
Sherborne
Stourton Caundle
Tarrant Monkton
Trent
Verwood
Westbourne
Weymouth
Winkton
Wyke Regis

THE BREWERIES

THE BADGER BREWERY

Blandford St Mary, Blandford Forum DT11 9LS
☎ *(01258) 452141*

 IPA 3.6% ABV
Well-hopped and refreshing.
DORSET BEST 4.1% ABV
Bitter fruitiness.
DEACON (for Gibbs Mew) 4.8% ABV
Pale and rounded.
TANGLEFOOT 5.1% ABV
Pale, full fruit, with bittersweet finish.
BISHOPS TIPPLE (for Gibbs Mew) 6.5% ABV

GOLDFINCH BREWERY

47 High East Street, Dorchester DT1 1HU
☎ *(01305) 264020*

 TOM BROWN'S BITTER 4.0% ABV
Hoppy throughout.
FLASHMAN'S CLOUT 4.5% ABV
Balanced and flavoursome.
MIDNIGHT BLINDER 5.0% ABV
Sweet malt with balancing hoppiness.
Plus occasional brews.

JC AND RH PALMER

The Old Brewery, West Bay Road, Bridport DT6 4JA
☎ *(01308) 422396*

 BRIDPORT BITTER 3.2% ABV
Refreshing, with hops and bitterness throughout.
BEST BITTER 4.2% ABV
Well-balanced and good hop character.
TALLY HO! 4.7% ABV
Nutty and distinctive.
200 5.0% ABV
Smooth, full-flavoured and complex.

POOLE BREWERY

68 High Street, Poole BH15 1DA
☎ *(01202) 682345*

 BEST BITTER or DOLPHIN 3.8% ABV
BEDROCK BITTER (occasional) 4.2% ABV
HOLES BAY HOG 4.5% ABV
BOSUN 4.6% ABV
DOUBLE BARREL (occasional) 5.5% ABV

THE QUAY BREWERY

Hope Square, Weymouth DT4 8TR
☎ *(01305) 777515*

WEYMOUTH HARBOUR MASTER 3.6% ABV
Rounded and easy-drinking.
WEYMOUTH SPECIAL PALE ALE 4.0% ABV
Gold and well-balanced.
WEYMOUTH JD 1742 4.2% ABV
Quenching bittersweet flavour.
BOMBSHELL BITTER 4.5% ABV
Sweet and malty.
STEAM ALE 4.5% ABV
OLD ROTT 5.0% ABV
Plus occasional beers.

THOMAS HARDY BREWING LTD

Weymouth Avenue, Dorchester DT1 1QT
☎ *(01305) 250255*

 **POPE'S TRADITIONAL 3.8% ABV**
HARDY COUNTRY 4.2% ABV
Well-balanced with clean bitterness in the finish.
ROYAL OAK 5.0% ABV
Warming, excellent balance and smooth finish.

THE PUBS

BENVILLE

The Talbot Arms
Benville, Dorchester DT2 0NN
☎ *(01935) 83381* Mr Skelcher

 A freehouse serving Smiles ales.

A country pub/restaurant with beer garden. Food served at lunchtime and evenings. Children allowed.

OPEN *12–2.30pm and 7–11pm (10.30pm Sun).*

BOURNEMOUTH

The Goat & Tricycle
27–9 West Hill Road, Bournemouth BH2 5PF
☎ *(01202) 314220* Sandra Gillard

Wadworth 6X, Henry's Original IPA and Farmer's Glory always available, plus four or five regularly changing guests including Morland Old Speckled Hen or brews from Bateman and Hop Back.

A traditional pub with family area and courtyard. No juke box, background music only. No children in the bar. Food served lunchtimes and evenings.

OPEN *12–3pm daily; 5.30–11pm Mon–Fri; 6–11pm Sat; 7–10.30pm Sun.*

Moon in the Square
4–8 Exeter Road, Bournemouth BH2 5AL
☎ *(01202) 314940*
Sue and Martin Groundwalker

Four guest real ales always available, perhaps from the Spinnaker range (Brewery on Sea) or other independents.

A traditional, Wetherspoons pub with no smoking at the bar. Food served all day. No children.

OPEN *All day, every day.*

BURTON BRADSTOCK

The Dove Inn
Southover, Burton Bradstock, Bridport DT6 4RD
☎ *(01308) 897897* Neil Walker

Branscombe Vale Branoc, Otter Ale, Morland Old Speckled Hen are among the brews usually available, plus one regularly changing guest, usually from a local or micro-brewery.

A listed building with thatched roof. Recently refurbished to convert three cottages into one building. One bar, restaurant area, large garden terrace, car park. Food served lunchtimes and evenings. Children allowed. Signposted from Burton Bradstock.

OPEN *All day, every day.*

CATTISTOCK

The Fox & Hounds
Duck Street, Cattistock
☎ *(01300) 320444* Anne Hinton

Lots of guest beers, two at any one time. These may include Fuller's London Pride, Charles Wells Bombadier and ales from Oakhill and Cottage breweries.

A fifteenth-century village inn with large fires, flagstones and a separate restaurant. Relaxing atmosphere. Bar and restaurant food available at lunchtime and evenings. Parking, garden and play area opposite. Campsite nearby. Accommodation. On the A37, look out for the sign for Cattistock, just past the Clay Pigeon Cafe from Yeovil or the sign on the road from Dorchester.

OPEN *12–2.30pm and 7–11pm.*

CHETNOLE

The Chetnole Inn
Chetnole, Sherborne DT9 6NU
☎ *(01935) 872337*

A freehouse. Branscombe Vale Branoc Ale always available, plus guests often from the Butcombe or Otter breweries.

A two-bar village pub with background music and occasional small live bands. Beer garden and dining area. Food served at lunchtime and evenings. Children allowed in garden and dining area. Opposite the church.

OPEN *11am–2.30pm and 6–11pm Mon–Sat; 12–3pm and 7–10.30pm Sun.*

CHILD OKEFORD
Saxon Inn
Hold Hill, Child Okeford DT11 8HD
☎ *(01258) 860310* Mr Pendleton

One Butcombe brewery bitter permanently available plus a guest, changed twice-weekly, which might perhaps be Shepherd Neame Spitfire or Fuller's London Pride.

An old-fashioned freehouse with log fires and beams. Food served at lunchtime and evening in a separate restaurant area. Children allowed. In a tucked-away location, down an alleyway between two houses. Signposted from the main road.

OPEN *11.30am–2.30pm and 7–11pm Mon–Sat; 12–3pm and 7–10.30pm Sun.*

CORFE MULLEN
Coventry Arms
Mill Street, Corfe Mullen BH21 3RH
☎ *(01258) 857284* Mrs Nikki

Owned by Greenalls, serving local beers straight from the barrel, including Ringwood Best and Old Thumper plus other guests as available.

An old-style, one-bar country pub with food served at lunchtime and evenings in a separate dining area. Children allowed. Located on the main A31.

OPEN *11am–3pm and 5.30–11pm Mon–Fri; all day Sat–Sun.*

HINTON ST MARY
The White Horse
Hinton St Mary, Sturminster Newton DT10 1NA
☎ *(01258) 472723* Mr Thomas

A freehouse serving a wide range of real ales (8–10 per week) on a rotating basis including Ringwood Best and True Glory plus brews from Tisbury and Cottage Breweries. One light beer (under 3.5% ABV) and one heavy (over 4% ABV) always available. On Fridays one real ale is selected for a special offer at £1 per pint.

A busy nineteenth-century thatched pub. Public bar, lounge bar and beer garden. Restaurant area in the lounge with à la carte menu and specials plus Sunday Roasts. Food served at lunchtime and evenings. Children allowed.

OPEN *11.15am–3pm and 6.15–11pm Mon–Sat; 12–3pm and 7–11pm Sun.*

HURN
Avon Causeway Hotel
Hurn, Christchurch BH25 6AS
☎ *(01202) 482714* Keith Perks

Up to five real ales available, including Rockingham Forest Gold and a Ringwood ale such as Best or Old Thumper, plus guests.

A quaint country hotel, ten minutes from Bournemouth. Formerly Hurn railway station, the pub is decorated with lots of railway bric-a-brac. Food served at lunchtime and evenings in a separate large lounge. Murder mystery nights are a feature, and make use of an old Victorian carriage. Beer garden with large children's play area. Inside, children are allowed in dining area only.

OPEN *All day, every day.*

LYME REGIS
The Nag's Head
Silver Street, Lyme Regis DT7 3HS
☎ *(01297) 442312* Mrs Hamon

A freehouse with up to four ales available, perhaps including Ward's Best and Ringwood Best.

A traditional one-bar pub with background music and beer garden. Separate dining area. Food served every lunchtime and Mon, Wed, Fri and Sat evenings. Children allowed in the bar or restaurant when eating.

OPEN *11am–3pm and 6–11pm Mon; all day Tues–Sun (10.30pm Sun).*

NORTH WOOTTON
The Three Elms
North Wootton, Nr Sherborne DT9 5JW
☎ *(01935) 812881* Mr and Mrs Manning

Fuller's London Pride, Shepherd Neame Spitfire Ale, Hop Back Summer Lightning, Smiles and Butcombe brews always available. Plus two or three guests (160 per year) to include Oakhill Somer Ale, Black Sheep Special, RCH Pitchfork, Smiles Mayfly and Bateman's Strawberry Fields.

A busy roadside pub with a large garden and car park. Contains a collection of 1000+ diecast model cars and lorries in display cabinets around the walls. Bar and restaurant food available at lunchtime and evenings. Children allowed. Accommodation. Situated on the A3030 Sherborne to Sturminster Newton road, two miles from Sherborne.

OPEN *11am–2.30pm Mon–Sat, 12–3pm Sun; 6.30–11pm Mon–Thurs, 6–11pm Fri–Sat, 7–10.30pm Sun.*

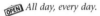

Branksome Railway Hotel

429 Poole Road, Parkstone, Poole BH12 1DQ
☎ *(01202) 769555* Dave Gough

A Whitbread pub with a guest beer policy. Brains Bitter always available, plus two weekly changing guests from Cottage Brewery and other small regional and local breweries.

A very basic locals' pub with one bar, function room, B&B. Sandwiches and pies only. Well-behaved children allowed. Located on the A35.

All day, every day.

PLUSH

The Brace of Pheasants

Plush DT2 7RQ
☎ *(01300) 348357* Mr Knights

A freehouse with Fuller's London Pride always available, plus one or two weekly rotated guests, including Hop Back Summer Lightning or something from Butcombe, Smiles or Tisbury breweries.

A sixteenth-century thatched village inn. Non-smoking family room, non-smoking restaurant area, large garden. Bar meals and snacks and à la carte restaurant food served lunchtimes and evenings. Children allowed in the garden and family room only. Situated off B3142 Dorchester/Sherborne road.

12–2.30pm and 7–11pm Mon–Sat; 12–3pm and 7–10.30pm Sun.

POOLE

The Bermuda Triangle

Parr Street, Lower Parkstone, Poole BH14 0JY
☎ *(01202) 748087* Mrs G Crane

Three real ales constantly changing. These may include Timothy Taylor Landlord, Fuller's ESB and London Pride, Adnams Broadside, Hop Back Summer Lightning, Greene King Abbot Ale, Ringwood Old Thumper and Fortyniner. Also Young's, Wychwood, Hampshire, Smiles and Shepherd Neame brews.

An interesting theme pub. German lagers on draught and at least 30 bottled beers from all around the world. Good music, great atmosphere. Bar food at lunchtime. Car park. Near Ashley Cross.

11.30am–3pm and 5.30–11pm.

The Blue Boar

29 Market Close, Poole BH15 1NE
☎ *(01202) 682247* Mr and Mrs Kellawar

A freehouse with Cottage Southern Bitter always available. Also regularly rotating guests including others from the Cottage range and ales from other independents.

An unusual three-storey pub. Top floor used as a conference room. Cellar bar with music twice a week and a children's licence. Games include table football and darts. Bar meals served at lunchtime.

11am–3pm and 5–11pm Mon–Sat; 12–4pm and 7–10.30pm Sun.

The Brewhouse

68 High Street, Poole BH15 1DA
☎ *(01202) 685288*

A Poole Brewery tied house with a range of Poole ales always available.

A drinker's pub. No food. No children.

All day, every day.

Sandacres Free House

3 Banks Road, Sandbanks, Poole BH13 8PW
☎ *(01202) 707244* Peter Fay

Ringwood Best and Gales HSB always available, plus up to four guests from breweries such as Poole, Wadworth, Smiles and Hampshire. Tries to support small and local breweries, and micro breweries.

A modern-style waterside pub in Poole Harbour with lovely views. One large bar, children's area, outside seating. Disabled facilities with no steps. Food served at lunchtime and evenings. Children allowed.

11am–3pm and 6–11pm (10.30pm Sun).

PULHAM

Halsey Arms

Pulham, Dorchester DT2 7DZ
☎ *(01258) 817344* Mrs Dunn

A freehouse serving Ringwood Best plus weekly changing guests including bitters from breweries such as Adnams, Bath and Fuller's.

A local's pub with dining area and occasional live entertainment. Food served at lunchtime and evenings. Children allowed.

11.30am–2.30pm and 6–11pm Mon–Sat; 12–3pm and 7–10.30pm Sun.

SHERBORNE

The Digby Tap
Cooks Lane, Sherborne DT9 3NS
☎ *(01935) 813148* Peter LeFevre

Twenty different beers served each week from a range of 100 per year. Brews from the Smiles, Teignworthy, Ringwood, Exmoor, Oakhill, Otter and Cottage breweries, plus many other regional producers.

A traditional, local, one-bar pub with flagstone floors. Bar snacks available at lunchtime (not on Sundays). Children are allowed at lunchtime only. Just 100 yards from the abbey, towards the railway station.

OPEN *11am–2.30pm and 5.30–11pm Mon–Sat; 12–2.30pm and 7–10.30pm Sun.*

STOURTON CAUNDLE

Trooper
Stourton Caundle, Stourminster Newton DT10 2JW
☎ *(01963) 362405* Mr Skeats

A freehouse. Cottage Champflower and Oakhill Bitter always available plus two monthly changing guests including perhaps Fuller's London Pride and Exmoor brews.

A very small pub with two bars and a skittle alley. Snacks served at lunchtime. Children allowed at lunchtime only. Situated off the main road, can be difficult to find.

OPEN *12–2.30pm and 7–closing daily.*

TARRANT MONKTON

The Langton Arms
Tarrant Monkton, Nr Blandford DT11 8RX
☎ *(01258) 830225* Mr and Mrs Davidson

Approximately 100 beers per year, none permanent, four at any one time. These may include Ringwood Fortyniner, Smiles Best, Tisbury Old Wardour, Shepherd Neame Spitfire, brews from Tally Ho! and many other micro-breweries.

An attractive seventeenth-century thatched inn with a separate restaurant (evenings only). Bar food available lunchtime and evenings. Car park, garden, children's room and play area. Accommodation. Less than two miles off the A354 Blandford to Salisbury road, five miles north of Blandford.

OPEN *11.30am–2.30pm and 6–11pm; all day Sat.*

TRENT

The Rose & Crown
Trent, Nr Sherborne DT9 4SL
☎ *(01935) 850776* Mr and Mrs Crawford

Butcombe Best and Shepherd Neame Spitfire always available plus two guest beers (24 per year) including Wadworth 6X, Charles Wells Bombardier, Otter Ale plus brews from Smiles, Hook Norton, Morland and Sam Smith.

A fifteenth-century part-thatched freehouse opposite Trent church. Bar and restaurant food available at lunchtime and evenings. Car park, garden, children's room and playground. Less than two miles north of the A30 between Sherborne and Yeovil.

OPEN *12–2.30pm and 7–11pm Mon–Sat; 12–3pm and 7–10.30pm Sun.*

VERWOOD

Albion Inn
Station Road, Verwood BH31 7LB
☎ *(01202) 825267* Rex Neville

An Enterprise Inns pub. Morland Old Speckled Hen and Ushers Salisbury Best always available.

A traditional two-bar layout. Was previously a railway-owned pub. Food served at lunchtime and evenings. Children allowed.

OPEN *All day, every day.*

WESTBOURNE

The Porterhouse
113 Poole Road, Westbourne BH4 9BG
☎ *(01202) 768586* Ray Rutter

Ringwood Best, True Glory, Fortyniner and Old Thumper always available, plus regular guests changed every few days such as Fuller's London Pride, Everards Mild, Hop Back Summer Lightning or Hogs Back Hop Garden Gold

A traditional one-bar pub on the main road. Food served at lunchtime only. No children under 14.

OPEN *All day, every day.*

King's Arms
15 Trinity Road, Weymouth DT4 8TJ
☎ *(01305) 770055* Martin Taylor

Wadworth 6X and Ringwood Best and Fortyniner always available, plus one regular guest from the Quay Brewery, perhaps Weymouth JD.

A n olde-worlde quayside pub owned by Greenalls with separate dining area. Two bars, pool table. Food served every lunchtime and Wed–Sat evenings. Children allowed.

All day, every day.

The Weatherbury Freehouse
7 Carlton Road North, Weymouth DT4 7PX
☎ *(01305) 786040* Mr and Mrs Cromack

Four beers (200 per year) which may include Townes IPA, Badger Tanglefoot, Wild's Redhead and Fuller's London Pride.

A busy town local in a residential position. Bar and restaurant food available at lunchtime and evenings. Car park, patio and dining area (where children are allowed). Dart board and pool table. Accommmodation. Coming in to Weymouth, turn right off the Dorchester road.

12–11pm (10.30pm Sun).

The Lamb Inn
Burley Road, Winkton BH23 7AN
☎ *(01425) 672427* Mr and Mrs J Haywood

Four real ale pumps, one serving Fuller's London Pride, the others with a range of ales such as Young's Special.

S ituated in the heart of the New Forest, this pub has a lounge and public bar. Bar and restaurant food available at lunchtime and evenings. Car park and garden. Children are allowed in the restaurant and garden.

11am–3pm and 5–11pm Mon–Sat; 12–3pm and 7–10.30pm Sun.

The Wyke Smugglers
76 Portland Road, Wyke Regis, Weymouth DT4 9AB
☎ *(01305) 760010* Mick Nellville

Ringwood Old Thumper always available plus two real ales served as guests which change weekly.

A local drinker's pub, sport orientated. No food. No children.

11am–2.30pm and 6–11.30pm.

★ *The Blue Raddle*, 8 Church Street, Dorchester
★ *The Cricketers*, Twerne Courtney
★ *The Queens Arms Inn*, Corton Denham, Sherborne
★ *Red Shoot*, Toms Lane, Linwood
★ *The Sheaf of Arrows*, 4 The Square, Cranborne, Wimborne
★ *Spyway*, Askerswell
★ *The Squirrel*, Laymore
★ *Tom Brown's*, 47 High East Street, Dorchester
★ *The Volunteer Inn*, 31 Broad Street, Lyme Regis

Places Featured:

Consett
Croxdale
Darlington
Durham
Forest in Teesdale
Framwellgate Moor
Great Lumley
Kirk Merrington

Middlestone Village
Newton Aycliffe
No Place
North Bitchburn
Rookhope
Shadforth
Tantobie

THE BREWERIES

CAMERONS BREWERY CO

Lion Brewery, Hartlepool TS24 7QS
☎ *(01429) 266666*

BITTER 3.6% ABV
Smooth and full-flavoured.
STRONGARM 4.0% ABV
An individual brew, very smooth.

CASTLE EDEN BREWERY

Castle Eden, Hartlepool TS27 4SX
☎ *(01429) 836007 (Brewery tours)*

BANNER 4.0% ABV
Well-balanced and fruity.
ALE 4.1% ABV
Smooth malt with hoppy aftertaste.
NIMMO'S BITTER 4.1% ABV
CONCILIATION 4.2% ABV
Fruity with good hoppy bitterness.
NIMMO'S XXXX 4.4% ABV

DARWIN BREWERY,

Unit 5, Castle Close, Crook, DL15 8LU
☎ *(01388) 763200*

EVOLUTION ALE 4.0% ABV
Good hoppiness.
HODGE'S ORIGINAL 4.0% ABV
Balanced.
TRAVELLERS BITTER 4.0% ABV
BITTER 4.5% ABV
KILLER BEE 6.0% ABV
Powerful honeyed flavour.

THE DURHAM BREWERY

Unit 5a, Bowburn North Industrial Est.,
Bowburn DH6 5PF
☎ *(0191) 377 1991*

GREEN GODDESS 3.8% ABV
Refreshing and spicy.
MAGUS 3.8% ABV
Pale, well-hopped lager-style beer.
BLACK VELVET 4.0% ABV
A weaker version of Black Friar.
WHITE GOLD 4.0% ABV
Pale, refreshing with citrus fruit flavours.
CELTIC 4.2% ABV
Award-winning, traditional premium ale.
DURHAM SOLSTICE 4.2% ABV
Darker, dry and bitter.
WHITE VELVET 4.2% ABV
Light, malty smoothness with flavour of fruit.
BLACK BISHOP 4.5% ABV
Black stout with powerful roast malt flavour.
BLACK FRIAR 4.5% ABV
Smooth porter.
CANNY LAD 4.5% ABV
Complex and malty with good bitterness.
INVINCIBLE 4.5% ABV
A strong version of Magus.
WHITE SAPPHIRE 4.5% ABV
Quenching, light and easy drinking.
WHITE BISHOP 4.8% ABV
Easy drinking and fruity with lager malt.
PAGAN 4.8% ABV
Golden, with some bitterness.
CUTHBERT'S ALE 5.0% ABV
Quenching, golden and fruity.
Plus seasonal brews.

THE PUBS

CONSETT

The Grey Horse
115 Sherburn Terrace, Consett DH8 6NE
☎ *(01207) 502585* Mrs Conroy

Home of the Grey Horse brewery with home beers brewed and always available on the premises, plus up to four other ales.

A brewpub with bar snacks available. No children.

MUTTON CLOG 3.8% ABV
STEEL TOWN 3.8 % ABV
RED DUST 4.2% ABV
SWORDMAKER 4.5% ABV
COAST 2 COAST 5.0% ABV
DERWENT DEEP 5.0% ABV

11am–11pm Mon–Sat; 12–10.30pm Sun.

CROXDALE

The Daleside Arms
Front Street, Croxdale, Durham DH6 5HY
☎ *(01388) 814165* Mr Patterson

A freehouse with Black Sheep Special and Mordue Workie Ticket always available. Four guest beers, which change weekly, include other favourites from Mordue, Black Sheep and Border breweries.

A village pub in a country setting, with en suite accommodation and two bars (a pub/lounge and restaurant). Food served in the evenings in the restaurant. Children allowed.

2–11pm Mon–Fri; all day Sat–Sun.

DARLINGTON

Number Twenty 2
Coniscliffe Road, Darlington DL3 7RG
☎ *(01325) 354590* Mr Wilkinson

Ten ales including Hambleton Nightmare, White Boar and Old Raby always available plus guests (500 per year) such as Dent Ramsbottom, Hadrian Gladiator and Butterknowle's Conciliation.

T raditional town-centre freehouse. Food available at lunchtime and evenings. Parking nearby, children allowed.

11am–11pm.

The Railway Tavern
8 High Northgate, Darlington DL1 1UN
☎ *(01325) 464963* Mr Greenhow

Tied to Whitbread, this pub offers Wadworth 6X and Greene King Abbot on a permanent basis. Three guest beers are changed weekly. These regularly include Black Sheep Bitter and Riggwelter and Durham Sanctuary. The pub tries to use small breweries when possible for its other guest beers.

T his small local pub was probably the first railway pub in the world, since the land on which it stands is owned by the Pease family, who founded Darlington Railway. On the main road through Darlington, the pub has two bars, a pool room with darts, and features live music on Fridays and occasionally on Sunday afternoons. Bar snacks at lunchtime and evenings. Children allowed if supervised.

12–11pm.

The Tap & Spile
99 Bondgate, Darlington DL3 7JY
☎ *(01325) 381679* Stella Bowden

Eight guests (100 per year) at any one time continually changing with brews from Marston's, Greene King, Butterknowle, Durham, Hadrian, Hambleton, Lees, Robinson's, Adnams, Bateman, Burtonwood, Exmoor, Jennings, Hardington, Morland, Nethergate, Steam Packet, Ridleys, Titanic, Ushers, Oak, Belhaven and Harviestoun.

A traditional town-centre alehouse where the policy is to offer one beer a month at a discounted price (£1.19–£1.24), sponsored by the brewer. Food available at lunchtime. Parking, children's room and non-smoking room.

11.30am–11pm Mon–Sat; 12–10.30pm Sun.

DURHAM

Neville's Cross Hotel
Barlington Road, Durham DH1 4JX
☎ *(0191) 384 3872* Mr Holland

Northumberland Brewery's Secret Kingdom, Black Sheep Bitter, Castle Eden Bitter and Butterknowle Banner usually available plus up to four others.

A n Edwardian freehouse, built in 1907 on the site of a tavern established in 1730. Open fireplace, two bars and pool room. Food served all day in a 40-seater restaurant. Accommodation. Children allowed. At the crossroads of A167 and A690.

All day, every day.

Ye Old Elm Tree

12 Crossgate, Durham DH1 4PS
☎ *(0191) 386 4621* Mr Dave Cruddace

 Ward's Waggle Dance and four others. Regular guests, two rotating every two weeks, may include Fuller's London Pride, Morland Old Speckled Hen or Bateman XXXB.

An alehouse dating from 1601, situated in the centre of Durham city, off Framwellgate Bridge. Two guest rooms, beer garden and patio. The bar is built round an elm tree. Quiz and folk nights held. Light snacks at lunchtime and evenings. Children allowed.

[OPEN] *12–3pm and 6–11pm Mon–Fri; 11am–11pm Sat; 12–4pm and 7–10.30pm Sun.*

FOREST IN TEESDALE

The High Force Hotel

Forest in Teesdale, Barnard Castle DL12 0XH
☎ *(01833) 622222/622264* Gary Wilson

Home of the High Force brewery with three own brews always available.

A country hotel, which is easy to find, serving food at lunchtime and evenings. Children allowed.

TEESDALE BITTER 3.8% ABV
FOREST XB 4.2% ABV
CAULDRON SNOUT 5.6% ABV

[OPEN] *11am–11pm Mon–Sat; 12–10.30pm Sun.*

FRAMWELLGATE MOOR

Tap & Spile

27 Front Street, Framwellgate Moor, Durham DH1 5EE
☎ *(0191) 386 5451* Jean McPoland

Up to nine beers available. Marston's Pedigree and Fuller's London Pride are usually among them.

A traditional pub with a family room, non-smoking room, and games room for darts and billiards. Pet-friendly. Snacks served all day. Children allowed. Two miles north of Durham city centre, on the old A1.

[OPEN] *11.30am–3pm and 6–11pm Mon–Sat; 12–3pm and 7–10.30pm Sun.*

GREAT LUMLEY

The Old England

Front Street, Great Lumley, Nr Chester le Street DH3 4JB
☎ *(0191) 388 5257* Mr Barkes

Three or four different ales a week are available in this freehouse, with a good mix of nationals and micro-breweries from all over the country. Regular guests include Hop Back Summer Lightning and brews from Caledonian and Wychwood.

A pub/restaurant set off the road, with a 200-seat lounge, 150-seat bar, separate dining area, darts, dominoes, pool. Food served mostly during evenings, lunchtime at weekends, but not on Sundays. Children allowed in dining area.

[OPEN] *11am–11pm Mon–Sat; 12–10.30pm Sun.*

KIRK MERRINGTON

The Half Moon Inn

Crowther Place, Kirk Merrington, Nr Spennymoor DL16 7JL
☎ *(01388) 811598* Mrs Crooks

Something from Durham Brewery always available in this freehouse. Favourite guest beers might come from the Kitchen Brewery, or include Elgood's Black Dog and Hart's Squirrels Hoards. Anything and everything has been tried.

A traditional pub on the village green, with one room, games area and car park. Bar meals at lunchtime and evening. Children allowed up to 8pm.

[OPEN] *All day, every day.*

MIDDLESTONE VILLAGE

The Ship Inn

Low Row, Middlestone Village, Bishop Auckland DL14 8AB
☎ *(01388) 810904* Mr Freeman

A freehouse with three real ales always available. Ales from local breweries, such as Castle Eden's Nimmo are popular. Stone's also a regular feature.

A well-appointed traditional pub with a small bar and lounge. Built into the hillside in walking country and offers panoramic views. Restaurant on first-floor balcony doubles as a function room. Food served from 5.30–9.30pm, and Saturday and Sunday lunchtimes. Children allowed if parents are eating.

[OPEN] *5–11pm Mon–Fri; 12–3pm and 5–11pm Sat; 12–3pm and 7–10.30pm Sun.*

NEWTON AYCLIFFE

The Blacksmith's Arms
Preston-le-Skerne, Newton Aycliffe DL5 6JH
☎ *(01325) 314873* Pat Cook

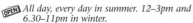 Three local beers are rotated each week (100 per year). Favourites come from Hambleton, Barnsley and a range of micro-brewers.

A country pub in the middle of farmland, in an isolated position two miles from Newton Aycliffe. Two bars, a one-acre beer garden, rabbits and a plant nursery. Ice creams served. Food available at lunchtime and evenings, outdoors in summer. Children allowed.

OPEN *All day, every day in summer. 12–3pm and 6.30–11pm in winter.*

NO PLACE

Beamish Mary Inn
No Place, Nr Stanley DH9 0QH
☎ *(0191) 370 0237* Graham Ford

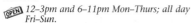 Black Sheep Special and Bitter and Jennings Cumberland Ale always available, plus three guests often including No Place, a beer brewed specially by Big Lamp Brewery. Others come from Border and other small local breweries.

Over 100 years old, this pub is a throw-back from the Beamish Museum housing many interesting artefacts. Live music four nights a week in the converted stables of the old barn. Food served 12–2pm and 7–9.30pm in a separate restaurant area. B&B. Children allowed.

OPEN *12–3pm and 6–11pm Mon–Thurs; all day Fri–Sun.*

NORTH BITCHBURN

Famous Red Lion
North Bitchburn Terrace, Barnard Castle DL15 8AL
☎ *(01388) 763561* Mr Kyte

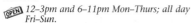 A freehouse with Black Sheep Special, Marston's Pedigree and Greene King Abbot always available. There is also a guest beer; Morland Old Speckled Hen is a favourite, but many others also served.

An easy-to-find, typical, olde-worlde inn with one bar and a small patio. Food served at lunchtime and evenings. Separate dining room. Children allowed.

OPEN *11am–11pm Mon–Sat; 12–10.30pm Sun.*

ROOKHOPE

The Rookhope Inn
Rookhope, Nr Stanhope DL13 2BG
☎ *(01388) 517215* Stephen Thompson

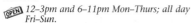 A freehouse offering a constantly changing choice of beers. A Hexhamshire and a Hadrian (Four Rivers) brew are always available, with Four Rivers Moondance and Hexhamshire Devil's Water particularly popular. Also Butterknowle Conciliation and Fuller's London Pride. No nationals; other guests are sourced as special offers through wholesalers or direct from small breweries.

A seventeenth-century pub with open fires and real beams. Three rooms (games/lounge/restaurant). Prior booking required for restaurant; soup and sandwiches served in bar and lounge. Children allowed in games room and restaurant.

OPEN *7–11pm daily, 12–3pm Sat–Sun (and weekdays by arrangement).*

SHADFORTH

The Plough Inn
South Side, Shadforth, Durham DH6 1LL
☎ *(0191) 372 0375* Jane Barber

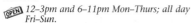 A freehouse with a varied and ever-changing range of beers, which change once or twice a week. Regular guests, which now number in the hundreds, come mainly from independents and micro-breweries. You name it, they've probably served it.

A small, traditional country pub, with one bar and lounge. No food. Children allowed.

OPEN *6.30–11pm Mon–Fri; 11am–11pm Sat; 12–10.30pm Sun.*

TANTOBIE

The Highlander

White-le-Head, Tantobie, Nr Stanley DH9 9SN
☎ *(01207) 232416* Mr CD Wright

Up to 100 beers per year changed weekly including something from Thwaites, Timothy Taylor, Black Sheep and Marston's, plus beers from many other smaller breweries as available.

One bar has games and music (pool, darts, etc). Also a small lounge and dining area. Hot food available on weekday evenings and weekend afternoons. Car park, beer garden, children's room and function room. Occasional accommodation. Ring to check. One mile off the A692 between Tantobie and Flint Hill.

7.30–11pm Mon–Fri; 12.30–3pm and 7.30–11pm Sat–Sun.

YOU TELL US

★ *The Blacksmith's Arms,* Ricknall Lane, Preston-le-Skerne
★ *Dun Cow,* Old White Lea, Billy Row
★ *Dun Cow,* 43 Front Street, Sedgefield
★ *The Malt Shovel,* Lower Wharn, Bishop Auckland
★ *Tap & Spile,* 13 Cockton Hill Road, Bishop Auckland
★ *Tap & Spile,* Church Street, Hartlepool
★ *Traders,* Blue Post Yard, Stockton-on-Tees

Places Featured:

Basildon	Manningtree
Billericay	Mill Green
Birdbrook	Moreton
Black Notely	Navestock Heath
Brentwood	Pebmarsh
Brightlingsea	Pleshey
Burnham-on-Crouch	Quendon
Chelmsford	Radwinter
Colchester	Ridgewell
Coxtie Green	Rochford
Epping	South Fambridge
Feering	Southend-on-Sea
Fyfield	Southminster
Gestingthorpe	Stock
Hatfield Broad Oak	Stow Maries
Herongate Tye	Tendring
Hutton	Thornwood Common
Leigh-on-Sea	Tillingham
Little Clacton	Toot Hill
Little Oakley	Wendens Ambo
Littlebury	Witham
Maldon	Woodham Water

THE BREWERIES

CROUCH VALE BREWERY LTD

12 Redhills Road, South Woodham Ferrers, Chelmsford CM3 5UP
☎ *(01245) 322744*

BEST DARK ALE 3.6% ABV
Easy-drinking mild.
WOODHAM IPA 3.6% ABV
Golden, with hoppy, fruity finish.
BEST BITTER 4.0% ABV
Malt and fruit, some hops. Bitter finish.
MILLENNIUM GOLD 4.2% ABV
Sharp fruit and hops. Malty bitter
STRONG ANGLIAN SPECIAL 5.0% ABV
Tawny. Clean-tasting bitter with dry aftertaste.
Plus occasional brews.

MIGHTY OAK BREWING CO.

9 Prospect Way, Hutton Industrial Estate, Brentwood CM13 1XA
☎ *(01277) 263007*

BARRACKWOOD IPA 3.6% ABV
Light amber with good hoppy bitterness.
HEARTSWOOD BITTER 3.8% ABV
Amber and malty with some sweetness.
BURNTWOOD BITTER 4.0% ABV
Malty with hoppy finish.

ALE DANCER 4.2% ABV
Soft malty flavour with balancing hoppiness.
MILLENNIUM RINGER 4.2% ABV
Complex combination of malt and hop flavours.
SIMPLY THE BEST 4.4% ABV
Refreshing hoppy bitterness.
TWENTY FIRST 4.4% ABV
Soft and delicate.
BITTER 4.8% ABV
Powerful, hoppy flavour.

TD RIDLEY AND SONS LTD

Hartford End Brewery, Chelmsford CM3 1JZ.
☎ *(01371) 820316*

IPA 3.5% ABV
Flavour of hops, with some malt.
MILD 3.5% ABV
Dark-coloured, with a fruity and rich malty flavour.
ESX BEST 4.3% ABV
Strong, well-hopped flavour.
WITCHFINDER PORTER 4.3% ABV
Based on traditional porter recipe.
SPECTACULAR 4.6% ABV
Very light-coloured, easy-quaffing ale.
RUMPUS 4.5% ABV
Ruby, with smooth nutty character.
WINTER ALE 5.0% ABV
Strong and warming.

THE PUBS

BASILDON

Moon on the Square

1–15 Market Square, Basildon SS14 1DF
☎ *(01268) 520360* Vic Jones

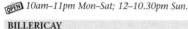 A Wetherspoon's pub. Eight guests, changed weekly, from a list that includes Shepherd Neame Spitfire, Adnams Clipper, Arundel Old Knuckler, Eldridge Pope's Royal Oak, Spinnaker and Hop Back brews amongst other independents.

A busy market pub with one large bar. A mixed clientele of business customers and lunchtime shoppers. Food served all day. No children.

10am–11pm Mon–Sat; 12–10.30pm Sun.

BILLERICAY

The Coach and Horses

36 Chapel Street, Billericay CM12 9LU
☎ *(01277) 622873* Mr J Childs

Greene King IPA and Abbot always available, plus two guest beers, one of which is changed each week,the other every fortnight. Guests include Ushers St George and the Dragon and Greene King Triumph. Tries to stock independent breweries' beers whenever possible.

A town pub with one bar. Friendly locals but clientele tend to be business lunchers during the day, regulars in the evening. Food available Mon–Sat lunchtime. Beer garden. No children. Next to Waitrose.

All day Mon–Sat; 12–3.30pm and 7–10.30pm Sun.

BIRDBROOK

The Plough

The Street, Birdbrook CO9 4BJ
☎ *(01440) 785336* Stuart Walton

Fuller's London Pride, Adnams Best and Greene King IPA always available, plus two rotating guests changing weekly. These might include Morland Old Speckled Hen and Adnams Broadside plus beers from smaller breweries such as Mighty Oak when possible.

A sixteenth-century thatched freehouse with a very low beamed ceiling. Two interlinking bars, safe beer garden. Food served every lunchtime and evening except Sunday evenings. Children allowed. Follow signs to Birdbrook from A1017.

11.30am–3pm and 6–11pm (10.30pm Sun).

BLACK NOTELY

The Vine Inn

105 The Street, Black Notely, Nr Braintree CM7 8LJ
☎ *(01376) 324269* Arthur Hodges

One Adnams brew and Ridleys IPA always available plus three guests changed three or four times a week. Of 192 beers served last year, regulars included Kelham Island Pale Rider and Nethergate Old Growler and Augustinian.

A country freehouse dating from 1640 with an old barn end, stone floor and a minstrel's gallery which is used as a small restaurant and for beer festivals. Food served at lunchtime and evenings. Children allowed. A couple of mile outside Braintree on the Notely Road

12–2pm and 6.30–11pm Mon–Fri; all day Sat–Sun.

BRENTWOOD

The Swan

123 High Street, Brentwood CM14 4RX
☎ *(01277) 211848* Nick Parade

Young's Special, Fuller's London Pride, Mighty Oak Burntwood Bitter, Shepherd Neame Spitfire, Wadworth 6X, Gales HSB and Greene King Abbot always available, plus four weekly changing guests such as Adnams Best, Shepherd Neame or Bateman brews

A thirteenth-century pub with a friendly atmosphere. Mainly a locals' pub with quiet background music. Food served 12–9pm. No children.

All day, every day.

BRIGHTLINGSEA

The Famous Railway Tavern

58 Station Road, Brightlingsea CO7 0DT
☎ *(01206) 302581* David English

Crouch Vale Best, a dark mild and a real cider always available, plus up to five guests from local breweries such as Tolly Cobbold amongst others. Gravity-fed in winter.

A friendly, traditional pub with real fire and floorboards. No fruit machines or juke box in the public bar. Garden, children's room. Table football, shove ha'penny, darts, cribbage, dominoes. Campsite opposite, 11 pubs within walking distance. Buskers' afternoon held once a month between October and April.

CRAB & WINKLE MILD 3.7% ABV
STRONGER EEL ALE 5.0% ABV
Seasonal. Other seasonals planned.

5–11pm Mon–Thurs; 3–11pm Fri; 12–11pm Sat; 12–3pm and 7–10.30pm Sun.

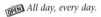

BURNHAM-ON-CROUCH

The Anchor Hotel
The Quay, Burnham-on-Crouch CM0 8AT
☎ *(01621) 782117* Mr Veal

Greene King IPA and Adnams and Crouch Vale brews usually available, plus three guests from breweries such as Titanic or Ridleys. Seasonal ales also stocked.

A locals' pub with a broad clientele in a small seaside town with seating on the sea wall. Two bars, dining area. Food available at lunchtime and evenings. Children allowed.

OPEN *All day, every day.*

CHELMSFORD

The Queen's Head
30 Lower Anchor Street, Chelmsford CM2 0AS
☎ *(01245) 265181* Mike Collins

One of two local Crouch Vale-owned houses. Crouch Vale Best and Woodham IPA always available, plus three guests changing almost daily, such as Elgood's Black Dog Mild, RCH Pitchfork or brews from Titanic, Buffy's, Green Jack or Porter. All ales come from independent breweries.

A traditional alehouse a mile from the cricket ground. Built in 1895 but totally refurbished – one bar with real fires, patio and beer garden. Pub games, no music. Food available every lunchtime and Mon–Sat evenings. Children allowed.

OPEN *11am–3pm and 5.30–11pm Mon–Thurs; all day Fri–Sun.*

The White Horse
25 Townfield Road, Chelmsford CM1 1QT
☎ *(01245) 269556*

Up to seven beers (600 per year) including Hambleton Stallion, Rooster's Yankee, Otter Bright, Bateman Strawberry Fields, Pilgrim Great Crusader, Freeminer Slaughter Porter and Hook Norton Haymaker.

L arge comfortable one-bar pub with a plethora of traditional pub games. Bar food available at lunchtime and evenings. Specialises in gourmet sausages cooked over a griddle. Turn right from the rear of the railway station.

OPEN *11am–3pm and 5.30–11pm.*

COLCHESTER

Odd One Out
28 Mersea Road, Colchester CO2 7ET
☎ *(01206) 578140* John Parrick

Tolly Original, Archers Best and a dark ale always available plus up to four guest beers which may include Nethergate Bitter, Tolly Mild, Mauldons Moletrap, Crouch Vale SAS, Swale Kentish Pride. Also up to three traditional ciders.

F riendly pub about 100 yards up the Mersea Road from St Botolph's roundabout. A traditional drinker's alehouse with garden.

OPEN *4.30–11pm Mon–Thurs; 11am–11pm Fri–Sat; 12–10.30pm Sun.*

The Tap & Spile
123 Crouch Street, Colchester CO3 3HA
☎ *(01206) 573572* Mr and Mrs Mathieson

Adnams Bitter, Marston's Pedigree and Nethergate Bitter always available plus up to five others including Morland Old Speckled Hen, Greene King Abbot Ale, Charles Wells Bombardier, Shepherd Neame ales, Thwaites Mild, Ushers Founders Ale, Everards Tiger, Black Sheep Best and many more.

T raditional English alehouse with no carpets, video machines or juke box. Soft background music. Bar food served at lunchtime. Outside patio. Children allowed. Just outside the town centre, opposite the Essex County Hospital, on Lexden Road.

OPEN *11am–2.30pm and 5.30–11pm Mon–Fri; all day Sat; 12–3pm and 7–10.30pm Sun.*

COXTIE GREEN

The White Horse
173 Coxtie Green Road, Coxtie Green, Brentwood CM14 5PX
☎ *(01277) 372410* Mr Hastings

Ridleys Rumpus, Fuller's London Pride and Adnams Bitter always available, plus three rotating guests such as Wolf Brewery's Coyote, Hop Back Summer Lightning, Timothy Taylor Landlord or Crouch Vale, Ash Vine or Mighty Oak brews. Over 100 guest beers served every year. Beer festival held each July with 30–40 real ales.

A semi-rural pub, with public bar and lounge. Darts, large garden. Barbecues in summer, some children's facilities in the garden. Food served at lunchtime and evenings. Children allowed. Situated off the A128 towards Ongar.

OPEN *11.30am–3.30pm Mon–Thurs; all day Fri–Sun.*

EPPING

The Moletrap

Tawney Common, Epping CM16 7PU
☎ *(01992) 522394* Mr and Mrs Kirtley

A freehouse with Fuller's London Pride always available plus ever-changing guests from all over the country with the emphasis on independent and micro-breweries.

A 250-year-old listed building which has recently been enlarged. Outside seating. Food served at lunchtime and evenings. Children allowed. Down a rural country lane, but five minutes from Epping.

Winter: 12–3pm and 7–11pm daily. Summer: 11.30am–3pm and 6–11pm daily.

FEERING

The Sun Inn

3 Feering Hill, Feering, Nr Kelvedon CO5 9NH
☎ *(01376) 570442* Mr and Mrs Scicluna

Five ever-changing beers (up to 20 per week). The emphasis is firmly on the more unusual micro-breweries.

A heavily timbered former mansion, richly decorated with carved beams and open fires. Bar and restaurant food is available at lunchtime and evenings. Car park and garden. Two beer festivals every year – Easter and August bank holiday. Small functions (up to 28 persons) catered for. Turn off the Kelveden bypass when coming from the north or south.

11am–3pm and 6–11pm Mon–Sat; 12–3pm and 7–10.30pm Sun.

FYFIELD

The Queen's Head

Queen Street, Fyfield, Ongar CM5 0RY
☎ *(01277) 899231* Nick Thain

Badger Best, Adnams Best and Broadside available plus three constantly changing guests from a range of independent and micro-breweries.

A friendly freehouse, reputed to be 500 years old and run by the same family for 25 years. Food served at lunchtime and evenings (not Sat evening). Children allowed.

11am–3pm and 6–11pm; all day Sat; 12–3pm and 7–10.30pm Sun.

GESTINGTHORPE

The Pheasant

Audley End, Gestingthorpe CO9 3AX
☎ *(01787) 461196*

Greene King IPA, Adnams Best and Broadside always available with a guest beer in summer.

T his recently refurbished multi-roomed, 400-year-old freehouse has exposed timbers, open fires and a warm friendly atmosphere. There are three bars, including a dining area. Food is available at lunchtime and evenings, except Sunday and Monday. Car park, garden. Children allowed. Well signposted, the only pub in the village.

12–3pm and 6–11pm Mon–Sat; 7–10.30pm Sun.

HATFIELD BROAD OAK

The Cock Inn

High Street, Hatfield Broad Oak CM22 7HF
☎ *(01279) 718273*
Miss Holcroft and Mr Sulway

Adnams Best and Fuller's London Pride always available, plus four guests changing twice-weekly. Independent brews always included.

A traditional country freehouse with open fires, non-smoking area, private function room, car park, disabled access and outside seating. Food served at lunchtime and evenings. Children allowed.

12–2.30pm and 6–11pm Mon–Sat; all day most Sundays.

HERONGATE TYE

The Old Dog Inn

Billericay Road, Herongate Tye, Brentwood CM13 3SD
☎ *(01277) 810337* Sheila Murphy

Ridleys IPA and Rumpus plus something from Mauldons, Nethergate, Adnams and Crouch Vale. Also two or three regularly changing guests, such as Fuller's London Pride or Shepherd Neame Spitfire.

A sixteenth-century family-owned and -run Essex weatherboard pub. One bar, garden, background music only. Food served at lunchtime and evenings in a separate dining area. Children allowed. Located off the A128 Brentwood/Tilbury Road.

11am–3pm and 6–11pm (10.30pm Sun).

HUTTON

Chequers
213 Rayleigh Road, Hutton, Brentwood
CM13 1PJ
☎ *(01277) 224980* Peter Waters

Greene King IPA always available plus a range of guest ales served on one pump. Tends towards the lighter brews.

A seventeenth-century coaching house. Two cosy bars, beer garden, main road location. Bar snacks available at lunchtime. Children allowed. Situated on the main road A129.

(OPEN) *All day, every day.*

LEIGH-ON-SEA

The Broker Free House
213–17 Leigh Road, Leigh-on-Sea SS9 1JA
☎ *(01702) 471932* Alan Glayne

Shepherd Neame Spitfire and Tolly Original always available, plus two guests which regularly include Fuller's London Pride, Young's Bitter, Morland Tanners Jack, Green Jack Honey Bunny and something from Hop Back, Harveys, Mansfield, Bateman and Cottage breweries. Often serves 14 beers over 10 days.

A family-run, welcoming freehouse, catering for 18–96 year olds! One big bar, beer garden, children's licence and dedicated children's area. Sunday night is live music or quiz night. Food served at lunchtime and evenings (lunchtime only on Sundays). Children allowed.

(OPEN) *11am–3pm and 6–11pm (opens 5.30pm Sat).*

The Elms
1060 London Road, Leigh-on-Sea SS9 3ND
☎ *(01702) 474687* Philip Thomas

Shepherd Neame Spitfire available, plus more than 100 guests every year such as Ringwood Old Thumper and Exmoor Beast. Twice-yearly beer festival.

A Wetherspoon's pub. Modern bar with an old-looking exterior. Outside seating. Non-smoking area. Food served 11am–10pm. No children.

(OPEN) *All day, every day.*

LITTLE CLACTON

The Apple Tree
The Street, Little Clacton CO16 9LS
☎ *(01255) 861026* Mrs Clarke

Charles Wells IPA always available plus three others (60+ per year) including Nethergate Old Growler, Morland Old Speckled Hen, Wadworth 6X, Adnams Broadside, Hook Norton Old Hooky, Brakspear Special, Everards Tiger and Gales HSB.

A well-run family pub with live entertainment every Saturday. Bar and restaurant food available at lunchtime and evenings. Car park and garden. Children allowed in the restaurant. Follow the 'old' road into Clacton (i.e. not the bypass).

(OPEN) *11am–11pm Mon–Fri; 11am–midnight Sat; 12–3pm and 7–10.30pm Sun.*

LITTLE OAKLEY

Ye Olde Cherry Tree Inn
Clacton Road, Little Oakley, Harwich CO12 5JH
☎ *(01255) 880333* Steve and Julie Chandler

Adnams Best and Broadside, Charles Wells Eagle IPA and Bombardier always available, plus one rotating guest changing weekly.

A traditional country pub with traditional pub games. One bar, beer garden and children's play area. Friendly, family atmosphere, overlooking the sea. Food served at lunchtime and evenings. Children allowed.

(OPEN) *11am–2.30pm and 5–11pm Mon–Fri; all day (subject to trade) Sat–Sun.*

LITTLEBURY

The Queen's Head
High Street, Littlebury, Nr Saffron Walden
CB11 4TD
☎ *(01799) 522251* Jeremy O'Gorman

Timothy Taylor Landlord among those beers always available plus four or five guests (140 per year) to include Border Rover, Burton Bridge Spring Ale, Fuller's London Pride, Marston's Pedigree and Mauldons Black Adder.

A sixteenth-century coaching inn with exposed beams, a snug and two open fires. Beer festival at Easter. Bar and restaurant food available at lunchtime and evenings. Non-smoking area, car park, garden. Accommodation. Children allowed. On the B1383, between Newport and junction 9 of the M11.

(OPEN) *12–11pm (10.30pm Sun).*

MALDON

MALDON

The White Horse

26 High Street, Maldon CM9 5PJ
☎ *(01621) 851708* Mr RJ Wood

 A Shepherd Neame tied house. So, Bishop's Finger, Spitfire, Master Brew X, Master Brew XX always available plus one rotating guest.

A typical high-street pub with pub grub served at lunchtime. Children allowed.

OPEN *All day, every day.*

MANNINGTREE

Manningtree Station Buffet

Station Road, Lawford, Manningtree CO11 2LH
☎ *(01206) 391114* Richard and Debbie Rowley

Adnams Best, Shepherd Neame Spitfire plus one Crouch Vale beer and one Fuller's beer always available.

A station buffet, built in 1846. Food served all day in a 24-seater restaurant. Restaurant menu in evenings, pies and breakfast until 2.30pm. Children allowed.

OPEN *5.30am–11pm Mon–Fri; 7am–11pm Sat; 8am–3pm Sun.*

MILL GREEN

The Viper

Mill Green Road, Mill Green, Nr Ingatestone CM4 0PT
☎ *(01277) 352010* Mr FW and Mr RDM Beard

Three real ales always available which will include Ridleys IPA, one from Mighty Oak Brewery and one other from around the country, changed weekly.

A small, traditional, unspoilt country pub with award-winning garden. Bar food available at lunchtime. Car park. Children allowed in garden only. Take the Ivy Barn road off the A12. Turn off at Margaretting. Two miles north-west of Ingatestone.

OPEN *12–3pm and 6–11pm Mon–Sat; 12–3pm and 7–10.30pm Sun.*

MORETON

The Nag's Head

Church Road, Moreton, Nr Ongar CM5 0LF
☎ *(01277) 890239* Richard Keep

Adnams Best and Fuller's London Pride always available plus one rotating guest, perhaps Greene King Abbot, Morland Old Speckled Hen or a Young's brew.

A country freehouse with B&B. Food served at lunchtimes and evenings in a separate dining area. Children allowed.

OPEN *11.30am–3pm and 6–11pm Mon–Fri; all day Sat–Sun.*

NAVESTOCK HEATH

The Plough Inn

Sabines Road, Navestock Heath RM4 1HD
☎ *(01277) 372296*

Marston's Pedigree and Fuller's London Pride among the beers always available in a varied selection of eight real ales (100+ per year) chosen from all across the land.

A one-bar public house with a small dining room and family room. Background music, no juke box, machines or pool table. Bar snacks and meals are available at lunchtime and evenings (except Sunday and Monday). Car park, two gardens, children allowed. The pub is difficult to find, so ring for directions.

OPEN *11am–11pm Mon–Sat; 12–10.30pm Sun.*

PEBMARSH

The King's Head

The Street, Pebmarsh, Nr Halstead CO9 2NH
☎ *(01787) 269306* Ian Miller

Greene King IPA always available plus three guest beers including Timothy Taylor Landlord, Fuller's London Pride, Woodforde's, Mauldons, Ridleys, Simpkiss and Rooster's brews.

An oak-beamed freehouse built in 1740. Bar snacks and meals available at lunchtime and evenings. Barbecues in season. Car park, garden, barn with skittle alley, children's room. One mile off the Halstead to Sudbury road.

OPEN *12–2pm and 7–11pm.*

PLESHEY

The White Horse

The Street, Pleshey, Chelmsford CM3 1HA
☎ *(01245) 237281* John Thorburn

Nethergate Umbel Ale, Tolly Original, Crouch Vale Millennium Gold, Mighty Oak Burntwood and Barrackwood IPA plus Ridleys IPA regularly available, plus other guests from breweries such as Cottage and Elgood's. No national beers served.

A village pub in very picturesque historic village. One bar and two eating areas, large garden, play area, car park. Food served at lunchtime and evenings during the week and all day at weekends. Children allowed.

OPEN *11am–3pm and 7–11pm Mon–Fri; all day Sat–Sun.*

QUENDON

The Cricketer's Arms
Rickling Green, Quendon, Saffron Walden CB11 3YG
☎ *(01799) 543210* Tim Proctor

A freehouse. with three guest ales always available from a list including Adnams Extra, Fuller's ESB, one best bitter and one dark mild. The focus is on stronger brews. Also a selection of Belgian beers.

A heavily timbered building dating from 1590, ten en suite bedrooms, three dining rooms (one non-smoking). Food served daily at lunchtime and evenings. Children not allowed in the main bar area. Facing the cricket green, just off the B1383 at Quendon.

All day, every day.

RADWINTER

The Plough Inn
Radwinter, Nr Saffron Walden CB10 2TL
☎ *(01799) 599222* Tony Birdfield

A freehouse with Adnams Best and Greene King IPA always available, plus two or three rotating guests such as Oakhill Mendip Gold, Jennings Cumberland Ale, Shepherd Neame Spitfire, Timothy Taylor Landlord, Nethergate Golden Gate and Hop Back Summer Lightning.

A seventeenth-century country freehouse with heavy emphasis on food and accommodation. Non-smoking area in the restaurant. Food available at lunchtime and evenings. Children and dogs welcome. From the junction of B1053 and B1054, four miles east of Saffron Walden.

12–3pm and 6.30–11pm (10.30pm Sun).

RIDGEWELL

The White Horse
Mill Road, Ridgewell CO9 4SG
☎ *(01440) 785532* Robin Briggs

A freehouse serving a constantly changing range of real ales May include Ridleys IPA, Fuller's London Pride or brews from Shepherd Neame, Belhaven, Cottage or other smaller breweries.

A rural village pub with games room, pool table and darts. Single bar covered in old pennies (4,200 in all). Large restaurant, beer garden and car park. Food served at lunchtime and evenings. Children allowed. Located on the old A604 between Halstead and Haverhill.

11am–3pm and 6–11pm (10.30pm Sun).

ROCHFORD

The Golden Lion
35 North Street, Rochford SS4 1AB
☎ *(01702) 545487* Sue Williams

Greene King Abbot Ale, Fuller's London Pride and Mansfield IPA usually available plus two guests changed every three days. Emphasis on unusual brews from smaller breweries.

A sixteenth-century traditional-style freehouse with one bar with beams and brasses and a small beer garden. Bar snacks served at lunchtime. Children and dogs welcome.

12–11pm.

SOUTH FAMBRIDGE

The Anchor Hotel
Fambridge Road, South Fambridge, Rochford SS4 3LY
☎ *(01702) 203535* Mr Cracknell

Greene King Abbot is one of two beers always available, plus two rotating guests such as Shepherd Neame Bishops Finger, Smiles Heritage, Ringwood Fortyniner, Morland Old Speckled Hen, Crouch Vale SAS or Young's Special.

A traditional country freehouse with two bars and a restaurant. Four minutes' walk from the sea wall of River Crouch. Good views. Food available at lunchtime and evenings. Children allowed.

11am–3pm and 6–11pm.

SOUTHEND-ON-SEA

Cork & Cheese
10 Talza Way, Victoria Circus, Southend-on-Sea SS2 5BG
☎ *(01702) 616914* John Murray

Cork & Cheese Best (from Tolly Cobbold) always available plus three guests (250 per year) including brews from Concertina, Butterknowle, Rooster's, Woodforde's, Titanic, Hop Back, Wild's and Clark's.

An alehouse with a cosmopolitan trade. Separate dining area for bar and restaurant meals. Food available at lunchtime. Multi-storey car park nearby. Patio in summer. Children allowed in the restaurant. Located on the basement floor of the Victoria Circus shopping centre in Southend.

11am–11pm Mon–Sat; closed Sun.

Last Post
5 Weston Road, Southend-on-Sea SS1 1BZ
☎ *(01702) 431682* Neil Sanderson

 Ridleys IPA always available, plus up to five daily-changing guests such as Morland Old Speckled Hen or Hop Back Summer Lightning. Anything and everything from brewers of real ale considered.

A busy two-bar operation with disabled access and toilets. No music, a real drinker's pub. Two non-smoking areas. Food served all day every day. No children. Opposite the railway station.

OPEN *10am–11pm.*

The Station Arms
39 Station Road, Southminster CM0 7EW
☎ *(01621) 772225* Martin Park

Crouch Vale Best always available plus three guest beers (150 per year) from Titanic, Hop Back, Concertina, Fuller's, Jennings, Rooster's and Timothy Taylor breweries.

A welcoming, one-bar, Essex weatherboard pub with open fire and traditional pub furniture. 1997–98 CAMRA East Anglia Pub of the Year. Pub games played. Restaurant and courtyard to the rear. Bar and restaurant food served in evenings only. Parking. Children allowed in the restaurant. Just 200 yards from Southminster railway station.

OPEN *12–2.30pm and 6–11pm Mon–Fri; 12–11pm Sat; 12–4pm and 7–10.30pm Sun.*

The Hoop
21 High Street, Stock CM4 9BD
☎ *(01277) 841137* Albert and David Kitchen

Up to ten beers available. Brews from Adnams, Crouch Vale, Wadworth and Charles Wells always served. Guests from Bateman, Archers, Ringwood, Hop Back, Jennings, Exmoor, Fuller's, Marston's, Nethergate, Rooster's and Shepherd Neame.

T he pub has been adapted from some late fifteenth-century beamed cottages. There is an extensive beer garden to the rear. Bar food available all day. Barbecues at weekends in summer, weather permitting. Parking. Children not allowed. Take the B1007 from the A12 Chelmsford bypass, then take the Galleywood-Billericay turn off.

OPEN *11am–11pm.*

The Prince of Wales
Woodham Road, Stow Maries CM3 6SA
☎ *(01621) 828971* Robert Walster

Fuller's Chiswick always available plus any four guests (too many to count) including a mild and a stout/porter from small independent and the better regional brewers.

A traditional Essex weatherboard pub with real fires and Victorian bakehouse. Bar food available at lunchtime and evenings. Car park, garden and family room. Under two miles from South Woodham Ferrers on the road to Cold Norton.

OPEN *11am–11pm Mon–Sat; 12–10.30pm Sun.*

The Cherry Tree
Crow Lane, Tendring CO16 9AP
☎ *(01255) 830340* Mr Whitnell

Greene King IPA, Abbot and Adnams Best always avaiable, plus a regularly changing guest.

A n olde-worlde pub and restaurant. One bar, big garden. Food served at lunchtime and evenings. Well-behaved children allowed.

OPEN *11am–3pm and 6–11pm Mon–Sat; all day Sun.*

The Carpenter's Arms
Carpenter's Arms Lane, Thornwood Common, Epping CM16 6LS
☎ *(01992) 574208* Martin Gale

Crouch Vale Best Bitter and SAS, Adnams Broadside and McMullen AK always available, plus two constantly changing guests, perhaps from Wye Valley, Woodforde's or Mighty Oak. One dark mild always available.

A traditional country pub. Three bars, two beer gardens, pub games, live music, Essex Pub of the Year 1998–99. Food served 12–2 pm. Children allowed.

OPEN *11am–3pm and 6–11pm Mon–Thurs; all day Fri–Sun.*

TILLINGHAM

Cap and Feathers

8 South Street, Tillingham CM70 7TH
☎ *(01621) 779212* Tony Burdfield

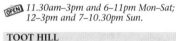 Crouch Vale Woodham IPA, Best Bitter, Dark Ale and Millennium Gold always available plus a guest (400 per year) which might include Morland Old Speckled Hen, Titanic Best, Buffy's Polly's Folly and Clark's Burglar Bill.

D ates from 1427, an old weatherboard building. Unspoilt, with a relaxed atmosphere. Bar food available at lunchtime and evenings. Car park, garden, non-smoking family room. Accommodation. Between Southminster and Bradwell.

11.30am–3pm and 6–11pm Mon–Sat; 12–3pm and 7–10.30pm Sun.

TOOT HILL

The Green Man and Courtyard Restaurant

Toot Hill, Nr Ongar CM5 9SD
☎ *(01992) 522255* Mr J Roads

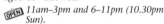 Crouch Vale Best always available plus two guests changing twice weekly including, perhaps, an Adnams brews or Fuller's London Pride. No strong bitters over 4.3% ABV.

A country freehouse with two restaurants, one bar, courtyard and beer garden. Food served at lunchtime and evenings. Children aged 11+ allowed.

11am–3pm and 6–11pm (10.30pm Sun).

WENDENS AMBO

The Bell

Royston Road, Wendens Ambo CB11 4JY
☎ *(01799) 540382* Geoff and Bernie Bates

Adnams Bitter and Ansells Dark Mild always available plus a couple of guests (50 per year) perhaps including Everards Tiger, Charles Wells Bombardier, Eldridge Pope Royal Oak, Adnams Broadside and Gales brews.

B uilt in 1576, beamed with open fires in winter. Background music only. Bar food available at lunchtime and evenings (not Monday). Car park, garden, children's play area.

11.30am–2.30pm and 6–11pm Mon–Sat; 12–3pm and 7–10.30pm Sun.

WITHAM

The Woolpack

7 Church Street, Witham CM8 2JP
☎ *(01376) 511195* Mrs Hazel Hadgraft

 Greene King IPA and Tolly Cobbold Original or Best always available, plus one rotating guest changed fortnightly.

A small community locals' drinking pub. Team orientated (darts, pool, cribbage etc). Sandwiches available at lunchtime. No children.

All day, every day.

WOODHAM WATER

The Bell

The Street, Woodham Water, Maldon CM9 6RF
☎ *(01245) 223437* Mr Alan Oldfield

A freehouse with Greene King's IPA permanently available, plus two guest pumps serving real ales such as Morland Old Speckled Hen, Fuller's ESB, Hook Norton Old Hooky or Everards Tiger or Triple Gold.

A traditional sixteenth-century village inn with beams, one bar and three adjoining rooms. No music or machines. Beer garden. Food available lunchtimes and evenings in a separate dining room. Children allowed.

12–3pm and 7–11pm (10.30pm Sun).

YOU TELL US

★ *The Angel*, 36 Bocking End, Bocking
★ *The Bell*, Main Road, Woodham Ferrers
★ *The Bell Inn*, Horndon on the Hill
★ *Boadicea*, St. John's Street, Colchester
★ *The Foxhound*, 18 High Road, Ossett, Grays
★ *The George Inn*, The Street, Shalford
★ *The Retreat*, 42 Church Street, Bocking
★ *The Royal Fusiliers*, Aingers Green Road, Aingers Green
★ *The Woodman*, 155 London Road, Stanford Rivers

Places Featured:

Apperley
Ashleworth
Avening
Awre
Bedminster
Birdlip
Bishopston
Bourton-on-the-Hill
Bourton-on-the-Water
Box
Bristol
Broad Campden
Cheltenham
Chipping Campden
Chipping Sodbury
Churchill
Cirencester
Cowley
Duntisbourne Abbots
Dursley
Ebrington
Ford

Frampton Cottrell
France Lynch
Gloucester
Hanham Mills
Kingswood
Lime Street
Littleton upon Severn
Longhope
Lower Apperley
Lower Swell
Newland
Pill
Pope's Hill
Sapperton
Sheepscombe
Sling
South Woodchester
Tewkesbury
Uley
Waterley Bottom
Westbury on Trym
Whitminster

THE BREWERIES

BERKELEY BREWING CO.
The Brewery, Bucketts Hill, Berkeley GL13 9NZ
☎ *(01453) 511799*

 OLD FRIEND 3.8% ABV
Gold-coloured, with well-balanced fruit and hops.
DICKY PEARCE 4.3% ABV
Plus seasonal brews.

BUTCOMBE BREWERY LTD
Rusling House, Butcombe, Bristol BS40 7XQ
☎ *(01275) 472240*

 BITTER 4.0% ABV
A dry, clean-tasting bitter with strong hop flavour.
WILMOT'S PREMIUM ALE 4.8% ABV
Smooth, malty and full-flavoured with bitterness in the finish.

DONNINGTON BREWERY
Upper Swell, Stow-on-the-Wold GL54 1EP
☎ *(01451) 830603*

 XXX 3.6% ABV
Light, hoppy, easy-quaffing.
BB 3.6% ABV
Plenty of flavour for gravity.
SBA 3.8% ABV
Smooth and malty.

FREEMINER BREWERY LTD
The Laurels, Sling, Coleford GL16 8JJ
☎ *(01594) 810408*

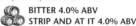 **BITTER 4.0% ABV**
STRIP AND AT IT 4.0% ABV
IRON BREW 4.2% ABV
SPECULATION ALE 4.8% ABV
CELESTIAL STEAM GALE 5.0% ABV
GOLD STANDARD 5.0% ABV
SHAKEMANTLE GINGER ALE 5.0% ABV
SLAUGHTER PORTER 5.0% ABV
DEEP SHAFT 6.0% ABV
TRAFALGAR IPA 6.0% ABV

GOFF'S BREWERY LTD
9 Isbourne Way, Winchcombe GL54 5NS
☎ *(01242) 603383*

 KNIGHT RIDER 3.6% ABV
Amber, hoppy and refreshing.
JOUSTER 4.0% ABV
Fruity, with hop flavours.
FALLEN KNIGHT 4.4% ABV
Hoppy with bittersweet aftertaste.
WHITE KNIGHT 4.7% ABV
Pale, with hoppiness throughout.

SMILES BREWING CO. LTD

Colston Yard, Colston Street, Bristol BS1 5BD
☎ *(0117) 929 7350*

 BA 3.3% ABV
Pale and refreshing.
GOLDEN BREW 3.8% ABV
Golden pale with thirst-quenching hoppy flavour.
BEST BITTER 4.1% ABV
Well-rounded, hop, fruit and malt flavours.
HERITAGE 5.2% ABV
Dark and rich with roast malt character.
Plus monthly brews.

STANWAY BREWERY

Stanway, Cheltenham GL54 5PQ
☎ *(01386) 584320*

 LORDS-A-LEAPING 4.5% ABV
Winter ale.
STANNEY BITTER 4.5% ABV
Quenching, with hoppiness throughout.
Plus seasonal brews.

ULEY BREWERY LTD

The Old Brewery, The Street, Uley, Dursley GL11 5TB
☎ *(01453) 860120*

 HOGSHEAD BITTER 3.5% ABV
Light in colour and well-hopped.
BEST BITTER 4.0% ABV
Balanced and full-flavoured.
OLD SPOT 5.0% ABV
Flagship ale. Powerful malt flavour with fruit and hops.
PIG'S EAR 5.0% ABV
Smooth IPA.

WICKWAR BREWERY CO.

The Old Cider Mill, Station Road, Wickwar, Wootton-under-Edge GL12 8NB
☎ *(01454) 294168*

 COOPERS WPA 3.5% ABV
Quenching, full-flavoured pale ale.
BRAND OAK BITTER 4.0% ABV
Characterful and well-balanced.
OLD MERRYFORD ALE 5.1% ABV
Flavoursome, with hoppy fruit aroma.
Plus seasonal and occasional brews.

THE PUBS

APPERLEY

Coal House Inn

Gadd Lane, Apperley GL19 4DN
☎ *(01452) 780211* Mrs McDonald

Wadworth 6X and Wickwar Coopers' WPA always available plus one regularly changing guest ale.

A large country freehouse with riverside garden. Food served at lunchtime and evenings. Children allowed.

OPEN *12–2.30pm and 6–11pm (10.30pm Sun).*

ASHLEWORTH

The Boat Inn

The Quay, Ashleworth GL19 4HZ
☎ *(01452) 700272* Mrs Nicholls

Arkell's 3B, RCH Pitchfork, Oakhill Yeoman 1767 and Wye Valley brews always available plus at least three constantly changing guest beers served straight from the cask including, for example, Exmoor Gold, Oakhill Somer Ale and Black Magic, Arkell's Summer Ale, Smiles Exhibition, brews from Hambleton, Church End, Goff's, Cottage, Sporting Ales and Eccleshall plus various Christmas ales.

A fifteenth-century cottage pub on the banks of the River Severn. Small and friendly, has remained in the same family for 400 years. Bar food available at lunchtime. Car park and garden. Children allowed. Ashleworth is signposted off the A417 north of Gloucester. The Quay is signed from the village.

OPEN *April–Sep: 11am–2.30pm and 6–11pm Mon–Sat; 12–3pm and 7–10.30pm Sun; Oct–Mar: 11am–2.30pm Thurs–Tues, closed Wed lunchtime; 7–11pm Mon–Sat; 12–3pm and 7–10.30pm Sun.*

AVENING

The Bell

29 High Street, Avening, Tetbury GL8 8NF
☎ *(01453) 836422* Melissa Bovey

A freehouse with Wickwar Brand Oak usually available plus two guests such as Berkeley Old Friend or a Smiles or Abbey brew.

A traditional Cotswold pub with log fire, dining area and garden. Food served at lunchtime and evenings. Children allowed. Accommodation.

OPEN *12–3pm and 6.30–11pm Mon–Fri; all day Sat–Sun.*

AWRE

The Red Hart Inn

Awre, Newnham GL14 1EQ
☎ *(01594) 510220* Herry Bedwell

 A freehouse with a Freeminer brew always available, plus two guests changing weekly. Examples include Fuller's London Pride, Wadworth 6X, or a Goff's, Sporting Ales or Ledbury ale. The landlord's policy is to support smaller breweries as much as possible.

A beamed hostelry dating from 1483 with one bar area. Non-smoking area. Outside seating in front garden. Bar snacks and à la carte menu available at lunchtime and evenings. Children allowed until 8pm, if well supervised. Accommodation. In the middle of nowhere! Turn off A48 between Newnham and Blakeney.

💢 *12–3pm and 6.30–11pm Mon–Sat; 12–3pm and 7–10.30pm Sun.*

BEDMINSTER

Robert Fitzharding

24 Cannon Street, Bedminster, Bristol BS3 1BN
☎ *(0117) 966 2757* John Baldwin

💢 A Wetherspoon's pub with Butcombe Bitter always available. Four guest pumps serve a range of 30 guests every quarter. Examples include Coniston Bluebird, Exmoor Beast, Caledonian Deuchars IPA or something from Burton Bridge.

A city suburb pub with non-smoking area. Two beer festivals held each year. Food served all day. No children.

💢 *All day, every day.*

BIRDLIP

The Golden Heart Inn

Nettleton Bottom, Nr Birdlip GL4 8LA
☎ *(01242) 870261*
Mr D Morgan and Miss C Stevens

💢 Marston's Pedigree, Hook Norton Best and Ruddles brews always available plus four guest beers (400 per year), perhaps from Greene King, Timothy Taylor and many local brewers.

A sixteenth–century pub with stone floors, beams and bric-a-brac. Bar food available at lunchtime and evenings. Car park, garden, children's room and function room. Situated on the A417 between Cheltenham, Gloucester and Cirencester, two miles from Birdlip.

💢 *10.30am–3pm and 6–11pm Mon–Sat; 12–3pm and 7–10.30pm Sun.*

BISHOPSTON

The Annexe

Seymour Road, Bishopston, Bristol BS7 9EQ
☎ *(0117) 949 3931* Mr Morgan

💢 A Courage tied house regularly serving Smiles and Young's brews plus Marston's Pedigree. Also a range of guests including York Brewery's Bug's Bitter, Morland Old Speckled Hen, and Archers Golden.

A town pub with disabled access, children's room, garden, darts etc. Bar food available at lunchtime and restaurant food in the evenings. Children allowed until 8.30pm in the children's room only.

💢 *11am–2.30pm and 6–11pm Mon–Fri; all day Sat–Sun.*

BOURTON-ON-THE-HILL

The Horse & Groom

Bourton-on-the-Hill, Moreton-in-the-Marsh GL56 9AQ
☎ *(01386) 700413* Linda Balhatchet

💢 A freehouse offering Hook Norton brews plus rotating guests such as Morland Old Speckled Hen.

A village pub on the main road with bar and restaurant area. Food served at lunchtime and evenings. Children allowed.

💢 *11.30am–3pm and 7–11pm (10.30pm Sun).*

BOURTON-ON-THE-WATER

The Kingsbridge Inn

Riverside, Bourton-on-the-Water, Cheltenham GL54 2BS
☎ *(01451) 820371* John and Julie Swan

💢 Caledonian 80/- and Deuchars IPA always available, plus two guests that change monthly. Brews include Morland Old Speckled Hen or Bourton Ale (a summer session ale brewed specially by Smiles).

An olde-worlde riverside pub in the Cotswolds with beer garden and tables out front. Family- and tourist-orientated. One bar with food served at lunchtime and evenings in both smoking and non-smoking dining areas. Children welcome, play area provided.

💢 *All day, every day.*

BOX

The Halfway House
Minchinhampton, Box, Stroud GL6 9AE
☎ *(01453) 832631*

Marston's Best Bitter and Pedigree, Banks's Bitter, and Timothy Taylor Landlord always available, plus one rotating guest – perhaps a Berkeley or Wickwar ale. Under new management.

A prettily situated freehouse with L-shaped bar, 70-seater function room, skittle alley, garden with children's play area and 50-seater restaurant. Food served at lunchtime and evenings. On the edge of Minchinhampton Common.

OPEN 12–3pm and 6–11pm (10.30pm Sun). Sometimes all day in summer.

BRISTOL

The Bag O'Nails
141 St Georges Road, Hotwells, Bristol BS1 5UW
☎ *(0117) 940 6776* Gordon Beresford

Fuller's London Pride usually available plus up to five others served on a guest basis (over 300 served in two years). Mainly supplied by smaller, independent breweries. The pub's own web page gives details of beers stocked at any one time (www.cix.co.uk/ bagonails/). For a monthly e-mail list of forthcoming beers send e-mail address to gordon@bagonails.cix.co.uk.

A small, quiet, gas-lit city-centre pub with one bar. Situated just 25 yards from the Dock. Simples lunches only served 12–2pm. No children.

OPEN 12–2.30pm and 5–11pm Mon–Thurs; all day Fri–Sun.

The Bell Inn
21 Alfred Place, Kingsdown, Bristol BS2 8HD
☎ *(0117) 907 7563* Anna Luke

A freehouse regularly offering Wickwar Brand Oak Bitter and Olde Merryford Ale. Also RCH Pitchfork plus occasional guests.

A small, one-bar locals' pub. Toasted sandwiches available at lunchtime only. No children. Situated off St Michael's Hill, at the back of the BRI hospital.

OPEN 12–2.30pm and 5.30–11pm (10.30pm Sun).

Cadbury House
68 Richmond Road, Montpelier, Bristol BS6 5EW
☎ *(0117) 924 7874* Rachel Bickerton

A freehouse serving Wickwar Brand Oak Bitter and Olde Merryford plus Quay Bombshell and one rotating guests. Wickwar Station Porter or other winter ales usually available from October.

A locals' pub in a residential area. Clientele a mix of regulars and students. Large beer garden. Bar meals served 12–6.30pm and traditional Sunday roasts. Children allowed.

OPEN All day, every day.

Commercial Rooms
43–5 Corn Street, Bristol BS1 1HT
☎ *(0117) 927 9681* Andrew Harvey

A freehouse serving Butcombe Bitter and Exmoor Gold plus two guests changing constantly.

A town-centre pub with twice-yearly beer festivals in April and October. Food served all day. No children.

OPEN 10.30am–11pm.

Cornubia
142 Temple Street, Bristol BS1 6EN
☎ *(0117) 925 4415* Nick Luke

A freehouse with no permanent beers, just a constantly changing range of guests. Local brewers generally favoured. Tries to include a dark porter or stout when possible.

A Georgian, listed building with traditional town-centre pub atmosphere. Food available at lunchtime only in a separate restaurant. Well-behaved children allowed.

OPEN 11am–11pm Mon–Fri; 7–11pm Sat; 12–4pm Sun.

The Highbury Vaults
164 St Michael's Hill, Cotham, Bristol BS2 8DE
☎ *(0117) 973 3203* Bradd Francis

Smiles Best, Golden and Heritage always available plus seasonal brews and Brains SA. Also guest beers, changed weekly, including Fuller's London Pride, Greene King Abbot, Adnams Broadside, Uley Old Spot, Hampshire Pendragon, Quay Bombshell, Ridleys Rumpus and Bateman XXXB.

Very traditional pub set in the heart of university land with no music, fruit machines, pool tables etc. Lots of atmosphere for young and old, students and locals. Cheap bar food available at lunchtime and evenings (nothing fried). Heated rear garden. Children allowed in garden.

OPEN 12–11pm (10.30pm Sun).

The Hope & Anchor

38 Jacobs Wells Road, Clifton, Bristol BS8 1DR
☎ *(0117) 929 2987* Martin Hughes

Six beers always available, changed every few days. Up to 30 brews per year including Fuller's London Pride, Gales HSB, Titanic Best, Felinfoel Double Dragon, Greene King Abbot, Palmers IPA and Badger Tanglefoot.

F riendly one-bar pub with relaxed atmosphere. No TV or games machines. Bar food available at lunchtime and evenings. Children allowed in beer garden. Near The Triangle in Clifton, north of Bristol city centre.

OPEN *12–11pm; (10.30pm Sun).*

The Phoenix

15 Wellington Street, St Judes, Bristol BS2
☎ *(0117) 955 8327* Jeffrey Fowler

Up to ten beers always available including those from Oakhill and Wickwar breweries plus Wadworth 6X. Also a selection from 100 guest beers per year. Brews from Young's, Shepherd Neame, Cottage, Bateman, Everards, Ash Vine, Uley, Burton Bridge, Burtonwood, Exmoor and many more.

S mall, local one-bar freehouse in Grade II listed building. Snacks available at lunchtime and evenings. Parking, garden, children's room, accommodation. On the edge of Broadmead shopping area.

OPEN *11.30am–11pm Mon–Sat; 12–3pm and 7–10.30pm Sun.*

The Swan with Two Necks

12 Little Ann Street, St Judes, Bristol BS2 9EB
☎ *(0117) 955 1893* John Lansall

Six beers always available from a range of hundreds per year. The emphasis is on unusual first brews from new breweries and brewpubs.

B asic one-bar pub ten minutes from city centre and docks. No music or machines. Bar food available at lunchtime. Parking. Well-behaved children allowed. Tricky to find. Coming into Bristol on M32, left at first set of lights, then 3rd left.

OPEN *11.30am–3pm and 5–11pm Mon–Thurs; 11.30am–11pm Fri; 12–11pm Sat; 12–3pm and 7–10.30pm Sun.*

The Woolpack Inn

Shepherds Way, St Georges, Bristol BA3 6SP
☎ *(01934) 521670* PW Sampson

Four beers always available, 30 per year to include Charles Wells Bombardier and Oakhill Best.

V illage freehouse in 200-year-old building. Bar and restaurant food at lunchtime and evenings. Car park, garden, conservatory planned. No children. Off M5, junction 21.

OPEN *12–2.30pm and 6–11pm Mon–Sat; 12–3pm and 7–10.30pm Sun.*

BROAD CAMPDEN

The Baker's Arms

Broad Campden, Nr Chipping Campden GL55 6UR
☎ *(01386) 840515* Sally and Ray Mayo

Marston's Bitter, Adnams Best and Timothy Taylor Landlord always available, plus three rotating guest ales.

A small, friendly Cotswold country pub with open fires. Bar food available at lunchtime and evenings. Car park, garden, patio and children's play area. In a village between Chipping Campden and Blockley.

OPEN *Winter: 11.30am–2.30pm and 6.30–11pm Mon–Sat 12–3pm and 7–10.30pm Sun. Summer: 12–3pm and 6–11pm Mon–Sat; 12–3pm and 7–10.30pm Sun.*

CHELTENHAM

Tailors

4 Cambray Place, Cheltenham GL50 1JS
☎ *(01242) 255453* S Yates

A Wadworth tied house with 6X and IPA always available. Three guest ales, changed fortnightly, might include Badger Tanglefoot or a Shepherd Neame brew.

A town-centre pub with cellar bar and comfortable armchairs. Live music on Thursdays. Two beer gardens. Food served every lunchtime except Sunday. Children allowed.

OPEN *All day, every day.*

CHIPPING CAMPDEN

The Volunteer

Lower High Street, Chipping Campden GL55 6DY
☎ *(01386) 840688* Mrs H Sinclair

Three ales including Fuller's London Pride always available plus two guests. Brews from Wood, Fat God's, Hampshire or Hook Norton are all popular.

A country inn with garden. Food served at lunchtime and evenings. Children allowed. Accommodation.

OPEN *11.30am–3pm and 5–11pm Mon–Sat; 12–3pm and 6.30–10.30pm Sun.*

CHIPPING SODBURY

Beaufort Hunt
*Broad Street, Chipping Sodbury, Bristol
BS37 6AG*
☎ (01454) 312871 Mrs Jarvis

Greene King IPA always available plus two guests including, perhaps, Wickwar Olde Merryford, Fuller's London Pride, Shepherd Neame Bishop's Finger or Everards Tiger.

An olde-style village pub with beer garden. Food available at lunchtime. Children aged 14–18 allowed in lounge bar only if eating. Under 14s not allowed.

OPEN *10.30am–3pm and 5–11pm (10.30pm Sun).*

CHURCHILL

The Crown Inn
The Batch, Skinners Lane, Churchill, Nr Bristol
☎ (01934) 852995

Butcombe Bitter, RCH PG Steam and Palmers Best always available straight from the barrel, plus up to five guest beers (100+ per year) to include Palmers Tally Ho, Greene King Abbot, Tomintoul Wild Cat, Otter Bright and Hop Back Summer Lightning.

An old pub with small rooms and flagstone floors. Large fires in winter. Food made and prepared to order when practical. Parking, garden, children's room. Children not allowed in bar area. South of Bristol, just off the A38, not far from M5.

OPEN *11.30am–3pm and 5.30–11pm.*

CIRENCESTER

The Bear Inn
12 Dyer Street, Cirencester GL7 2PF
☎ (01285) 653472 Serena McBride

A Mole's Brewery tied house. Wadworth 6X always available, plus Mole's Best in summer and a range of seasonal brews.

A town-centre pub, soon to be refurbished in the style of an old coaching inn. Home-cooked food served at lunchtime and evenings in a separate dining area. Children allowed.

OPEN *All day, every day.*

Corinium Court Hotel
12 Gloucester Street, Cirencester GL7 2DG
☎ (01285) 659711 Mr Harding

Wadworth 6X and Hook Norton Best and Old Hooky always available.

A two-star hotel with bar. Food served at lunchtime and evenings. Children allowed.

OPEN *11am–2.30pm and 7–11pm (10.30pm Sun).*

The Drillman's Arms
84 Gloucester Road, Cirencester GL7 2JY
☎ (01285) 653892 Richard Elby

A freehouse serving Archers Best and Village plus either Wadworth 6X or Greene King Abbot Ale. Also a rotating guest from local brewers such as Berkeley or Hampshire.

A village pub with log fire and function room. Food served at lunchtime and evenings. Children allowed.

OPEN *11am–3pm and 5.30–11pm Mon–Fri; all day Sat; 11am–4pm and 7–10.30pm Sun.*

COWLEY

The Green Dragon
Cockleford, Cowley, Nr Cheltenham GL53 9NW
☎ (01242) 870271 Pia-Maria Boast

Smiles Best, Brewery Bitter and Exhibition always available plus up to three guest beers (30 per year) which may include Fuller's ESB, Dorset Best Badger and Tanglefoot, Marston's Owd Roger, Hook Norton Best, Cotleigh Old Buzzard, Greene King Abbot, Bateman Victory and Shepherd Neame Spitfire.

A traditional seventeenth-century pub with flagstones, open fires and candles. Bar food served at lunchtime and evenings. Car park and patio. Private function room and bar available for wedding receptions and parties.

OPEN *11.30am–2.30pm and 6–11pm.*

DUNTISBOURNE ABBOTS

Five Mile House
Gloucester Road, Duntisbourne Abbots, Cirencester GL7 7JR
☎ (01285) 821432 JW Carrier

A freehouse serving Marston's Bitter and Timothy Taylor Landlord plus one guest of 3.8% ABV or less. Archers Village is a popular example.

A traditional country pub with old bar, family room and garden. Food served at lunchtime and evenings in non-smoking restaurant. Children allowed.

OPEN *12–3pm and 6–11pm (7–10.30pm Sun).*

DURSLEY

Old Spot Inn
Hill Road, Dursley GL11 4JQ
☎ *(01453) 542870*

 Uley Old Spot and Old Ric always available plus a couple of guests (40 per year) which may include Adnams May Day, Fuller's London Pride, McMullen Gladstone, Robinson's Frederics, Burtonwood Top Hat and other Uley brews.

Originally a farm cottage, then a school, built in 1776 on the Cotswold Way, beamed with open fires. Bar snacks available at lunchtime. Live music. Parking, garden. No children.

OPEN *11am–11pm Mon–Sat; 12–3pm and 7–10.30pm Sun.*

EBRINGTON

The Ebrington Arms
Ebrington, Nr Chipping Campden GL55 6NH
☎ *(01386) 593223* Gareth Richards

 Hook Norton Best and Donnington SBA always available plus a guest beer (52 per year), perhaps from Wadworth, Fuller's, Wychwood, Goff's, Uley, or Greene King breweries.

An unspoilt traditional Cotswold village pub. No music or machines. Traditional games. Bar and restaurant food at lunchtime and evenings. Car park and garden. Children in the restaurant only. The owner has a pottery in the courtyard where he makes bowls, jugs and cruet sets used in the restaurant. Accommodation.

OPEN *11am–2.30pm and 6–11pm Mon–Sat; 12–3pm and 7–10.30pm Sun.*

FORD

The Plough Inn
Ford, Temple Guiting GL54 5RU
☎ *(01386) 584215* Chris Turner

 A Donnington Brewery house always serving BB and SBA.

A thirteenth-century Cotswold stone inn with inglenook fireplace, beams and flagstone floor. Food served at lunchtime and evenings in a separate dining area. Children allowed. Located on the main road between Stow-on-the-Wold and Tewkesbury

OPEN *All day, every day.*

FRAMPTON COTTERELL

The Rising Sun
43 Ryecroft Road, Frampton Cotterell, Nr Bristol BS17 2HN
☎ *(01454) 772330* Roger Stone

 Six beers always available with up to 30 featured per year. Examples include Smiles brews, Phoenix Mayfly, Crown Buckley Rev James Original and Buchanan Original.

Small, friendly, single-bar local. CAMRA Pub of the Year for Avon in 1995. Bar food available at lunchtime. Large patio area.

OPEN *11.30am–3pm and 7–11pm Mon–Sat; 12–3pm and 7–10.30pm Sun.*

FRANCE LYNCH

The King's Head
France Lynch, Stroud GL6 8LT
☎ *(01453) 882225* Mike Duff

A freehouse serving Hook Norton and Archers brews, plus one guest that changes frequently.

A small, traditional, country pub with large garden. No juke box. Food served at lunchtime and evenings. Children allowed.

OPEN *12–2.30pm and 6–11pm Mon–Fri; 12–4pm and 6–11pm Sat; all day Sun.*

GLOUCESTER

England's Glory
66–8 London Road, Gloucester GL1 3PB
☎ *(01452) 302948* Sarah Chapel

A Wadworth-managed house with IPA, 6X and Badger Tanglefoot always available. Three guests might include Mayhem's Odda's Light or seasonal Wadworth beers such as Summersault.

A food-oriented pub on the outskirts of town. Disabled access, non-smoking area, beer garden. Food available at lunchtime and evenings. Children allowed in the non-smoking area only.

OPEN *11.30am–2.30pm and 5–11pm Mon–Fri; 12–2.30pm and 6–11pm Sat; 12–3pm and 7–10.30pm Sun.*

The Linden Tree

73–5 Bristol Road, Gloucester GL1 5SN
☎ *(01452) 527869* Simon Cairns

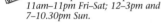 Hook Norton Best, Smiles Exhibition, Wadworth 6X and IPA and Badger Tanglefoot always available plus two guest beers (more than 100 per year) which may include Exmoor Stag, Crown Buckley Rev James Original and Wadworth Old Timer.

A true country pub in the heart of Gloucester, south of the city centre. Large Georgian Grade II listed building. Bar food available at lunchtime and evenings. Parking, skittle alley, function room. Children allowed. Accommodation. Follow the Bristol road from the M5.

OPEN *11am–2.30pm and 5–11pm Mon–Thurs; 11am–11pm Fri–Sat; 12–3pm and 7–10.30pm Sun.*

The Regal

32 St Aldate Street, King's Square, Gloucester GL1 1RP
☎ *(01452) 332344* Neil Marther

A Wetherspoon's pub. Archers Golden, Morland Old Speckled Hen and a Banks's brew always available plus up to ten guests changed on a weekly basis.

A large town pub with non-smoking areas, disabled access and toilets. Beer garden. Food served all day. No children. Regular beer festivals held.

OPEN *All day, every day.*

HANHAM MILLS

Old Lock & Weir

Hanham Mills, Bristol BS15 3NU
☎ *(0117) 967 3793* Mark Brian

A freehouse usually serving Exmoor Gold and Stag, Marston's Pedigree and Towpath Tippler (a special house brew).

A riverside country pub with dining area and garden. Food available at lunchtime and evenings. Children allowed in dining area and garden only.

OPEN *All day, every day.*

KINGSWOOD

Dinneywicks Inn

The Chippings, Kingswood, Wotton-under-Edge GL12 8RT
☎ *(01453) 843328* Mrs Thomas

A Wadworth house serving 6X and IPA with other seasonal guests. Also Adnams Broadside.

A recently refurbished village pub with garden and petanque court. Food served at lunchtime and evenings, including traditional Sunday lunch. Children allowed.

OPEN *11.30am–3pm and 6–11pm (all day Sat in winter).*

LIME STREET

The Greyhound Inn

Lime Street, Eldersfield GL19 4NX
☎ *(01452) 840381* Matthew and Kate Brown

A freehouse with Wadworth 6X and a Butcombe brew always available, plus a weekly changing guest beer from an independent brewery such as Dorothy Goodbody's (Wye Valley), Ledbury, Wickwar, Coopers, Smiles or Oakhill.

A rural country inn with two bars and real fires, skittle alley/function room. Large garden with play area. Food served every lunchtime and Tues–Sun evenings. Children allowed. Look for Lime Street on the map, not Eldersfield!

OPEN *11.30am–3pm Mon–Sat; 12–3pm Sun; 7–11pm Sun–Mon; 6–11pm Tues–Sat.*

LITTLETON UPON SEVERN

The White Hart Inn

Littleton upon Severn, Nr Bristol BS12 1NR
☎ *(01454) 412275* Mr and Mrs Berryman

Smiles Best and Exhibition always available plus two or three guest beers to include Burton Bridge Bitter, Wadworth 6X, Bateman XB, Fuller's London Pride, Spitfire Ale and Greene King Abbot.

Near the Severn Bridges and Thornbury Castle. Bar food at lunchtime and evenings. Children not allowed. Leave the M4 at junction 21. Head towards Thornbury, then Elberton village. Signposted from there.

OPEN *11.30am–3pm and 6–11pm weekdays; 11.30am–11pm Sat;*

LONGHOPE

The Glasshouse Inn

May Hill, Longhope GL17 0NN
☎ *(01452) 830529* Mr S Pugh

A freehouse reguarly serving Butcombe brews. Guests served straight from the barrel include ales from Adnams and Hook Norton.

An old-fashioned country pub with garden. Food served at lunchtime and evenings. Well-behaved children allowed.

OPEN *11.30am–3pm and 6.30–11pm Mon–Sat; 12–3pm and 7–10.30pm Sun.*

LOWER APPERLEY

The Farmer's Arms
Ledbury Road, Lower Apperley GL19 4DR
☎ *(01452) 780307* Viv Healey

 Home of the Mayhem Brewery. Odda's Light and Sundowner's Heavy always available plus six other guests, which may include Marston's Pedigree and Wadworth 6X.

A n eighteenth-century inn with one bar, oak beams and open fires. The brewery was opened in the grounds in 1992. Bar and restaurant food available at lunchtime and evenings. Car park, garden, children's play area. B4213 Ledbury Road, four miles south of Tewkesbury.

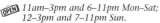 **ODDA'S LIGHT 3.8% ABV**
SUNDOWNER'S HEAVY 4.5% ABV

OPEN *11am–3pm and 6–11pm Mon–Sat; 12–3pm and 7–11pm Sun.*

LOWER SWELL

The Golden Ball Inn
Lower Swell, Nr Cheltenham GL54 1LF
☎ *(01451) 830247* Pat Heads

 Tied to the nearby Donnington Brewery, so BB and SBA are always available. No guest beers.

A seventeenth-century, Cotswold stone, village local with log fires in winter. Accommodation available. Typical old pub games played (darts, dominoes, cribbage, Aunt Sally). Bar food served at lunchtime and evenings. Car park and garden. Children welcome. On the B4068, one mile from Stow-on-the-Wold.

OPEN *12–2.20pm and 6.30–11pm Mon–Fri; 12–3pm and 6.30–11pm Sat; 12–3pm and 7–10.30pm Sun.*

NEWLAND

The Ostrich Inn
Newland, Nr Coleford GL16 8NP
☎ *(01594) 833260* Mr and Mrs Dewe

 Wadworth 6X, Shepherd Neame Spitfire and RCH Old Slug Porter always available plus four guest beers (50 per year) which may include Otter Head, RCH Pitchfork, Moles Tap, Vale Ale, Durham Pagan, Uley Pig's Ear, Ridleys Spectacular, Bull Mastiff Best, Marston's Pedigree, Black Sheep Bitter and Exmoor Gold. Also real cider and German lager.

A thirteenth-century inn in the Forest of Dean with beams, log fire, settles and candles. Bar and restaurant food available at lunchtime and evenings. Garden and accommodation. In the village centre, opposite the church.

OPEN *12–2.20pm and 6.30–11pm Mon–Fri; 12–3pm and 6.30–11pm Sat; 12–3pm and 7–10.30pm Sun.*

PILL

The Star Inn
13 Bank Place, Pill, Nr Bristol BS20 0AQ
☎ *(01275) 374926* Mrs Fey

 Approximately 300 different ales sold in the past eight years. Small regional brews favoured. Butcombe Bitter always available plus two or three from a selection of 50–60 brews per year including Bullmastiff Son of a Bitch, Ringwood Old Thumper, Wychwood Hobgoblin, Gibbs Mew Wake Ale and Moorhouse's Pendle Witches Brew.

L ocal village pub with a wide range of customers. Parking. Children allowed in bar. Junction 19 off the M5.

OPEN *12–4pm and 7–11pm.*

POPE'S HILL

The Greyhound Inn
The Slad, Pope's Hill, Gloucester GL14 1JX
☎ *(01452) 760344* Mr Pammenter

 A freehouse serving Timothy Taylor and Freeminer brews. One twice-weekly changing guest from any brewery in the UK. Ledbury and Ash Vine are examples.

A country pub with non-smoking family room and garden. Food served at lunchtime and evenings. Children allowed in the family room only.

OPEN *11am–3pm and 5.30–11pm (12–3pm Sun).*

SAPPERTON

The Daneway
Sapperton, Nr Cirencester GL7 6LN
☎ *(01285) 760297*

 Five real ales always available including Wadworth 6X, Archers Best and Daneway Bitter. Guests (30+ per year) might come from the West Berkshire Brewery or Greene King.

B uilt in 1784, this beamed pub is set in some wonderful Gloucestershire countryside. It features a lounge and public bar, plus small non-smoking family room. No music, machines or pool but traditional pub games. Bar food is available at lunchtime and meals in the evening. Car park, garden, children allowed in family room. Less than two miles off the A419 Stroud–Cirencester road.

OPEN *11am–2.30pm and 6.30–11pm.*

The Butcher's Arms

Sheepscombe, Painswick GL6 7RH
☎ *(01452) 812113*
Johnny and Hilary Johnstone

 A freehouse with Hook Norton Best, Uley Old Spot and an Archers brew always available.

A country pub with restaurant. Food served at lunchtime and evenings. Children allowed.

 11.30am–3pm and 6.30–11pm (10.30pm Sun).

The Miners Arms

Sling, Coleford GL16 8LH
☎ *(01594) 836632* Mrs Jeynes

A freehouse serving four Freeminer brews.

Old-fashioned, one-bar locals' pub in tourist area. Nice walking and views. Large garden, juke box and darts. Food served all day. Children allowed. Situated on the main road from Chepstow to Coleford and the Forest of Dean

All day, every day.

The Ram Inn

Station Road, South Woodchester, Nr Stroud GL5 5EL
☎ *(01453) 873329* Mike McAsey

Uley Bitter and Old Spot, Archers Best and Ruddles Best always available plus two guests (200 per year) including Hook Norton Best and Old Hooky, Buchanan brews, Fuller's London Pride, Exmoor Gold, Smiles brews, Morland Old Speckled Hen, Robinson's, Butcombe, Charles Wells, Badger, Cotleigh and Ash Vine brews.

A bustling sixteenth-century Cotswold inn with beautiful views. Open fires in winter, plenty of outside seating in summer. Bar and restaurant food available at lunchtime and evenings. Car park and garden. Children allowed. Off the A46 from Stroud towards Nailsworth. After approximately two miles, turn right to South Woodchester village.

11am–11pm Mon–Sat; 12–10.30pm Sun.

The Berkeley Arms

8 Church Street, Tewkesbury GL20 5PA
☎ *(01684) 293034* Mr and Mrs K Mather

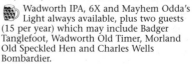 Wadworth IPA, 6X and Mayhem Odda's Light always available, plus two guests (15 per year) which may include Badger Tanglefoot, Wadworth Old Timer, Morland Old Speckled Hen and Charles Wells Bombardier.

A small, homely fifteenth-century pub. Bar and restaurant food available. Street parking. The restaurant can be hired for functions. Children allowed in the restaurant.

11am–3pm and 5–11pm Mon–Thur; all day Fri–Sun.

The White Bear

Bredon Road, Tewkesbury GL20 5BU
☎ *(01684) 296614* H and G Stone

A freehouse serving Wye Valley Bitter, plus two guests from breweries such as Wood, Hook Norton, RCH, Wyre Piddle and Banks's.

A games-orientated, male-dominated boozer! No food. Children allowed in the garden only.

All day, every day.

Old Crown Inn

The Green, Uley, Dursley GL11 8SN
☎ *(01453) 860502* Mrs Morgan

A freehouse with Uley Bitter and Pig's Ear regularly available, plus three weekly changing guests from breweries such as Cotleigh, Greene King, Hook Norton, Hampshire or Hop Back.

A village pub with games room, garden and accommodation. Home-cooked pub food served at lunchtimes and evenings. Children allowed.

11.30am–3pm and 7–11pm (10.30pm Sun).

WATERLEY BOTTOM

The New Inn
Waterley Bottom, North Nibley, Nr Dursley GL11 6EF
☎ *(01453) 543659* Ruby Sainty

Cotleigh Hobby Ale and Tawny, Greene King Abbot plus Smiles Best and Exhibition always available. Also occasional guests (104 per year) to include B&T Dragonslayer and Adnams May Day.

A remote freehouse with two bars, set in a beautiful valley. Bar food available at lunchtime and evenings. Car park, garden and accommodation. CAMRA Gloucestershire Pub of the Year 1992–93. From North Nibley, follow signs for Waterley Bottom.

OPEN *12–2.30pm and 7–11pm (10.30pm Sun).*

WESTBURY ON TRYM

The Post Office Tavern
17 Westbury Hill, Westbury on Trym, Nr Bristol BS9 3AH
☎ *(0117) 940 1233* Steve Fitzgerald

Up to ten beers available from an extensive range including Shepherd Neame Spitfire Ale, Fuller's London Pride and Smiles brews.

E arly twentieth-century alehouse full of post office memorabilia. Non-smoking lounge. Bar food lunchtime and evenings. Street parking, small patio. Children allowed with parents for food in early evenings only. On main road in Westbury village.

OPEN *11.30am–11pm Mon–Sat; 12–3pm and 7–10.30pm Sun.*

The Victoria Inn
20 Chock Lane, Westbury on Trym, Bristol BS9 3EX
☎ *(0117) 950 0441* Mr Deas

A Wadworth tied house with 6X and Henry's IPA and Adnams Broadside usually available, plus two weekly changing guests such as Young's Bitter, Charles Wells Bombardier and seasonal brews.

A village pub with garden. Food available at lunchtime and evenings. Children allowed.

OPEN *12–2.30pm and 5.30–11pm.*

WHITMINSTER

The Old Forge
Bristol Road, Whitminster GL2 7NY
☎ *(01452) 741306* Peter Brian

A freehouse serving Exmoor Gold, Exmoor Ale and Uley Bitter plus one rotating guest from breweries such as York or Cotleigh.

A n old, traditional pub with dining area and beer garden. Food served at lunchtime and evenings. Children allowed.

OPEN *11am–3pm and 7–11pm Mon–Fri; all day Sat; 12–3pm and 7–11pm Sun.*

YOU TELL US

★ *Adam & Eve*, 8 Townsend Street, Alstone, Cheltenham
★ *The Angel Hotel*, Market Place, Coleford
★ *Bayshill Inn*, 85 St George's Place, Cheltenham
★ *The Beaufort Arms*, High Street, Hawkesbury Upton, Badminton
★ *The Brewery Tap*, Colston Street, Bristol
★ *The Bristol Brewhouse*, Stokes Croft, Bristol
★ *The Butchers Arms*, Oakridge, Stroud
★ *The Cat & Wheel*, Cotham Brow, Bristol
★ *The Coach and Horses*, Longborough, Moreton-in-the-Marsh
★ *The Green Dragon*, Elkstone
★ *The Hare on the Hill*, 41 Thomas Street, North Kingsdown, Bristol
★ *Kemble Brewery Inn*, 27 Fairview Street, Cheltenham
★ *The King's Head*, Bledington
★ *The Lamb*, High Street, Clearwell
★ *The Little Thatch Hotel*, 141 Bristol Road, Quedgeley
★ *The Prince Albert*, Two Mile Hill Road, Kingswood, Bristol
★ *The Ram Inn*, Station Road, Woodchester
★ *The Red Hart*, Blaisdon
★ *Robert Fitzharding*, 24 Cannon Street, Bedminster, Bristol
★ *The Rose & Crown*, High Street, Iron Acton
★ *Salutation Inn*, Ham, Berkeley
★ *The Snowshill Arms*, Snowshill
★ *The Swan*, Pillowell
★ *The Twelve Bells*, 12 Lewis Lane, Cirencester
★ *The Woolpack*, Slad, Stroud

Places Featured:

Aldershot
Beauworth
Bentworth
Bishops Waltham
Chalton
Charter Alley
Cheriton
Dunbridge
Easton
Fareham
Farnborough
Freefolk Priors
Frogham
Froxfield
Hamble
Hartley Wintney
Horndean

Lasham
Liss
Little London
Meonstoke
Micheldever
Ovington
Portsmouth
Priors Dean
Ringwood
Rotherwick
Shedfield
Southampton
Southsea
Titchfield
Weyhill
Whitsbury

THE BREWERIES

BALLARD'S BREWERY LTD
Unit C, The Old Sawmill, Nyewood, Rogate,
Petersfield GU31 5HA
☎ *(01730) 821362*

MIDHURST MILD 3.5% ABV
Winter brew, dark and smooth.
TROTTON BITTER 3.6%
Well-flavoured, well-hopped session bitter.
BEST BITTER 4.2% ABV
Nutty and well-balanced, with hops and
bitterness in the finish.
NYEWOOD GOLD 5.0% ABV
Golden, hoppy brew.
WASSAIL 6.0% ABV
Malty and powerful, but not over-sweet.
Plus a powerful Christmas ale.

BECKETT'S BREWERY LTD
8 Enterprise Court, Rankine Road, Basingstoke
RG24 8GE
☎ *(01256) 472986*

OLD TOWN BITTER 3.7% ABV
ORIGINAL BITTER 4.0% ABV
GOLDEN GRALE 4.5% ABV
FORTRESS ALE 5.0% ABV
Plus occasional brews.

THE CHERITON BREWHOUSE
Cheriton, Alresford SO24 0QQ
☎ *(01962) 771166*

POTS ALE 3.8% ABV
Golden, with hoppiness throughout.
BEST BITTER 4.2% ABV
Pronounced fruit and malt flavour.
DIGGERS GOLD 4.6% ABV
Powerful hoppiness and bitter finish.
FLOWER POWER 5.2% ABV
TURKEY'S REVENGE 5.9% ABV
A Christmas ale.

CLARENCE TAVERN AND OLD CHAPEL BREWERY
1 Clarence Road, Gosport PO12 1BB
☎ *(01705) 529726*

OLD CHAPEL 3.8% ABV
BUCKLAND'S BEST 4.1% ABV
INVINCIBLE STOUT 4.5% ABV
WHOLE HEARTED 4.7% ABV
BLAKE'S GOSPORT BEST 5.2% ABV

GEORGE GALE & CO. LTD
The Brewery, Horndean PO8 0DA
☎ *(01705) 571212*

BUTSER BREW 3.4% ABV
A sweet brew, with fruit throughout.
GB 4.0% ABV
Malt flavour with some fruitiness. Bitter.
FESTIVAL MILD 4.8% ABV
Sweet and dark, with fruitiness.
HSB 4.8% ABV
Sweet and malty.
Plus seasonal brews.

HAMPSHIRE BREWERY LTD

Romsey Industrial Estate, Greatbridge Road,
Romsey SO51 0HR
☎ *(01794) 830000*

 KING ALFRED'S BITTER 3.8% ABV
Amber, light, refreshing and complex.
LIONHEART 4.2% ABV
Golden and refreshing with subtle hop finish.
IRONSIDE 4.2% ABV
Amber, with crisp hop flavour and bitter finish.
PENDRAGON 4.8% ABV
Excellent balance. Bursting with malt hops.
PRIDE OF ROMSEY 5.0% ABV
Fragrant with distinctive bitterness.
1066 6.0% ABV
Light, powerful pale ale. Clean and subtle.
Plus seasonal brews.

ITCHEN VALLEY BREWERY

Shelf House, New Farm Road, Alresford
SO24 9QE
☎ *(01962) 735111*

 GODFATHERS 3.8% ABV
FAGIN 4.1% ABV
JUDGE JEFFREYS 4.5% ABV
Plus occasional brews.

PACKHORSE BREWERY

5 Somers Road, Southsea PO5 4PR
☎ *(01705) 750450*

 PACKHORSE BITTER 3.8% ABV

RINGWOOD BREWERY LTD

138 Christchurch Road, Ringwood BH24 3AP
☎ *(01425) 471177*

 BEST BITTER 3.8% ABV
Sweet malt flavour, becoming dry.
Bitterness in the finish.
TRUE GLORY 4.3% ABV
Smooth and malty throughout, with some fruit.
XXXX PORTER 4.7% ABV
Full-bodied, winter brew. Fruit, coffee and
vanilla flavours.
FORTYNINER 4.9% ABV
Hop and malt flavour with malty finish.
OLD THUMPER 5.6% ABV
Golden with various fruit flavours.

TRIPPLE FFF BREWING CO.

Magpie Works, Unit 3, Station Approach, Four
Marks, Alton GU34 4HN
☎ *(01420) 561422*

BILLERICAY DICKIE 3.8% ABV
Hoppy session brew.
PRESSED RAT AND WARTHOG 3.8% ABV
Dark and malty with hoppy bitterness.
MOONDANCE 4.2% ABV
Golden with fruity, hoppy flavour.
DAZED AND CONFUSED 4.6% ABV
Pale and hoppy.
STAIRWAY TO HEAVEN 4.6% ABV
Excellent balance.
COMFORTABLY NUMB 5.0% ABV
Dark and fruity.

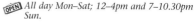

THE PUBS

ALDERSHOT

The Red Lion

Ash Road, Aldershot GU12 4EZ
☎ *(01252) 403503* Mr Freeth

A freehouse serving a range of up to six
weekly changing beers including
Timothy Taylor Dark Mild, Oakham Perrywig
and many, many more.

A traditional pub with beer garden. No
music or pool. Food available Tues–Fri
lunchtimes. Well-behaved children allowed.

 All day Mon–Sat; 12–4pm and 7–10.30pm
Sun.

BEAUWORTH

The Milburys

Beauworth, Alresford SO24 0PB
☎ *(01962) 771248* Mr Larden

A freehouse with Milbury's Best (house
beer) plus Hampshire Pride of Romsey
and King Alfred's always available. Two
guests change every couple of months.

A country pub with dining area and beer
garden. Food available at lunchtime and
evenings. Children allowed.

11am–3pm and 6–11pm (10.30pm Sun).

BENTWORTH

The Sun Inn

Bentworth, Nr Alton GU34 5JT
☎ *(01420) 562338* Mary Holmes

Ringwood Best, Cheriton Pots Ale,
Hampshire Sun (house beer) and Bunces
Pigswill always available, plus at least four
guest ales changed weekly. Regulars include
Hogs Back TEA, Timothy Taylor Landlord,
Ringwood Old Thumper, Badger Best and
Abbey Bellringer.

A pretty seventeenth-century country inn
with three connecting rooms. Stone and
wooden floors. Food available at lunchtime
and evenings. Children allowed.

12–3pm and 6–11pm Mon–Sat; all day
Sun.

BISHOPS WALTHAM

The Hampshire Bowman
Dundridge Lane, Bishops Waltham,
Southampton SO32 1GD
☎ *(01489) 892940* Jim Park

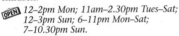 A freehouse serving Archers Village and Golden and Ringwood Fortyniner plus guests such as Cheriton Flower Power.

F reehouse in a rural setting with beer garden. Archery next door. Food available at lunchtime and evenings. No children.

OPEN *12–2pm Mon; 11am–2.30pm Tues–Sat;*
12–3pm Sun; 6–11pm Mon–Sat;
7–10.30pm Sun.

CHALTON

The Red Lion
Chalton, Waterlooville PO8 0BG
☎ *(01705) 592246* Mr McGee

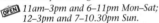 A Gales brewery tied house, serving HSB, Butser Bitter and GB plus one rotating guest changed monthly. This might be Marston's Pedigree, Shepherd Neame Spitfire, Charles Wells Bombardier or Wadworth 6X.

R eputed to be the oldest in Hampshire, this country pub with garden overlooks the Downs. Thatched roof, non-smoking dining area. Food available at lunchtime and evenings (not Sunday evenings). Under 14s allowed only if eating.

OPEN *11am–3pm and 6–11pm Mon–Sat;*
12–3pm and 7–10.30pm Sun.

CHARTER ALLEY

The White Hart
White Hart Lane, Charter Alley, Tadley
RG26 5QA
☎ *(01256) 850048* Howard Bradley

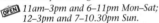 A freehouse with Greene King Abbot Ale always available, plus two guest beers. Brews from Otter and Harveys breweries are popular.

A village pub with dining area, skittle alley and garden. Food available at lunchtime and evenings. Children allowed in certain areas.

OPEN *12–2.30pm Mon–Fri; 12–3pm Sat–Sun;*
7–11pm Mon–Sat; 7–10.30pm Sun.

CHERITON

The Flower Pots Inn
Cheriton, Alresford SO24 0QQ
☎ *(01962) 771318*
Paul Tickner and Jo Bartlett

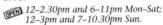 The Cheriton Brewhouse is situated very close to this pub, hence the full range of Cheriton brews are always available, plus occasional Cheriton specials. The two businesses are run separately though, and this is not the 'brewpub' that it is often mistaken for.

T he pub is an unspoilt traditional inn on the edge of the village. Bar food is available every lunchtime and Mon–Sat evenings. Car park, garden, small children's room, accommodation. Children not allowed in the pub. CAMRA regional pub of the year 1995.

OPEN *12–2.30pm and 6–11pm Mon–Sat;*
12–3pm and 7–10.30pm Sun.

DUNBRIDGE

The Mill Arms
Barley Hill, Dunbridge, Nr Romsey SO51 0LF
☎ *(01794) 343401* Terry Lewis

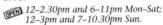 A freehouse with up to four real ales changed every few days. These often include something from the Hampshire, Ringwood or Badger breweries.

A quiet country pub in the middle of nowhere! Two open fires, conservatory, restaurant, function room and B&B. Large garden. Food available at lunchtime and evenings. Children and dogs welcome.

OPEN *11am–3pm and 6–11pm (12–3pm during*
winter).

EASTON

The Cricketers Inn
Easton, Winchester SO21 1ET
☎ *(01962) 779353* John Sturges

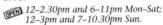 A freehouse with a Ringwood brew and Otter Ale always available. Three weekly changing guests might be Hop Back Summer Lightning or a brew from Cottage or Sharp's.

A traditional village pub with drinking terrace and non-smoking dining area. Food available at lunchtime and evenings. B&B. Children allowed.

OPEN *11am–3pm and 6–11pm (10.30pm Sun).*

Osborne View Hotel
67 Hill Head Road, Fareham PO14 3JP
☎ *(01329) 664623* Ian Reabman

A Hall and Woodhouse (Badger) tied pub. Badger Best and IPA, Tanglefoot and Golden Champion always available plus two guests such as Gribble Blackadder.

A seafront pub on three levels. Non-smoking area, sea views, parking. Food available at lunchtime and evenings. Children and dogs welcome.

OPEN *11am–11pm (10.30pm Sun).*

The Prince of Wales
184 Rectory Road, Farnborough GU14 8AL
☎ *(01252) 5545578*

Brakspear Bitter, Badger Best and Tanglefoot, Fuller's London Pride, Hog's Back TEA and Ringwood Fortyniner always available plus up to four guest beers at any one time, which may include Hop Back Summer Lightning, Cheriton Pots Ale and Gales Festival.

An Edwardian freehouse with antique touches in three small connecting rooms. A busy, traditional pub serving food at lunchtime. Just around the corner from Farnborough North railway station. Children over 14 allowed.

OPEN *11.30am–2.30pm and 5.30–11pm Mon–Sat; 12–3.30pm and 7–10.30pm Sun.*

The Watership Down Inn
Freefolk, Nr Whitchurch RG28 7NJ
☎ *(01256) 892254* Mark and Alison Lodge

Real ale on five pumps with Archers Best, Brakspear IPA and a mild always available plus two constantly changing guests usually from smaller breweries including Ringwood, Otter, Moor, Juwards, Beckett's, Itchen Valley, Oakhill, Triple FFF and Butts.

Built in 1840, renamed after the Richard Adams novel that was set locally, a one-bar pub with an open fire and pretty garden with many outside tables. Bar and restaurant food available at lunchtime and evenings. Car park, children's play area. Children allowed in the restaurant. On the B3400 between Whitchurch and Overton.

OPEN *11.30am–3.30pm and 6–11pm (10.30pm Sun).*

The Forester's Arms
Abbots Well Road, Frogham, Fordingbridge SP6 2JA
☎ *(01425) 652294* Mr M Harding

A Wadworth tied house with 6X and Henry's IPA always available plus two seasonal or special brews such as Mayhem Odda's Light.

A country inn in the New Forest area. Dartboard, garden children's play area. Food available at lunchtime and evenings in a separate restaurant. Children and dogs welcome.

OPEN *11am–3pm and 6–11pm Mon–Sat; 12–3pm and 7–10.30pm Sun.*

The Trooper Inn
Froxfield, Petersfield GU32 1BD
☎ *(01730) 827293* Mr Matini

A freehouse serving Ringwood Fortyniner and Best plus a couple of weekly changing guests from breweries such as Ballard's.

A country pub with dining area, function room and garden. Food available at lunchtime and evenings. Children allowed.

OPEN *All day, every day.*

The King & Queen
High Street, Hamble, Southampton SO31 4HA
☎ *(01703) 454247* Ken Smith

A Whitbread house with Fuller's London Pride, Wadworth 6X, and a Brakspear brew always available, plus a changing guest from local breweries such as Cottage or Hampshire.

A sailing pub with log fires and billiards. Separate restaurant serving food at lunchtime and evenings. Children allowed in the restaurant only.

OPEN *11am–11pm (10.30pm Sun).*

The Wagon & Horses
High Street, Hartley Wintney, Nr Hook RG27 8NX
☎ *(01252) 842119* Neil Scott

A freehouse with Gales HSB always available, plus two guest beers, often brews from Ringwood but changing all the time.

A typical village pub with secluded garden. Food available at lunchtime. No children.

OPEN *11am–11pm Mon–Sat; 12–3pm and 7–10.30pm Sun.*

HORNDEAN

Ship & Bell Hotel

6 London Road, Horndean, Waterlooville
PO8 0BZ
☎ *(01705) 592107* Allan Clarke

 A Gales Brewery house serving Butser, HSB and GB plus seasonal specials and a range of other guests perhaps including Everards Tiger.

A village pub with separate dining area and accommodation. Children allowed if eating.

All day, every day.

LASHAM

The Royal Oak

Lasham, Nr Alton GU34 5SJ
☎ *(01256) 381213* Rob Caithness

Ringwood Best, Fuller's London Pride, Hogs Back TEA and a house ale brewed by Beckett's of Basingstoke, plus guests from independent breweries including Sharp's, Triple FFF and Stonehenge Ales. Cask marque approved.

A cosy, two-bar pub with open fires, beams and brickwork. Quiet, enclosed beer garden. Pool table and dartboard in the village bar. Bar food available at lunchtime and evenings. Car park. Just off the A339, four miles from Alton, six miles from Basingstoke.

11am–2.30pm and 6–11pm Mon–Fri; 11am–3pm and 6–11pm Sat; 12–3pm and 7–10.30pm Sun.

LISS

The Bluebell

Farnham Road, Liss GU33 6JE
☎ *(01730) 892107* George Doa

A freehouse with Fuller's London Pride always available plus three guests including, perhaps, Hogs Back Triple and Moondance, Ballard's Best, Beckett's Original or Gales GB.

A pub/restaurant, half smoking and half non-smoking. International cuisine served at lunchtime and evenings, with a choice of either à la carte or bar menu. Beer garden. Children allowed.

11.30am–3pm and 5–11pm (10.30pm Sun).

LITTLE LONDON

The Plough Inn

Silchester Road, Little London, Tadley RG26 5EP
☎ *(01256) 850628* Mr Brown

A freehouse with Ringwood Best and True Glory usually available plus a large selection of guest ales.

A country pub with nice gardens and log fires in winter. Hot, filled baguettes served at lunchtime. Children allowed.

12–2.30pm and 6–11pm Mon–Sat; 12–3pm and 7–10.30pm Sun.

MEONSTOKE

The Bucks Head

Bucks Head Hill, Meonstoke, Southampton
SO32 3NA
☎ *(01489) 877313* Stewart McKenzie

A Morland house with Old Speckled Hen and Ruddles Best always available plus two guests from a list including Charles Wells Bombardier and Cheriton Best.

A rural country pub on the banks of the river. Tourist Board recommended with separate restaurant and B&B. Food available at lunchtime and evenings. Well-behaved children and dogs allowed. Situated just off the A32 north of Dropsford

11am–3pm and 6–11pm Mon–Fri; all day Sat–Sun and bank holidays.

MICHELDEVER

The Dever Arms

Winchester Road, Micheldever SO21 3DG
☎ *(01962) 774339* Mr and Mrs Penny

Cheriton Pots Ale and Badger Best always available plus up to four guest beers which may include Smiles Best, Fuller's London Pride and Timothy Taylor Landlord.

A popular country pub with restaurant and gardens. Bar and restaurant food served at lunchtime and evenings. Car park, garden and children's room. Less than a mile off the A33, six miles north of Winchester, 12 miles south of Basingstoke.

11.30am–3pm and 6–11pm.

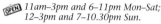

OVINGTON

The Bush Inn

Nr Arlesford, Ovington SO24 0RE
☎ *(01962) 732764* Nick Young

Wadworth 6X and IPA and Hall and Woodhouse (Badger) Tanglefoot permanently available, plus two guests changing every two weeks. Wadworth Farmer's Glory is a regular feature.

A seventeenth-century up and down pub with lots of little rooms and antique memorabilia. Real fires make it cosy in the winter. One main bar in the middle of the pub. Beer garden. Food available every lunchtime and Mon–Sat evenings. Well-behaved children allowed. Situated off the A31 towards Winchester.

11am–3pm and 6–11pm Mon–Sat; 12–3pm and 7–10.30pm Sun.

PORTSMOUTH

The Dolphin

41 High Street, Portsmouth PO1 2LV
☎ *(01705) 823595* Romayne Spooner

Eight real ales on tap including Wadworth 6X, Badger Tanglefoot, Gales HSB and Marston's Pedigree plus something from Ringwood and Fuller's and many other guests on a constantly rotating basis. Local brewers supported whenever possible.

A sixteenth-century coaching inn with wood and flagstone floors. Historic area with good walks nearby. The pub boasts Nelson's signature on a piece of glass in the bar! Bar food available at lunchtime and evenings. Small function room. Children allowed. Directly opposite the cathedral in old Portsmouth.

11am–11pm Mon–Sat; 12–10.30pm Sun.

The Tap

17 London Road, North End, Portsmouth PO2 0BQ
☎ *(01705) 614861*

Up to 11 beers available including Ruddles Best and Ringwood Old Thumper. Guests (100 per year) will include Ringwood Best, Badger Tanglefoot, Gales HSB and brews from the Brewery on Sea. Micro-breweries particularly favoured.

A one-bar drinking pub in the town centre with no juke box or fruit machines. Formerly the brewery tap for the now defunct Southsea Brewery. Bar meals available at lunchtime. Street parking opposite, small yard, disabled toilet. Children not allowed.

10.30am–11pm Mon–Sat; 12–10.30pm Sun.

The Wellington

62 High Street, Portsmouth PO1 2LY
☎ *(01705) 818965* Mr Western

Ansells Bitter, Wadworth 6X and Greene King IPA available plus a guest from breweries such as Fuller's.

A traditional community pub with a reputation for good food served at lunchtime and four evenings per week. Use the harbour entrance. Children allowed.

11am–11pm (10.30pm Sun).

Wetherspoons

2 Guildhall Walk, Portsmouth PO1 2DB
☎ *(01705) 295112* Dave Lea

Hop Back Bitter and Spinnaker Buzz always available plus two guests changed daily including, perhaps, Tom Wood Harvest Bitter (High Wood), Hook Norton Generation or Bateman Spring Breeze.

A friendly town pub with non-smoking area. Food served all day. No children.

11am–11pm Mon–Sat; 12–10.30pm Sun.

PRIORS DEAN

The White Horse Inn

Priors Dean, Nr Petersfield GU32 1DA
☎ *(01420) 588387* Mr J Eddleston

Gales Festival Mild, HSB and Butser Brew Bitter, Ballard's Best plus Ringwood Fortyniner always available and guest beers (ten per year) including Wadworth 6X, Bateman Summer Breeze, Gales IPA and Porter, plus a range of one-off brews from Gales.

An olde-world pub untouched for years with log fires, rocking chairs, antique furniture and a grandfather clock. Bar food available at lunchtime. Car park and garden. Nearby caravan site. Tricky to find. Midway between Petersfield and Alton, five miles from Petersfield, seven miles from Alton.

11am–2.30pm and 6–11pm Mon–Fri; 11am–3pm and 6–11pm Sat; 12–3pm and 7–10.30pm Sun.

RINGWOOD

Inn on the Furlong

12 Meeting House Lane, Ringwood BH24 1EY
☎ *(01425) 475139* Joyce Perkins

Tied to the Ringwood brewery, so Best, Fortyniner and Old Thumper available, plus a seasonal beer.

An old building with log fire, conservatory and beer garden. Food available at lunchtime. Children allowed.

All day Wed/Fri/Sat; closed afternoons Mon/Tue/Thurs.

The Falcon

The Street, Rotherwick, Hook RG27 9BL
☎ *(01256) 762586* Robert Tilbrook

An Eldridge Pope tied house with Brakspear Bitter plus three guests such as Hampshire Pendragon or Gibbs Mew The Bishop's Tipple.

A traditional family pub with restaurant and beer garden. Food available at lunchtime and evenings. Children allowed.

All day, every day.

The Wheatsheaf Inn

Botley Road, Shedfield, Southampton SO32 2JG
☎ *(01329) 833024* Mr Rennie

A freehouse serving Cheriton Pots Ale, Mansfield Four Season, Cotleigh Tawny, and Hop Back Summer Lightning plus two different guests every week.

A country pub with garden. Food available at lunchtime. Children allowed in the garden only.

All day, every day.

The Alexandra

6 Belle Vue Road, Southampton SO15 2AY
☎ *(01703 223012)* Miss Niles

A Whitbread house with Wadworth 6X and Fuller's London Pride always available, plus two guests per week, such as Gales HSB, Hop Back Summer Lightning or a Ringwood brew.

A town-centre pub with traditional building. One bar with big TV and juke box. Disabled access. Food available at lunchtime. No children.

All day, every day.

The Crown Inn

9 Highcrown Street, Southampton SO17 1QE
☎ *(01703) 315033* Jackie Hayer

A Whitbread house with Wadworth 6X and Fuller's London Pride always available plus a rotating guest ale, often from Archers.

A city pub and restaurant with food available at lunchtime and evenings. Children allowed in the restaurant only.

11am–11pm Mon–Sat; 12–10.30pm Sun.

The Duke of Wellington

36 Bugle Street, Southampton SO14 2AH
☎ *(01703) 339222* Mr Wyle

A freehouse offering Ringwood Best and Wadworth 6X plus about 100 guests each year, from a range including Hop Back GFB, Cheriton Best and Pots Ale, Hop Back Best or Hampshire King Alfred

B uilt in the twelfth century, this is the oldest pub in Southampton. Food available at lunchtime and evenings in a separate dining area. Function room. No children.

All day, every day.

The Eagle

1 Palmerston Road, Southampton SO14 1LL
☎ *(01703) 333825* Tina Austin

A Whitbread house with Wadworth 6X and Fuller's London Pride always available, plus four guests from a range of ales such as Gibbs Mew The Bishop's Tipple, Ringwood Porter (winter only), Old Thumper, Fortyniner or Marston's Pedigree.

A traditional town-centre pub with darts and pool. Food available at lunchtime. No children.

All day, every day.

The Hedgehog & Hogshead

163 University Road, Southampton SO17 1TS
☎ *(01703) 581124* Kelvin Jiggle

Gales HSB and a couple of guests always on offer. Something like Brains SA, Ruddles Best or perhaps Fuller's London Pride.

A city-based student pub with food served at lunchtimes only. No children.

11am–11pm Mon–Sun.

The South Western Arms

36–40 Adelaide Road, Southampton SO17 2HW
☎ *(01703) 324542* Simon Woodall

Wadworth 6X, Fuller's London Pride, Gales HSB and Badger Tanglefoot are permanent fixtures, plus three guests such as Greene King Abbot.

A split-level pub with the bar on the ground floor and a games area with TV on the first floor. Food available at lunchtimes only. Children allowed upstairs only.

11am–3pm and 7–11pm Mon–Thurs; all day Fri–Sun.

The Standing Order

30 High Street, Southampton SO14 3HT
☎ *(01703) 222121* Wayne Ellis

A Wetherspoon's pub with Bateman Dark Mild, Shepherd Neame Spitfire and Marston's Pedigree always available, plus about ten different real ale guests per week.

A traditional high-street pub with non-smoking area. Food available all day. No children.

OPEN *10am–11pm Mon–Sat; 12–10.30pm Sun.*

Waterloo Arms

101 Waterloo Road, Southampton SO15 3BS
☎ *(01703) 220022* Paul Osgood

A Hop Back pub serving Summer Lightning, Thunderstorm, GFB, Festive Stout and Best, plus guests rotated weekly on one pump, perhaps King and Barnes Festive, Woodforde's Wherry or something from the Hampshire Brewery.

A local, traditional, village pub with garden. Food available at lunchtime and evenings. Children allowed.

OPEN *All day, every day.*

The Wellington Arms

56 Park Road, Freemantle, Southampton SO15 3DE
☎ *(01703) 227356* Charles Oliver

A freehouse with Wadworth 6X, Ringwood Old Thumper and Best, Fuller's London Pride and ESB always available, plus four constantly changing guests. Has served 2,300 real ales (54 different ones in April 1999 alone). Also serves one Belgian and one German brew.

A town pub with garden and à la carte restaurant. Bar or restaurant food served at lunchtime and evenings. Children allowed in the garden.

OPEN *11.30am–3pm Mon–Sat; 12–4pm Sun; 5.30–11pm Mon–Thurs; 5–11pm Fri; 6–11pm Sat; 6.30–10.30pm Sun.*

SOUTHSEA

The Artillery Arms

Hester Road, Southsea PO4 8HB
☎ *(01705) 733610* Tom Forsythe

A freehouse with Gales, Hampshire and Burton brews always available, plus up to four others including brews from Arundel and Hop Back.

A traditional pub with garden. Food available at lunchtime and evenings. Children allowed until 9pm (8pm Sat).

OPEN *11am–3pm and 6–11pm Mon–Thurs; all day Fri–Sun.*

TITCHFIELD

The Wheatsheaf Inn

1 East Street, Titchfield, Fareham PO14 4AD
☎ *(01329) 842965* Adrienne DoNoia

A freehouse serving Fuller's London Pride and Woodforde's Wherry plus two guests changed weekly. Examples may include Hook Norton Best and Exmoor Gold.

A village pub with dining area, open fire, patio and garden. Food available at lunchtime and evenings. Children allowed in the dining area only.

OPEN *12–3pm and 6–11pm Mon–Thurs; all day Fri; 12–3pm and 6–11pm Sat; 12–3pm and 7–10.30pm Sun.*

WEYHILL

Weyhill Fair

Weyhill Road, Weyhill, Nr Andover SP11 0PP
☎ *(01264) 773631* Mr and Mrs Rayner

Fuller's London Pride, Chiswick and ESB always available plus three guest beers (200 per year) including brews from Shepherd Neame, Adnams and Ringwood.

A friendly local freehouse offering bar food at lunchtime and evenings. Car park, garden and non-smoking family room. On the A342 west of Andover.

OPEN *11am–3pm and 6–11pm Mon–Thurs; 11am–3pm and 5–11pm Fri; 11am–3pm and 6.30–11pm Sat; 12–3pm and 7–10.30pm Sun.*

WHITSBURY

The Cartwheel

Whitsbury Road, Whitsbury, Nr Fordingbridge SP6 3PQ

☎ *(01725) 518362* Gini McGraghan

Up to six beers always available (120 per year) but brews continually changing. Breweries favoured include Adnams, Shepherd Neame, Bunces, Hop Back, Ringwood and Mole's. Seasonal beers and small breweries preferred.

A relaxed bar with exposed beams and open fire, in good walking country. Bar and restaurant food available at lunchtime and evenings. Car park and garden. Children allowed in the restaurant. Turn west of Salisbury onto the Fordingbridge road at Breamore. Signposted from the A338.

11am–2.30pm and 6–11pm; all day Sun in summer.

YOU TELL US

- ★ *The Axford Arms*, Farleigh Road, Axford
- ★ *The Bevois Castle*, 63 Onslow Road, Bevois Valley, Southampton.
- ★ *The Connaught Arms*, 118 Guildford Road, Fratton, Portsmouth
- ★ *The Eagle Hotel*, City Road, Winchester
- ★ *Hawkley Inn*, Pococks Lane, Hawkley, Liss
- ★ *The Newport Inn*, Newport Lane, Brashfield
- ★ *The Old Oyster House*, 291 Locksway Road, Milton, Portsmouth
- ★ *The Old Gaol House*, 11 Jewry Street, Whitchurch
- ★ *The Plough*, Ashmansworth
- ★ *Queen Hotel*, 143 Queens Road, Gosport
- ★ *The Raven*, Bedford Street, Portsmouth (brewpub)
- ★ *The Rampant Cat*, Broad Layings, Woolton Hill
- ★ *Sir Robert Peel*, Astley Street, Southsea
- ★ *The Winchester Arms*, 99 Winchester Road, Portsmouth (brewpub)
- ★ *Wine Vaults*, 43–7 Albert Road, Southsea

Places Featured:

Aston Crews
Aymestry
Birtsmorton
Bretforton
Broadway
Bromyard
Dodford
Evesham
Fromes Hill
Hanley Castle
Hereford

Kempsey
Kidderminster
Ledbury
Leominster
Much Dewchurch
Pensax
Pershore
Ross-on-Wye
Stourport-on-Severn
Tenbury Wells
Uphampton

THE BREWERIES

BRANDY CASK BREWING CO.
25 Bridge Street, Pershore WR10 1AJ
☎ *(01386)552602*

WHISTLING JOE 3.6% ABV
BRANDY SNAPPER 4.0% ABV
JOE BAKER'S ORIGINAL 4.8% ABV

FROME VALLEY BREWERY
Bishop's Frome WR6 5AS
☎ *(01531) 640321*

PREMIUM BITTER 3.8% ABV
MAD MAJOR PALE ALE 4.2% ABV
MAD MAJOR TAWNY ALE 4.2% ABV
MAD MAJOR STOUT 4.5% ABV
BLACKMOOR 5.0% ABV
Plus occasional brews.

HOBSONS BREWERY & CO.
*Newhouse Farm, Tenbury Road, Cleobury
Mortimer, Kidderminster DY14 8RD*
☎ *(01299) 270837*

BEST BITTER 3.8% ABV
Excellent, hoppy session bitter.
TOWN CRIER 4.5% ABV
Smooth, mellow sweetness with balancing hops.
OLD HENRY 5.2% ABV
Darker, smooth and flavoursome.
Plus occasional brews.

MALVERN HILLS BREWERY
*15 West Malvern Road, North Malvern
WR14 4ND*
☎ *(01684) 577336*

BITTER 3.9% ABV
WORCESTERSHIRE WHYM 4.1% ABV
BLACK PEAR 4.4% ABV

MARCHES ALES
*Unit 6, Western Close, Southern Avenue
Industrial Estate, Leominster HR6 0QD*
☎ *(01568) 611084*

SP SPORTING ALES LTD
*Cantilever Lodge, Stoke Prior, Leominster
HR6 0LG*
☎ *(01568) 760226*

WINNERS 3.5% ABV
Amber, refreshing and full-flavoured for
gravity.
DOVES DELIGHT 4.0% ABV
Dark amber, rich and well-balanced.
JOUST 'PERFIC' 4.5% ABV
Smooth and creamy.
Plus seasonal brews.

ST GEORGE'S BREWERY
*The Old Bakehouse, Bush Lane, Callow End,
Worcester WR2 4TF*
☎ *(01905) 831316*

PRIDE 3.8% ABV
WAR DRUM 4.1% ABV

WOODBURY BREWERY LTD
*Home Farm Cottage, Great Witley, Worcester
WR6 6JJ*
☎ *(01299) 896219*

WHITE GOOSE 3.8% ABV
Pale, refreshing with clean, hoppy
bitterness.
OLD HOUSE 4.3% ABV
Full-bodied, malty with a touch of wheat.
MONUMENTAL 5.0% ABV
A stronger version of Old House.
WITLEY WONOFFS
Occasional brews, seasonal or just for the
fun of it!

WOODHAMPTON BREWERY
Aymestrey
☎ (01568) 770503

WYRE PIDDLE BREWERY
Craycombe Farm, Fladbury, Evesham
WR10 2QS
☎ (01386) 860473

 PIDDLE IN THE HOLE 3.9% ABV
PIDDLE IN THE WIND 4.2% ABV
Plus occasional and seasonal brews.

THE PUBS

ASTON CREWS

The Ha'Penny
Aston Crews, Nr Ross-on-Wye, Herefordshire
HR9 7LW
☎ (01989) 750203

Wadworth 6X, Marston's Pedigree and Bitter and Banks's Mild always available plus two guests (20 per year) including Morland Old Speckled Hen, Timothy Taylor Landlord and Adnams Best and others from smaller breweries.

A beautifully restored old pub in glorious countryside. Bar food available at lunchtime and evenings. Car park, garden and games room. Turn off the A40 Ross to Gloucester road at Lea, onto the B4222.

(OPEN) 12–3pm and 6–11pm.

The Penny Farthing
Aston Crews, Nr Ross-on-Wye, Herefordshire
HR9 7LW
☎ (01989) 750366 Mr and Mrs Brown

Marston's Pedigree and Bitter and Wadworth 6X always available plus a guest beer (ten per year) which may be Shepherd Neame Spitfire, Morland Old Speckled Hen or from Robinson's or Hook Norton breweries.

A country inn and restaurant. Bar and restaurant food available at lunchtime and evenings. Car park and garden. Children allowed in the restaurant. Turn off the A40 Ross-on-Wye to Gloucester road at Lea, on to the B4222 (signposted to Newent). The Penny Farthing is one mile down this road.

(OPEN) 12–3pm and 7–11pm.

AYMESTREY

The Riverside Inn
Aymestry, Leominster, Herefordshire HL6 9ST
☎ (01568) 708440 Steve Bowen

Beers from the nearby Woodhampton Brewery including Red Kite, Kingfisher and Jack Snipe. Also one guest, which could be Timothy Taylor Landlord or Marston's Pedigree.

A rural village pub with one bar, dining area and riverside garden. Limited disabled access, but willing. Food available at lunchtime and evenings. Children over seven permitted.

(OPEN) 12–3pm and 6.30–11pm (10.30pm Sun).

BIRTSMORTON

The Farmer's Arms
Birts Street, Birtsmorton, Malvern, Worcestershire
WR13 6AP
☎ (01684) 833308 Julie Moore

Hook Norton Best and Old Hooky always available plus one guest from breweries such as Ledbury, Cottage or Cannon Royall.

A traditional two-bar country freehouse with beer garden. Food available at lunchtime and evenings in a separate dining area at one end of the bar. Children allowed.

(OPEN) 11am–3pm and 6–11pm Mon–Sat; 12–4pm and 7–10.30pm Sun.

BRETFORTON

The Fleece Inn
The Cross, Bretforton, Worcesterhire WR11 5JE
☎ (01386) 831173 Graham Brown

Hook Norton and Uley brews always available, plus guests.

This pub is 650 years old and has been used by the BBC as a film location. Owned by the National Trust, it is also a working museum. Non-smoking family room. East of Evesham, in the middle of the village.

(OPEN) 11am–3pm and 6–11pm Sun–Fri; all day Sat.

BROADWAY

The Crown & Trumpet Inn
Church Street, Broadway. Worcestershire
WR12 7AE
☎ *(01386) 853202* Andy Scott

Morland Old Speckled Hen, Wadworth 6X and Cutterswall Gold (produced especially by Stanway Brewery) always available.

A seventeenth-century village inn built from Cotswold stone. Food at lunchtimes and evenings. Beer garden. Accommodation. Well-behaved children allowed.

11am–2.30pm and 5–11pm Sun–Fri; all day Sat.

BROMYARD

The Rose & Lion Inn
5 New Road, Bromyard, Herefordshire HR7 4AJ
☎ *(01885) 482381* Mrs Herdman

A Wye Valley tied house always serving Bitter, Hereford Pale Ale, Dorothy Goodbody's and Butty Back beers. One weekly changing guest, sometimes a seasonal Wye Valley ale such as Springtime, or brews such as Coach House Gunpowder Strong Mild.

A two-bar drinking house. Old, traditional building with garden. No food. Children allowed in the garden only.

11am–3pm and 6–11pm Mon–Fri; all day most Sat–Sun.

DODFORD

The Dodford Inn
Whinfield Road, Dodford, Bromsgrove,
Worcestershire B61 9BG
☎ *(01527) 832470* Larry Bowen

Greenalls Bitter always available plus three guests from breweries such as Titanic, Stafford, Evesham and Young's. Some 2000 beers served over five years.

A traditional country pub situated in an historic village. Beamed ceilings, very large garden and campsite plus two patios. Food served at lunchtime and evenings. Children allowed.

12–3pm and 6–11pm Mon–Fri; all day Sat; 12–3pm and 6–10.30pm Sun.

EVESHAM

The Green Dragon
17 Oat Street, Evesham, Worcestershire
WR11 4PJ
☎ *(01386) 443462*

Home of the Evesham Brewery. Two Asum brews produced and sold, 'Asum' being the local pronunciation of 'Evesham'. Other guest ales also offered.

T he brewery is housed in the old bottle store. A Grade II listed pub with a cosy lounge. Bar and restaurant food is served at lunchtime and evenings. Car park, garden, large function room. Children allowed.

ASUM ALE 3.8% ABV
A malty session ale.
ASUM GOLD 5.2% ABV
Fruity, malty and sweet strong ale.

11am–11pm Mon–Thur; 11pm–1am Fri–Sat.

FROMES HILL

Wheatsheaf Inn
Fromes Hill, Ledbury, Herefordshire HR8 1HT
☎ *(01531) 640888* Mr Mirfin

A brewpub serving Fromes Hill Buckswood Dingle and Overture. Also occasional guests.

A country inn with one bar, dining area and garden. Food served at lunchtime and evenings. Children allowed.

BUCKSWOOD DINGLE 3.6% ABV
EIGHTH OVERTURE 4.2% ABV

All day, every day.

HANLEY CASTLE

The Three Kings
Church End, Hanley Castle, Worcestershire
WR8 0BL
☎ *(01684) 592686* Mrs Sheila Roberts •

Thwaites and Butcombe brews available plus three guest beers (more than 150 per year) perhaps from Brandy Cask, Evesham, Mildmay, Fromes Hill, Crouch Vale, Berkeley, Otter, Hop Back, Dyffryn Clwyd, Goff's, Stanway Woods and Belhaven breweries.

A traditional fifteenth-century freehouse that has been in the same family for 87 years. Bar food available at lunchtime and evenings. Parking, garden and children's room. CAMRA pub of the Year 1993. Just off the B4211, Upton-upon-Severn to Malvern road. Take the third turn on the left from Upton.

11am–3pm and 7–11pm Mon–Sat; 12–3pm and 7–10.30pm Sun.

The Barrels & Wye Valley Brewery

69 Owen Street, Hereford, Herefordshire HR1 2JQ
☎ *(01432) 274968* Carey Spry

The Wye Valley brewpub, with Bitter, Hereford Pale Ale, Butty Bach, Dorothy Goodbody's seasonal ales, Dorothy Goodbody's Wholesome Stout, and Travellers Best usually available. Also offers one guest ale, such as O'Hanlon's Red.

A town boozer. One of the last multi-roomed public houses in Hereford. Clientele a mix of old regulars and students. Occasional live music. Outside seating and fishpond. Annual beer festival on August bank holiday weekend, during which over 50 beers and ciders are available. No food. No children.

BITTER 3.5% ABV
HEREFORD PALE ALE 4% ABV
SUPREME 4.3% ABV
BREW 69 5.6% ABV
DOROTHY GOODBODY'S WONDERFUL SPRINGTIME BITTER 4% ABV
DOROTHY GOODBODY'S GOLDEN SUMMERTIME ALE 4.2% ABV
DOROTHY GOODBODY'S AUTUMN DELIGHT 4.5% ABV
DOROTHY GOODBODY'S WHOLESOME STOUT 4.6% ABV
DOROTHY GOODBODY'S WARMING WINTERTIME ALE 4.9% ABV

OPEN *All day, every day.*

Lichfield Vaults

11 Church Street, Hereford, Herefordshire HR1 2LR
☎ *(01432) 267994* Charles Wenyon

Marston's Pedigree usually available plus up to seven guest ales including, perhaps, Hoskins & Oldfield Ginger Tom, Shepherd Neame Spitfire or a Greene King brew.

A traditional town-centre pub, one bar, patio. Food served at lunchtime only. No children.

OPEN *All day Mon–Sat; 7–10.30pm Sun.*

The Victory

88 St Owen Street, Hereford, Herefordshire HR1 2QD
☎ *(01432) 274998* Miss Brooks

A freehouse serving local brews such as Wye Valley Bitter, HPA and Dorothy Goodbody's ales. Plus two guests on from any independent brewery in the country, such as Ridleys Rumpus.

A two-bar boozer with a nautical theme. Live music from Thursday to Sunday. Beer Garden. Food served at lunchtime only. Children allowed at lunchtime only.

OPEN *All day, every day.*

Walter de Cantelupe Inn

Main Road, Kempsey, Worcestershire WR5 3NA
☎ *(01905) 820572* Martin Lloyd Morris

A freehouse with Marston's Bitter and Timothy Taylor Landlord among the brews always available, plus one guest from a wide range. Examples include Greene King Abbot, Cannon Royall Arrowhead, Wood Shropshire Lad, Orkney Raven Ale and Felinfoel Double Dragon.

A Tudor village pub with wooden beams and stone floors. One bar, dining area and garden. Food available Tues–Sun lunchtime and evenings. Children allowed during the day only.

OPEN *12–2.30pm and 6–11pm Mon–Sat; 7–10.30pm Sun.*

KIDDERMINSTER

The Boar's Head

39 Worcester Street, Kidderminster,
Worcestershire DY10 1EA
☎ *(01562) 862450* Andy Hipkiss

Banks's Bitter and Original, Camerons Strongarm, Tap House Bitter and Marston's Pedigree always available plus three guests such as Fuller's London Pride, Cains Formidable and Brewery Bitter or a selection from Bateman.

A two-bar town-centre pub with stone floors and beamed ceilings. Small beer garden and all-weather bricked courtyard covered with a glass pyramid. Food available Mon–Sat 12–3pm. Children allowed in the courtyard only.

12–11pm Mon–Sat; 12–3pm and 7–10.30pm Sun.

The King & Castle

Severn Valley Railway Station, Comberton Hill,
Kidderminster, Worcestershire
☎ *(01562) 747505* Peter Williamson

Batham Best is among the brews always available plus guest beers (250 per year) from Enville, Hobsons, Hanby, Three Tuns, Timothy Taylor, Holt, Holden's, Berrow, Wood, Burton Bridge and Wye Valley breweries.

The pub is a copy of the Victorian railway refreshment rooms, decorated in the 1930s, GWR-style. Bar food available. Car park and garden. Children allowed until 9pm. Located next to Kidderminster railway station.

11am–4pm and 5–11pm.

LEDBURY

The Horseshoe Inn

The Homend, Ledbury, Herefordshire HR8 1BP
☎ *(01531) 632770* David Tegg

A freehouse with Hobsons Bitter and Flowers IPA always available. Two guests could well come from Wye Valley.

A small family inn in Ledbury town with one bar and garden. Food available at lunchtime only. Children allowed.

All day, every day.

The Royal Oak Hotel

The Southend, Ledbury, Herefordshire HR8 2EY
☎ *(01531) 632110* Mr Barron

The home of the Ledbury Brewery with the range of Ledbury brews produced and served on the premises. Also Wadworth 6X and seasonal Ledbury ales plus occasional guests such as Morland Old Speckled Hen and Greene King Abbot.

B uilt in 1420, with the main building added in 1645, this was the original Ledbury inn. Bar and restaurant food served at lunchtime and evenings. Car park and accommodation. Children allowed.

DOGHILL BITTS 3.6% ABV
LEDBURY SB 3.8% ABV
LEDBURY BEST 4.2% ABV
EXHIBITION 5.1% ABV
XB 7.5% ABV

11am–11pm daily.

LEOMINSTER

The Black Horse Coach House

South Street, Leominster, Herefordshire HR6 8JF
☎ *(01568) 611946* Peter Hoare

A freehouse serving Marches Black Horse (house ale) and Hobsons Town Cryer plus two guests such as Fuller's London Pride, Hobsons Best or other micro-brews. Has served 150 beers over the past 12 months.

A town pub in a traditional building. Two bars, restaurant and garden. Food served every lunchtime and Mon–Sat evenings. Children allowed.

11am–2.30pm and 6–11pm Mon–Fri; all day Sat; 12–3 pm and 7–10.30pm Sun.

The Grape Vaults

Broad Street, Leominster, Herefordshire HR6 8BS
☎ *(01568) 611404* Mrs Greenwold

 A freehouse offering Marston's Pedigree and Best and Banks's Mild plus one rotating guest such as a Marston's special brew or Timothy Taylor Landlord, Morland Old Speckled Hen, Greene King Abbot or Fuller's London Pride.

A small pub in the town centre. Old-fashioned with log fire, no music. Bar snacks available at lunchtime and evenings. Children allowed if eating.

OPEN *11am–3pm and 5–11pm Mon–Fri; 11am–3.30pm and 6–11pm Sat; 12–4pm and 6.30–10.30pm Sun.*

MUCH DEWCHURCH

The Black Swan Inn

Much Dewchurch, Hereford, Herefordshire HR2 8DJ
☎ *(01981) 540295* A Davies

Beers from breweries such as Timothy Taylor, Badger and Adnams usually available plus one rotating guest such as Reverend James' Shropshire Lad or a beer from Frome Valley or Hook Norton breweries.

A fourteenth-century freehouse with lounge and public bar. Dining area in lounge. Patio. Food available at lunchtime and evenings. Children allowed.

OPEN *12–3pm and 6–11pm Mon–Fri; 11.30am–3pm and 6–11pm Sat; 12–3pm and 7–10.30pm Sun.*

PENSAX

The Bell

Pensax, Abberley, Worcestershire WR6 6AE
☎ *(01299) 896677* Graham Titcombe

Five beers available at any one time from a constantly changing list of approximately 500 brews per year. Green Cucumber Gandolf, Marches Autumn Ale, Pat Catney's Irish Stout, Fromes Hill Overture, Tipsy Toad Horny Toad may be among them. Occasional beer festivals.

Attractive, rural Tudor-style pub with various traditional drinking areas and dining room. Large garden, superb views, three real fires in winter. Bar and restaurant food served at lunchtimes and evenings. Located on the B4202 Great Witley to Cleobury Mortimer road, between Abberley and Clows Top.

OPEN *12–2.30pm and 5–11pm Mon–Fri; 11am–11pm Sat; 12–10.30pm Sun.*

PERSHORE

The Brandy Cask

25 Bridge Street, Pershore, Worcestershire WR10 1AJ
☎ *(01386) 552602*

The ales brewed here now supply 30 outlets. Also Ruddles Best and County available plus guest beers.

Town-centre freehouse. Bar and restaurant food is served at lunchtime and evenings. Large riverside garden. Children allowed.

BRANDY SNAPPER 4% ABV
JOHN BAKER'S ORIGINAL 4.8% ABV

OPEN *11.30am–2.30pm and 7–11pm.*

ROSS-ON-WYE

The Crown & Sceptre

Market Place, Ross-on-Wye, Herefordshire HR9 5NX
☎ *(01989) 562765* Mr Lesever

A Whitbread pub serving Archers Best, Morland Old Speckled Hen and Greene King Abbot Ale plus two changing guests such as Young's Special, Brains SA or Gales HSB

A town pub with a friendly atmosphere and mixed clientele. One bar, patio and garden. Bar food served at lunchtime. Well-behaved children allowed.

OPEN *All day, every day.*

STOURPORT-ON-SEVERN

The Rising Sun

50 Lombard Street, Stourport-on-Severn, Worcestershire DY13 8DU
☎ *(01299) 822530* Robert Hallard

Banks's Original, Bitter and Hanson's Mild plus Marston's Pedigree always available, plus one guest such as Goddards Inspiration. Seasonal and celebration ales served whenever available.

A 200-year-old canalside pub. One bar, small dining area and patio. Food available at lunchtime and evenings. Children allowed in the dining room and patio only.

OPEN *All day, every day.*

The Ship Inn

Teme Street, Tenbury Wells, Worcestershire
WR15 8AE
☎ *(01584) 810269* Michael Hoar

 A freehouse with Hobsons Best always available plus a guest such as Morland Old Speckled Hen or Shepherd Neame The Bishop's Finger.

A seventeenth-century, market town pub with beamed ceilings and two separate non-smoking dining areas. Food available at lunchtime and evenings. Beer garden. Children allowed.

OPEN *11am–3pm and 7–11pm (10.30pm Sun).*

The Fruiterer's Arms

Uphampton, Ombersley, Worcestershire
WR9 0JW
☎ *(01905) 621161*

Cannon Royall brews produced and served on the premises plus a guest beer.

B rewing began in this converted cider house in July 1993. The maximum output is now 16 barrels per week and there are plans for expansion. The pub has two bars and a log fire in winter. Bar food is served at lunchtime. Car park. Children allowed.

KPA 3.4% ABV
A new summer beer.

FRUITERER'S MILD 3.7% ABV
Replaces Millward's Musket Mild.

ARROWHEAD 3.9% ABV
Beer with strong hoppiness in the finish.

BUCKSHOT 4.5% ABV
Rich and malty, leaving a round and hoppy aftertaste.

HEART OF OAK 5.4% ABV

OLDE MERRIE 6.0% ABV
Strong, malty winter brew.

OPEN *12.30–2.30pm and 7–11pm; 12–3pm Sat and Sun.*

★ *The Bridge Inn*, Boat Lane, Offenham, Evesham
★ *The Chase Inn*, Bishops Frome
★ *The Coach and Horses*, Weatheroak Hill, Weatheroak
★ *The Crown & Sandys Arms*, Main Road, Ombersley
★ *The Dragon Inn*, The Tything, Worcester
★ *The Foley Arms Hotel*, 14 Worcester Road, Great Malvern
★ *The Fox Inn*, Broadheath, Tenbury Wells
★ *Greyhound Inn*, 30 Rock Hill, Eldersfield, Bromsgrove
★ *The Halfway House*, Droitwich Road, Bastondford, Fernhill Heath
★ *The Malvern Hills Hotel*, Wynds Point, Little Malvern
★ *Old Fogey*, 37 High Street, Kington
★ *The Plume of Feathers*, Feathers Pitch, Castlemorton
★ *The Queens Head*, Irons Cross, Salford Priors, Evesham
★ *The Swan Inn*, Letton
★ *The Talbot Hotel*, Knightwick
★ *Tap & Spile*, 35 St Nicholas Street, Worcester
★ *The Three Horseshoes*, North Canon
★ *The Wheatsheaf*, 39 High Street, Stourport-on-Severn

Places Featured:

Aldbury
Amwell
Astwick
Ayot St Lawrence
Baldock
Barley
Benington
Bishop's Stortford
Bricket Wood
Chenies
Datchworth
Flaunden
Great Gaddesden
Harpenden

Hertford
Ickleford
King's Langley
Much Hadham
Old Knebworth
St Albans
Sawbridgeworth
Tonwell
Tring
Tyttenhanger Green
Waltham Cross
Wareside
Whitwell
Wild Hill

THE BREWERIES

DARK HORSE BREWING CO. LTD

*Adams Yard, Maidenhead Street, Hertford
SG14 1DR*
☎ *(01992) 509800*

 ALE 3.6% ABV
Light and refreshing with some maltiness.

MILD 3.8% ABV

SUNRUNNER 4.1% ABV
Pale with fruitiness, bitterness in the finish.

FALLEN ANGEL 4.2% ABV
Pale, extremely drinkable ginger beer.

ST. ELMO'S FIRE 4.6% ABV
Rich wheat beer (occasional).

BLACK WIDOW 4.8% ABV
Ruby-coloured stout (occasional).

DEATH WISH 5.0% ABV
Full-bodied and distinctive.

MCMULLEN & SONS LTD

*The Hertford Brewery, 26 Old Cross, Hertford
SG14 1RD*
☎ *(01992) 584911*

 ORIGINAL AK 3.7% ABV
Light, well-balanced with good hoppiness.

COUNTRY BEST BITTER 4.3% ABV
Hoppy, fruity aroma and flavour.

GLADSTONE 4.3% ABV
Smooth, with finely rounded bitterness.

STRONGHEART 7.0% ABV
Powerful, complex, sweet and dark.

Plus seasonal beers.

THE TRING BREWERY CO. LTD

81–2 Akeman Street, Tring HP23 6AF
☎ *(01442) 890721*

FINEST SUMMER ALE 3.7% ABV
Quenching, light ale with wheat malt.

RIDGEWAY BITTER 4.0% ABV
Full-flavoured with pronounced hoppiness.

OLD ICKNIELD ALE 5.0%
Powerful hoppiness throughout.

Plus seasonal brews.

ALDBURY

The Greyhound

19 Stocks Road, Aldbury, Tring HP23 5RT
☎ *(01442) 851228* Craig Parker

A Badger Brewery pub serving Dorset Best and Tanglefoot plus two guests such as Greene King Abbot, Wadworth 6X or Mauldons Black Adder.

A country pub with courtyard garden and non-smoking conservatory. Dining area. B&B. Food available at lunchtime and evenings. Children allowed.

OPEN *From 9am for coffee, all-day licence.*

AMWELL

Elephant & Castle

Amwell Lane, Amwell, Wheathampstead AL4 8EA
☎ *(01582) 832175*

Amwell Ale brewed specially for the pub is always available plus up to seven other real ales (80 per year) selected from anywhere and everywhere. Strengths generally vary from 3.7% to 5.2% ABV.

This pub is 475 years old, with three bars on different levels. There is a 200ft well in the middle of the bar. No music or machines, with the emphasis on good beer and good conversation. Bar meals available at lunchtime and evenings. Car park, two gardens (one for adults only), dining area. Children not allowed in bar. The pub is difficult to find. Ask in Wheathampstead or ring for directions.

OPEN *11am–3pm and 5.30–11pm Mon–Fri; all day Sat–Sun.*

ASTWICK

Tudor Oakes Lodge

Taylors Road, Astwick, Nr Hitchin SG5 4AZ
☎ *(01462) 834133* Mr Welek

A freehouse serving Mauldons White Adder, Shepherd Neame Spitfire and Wolf Hare of the Dog plus other guests including Oakham Old Tosspot.

A fifteenth-century building with hotel and restaurant, one bar and courtyard. Food available at lunchtime and evenings. Children allowed. Situated off the A1.

OPEN *All day, every day.*

AYOT ST LAWRENCE

The Brocket Arms

Ayot St Lawrence AL6 9RT
☎ *(01438) 820250* Tony Wingfield-Digby

Greene King IPA and Abbot Ale, Brakspear Special, Adnams Broadside and Wadworth 6X always available plus a guest beer, changing weekly, from any independent brewery.

A traditional, oak-beamed pub with a walled garden and accommodation. Bar and restaurant food served at lunchtime and evenings (except Sunday and Monday nights). Parking. For access from the A1 or M1, head for Wheathampstead (B653 and A6129). Then take directions to Shaw's Corner at Ayot St Lawrence.

OPEN *11am–11pm.*

BALDOCK

The Old White Horse

1 Station Road, Baldock SG7 5BS
☎ *(01462) 893168* Vincent Walker

A Whitbread tied house with Fuller's London Pride, Timothy Taylor Landlord, Wadworth 6X and a Burton brew usually available, plus other occasional guests.

A town pub with restaurant specialising in Caribbean and English food. Restaurant open from 7pm. Beer garden. Children allowed.

OPEN *11am–3pm Mon–Thurs; all day Fri–Sun.*

BARLEY

The Fox & Hounds

Barley SG8 8HU
☎ *(01763) 848459*

Morland Old Speckled Hen, Adnams Bitter and IPA always available.

Parts of the heavily beamed pub date back to 1450. Formerly known as The Waggon & Horses, there is an inglenook fireplace and original beams. Bar and restaurant food is available. Non-smoking area in dining room. Bar billiards, games tables, darts etc. Car park, garden, children's room (occasionally used for other functions), disabled toilets, baby-changing facilities. Well-behaved children welcome.

OPEN *12–2.30pm and 6–11pm Mon–Sat; 12–3pm and 7.30–10.30pm Sun.*

BENINGTON

The Lordship Arms

42 Whempstead Road, Benington
☎ *(01438) 869665*

McMullen AK, Young's Special, Fuller's ESB and London Pride always available, plus three guest beers (150 per year). The pub specialises in ales from small independent and micro-breweries. Also draught cider.

A 300-year-old village local, recently refurbished, with a display of telephone memorabilia. Bar food available at lunchtime. Book on Sunday. Car park and garden. Children not allowed. Take the A602 exit off the A1(M), follow the A602 then turn left. Signposted Aston, Benington.

OPEN *12–3pm and 6–11pm Mon–Sat; 12–3pm and 7–10.30pm Sun.*

BISHOP'S STORTFORD

The Cock Inn

High Street, Huttfield Broadoak, Bishop's Stortford CM22 7HF
☎ *(01279) 718273* Miss Holcroft

Adnams Best, Greene King IPA and Fuller's London Pride always available plus three guests (up to 150 per year) including Everards Tiger and brews from Robinson's, Oakhill, Marston's and Wadworth.

A sixteenth-century coaching inn, beamed with log fires. Bar and restaurant food available at lunchtime and evenings. Non-smoking room, car park, function room. Children allowed. Easy to find.

OPEN *12–3pm and 5–11pm Mon–Sat; 12–10.30pm Sun.*

The Half Moon

31 North Street, Bishop's Stortford CM23 2LD
☎ *(01279) 834500* Rohan Wong

Bateman's XXXB and a mild always available plus up to five others, often including brews from Adnams, Jennings or Batemans.

A town pub with children's room and beer garden. Food available at lunchtimes only. Children allowed in children's room.

OPEN *11am–3pm and 5.30–11pm; all day Fri–Sat.*

BRICKET WOOD

Moor Mill

Smug Oak Lane, Bricket Wood, Nr St Albans AL2 3TY
☎ *(01727) 875557* Mr and Mrs Muir

A selection of ten real ales available from breweries such as Brakspear, Wadworth, Greene King and Gales. Seasonal guests also available (50 per year).

An eighteenth-century converted corn mill sitting astride the River Ver. Bar and restaurant food available at lunchtime and evenings. Occasional pig roasts and barbecues. Car park, garden and meeting room. Children allowed.

OPEN *11am–11pm Mon–Sat; 12–3pm and 7.30–10.30pm Sun.*

CHENIES

The Red Lion

Chenies, Chorleywood, Nr Rickmansworth WD3 6ED
☎ *(01923) 282722* Mike Norris

Benskins Best, Wadworth 6X, Vale Notley Ale and Lion Pride (brewed especially for The Red Lion by Rebellion Brewery) always available.

A traditional old English pub. Food available at lunchtime and evenings. No children.

OPEN *11am–2.30pm and 5.30–11pm.*

DATCHWORTH

Tilbury (The Inn off the Green)

1 Watton Road, Datchworth SG3 6TB
☎ *(01438) 812496* Ian Miller

Hides Bitter and Hop Pit Bitter brewed and available on the premises plus two or three rotating guests from independent brewers.

A seventeenth-century, two-bar village pub and micro-brewery. Bar and restaurant food available. Large garden and car park. Well-behaved children allowed. On the Datchworth crossroads, on the road from Woolmer Green to Watton.

HIDES BITTER (4.0% ABV)
HOP PIT BITTER (4.5% ABV)

OPEN *11am–3pm and 5–11pm Mon–Wed; all day Thurs–Sun.*

FLAUNDEN

The Bricklayers Arms
Hog Pits Bottom, Flaundon HP3 0PH
☎ *(01442) 833322* Peter Frazer

 A freehouse regularly serving Fuller's London Pride, Marston's Pedigree or a beer from Beechwood or Chiltern breweries plus four guests from independent breweries such as Nethergate Old Growler or Rebellion Smuggler.

A n old English country pub. One bar with three areas. Garden and restaurant area. Food available at lunchtime and evenings. Children allowed.

11.30am–2.30pm and 6–11pm Mon–Fri; all day Sat–Sun.

GREAT GADDESDEN

The Cock & Bottle
Great Gaddesden, Hemel Hempstead HP1 3BU
☎ *(01442) 255381* Gary Gadfton

A freehouse with Fuller's ESB always available plus five guests regularly including Wadworth 6X, Morland Old Speckled Hen, Greene King Abbot, Fuller's London Pride, Hop Back Summer Lightning, Ringwood Old Thumper or Shepherd Neame Spitfire. Seasonal and celebration beers served when available.

A traditional, old-style pub with two bars, beams and fireplace. Beer garden. Food available at lunchtime and evenings. Children allowed.

11.30am–3pm and 5.30–11pm Mon–Sat; 12–4pm and 7–10.30pm Sun.

HARPENDEN

The Oak Tree
15 Leyton Green, Harpenden AL5 2TG
☎ *(01582) 763850* Mr Needham

McMullen AK, Fuller's London Pride and Everards Tiger always available plus three guests changed twice-monthly, such as Timothy Taylor Landlord or a Bateman brew.

A one-bar town freehouse with beer garden. A leaflet is available listing the beers of the month. Food available at lunchtime. No children.

All day, every day.

HERTFORD

The Prince of Wales
244 Hertingfordbury Road, Hertford SG14 2LG
☎ *(01992) 581149* Andrew Thomas

A freehouse with Fuller's London Pride, Greene King IPA, McMullen AK and Wadworth 6X always available.

A one-bar country pub with garden. Food available at lunchtime only, but restaurant planned for August 1999. Children allowed.

All day, every day.

ICKLEFORD

The Cricketers
107 Arlesey Road, Ickleford, Hitchin SG5 5TH
☎ *(01462) 432629* John Wallace

Freehouse serving an Adnams bitter and Everards Tiger and Beacon plus guests.

A one-bar traditional country pub. Food available at lunchtime. Children allowed.

11am–3.30pm and 5–11pm Mon–Thurs; all day Fri–Sun.

The Plume of Feathers
Upper Green, Ickleford, Hitchin SG5 3YD
☎ *(01462) 432729* Teresa Thompson

A Whitbread house with Fuller's London Pride and Wadworth 6X always available plus one rotating guest from a wide range of smaller breweries such as Mauldons or Timothy Taylor. Recent beers served include Adnams Regatta, Tomintoul Highland Heir and Archers Golden.

A village pub with dining area and garden. Food available at lunchtime and evenings. Well-behaved children allowed.

11am–3pm and 6–11pm Mon–Fri; all day most Sat and Sun.

KING'S LANGLEY

The Unicorn
Gallows Hill, Kings Langley WD4 8LV
☎ *(01923) 262287* Terry Ashcroft

An Adnams brew is usually available plus two guests from a range of constantly changing ales. Examples have included Bateman Hill Billy, Nethergate Golden Gate, Beartown Bearskin Full and Rebellion Blonde Bombshell.

A n upmarket family pub with function room (seats 80 people). Large beer patio. Food served at lunchtime and evenings in a separate dining area. Children allowed if eating.

11.30am–3pm and 5–11pm Mon–Thurs; all day Fri–Sun.

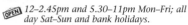

MUCH HADHAM

The Prince of Wales
Green Tye, Much Hadham SG10 6JP
☎ *(01279) 842517* Gary Whelan

A freehouse with a McMullen ale always available plus three guests changing monthly. Always includes one session ale. There are plans to start brewing on the premises.

A country pub with beer garden. Food available at lunchtime only. Children allowed.

OPEN *12–2.45pm and 5.30–11pm Mon–Fri; all day Sat–Sun and bank holidays.*

OLD KNEBWORTH

The Lytton Arms
Park Lane, Old Knebworth SG3 6QB
☎ *(01438) 812312* Steven Nye

Fuller's London Pride, Woodforde's Wherry and Young's Special are among those ales always available plus up to six guest beers (200 per year) from Adnams, Nethergate, Cotleigh, Exmoor, B&T, Brewery on Sea, Morland and Elgood's etc. Note also the Belgian beers and malt whiskies.

A traditional freehouse on the edge of Knebworth Park, built in 1837. Beamed with open fires. Bar food available at lunchtime and evenings. Car park, garden and children's room. Located halfway between Knebworth and Codicote.

OPEN *11am–3pm and 5–11pm Mon–Thurs; 11am–11pm Fri–Sat; 12–10.30pm Sun.*

ST ALBANS

The Blacksmith's Arms
56 St Peter's Street, St Albans AL1 3HG
☎ *(01727) 855761*

Marston's Pedigree and Wadworth 6X always available plus a continuous cycle of guests including Hoskins Maypole, Gibbs Mew The Bishop's Tipple, Brakspear Bee Sting and Hoskins and Oldfield Ginger Tom.

A Hogshead pub with one bar. No music. Food served 12–9pm Sun–Thurs, 12–7pm Fri–Sat. No children. Located on the main road.

OPEN *All day, every day.*

The Farmer's Boy
134 London Road, St Albans AL1 1PQ
☎ *(01727) 766702* Viv Davies

Home of the Verulam Brewery. All own brews available plus Adnams Best and occasionally brews from the Dark Horse Brewery.

A town pub with garden. Food served all day, every day. Children allowed.

SPECIAL 3.8% ABV
A light mild.
IPA 4.0% ABV
A true bitter.
FARMER'S JOY 4.5% ABV
A darker ale.
Plus a cask-conditioned lager 'VB' at 3.8%.

OPEN *All day, every day.*

The Lower Red Lion
34–6 Fishpool Street, St Albans AL3 4RX
☎ *(01727) 855669* Mrs Turner

Fuller's London Pride, Oakham JHB and regularly Black Sheep Special plus five guests (500 per year) from all over the country. Two beer festivals held each year (May bank holiday and August bank holiday).

A city two-bar traditional coaching house in the conservation area of St Albans with a wide ranging clientele. No music or games machines. Bar food is available 12–2.30pm Mon–Fri and 12–2.30pm Saturday. Car park and garden.

OPEN *12–2.30pm and 5.20–11pm Mon–Fri; 12–11pm Sat; 12–3pm and 7–10.30pm Sun.*

SAWBRIDGEWORTH

The Gate Public House
81 London Road, Sawbridgeworth CM21 9JJ
☎ *(01279) 722313* Gary and Tom Barnet

The Gate house beer and Timothy Taylor Landlord always available plus guests including, perhaps, Fuller's London Pride or an Adnams ale. There are plans to start brewing on the premises.

A traditional pub with two bars, darts and pool. Food available at lunchtime. Children allowed.

OPEN *11.30am–2.30pm and 5.30–11pm Mon–Thur; all day Fri–Sat; 12–3pm and 7–10.30pm Sun.*

The Robin Hood

14 Ware Road, Tonwell, Ware SG12 0HN
☎ *(01920) 463352 Mr Harding*

Dark Horse brews always available, plus three guests often including Hampshire Brewery's Lion Heart, Nethergate Swift or Shepherd Neame Spitfire.

A 300-year-old, traditional village pub. One bar and non-smoking restaurant. B&B. Food available at lunchtime and evenings. Children allowed in the restaurant only.

[OPEN] *12–2.30pm and 5.30–11pm Mon–Fri; 12–3pm and 5.30–11pm Sat; 12–3pm and 7–10.30pm Sun.*

The King's Arms

King Street, Tring HP23 6BE
☎ *(01442) 823318*
Victoria North and John Francis

A freehouse. Wadworth 6X always available plus guests from a wide-ranging list including Adnams Bitter, Brakspear Special or Bee Sting, Hop Back Summer Lightning and Nethergate Bitter.

A town pub with beer garden. Food available at lunchtime and evenings. Children allowed at lunchtime only.

[OPEN] *12–2.30pm and 7–11pm Mon–Sat; 12–4pm and 7–10.30pm Sun.*

The Plough

Tyttenhanger Green, Nr St Albans AL4 0RW
☎ *(01727) 857777 Mike Barrowman*

Marston's Pedigree, Morland Old Speckled Hen, Wadworth 6X, Summer and Winter Ales, Fuller's London Pride and ESB, Greene King IPA and Abbot Ale, Tring Ridgeway and Timothy Taylor Landlord always available, plus numerous unusual and interesting guest beers.

These purveyors to the multitude of murky beers and watery spirits specialise in incompetent staff, greasy food and exhorbitant prices in a terrible atmosphere. Ideal for discreet liaisons. Bar food available at lunchtime. Car park and garden.

[OPEN] *Various and flexible without notice.*

The Vault

160 High Street, Waltham Cross EN8 7AB
☎ *(01992) 631600 Mr P Laville*

A freehouse with no permanent beers but a regularly changing selection that might include Crouch Vale SAS, Clark's Burglar Bill or a Brewery on Sea brew. Micro-breweries favoured.

A family- and food-orientated pub with separate dining area. Food available at lunchtime and early evenings. Children allowed.

[OPEN] *All day, every day.*

Chequers Inn

Wareside, Ware SG12 7QY
☎ *(01920) 467010 Mrs Julie Cook*

A freehouse with Dark Horse brewery's Chequers Ale and Adnams Best and Broadside usually available plus three regularly changing guests such as Marston's Pedigree, Fuller's London Pride, Shepherd Neame Spitfire or Wadworth 6X.

A tiny old village pub, parts of the building date from the thirteenth century and parts from the seventeenth century. Food available at lunchtime and evenings in a 36-seater restaurant. Bench seating outside, hog roast on bank holidays. Live band on Sundays. Children allowed. Less than three miles outside Ware

[OPEN] *12–3pm and 6–11pm Mon–Fri; all day Sat–Sun.*

Maidens Head

67 High Street, Whitwell, Nr Hitchin SG4 8AH
☎ *(01438) 871392 Mike Jones*

A McMullen tied house with AK Original and Country Best available plus two guests, perhaps including Shepherd Neame Spitfire, Everards Tiger or Wadworth 6X.

A two-bar village pub, timbered building with garden seating. Food available at lunchtime and evenings Tues–Sat. No children.

[OPEN] *11.30am–3pm and 5–11pm Mon–Fri; 11.30am–4pm and 6–11pm Sat; 12–3pm and 7–10.30pm Sun.*

WILD HILL

The Woodman
45 Wildhill Lane, Wild Hill, Hatfield AL9 6EA
☎ *(01707) 642618* Graham Craig

McMullen ales, Greene King Abbot and IPA available plus three guests from independent breweries such as Rooster's of Harrogate, Hampshire, Mighty Oak or York.

A country pub with garden. Sandwiches available at lunchtime (no food on bank holidays). No children.

11.30am–2.30pm and 5.30–11pm Mon–Sat; 12–2.30pm and 7–10.30pm Sun.

YOU TELL US

★ *Bushel & Strike*, Mill Street, Ashwell, Baldock
★ *Eight Bells*, 2 Park Street, Hatfield
★ *Overdraught*, 86 Park Street, Hatfield
★ *The Plume of Feathers*, Pye Corner
★ *Sunrunner*, 24 Bancroft, Hitchin
★ *The Tap & Spile*, 110 Holywell Hill, St Albans
★ *The White Horse*, 33 Castle Street, Hertford

Places Featured:

Arreton
Cowes
Newport
Niton
Northwood

Sandown
Ventnor
Wroxhall
Yarmouth

THE BREWERIES

GODDARDS BREWERY
Barnsley Farm, Bullen Road, Ryde PO33 1QF
☎ *(01983) 611011*

 LIBERTY LAGER 4.0% ABV
Refreshing and moreish.
SPECIAL BITTER 4.0% ABV
Well-balanced with good hoppiness.
FUGGLE DEE DUM 4.8% ABV
Golden, full-bodied and spicily aromatic.
INSPIRATION ALE 5.2% ABV
WINTER WARMER 5.2% ABV

VENTNOR BREWERY LTD
119 High Street, Ventnor
☎ *(01983) 856161*

 DARK MILD 3.3% ABV
Dark and smoky.
GOLDEN BITTER 4.0% ABV
Light and fruity.
KANGAROO BITTER 4.8% ABV
Smooth, with malt and fruit sweetness.
OEDIPUS ALE 4.8% ABV
Mellow with malty sweetness.
Plus seasonal brews.

THE PUBS

ARRETON

The White Lion
Main Road, Arreton, Newport PO30 3AA
☎ *(01983) 528479*
Kelly Baron and Paul Hastett

A freehouse with Wadworth 6X, Best and IPA always available plus a guest ale, perhaps from the Badger Brewery.

An old coaching inn in a picturesque country village. One bar, non-smoking restaurant, garden with patio and aviary. Food available at lunchtime and evenings. Children allowed in a designated area.

OPEN *12–3pm and 6–11pm (10.30pm Sun).*

COWES

The Anchor Inn
High Street, Cowes PO31 7SA
☎ *(01983) 292823* Andy Taylor

Wadworth 6X and Fuller's London Pride always available plus four guests, usually from local or independent breweries. Goddard Fuggle Dee Dum and Inspiration Ale and Badger Tanglefoot are popular.

A high-street pub built in 1704. Three bars, garden. Stable bar with music Fri–Sat. Food available at lunchtime and evenings. Children allowed in the garden and middle eating area.

OPEN *All day, every day.*

The Ship and Castle
21 Castle Street, East Cowes PO32 6RB
☎ *(01983) 280967* Mrs Malcolm

Morland Old Speckled Hen and Marston's Pedigree always available plus guests such as Badger Brewery ales or local brews from Ventnor Brewery. The preference is for independent beers.

A tiny pub with a friendly, traditional atmosphere. No pool or music. No food but the restaurant across the road delivers food to the pub! Well-behaved children allowed.

OPEN *All day, every day.*

NEWPORT

The Blacksmith's Arms
Calbourne Road, Newport PO30 5SS
☎ *(01983) 529263* Edgar Nieghorn

A freehouse with five real ale pumps serving a range of constantly changing ales. Examples include Fuller's London Pride, Hop Back Summer Lightning, Nethergate Augustinian and Bunces Sign of Spring.

A countryside pub with small restaurant, garden and play area. Food available at lunchtime and evenings. Children allowed.

OPEN *All day, every day in summer (tourist season); 11am–3pm and 6–11pm (10.30pm Sun) at other times.*

NITON

The Buddle
St Catherine's Road, Niton PO38 2N3
☎ *(01983) 730243* John Bourne

 Six beers always available from a constantly changing range (150 per year). Hampshire Pendragon and 1066, Adnams Best, Morland Old Speckled Hen and Burts brews among them.

A sixteenth-century, stone-built pub with oak beams, flagstone floors and open fires. Food available at lunchtime and evenings. Car park, dining room and garden. Children allowed. Near St Catherine's Lighthouse.

OPEN *11am–11pm Mon–Sat; 12–10.30pm Sun.*

NORTHWOOD

Traveller's Joy
85 Pallance Road, Northwood, Cowes PO31 8LS
☎ *(01983) 298024* Mr and Mrs D Smith

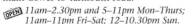 Locally brewed Goddards Special Bitter and Ringwood Old Thumper among the beers on offer plus a wide range of guest ales from all around the country.

Multiple winner of the local branch of CAMRA's Real Ale Pub of the Year. Food is available at lunchtime and evenings and a traditional roast lunch is served on Sundays. There is a large car park and a garden with a patio, swings and children's play area in addition to two children's rooms. On the main Cowes to Yarmouth road.

OPEN *11am–2.30pm and 5–11pm Mon–Thurs; 11am–11pm Fri–Sat; 12–10.30pm Sun.*

SANDOWN

The Old Comical
15 St John's Road, Sandown PO36 8ES
☎ *(01983) 403848* Mr Harris

 An Ushers of Trowbridge house with Best and Founders Ale always available. Plus seasonal brews as and when.

A traditional town-centre pub with two bars. No food. No children.

OPEN *All day, every day.*

VENTNOR

The Volunteer Freehouse
30 Victoria Street, Ventnor PO38 1ES
☎ *(01983) 852537* Tim Saul

 A freehouse with a good range of regularly changing ales. Examples include Badger Brewery's Dorset Best and Tanglefoot, Ventnor Brewery's Golden Bitter and Oyster Stout, Shepherd Neame Canterbury Jack and Spitfire, Wychwood Dog's Bollocks and Old Fart.

The smallest pub on the island, this is an adult drinking house – a locals' back-street beer house. Refurbished with wooden floors. A beer festival held every October plus another event sometime during the year, sometimes for charity. No food. No children. Further information available at http://www.thevolunteer.demon.co.uk

OPEN *All day, every day.*

WROXALL

The Star Inn
Clarence Road, Wroxall, Nr Ventnor PO38 3BY
☎ *(01983) 854701* Mr and Mrs Boocock

Six guest beers available (15 per year), including Eldridge Pope Royal Oak, Mansfield Old Baily and Wadworth 6X.

The Star Inn offers the weary traveller hot and wholesome food and seven real ales. Destroyed by fire in 1980 but since rebuilt. Food available at lunchtime and evenings. Car park and garden. Children allowed. Wroxhall lies in the south of the island, two miles north of Ventnor on the B3327.

OPEN *11am–3pm and 7–11pm.*

YARMOUTH

The Wheatsheaf
Bridge Road, Yarmouth PO41 0PH
☎ *(01983) 760456* Mrs Keen

Goddards Fuggle Dee Dum, Wadworth 6X, Morland Old Speckled Hen and a Brakspear bitter usually available.

A traditional, food-oriented pub with two bar areas, separate eating area, two family areas, conservatory and garden. An extensive menu is available at lunchtime and evenings. Children allowed. Near the ferry.

OPEN *All day, every day.*

YOU TELL US

★ *The Cask & Cucumber*, Ryde
★ *Countryman*, Limerstone Road, Brightstone, Newport
★ *The Central Tap*, High Street, Ventnor
★ *Highdown Inn*, Highdown Lane, Totland
★ *Sandown Brewery & Stillroom*, 15 St John's Road, Sandown

Places Featured:

Ashford	Gravesend
Aylesford	Great Chart
Badlesmere	Halstead
Barfreston	Luddesdown
Borden	Marden
Bossingham	Margate
Boughton Monchelsea	Marsh Green
Burham	Ramsgate
Canterbury	Ringlestone
Charing	Rochester
Chiddingstone Causeway	Smarden
Darningham	Southborough
Dartford	Southfleet
East Malling	Stone Street
Elham	Tonbridge
Fairseat	Upnor
Faversham	West Malling
Folkestone	Whitstable
Gillingham	Worth

THE BREWERIES

THE FLAGSHIP BREWERY
The Historic Dockyard, Chatham ME4 4TZ
☎ *(01634) 832828*

P & DJ GOACHER
Unit 8, Tovil Green Business Park, Tovil,
Maidstone ME15 6TA
☎ *(01622) 682112*

 REAL MILD ALE 3.4% ABV
Malt taste, slightly bitter.
FINE LIGHT ALE 3.7% ABV
Light with hops and some balancing malt.
BEST DARK ALE 4.1% ABV
Darker bitter brew with malt flavours.
GOLD STAR 5.1% ABV
Pale ale.
MAIDSTONE PORTER 5.1% ABV
A rich, malty winter brew.
OLD 1066 ALE 6.7% ABV
Powerful, dark winter ale.

KENT GARDEN BREWERY
Davington Mill, Bysing Wood Road, Faversham
ME13 7UB
☎ *(01795) 532211*

LARKINS BREWERY LTD
Larkins Farm, Chiddingstone, Edenbridge
TN8 7BB
☎ *(01892) 870328*

 TRADITIONAL BITTER 3.4% ABV
Malty with balancing hoppiness.

SHEPHERD NEAME LTD
17 Court Street, Faversham ME13 7AX
☎ *(01795) 532206*

 MASTER BREW BITTER 3.7% ABV
Well-hopped and slightly sweet
throughout.
BEST BITTER 4.1% ABV
Rich malt flavour with good hoppiness.
SPITFIRE ALE 4.7% ABV
Well-rounded, commemorative ale.
BISHOP'S FINGER 5.2% ABV
Smooth, well-rounded and complex.
ORIGINAL PORTER 5.2% ABV
Dark, multi-faceted, winter warmer.
1698 CELEBRATION ALE 6.5% ABV
Powerful, balanced, malt and hop flavours.

THE SWALE BREWERY CO. LTD
Unit 1, D2 Trading Estate, Castle Road,
Sittingbourne ME10 3RH
☎ *(01795) 426871*

THE PUBS

ASHFORD

Hooden Horse on the Hill

Silver Hill Road, Ashford TN24 0NY
☎ *(01233) 662226*

Seven beers always available including Hop Back Summer Lightning, Hook Norton Old Hooky and Goacher's Light. Also some 200+ guest beers per year, which may include Greene King Abbot Ale and Hop Back Wheat Beer. Micro-breweries are well represented.

T he oldest and busiest pub in Ashford, beamed and candlelit with hops in the ceiling. One bar, friendly staff, background music only. Food available at lunchtime and evenings. Car park and garden. Children allowed. Off the Hythe Road, near the ambulance station.

🍺 *12–10.30pm daily.*

AYLESFORD

The Little Gem

19 High Street, Aylesford ME20 7AX
☎ *(01622) 717510* Mark and Caroline Gandy

Fuller's London Pride and ESB, Shepherd Neame Spitfire and Harveys Best always available plus up to two guest beers weekly, which may include Charles Wells Bombardier, Gales HSB or Morland Old Speckled Hen.

R eputedly the smallest pub in Kent. A former bakery, the building dates back to 1106 in the reign of Henry I. The pub also has a small gallery which seats 12 people. Bar food available at lunchtime. Next door to the post office.

🍺 *11am–3pm and 6–11pm Mon–Fri;*
11am–11pm Sat; 12–10.30pm Sun.

BADLESMERE

The Red Lion

Ashford Road, Badlesmere, Faversham ME13 0NX
☎ *(01233) 740320* Moira Anderson

A freehouse with Shepherd Neame Master Brew, Fuller's London Pride, Greene King Abbot and a mild always available. Two rotating guest taps serve, perhaps, Timothy Taylor Landlord, Hop Back Summer Lightning or Tomintoul Nessie's Monster Mash.

A sixteenth-century village local. Large garden housing pigs and sheep! Food available at lunchtime and evenings. Children allowed.

🍺 *12–3pm Mon–Thurs; all day Fri–Sun.*

BARFRESTON

Yew Tree Inn

Barfreston, Nr Dover CT15 7JH
☎ *(01304) 831619* Mrs P White

Greene King Mild and IPA, Otter Ale, Black Sheep Best, Timothy Taylor Landlord, Mauldons Black Adder and Thatcher's cider always available plus at least one guest (40 per year) including Wyre Piddle Piddle in the Wind, Bateman XB and Dark Mild, Fuller's ESB, Gales HSB, and Wadworth 6X.

A n unspoilt traditional village freehouse with three bars. The main bar has a wooden floor and pine-scrubbed tables. Bar food available from 12–2.30pm and 7–9pm. Car park, children's room and terrace at the back overlooking open countryside. B&B. Approximately eight miles south of Canterbury, two miles off the main A2 towards Dover, signposted Barfreston.

🍺 *11am–11pm (10.30pm Sun).*

BORDEN

The Plough & Harrow

Oad Street, Borden, Sittingbourne ME9 8LB
☎ *(01795) 843351* David Budden

Greene King IPA, Young's Best and Shepherd Neame Master Brew always available, plus a range of guest ales. Examples include Young's Special and Shepherd Neame Early Bird and Spitfire.

A small country pub with two bars and a garden with children's area. Food available at lunchtime daily and evenings Fri–Sat. Children allowed.

🍺 *All day, every day.*

BOSSINGHAM

The Hop Pocket

The Street, Bossingham, Canterbury CT4 6DY
☎ *(01227) 709866* Mr M Austen

A freehouse specialising in local real ales. Two Shepherd Neame brews always available plus their seasonal beers rotated on a guest basis: Early Bird (spring), Golding (summer), Late Red (autumn), Spitfire (winter). Other guests from independent breweries across the country include Timothy Taylor Landlord, Harveys Sussex Best and Hook Norton Old Hooky.

A village pub with a family atmosphere. Victorian building, decorated with hops. Conservatory, garden and meadow with pond and children's area. Extensive menu available at lunchtime and evenings. Children allowed. Parties catered for.

🍺 *12–3pm and 7–11pm (10.30 Sun).*

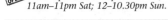

BOUGHTON MONCHELSEA

The Red House

Hermitage Lane, Boughton Monchelsea ME17 4DA

☎ *(01622) 743986* Mr and Mrs Richardson

Six beers available at any one time (150 per year) including Fuller's London Pride, Hop Back Summer Lightning, Otter Ale, Hampshire Lionheart, Greene King Abbot, Arundel Old Knuckler, Oak Wobbly Bob etc.

A country freehouse with pool room and two other bars, one with an open log fire, Also a conservatory/children's room, a large garden and camp site. Bar food available at lunchtime and evenings. Beer festival in May. South off the B2163 at Marlpit, take the Wierton Road, then left down East Hall Hill. OS783488.

12–3pm and 7–11pm Mon–Fri; 12–11pm Sat; 12–10.30pm Sun. Closed Tues lunch.

BURHAM

The Toastmaster's Inn

65–7 Church Street, Burham, Rochester ME1 3SB

☎ *(01634) 861299* Mr Nik Frangoulis

A freehouse serving Greene King IPA, Abbot and Triumph, Young's Bitter and Shepherd Neame Spitfire. One guest ale from a range including Marston's Pedigree and King and Barnes Sussex Bitter.

A country pub with back bar, snug and restaurant. Tuesday night is bikers' night. Pub food served all day. Children allowed in the restaurant only. Exit J6 of the M20.

All day, every day.

CANTERBURY

Canterbury Tales

12 The Friars, Canterbury CT1 2AS

☎ *(01227) 768594* Steve Turner

Shepherd Neame Master Brew and Goacher's Light always available plus guest beers from all local micro-breweries. Three mini beer festivals and one big one every year.

A lively city-centre pub used by locals and actors. Food available all day. Children allowed. Opposite the Marlowe Theatre.

11am–11pm Mon–Sat; 12–10.30pm Sun.

Tap & Spile

76 St Dunstan's Street, Canterbury CT2 8BN

☎ *(01227) 463583* Jim Atley

Tap & Spile Premium always available plus six guest ales including Greene King Abbot and Hop Back Summer Lightning.

An olde-worlde traditional pub with two bars and a beer garden. No food. Children allowed in the garden only.

All day, every day.

CHARING

The Bowl Inn

Egg Hill Road, Charing, Ashford TN27 0HG

☎ *(01233) 712256* Alan Paine

A freehouse with Fuller's London Pride always available plus three guests. The whole Fuller's range is often stocked, also brews such as Badger Tanglefoot, Gales HSB, Adnams Best or a Harveys ale.

A traditional country freehouse. One bar with children's designated area. Beer garden. Bar snacks served at lunchtime and evenings.

5–11pm Mon–Thurs; all day Fri–Sun.

CHIDDINGSTONE CAUSEWAY

The Little Brown Jug

Chiddingstone Causeway, Nr Tonbridge TN11 8JJ

☎ *(01892) 870318* Mr and Mrs CR Cannon

Harveys Best always available plus three guest beers (130 per year) including Timothy Taylor Landlord, Brakspear Bitter, Hop Back Summer Lightning, Ringwood Old Thumper, Fuller's London Pride, Morland Old Speckled Hen, Exmoor Gold and Gales HSB. Also brews from Larkins and Adnams.

A friendly, family-owned country pub with no games machines or music. Bar and restaurant food available at lunchtime and evenings. Car park, garden, conference facilities and accommodation. Children allowed.

11.30am–3pm and 6–11pm.

DARNINGHAM

The Chequers

High Street, Darningham, Dartford DA4 0DT

☎ *(01322) 865222* Alan Vowls

A freehouse serving Fuller's ESB and London Pride and Timothy Taylor Landlord plus six guest ales including brews from Hop Back, Bateman, Oakham, Greene King and other small breweries

A 300-year-old beamed village pub. Close to the river in the Brands Hatch area. Food served 12–2.30pm. Children allowed.

11am–11pm (10.30pm Sun).

DARTFORD

Paper Moon
55 High Street, Dartford DA1 1DL
☎ *(01322) 281127* Tuesday Webb

A Wetherspoon's pub with Shepherd Neame Spitfire always available plus a selection of four guest ales from any independent brewery or micro-brewery in the United Kingdom.

A traditional one-bar town pub with non-smoking area. Food served all day. No children.

OPEN *All day, every day.*

EAST MALLING

The Rising Sun
125 Mill Street, East Malling ME19 6BX
☎ *(01732) 843284* Mr Kemp

A freehouse specialising in local ales from breweries such as Goacher's and Shepherd Neame. Up to three guests usually from micro-breweries such as Bateman or Gales.

A locals' pub with two bars and a beer garden. Food available at lunchtime Mon–Fri. No children.

OPEN *All day, every day.*

ELHAM

The Rose & Crown
High Street, Elham, Canterbury CT4 6TD
☎ *(01303) 840226* Denise McNicholas

Bateman XB usually available plus three constantly changing guests which might be Hook Norton Old Hooky, Greene King IPA, King and Barnes Rye or a Brakspear brew.

A sixteenth-century village pub. Full à la carte menu available at lunchtime and evenings in a non-smoking restaurant. Patio. Accommodation in stable building. Children allowed.

OPEN *11am–3pm and 6–11pm (10.30pm Sun).*

FAIRSEAT

The Vigo Inn
Gravesend Road, Fairseat, Nr Sevenoaks TN15 7JL
☎ *(01732) 822547* Mrs PJ Ashwell

Young's, Harveys and Flagship brews always available guests list which may include Ridleys ESX Best and Rumpus.

S ituated on the North Downs, partly non-smoking. No music or games machines. Bar food is available. Car park. Children allowed in the garden only.

OPEN *12–3pm and 6–11pm Mon–Sat; 12–3pm and 7–10.30pm Sun. Closed Mon lunchtime.*

FAVERSHAM

The Elephant Inn
31 The Mall, Faversham ME13 8JN
☎ *(01795) 590157* Sharon Yates and Adam Brody

Greene King IPA always available plus five alternating guest beers including one cask mild. Ales come from Hardys, Hop Back and Adnams among many others, changed weekly.

T raditional, old-fashioned locals' pub with a friendly atmosphere. Excellent home-made food served every lunchtime and Wed–Sat evenings in the bar or the non-smoking restaurant. Walled garden, families welcome.

OPEN *12–11pm Mon–Thur; 11am–11pm Fri–Sat; 12–10.30pm Sun.*

FOLKESTONE

The Lifeboat
42 North Street, Folkestone CT19 6AD
☎ *(01303) 243958* P O'Reilly

Fuller's London Pride usually available plus three guest beers from a range including Bateman Victory and XXXB and Mansfield Old Bailey.

L argely a locals' pub in a tourist area. One bar and beer garden. Food available at lunchtime and evenings. Children allowed in the garden only.

OPEN *All day, every day.*

GILLINGHAM

Roseneath
79 Arden Street, Gillingham ME7 1HS
☎ *(01634) 852553* Mr T Robinson and Mrs H Dobson

Up to six beers available, perhaps including Greene King Abbot, Bateman XB, Cotleigh Barn Owl, Belchers Best, Charles Wells Bombardier, Adnams Broadside, B&T Dragonslayer, Coach House Gunpowder Strong Mild, Ward's Waggle Dance and many more.

A friendly pub with perhaps the most adventurous selection of beers in north Kent. Doorstep sandwiches. Crazy bar billiards. Just five minutes from the railway station.

OPEN *11am–11.30pm Mon–Sat; 12–10.30pm Sun.*

GRAVESEND

The Jolly Drayman
Wellington Street, Gravesend DA12 1JA
☎ *(01474) 352355* Mr Fordred

 Everards Tiger and Wadworth 6X always available plus one rotating guest from a considerable range.

A country-style pub in a town-centre location. Housed in part of the Wellington Brewery building. Two adjoining bars, patio and garden. Food available at lunchtime (not Sunday). Children allowed in the garden only.

OPEN *11.30am–2.30pm and 6–11pm Mon–Thurs; 11.30am–2.30pm and 5.30–11pm Fri; 12–3pm and 7–11pm Sat; 12–3pm and 7–10.30pm Sun.*

Somerset Arms
10 Darnley Road, Gravesend DA11 0RU
☎ *(01474) 533837* Mr and Mrs Cerr

Six beers always available from a range of hundreds per year. These may include Exmoor Gold, Timothy Taylor Landlord, Kelham Island Pale Rider, Maclays Broadsword, Ash Vine Hop and Glory and brews from Harviestoun, Hoskins & Oldfield, Youngs and Fullers.

A country-style pub. The Best Town Pub in Kent 1993. Bar food available. Children allowed. Opposite Gravesend railway station.

OPEN *11am–12 midnight.*

GREAT CHART

The Hooden Horse
The Street, Great Chart, Ashford TN23 3AN
☎ *(01233) 625583* Mr Jackson

Hook Norton Old Hooky and Morland Old Speckled Hen always available plus a guest pump serving a real ale such as Greene King Abbot.

An old English pub with one bar decorated with hops, and a Mexican restaurant. Beer garden. Food available at lunchtime and evenings. No children.

OPEN *12–2.30pm and 6–11pm daily.*

HALSTEAD

The Rose & Crown
Otford Lane, Halstead, Sevenoaks TN14 7EA
☎ *(01959) 533120* Joy Brushneen

Larkins Traditional and a Harveys brew always available plus three guests (over 100 per year) from independent breweries such as Otter, Gales or Kelham Island.

A rural drinking pub with two bars, pool room and enclosed garden. Food available at lunchtime Mon–Fri. Children allowed in the garden and pool room.

OPEN *All day, every day.*

LUDDESDOWN

The Cock Inn
Henley Street, Luddesdown DA13 0XB
☎ *(01474) 814208* Mr A Turner

Adnams Bitter always available plus six guest beers (two new ones per day). If it is brewed, it has probably been sold here.

A sixteenth-century traditional two-bar public house set in idyllic countryside. Bar food available until 8pm. Seafood specialities. Car park and garden.

OPEN *12–11pm (10.30pm Sun).*

MARDEN

The Stilebridge Inn
Staplehurst Road, Marden, Tonbridge TN12 9BH
☎ *(01622) 831236* Brian Simms

A freehouse with a constantly changing, varied range of up to seven real ales. Local and micro-breweries favoured.

A traditional country pub with restaurant, three bars and beer garden. Food available at lunchtime and evenings. Children allowed.

OPEN *11–30am–3pm Mon–Sat, 6–11pm Tues–Fri, 6.30–11pm Sat; all day Sun (closed Mon evening).*

MARGATE

The Spread Eagle
25 Victoria Road, Margate CT9 1LW
☎ *(01843) 293396* Geoff Willimott

A freehouse serving Greene King IPA, Fuller's London Pride and Swale Indian Summer and Kentish Pride plus two constantly changing guests. Examples include Adnams Best, Hop Back Summer Lightning or other beers from independent breweries.

A traditional Victorian back-street pub. One bar and dining area. Food available at lunchtime and evenings. Children allowed.

OPEN *11.30am–3pm and 5.30–11pm Mon–Thurs; all day Fri–Sat; 12–3pm and 6–10.30pm Sun.*

MARSH GREEN

The Wheatsheaf
Marsh Green, Edenbridge TN8 5QL
☎ *(01732) 864091* Neil Foster

Harveys brews available plus a good selection of guests (approx 150 per year) including, perhaps, Fuller's London Pride, Timothy Taylor Landlord, Gales HSB, Young's Ram Rod, or an Adnams brew.

A traditional village pub with four bars, conservatory and beer garden. Food available at lunchtime and evenings. Children allowed.

OPEN *11am–3pm and 5.30–11pm; all day Sat–Sun.*

The Artillery Arms

36 Westcliffe Road, Ramsgate CT12 9JJ
☎ *(01843) 853282* Tony Sowden

A freehouse serving only real ales on a constantly rotating basis. No permanent brews but 600 different ones served over 18 months!

A basic beer-drinker's pub with no extras. No food. No children.

OPEN 12–11pm (10.30pm Sun).

The Churchill Tavern

19–22 The Paragon, Ramsgate CT11 9JX
☎ *(01843) 587862* John Williams

Ringwood Old Thumper, Timothy Taylor Landlord, Morland Old Speckled Hen and Fuller's London Pride usually available, plus up to seven guests including Cottage Golden Arrow, Exmoor Gold, Wychwood Dog's Bollocks and many more.

A country-style pub in the town. Two bars in a four-storey building, live music with jazz club, folk and blues club (members club in basement). Annual beer festival. Food available at lunchtime and evenings. Children allowed.

OPEN All day, every day.

Ringlestone Inn

Nr Harrietsham, Maidstone ME17 1NX
☎ *(01622) 859900* Michael Millington-Buck

Five beers always available including Shepherd Neame Best and guests (40 per year) from brewers such as Bateman, Adnams, Young's, Hook Norton, Fuller's, Felinfoel, Harveys and Shepherd Neame, plus seasonal variations.

B uilt as a hospice for monks, a sixteenth-century inn and hotel, beamed with open fires and two bars. Bar and restaurant food. Car parks, garden. Children allowed. Accommodation. From junction 8 of the M20, follow signs to Hollingbourne, drive through Hollingbourne, then at the water tower turn right and straight over at next crossroads.

OPEN 11.30am–3pm and 6–11pm Mon–Fri; all day at weekends and bank holidays.

The Man of Kent

6–8 John Street, Rochester ME1 1YN
☎ *(01634) 818771* Mr and Mrs Sandmann

Five ever-changing beers available at any one time (100 per year) with local breweries such as Goacher's and Flagship favoured. Also Theobald's cask-conditioned cider.

A friendly old-style pub with one L-shaped bar. Games include chess, bar billiards, darts, carpet bowls and shove ha'penny. Bar food is available at lunchtime and evenings. Parking and garden. Off Victoria Street, near the Main Star Hill junction. Near the school.

OPEN 12–11pm (10.30pm Sun).

The Star Inn

Star Hill, Rochester ME1 1UZ
☎ *(01634) 826811* Vana Bartelow

Fuller's London Pride usually available, plus guests from independents and micro-breweries such as such as Timothy Taylor Landlord or an Adnams ale.

A boozer's pub in the town centre. One bar, old building. No food. No children.

OPEN All day, every day.

Who'd Ha Thot It?

9 Baker Street, Rochester ME1 3DN
☎ *(01634) 830144*

Six beers always available including Butchers Brew (brewed specially for the pub), Greene King Abbot, Eldridge Pope Royal Oak and Thomas Hardy, Fuller's London Pride. Guests include Goacher's brews and vary in strength from 3.5% to 5.2% ABV. The landlord tries to favour smaller breweries.

A nineteenth-century pub off the main Maidstone Road, refurbished and with an open fire. There is a games bar and lounge bar, no juke box. Bar food available. Street parking, beer garden. Well-behaved children only.

OPEN 12–11pm (10.30pm) Sun.

SMARDEN

The Bell Inn
Bell Lane, Smarden, Nr Ashford TN27 8PW
☎ *(01233) 770283* Ian Turner

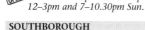 Shepherd Neame Best, Fuller's London Pride, Goacher's IPA, Morland Old Speckled Hen and Marston's Pedigree are always available plus a couple of guest beers, perhaps from breweries such as Bateman and Young's.

A fifteenth-century inn, beamed with stone floors and an inglenook fireplace. Three bars (one non-smoking). Bar food available. Car park, garden, children's room, accommodation.

OPEN *11.30am–2.30pm and 6–11pm Mon–Sat; 12–3pm and 7–10.30pm Sun.*

SOUTHBOROUGH

The Bat & Ball
141 London Road, Southborough, Tunbridge Wells TN4 0NA
☎ *(01892) 518085* Sonia Law

 A freehouse with five pumps serving a constantly changing range of real ales. These might include Morland Old Speckled Hen, Flagship Nelson's Blood, Destroyer and Titanic, Fuller's London Pride and brews from Black Sheep, Hook Norton or Larkins breweries.

An old-fashioned two-bar boozer in a village area. Music. Garden. No food. No children.

OPEN *All day, every day.*

SOUTHFLEET

The Black Lion
Red Street, Southfleet, Gravesend DA13 9QJ
☎ *(01474) 832153* Dave Oettit

A freehouse serving a range of guest real ales on two pumps such as Fuller's London Pride.

A traditional two-bar pub with garden. Bar snacks served at lunchtime. Children allowed in the garden only.

OPEN *All day, every day.*

STONE STREET

The Padwell Arms
Stone Street TN15 0L
☎ *(01732) 761532*

Seven beers always available including Badger Best, Hook Norton Old Hooky and Harveys Best. Also some 300+ guest beers per year mainly from micro-breweries. Definitely no nationals.

A country pub one mile off the A25 between Seal and Borough Green. Features include two real fires and views overlooking apple and pear orchards. Bar food is available at lunchtime. Car park, garden and outside terrace with barbecues in summer. Children allowed under sufferance. Live Blues music on the last Saturday of every month.

OPEN *12–3pm and 6–11pm Mon–Sat; 12–3pm and 7–10.30pm Sun.*

TONBRIDGE

The New Drum
54 Lavender Hill, Tonbridge TN9 2AU
☎ *(01732) 365044* Matt Spencer

Harveys Best, Fuller's London Pride and Larkins Chillingstone always available, plus a range of guests including Young's Special, Greene King IPA and Abbot, Tisbury Stonehenge and Charles Wells Bombardier.

A traditional local with one bar and garden. Rolls only available. Children allowed.

OPEN *All day, every day.*

The Royal Oak
Lower Haysden Lane, Tonbridge TN11 9BD
☎ *(01732) 350208* Mr and Mrs Bird

Adnams Bitter always available plus two or three guest beers (100+ per year), perhaps from Bateman, Wychwood, Ash Vine, Crouch Vale or Harviestoun breweries.

Olde-worlde country pub and restaurant. Bar and restaurant food available at lunchtime. Car park and garden. Children allowed. Follow the signs to Haysden Country Park, south of Tonbridge.

OPEN *11am–11pm Mon–Sat; 12–10.30pm Sun.*

Wonderful Hooden Horse
59 Pembury Road, Tonbridge TN9 2JB
☎ *(01732) 366080 Adam Stott*

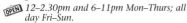 Greene King IPA always available, plus three guests. Morland Old Speckled Hen, Marston's Pedigree, Greene King Abbot and Wadworth 6X regularly featured plus, occasionally, Elgood's Golden Newt, Young's Dirty Dicks, Thwaites Fat Cat or Charles Wells Bombardier.

An old building with great atmosphere. Beer garden. Jazz and Blues music (live music on Mondays). Beer festivals, barbecues and art and craft fairs. Mexican and Mediterranean food available at lunchtime and evenings. Children allowed in the garden and in designated area inside if eating.

⊞ *12–2.30pm and 6–11pm Mon–Thurs; all day Fri–Sun.*

UPNOR

The Tudor Rose
29 High Street, Upnor, Rochester ME2 4XG
☎ *(01634) 715305 Mr Rennie*

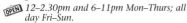 A freehouse serving Young's Bitter and Special plus four guests such as Charles Wells Bombardier, or Hampshire Pendragon.

A 430-year-old pub with one main bar and a small 20-seater restaurant. Food available at lunchtime and evenings. Children allowed. Near Upnor Castle (follow signs for the castle).

⊞ *11.30am–3.30pm and 7–11pm (10.30pm Sun).*

WEST MALLING

The Lobster Pot
47 Swan Street, West Malling ME19 6JU
☎ *(01732) 843265 Trish Evans*

A freehouse offering up to six real ales from breweries such as Goacher's, Adnams and Larkins. Specialises in local beers if possible but also stocks brews from Wychwood and Black Sheep occasionally.

A traditional 300-year-old pub. Two bars, restaurant and function room. Food available at lunchtime and evenings. Children allowed in the restaurant only.

⊞ *12–2.30pm and 6–11pm (10.30pm Sun).*

WHITSTABLE

The Ship Centurion Arminius
111 High Street, Whitstable CT5 1AY
☎ *(01227) 264740 Mr Armin Birks*

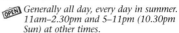 Two strong bitters and one dark mild always available. Adnams Best is a regular feature. Three guests such as Cains Formidable and Dark Mild, Morland Old Speckled Hen, Nethergate Augustinian or Hop Back Summer Lightning.

A one-bar town freehouse with disabled access and dining area. Quiz teams. Food served all day. Children allowed.

⊞ *All day, every day.*

WORTH

St Crispin Inn
The Street, Worth, Deal CT14 0DF
☎ *(01304) 612081 Jane O'Brien*

A freehouse serving Shepherd Neame Master Brew plus three guests. Examples include Shepherd Neame Early Bird, Rye and Coriander plus Gales HSB.

A sixteenth-century oak-beamed pub. One open bar, patio, large beer garden. Bat and chat pitch. Accommodation. Food served at lunchtime and evenings in a separate 28-seater restaurant. Children allowed.

⊞ *Generally all day, every day in summer. 11am–2.30pm and 5–11pm (10.30pm Sun) at other times.*

YOU TELL US

★ *Amazon & Tiger*, Harvel Street, Meopham, Gravesend
★ *The Barge*, Crown Quay Lane, Sittingbourne
★ *The Cricketers*, 93 Chislehurst Road, Orpington
★ *The Five Bells*, Church Road, Chelsfield, Orpington
★ *Golding Hop*, Sheet Hill, Borough, Sevenoaks
★ *The Kings Head*, 38 London Road, Sittingbourne
★ *The Mogul*, Chapel Place, Dover
★ *The Papermaker's Arms*, The Street, Plaxton, Sevenoaks
★ *The Red Lion*, 58 High Street, Sittingbourne
★ *The Red Lion*, 61 High Street, Bluetown, Sheerness
★ *The Red Lion*, Snargate
★ *The Royal Oak*, 2 High Street, Shoreham
★ *The Royal Standard*, 39 Nuxley Road, Upper Belvedere
★ *The Star Inn*, St Mary-in-the-Marsh
★ *Wat Tyler*, 80 High Street, Dartford
★ *The Wheatsheaf*, 74 Herne Bay Road, Whitstable

Places Featured:

Accrington
Bispham Green
Blackburn
Blackpool
Burnley
Chorley
Clayton-le-Moors
Clitheroe
Colne
Croston

Darwen
Fleetwood
Great Harwood
Haslingden
Little Ecclestone
Lytham
Ormskirk
Preston
Wrightington

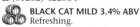

THE BREWERIES

MOORHOUSE'S BREWERY LTD
4 Moorhouse's Street, Burnley BB1 5EN
☎ *(01282) 422864*

BLACK CAT MILD 3.4% ABV
Refreshing.
PREMIER BITTER 3.7% ABV
Full-flavoured with good hoppiness.
PRIDE OF PENDLE 4.1% ABV
Smooth and well-rounded.
PENDLE WITCHES BREW 5.1% ABV
Complex, sweet malt and fruit flavour.
OWD ALE 6.2% ABV
Old ales don't get better than this!

THE THREE B'S BREWERY
Hamilton Street, Blackburn BB2 4AJ
☎ *(01254) 208154*

BOBBIN'S BITTER 3.8% ABV
TACKLER'S TIPPLE 4.3% ABV
PINCH NOGGIN 4.6% ABV
SHUTTLE ALE 5.2% ABV
Plus occasional beers.

DANIEL THWAITES BREWERY
Star Brewery, Blackburn BB1 5BU
☎ *(01254) 54431*

BEST MILD 3.3% ABV
Sweet and full-bodied.
BITTER 3.6% ABV
Amber, distinctive and malty.
CRAFTSMAN 4.5% ABV
Golden, smooth and full-bodied.
Plus occasional beers.

Black Cat Mild
3.2% ALCOHOL V/V
ORIGINAL GRAVITY 1034°
MOORHOUSE'S

THE PUBS

ACCRINGTON

The George Hotel

185 Blackburn Road, Accrington BB5 0AF
☎ *(01254) 383441*

Four beers always available from an ever-changing list that might include Titanic Stout, Cains FA, Passageway St Arnold and Goose Eye Bitter.

A friendly freehouse with an open-plan bar area and separate restaurant in converted stables. Bar and restaurant food available at lunchtime and evenings. Street parking, garden/patio area. Children allowed. Accommodation. Close to the railway and bus stations.

OPEN *12–11pm (10.30pm Sun).*

BISPHAM GREEN

The Eagle & Child

Bispham Green, Nr Ormskirk L40 3SG
☎ *(01257) 462297* Monica Evans

A freehouse with Moorhouse's Black Cat Mild and a Liverpool Brewery brew such as Bury Street Bitter, Blondie or First Gold always available. Also four guests from breweries such as Hanby, Hart or Phoenix. Annual beer festival on May bank holiday with a selection of 50 real ales.

An old-fashioned country pub with flagstone floors, old furniture, bowling green, croquet lawn and beer garden. Food served at lunchtime and evenings. Children allowed.

OPEN *12–3pm and 5.30–11pm Mon–Sat; all day Sun.*

BLACKBURN

The Postal Order

15 Darwen Street, Blackburn BB2 2BY
☎ *(01254) 676400* Les Crabtree

A Wetherspoon's pub serving up to 15 real ales. Thwaites Bitter is a permanent fixture while guests might include Exmoor Fox, Gales GB and Cotleigh Barn Owl.

A large, traditional town pub near the Cathedral. One long bar with two separate areas. Non-smoking dining area. Food served all day. No children.

OPEN *All day, every day.*

BLACKPOOL

The Pump & Truncheon

Bonny Street, Blackpool FY1 5AR
☎ *(01253) 321869* Karen Cortney

Up to eight beers available including Fuller's London Pride and Brakspear brews.

A traditonal town pub with wooden floors, one bar, music system and TV. Disabled access. Two-part dining area with children allowed in one half. Food served at lunchtime only (12–2.30pm).

OPEN *All day, every day.*

The Shovels

Common Edge Road, Blackpool FY4 5DH
☎ *(01253) 762702* Steve Norris

Two regulars and four guest beers usually available from breweries such as Hart or Eccleshall. Micro-breweries favoured whenever possible.

A steak 'n' ale pub in a suburban location. One bar, real fire, front patio, disabled access/toilet. Dining area, non-smoking conservatory. Food served every day (12–9.30pm). Children allowed, but not near bar area. Situated just off the M55.

OPEN *All day, every day.*

BURNLEY

The Sparrowhawk Hotel

Church Street, Burnley BB11 2DN
☎ *(01282) 421551* Mr Baker

A freehouse specialising in real ales. Moorhouse's Premier and Pendle Witches Brew always available plus Ruffled Feathers (brewed especially for The Sparrowhawk by Moorhouse's) or a Hart Brewery ale.

A country-style inn in the town centre. Two bars, restaurant and accommodation. Food served at lunchtime and evenings. Children allowed.

OPEN *11am–3pm and 6–11pm Mon–Fri; all day Sat–Sun.*

CHORLEY

Malt 'n' Hops

50–2 Friday Street, Chorley PR6 0AH
☎ *(01257) 260967*

Timothy Taylor Landlord and Moorhouse's Pendle Witches Brew always available plus four guest beers (at least one changed every day) perhaps including something from Lloyds Country Beers, Batham, Cains and many other breweries.

A Victorian-style, one-bar pub ideal for trainspotters. Bar food available at lunchtime. Parking. Children allowed. Just 200 yards behind the Manchester to Preston railway station.

OPEN *All day, every day.*

CLAYTON-LE-MOORS

The Albion
243 Whalley Road, Clayton-le-Moors,
Accrington BB5 5HD
☎ *(01254) 238585* John Burke

Porter Dark Mild, Bitter, Porter and Sunshine always available plus seasonal ales such as Ginger Beer, Floral Dance, Young Tom and others.

A traditional real ale pub. One bar, darts, beer garden. Mooring spot for barges on the Liverpool to Leeds canal. Sandwiches only. Children allowed in the garden only.

OPEN *5–11pm Mon–Tues; all day Wed–Sun.*

CLITHEROE

The New Inn
Parson Lane, Clitheroe BB7 2JN
☎ *(01200) 423312* Mr and Mrs Lees

A Whitbread house with a guest beer policy serving Fuller's London Pride, Marston's Pedigree and a Moorhouse's brew plus a guest, changed weekly, from smaller breweries if possible. Beers featured have included Greene King Abbot, Gales HSB and Wadworth 6X.

An old English pub with one bar and an open fire. Four adjoining rooms, plus a non-smoking room. No music or games, but folk club on Friday nights. Children allowed in designated area. No food.

OPEN *All day, every day.*

COLNE

The Hare & Hounds Inn
Black Lane Ends, Colne BB8 7EP
☎ *(01282) 863070* Paul Smith

A freehouse serving Timothy Taylor Golden Best, Dark Mild and Landlord on a regular basis plus various guests such as Black Sheep Bitter or Riggwelter.

A country pub. One bar, real fires, stone and wood floors and beams. Food available all day. Children allowed.

OPEN *All day, every day.*

CROSTON

The Black Horse
Westhead Road, Croston, Nr Chorley PR5 7RQ
☎ *(01772) 600338* Mr S Welsh

At least four regular and guest ales (650 per year) from breweries such as Cains, Hydes, Mansfield, Hanby, Lloyds, Tom Wood, Banks, Timothy Taylor, Coach House, Sutton and Bushy. Emphasis on micro-breweries and unusual brews.

A family-run traditional village freehouse. Bar and restaurant food is served at lunchtime and evenings. Car park, garden, children's play area, bowling green, French boules pitch. Children allowed in the restaurant. In the village of Croston, close to Chorley and midway between Preston and Southport.

OPEN *All day, every day.*

DARWEN

Greenfield Inn
Lower Barn Street, Darwen BB3 2HQ
☎ *(01254) 703945* John Howard

A freehouse with Thwaites Mild and Bitter plus Timothy Taylor Landlord always available. Also three guests including, perhaps, Shepherd Neame Spitfire, Greene King Abbot, Moorhouse's Pendle Witches Brew or special Porter's ales.

A traditional one-room pub with beer garden. Food served at lunchtime and evenings. Children allowed. Situated on the outskirts of Blackburn.

OPEN *12–3.30pm and 5–11pm Mon, Wed, Thur; 5.30–11pm Tues; all day Sat–Sun.*

FLEETWOOD

Wyre Lounge Bar
Marine Hall, The Esplanade, Fleetwood FY7 6HF
☎ *(01253) 771141*

Eight beers always available including Moorhouse's brews. Also 200+ guest beers per year which may come from Young's, Charles Wells, Banks's and Timothy Taylor.

Part of the Marine Hall Sports Complex in Fleetwood. Food available at lunchtime. CAMRA pub of the year. Car park, garden, function room. No children.

OPEN *11am–4.30pm and 7–11pm Mon–Sat; 12–4pm and 7–10.30pm Sun.*

GREAT HARWOOD

The Dog & Otter

Cliffe Lane, Great Harwood, Blackburn BB6 7PG
☎ *(01254) 885760* Alberto Rodriguez

A Jennings-managed house with Jennings Bitter and Cumberland Ale always available, plus one rotating guest ale, perhaps Fuller's London Pride or a Marston's brew.

A pub/restaurant with one bar and outside tables. Old-style building with extension. Food served at lunchtime and evenings Mon–Sat, all day Sun. Children allowed.

OPEN *11.30am–3pm and 5.30–11pm (10.30pm Sun).*

The Royal Hotel

Station Road, Great Harwood, Blackburn BB6 7BA
☎ *(01254) 883541* Mr Hughes

A freehouse with five guest ales constantly changing. Moorhouse's Premier, Charles Wells Bombardier, Cains Bitter, Tomintoul Wild Cat and Culloden, RCH East Street Cream or a Burtonwood brew regularly featured.

A Victorian pub/hotel. One bar, dining area, garden, accommodation. Food available at lunchtime and evenings. Children allowed.

OPEN *12–2pm and 7–11pm (10.30pm Sun).*

HASLINGDEN

The Griffin Inn

84 Hud Rake, Haslingden, Rossendale BB4 5AF
☎ *(01706) 214021* David Porter

Home of the Porter Brewing Company. A brewpub with Dark Mild, Bitter, Porter, Sunshine and Rossendale Ale brewed and served on the premises.

A traditional no-frills alehouse and local community pub on the northern edge of town. No music or TV. No food. No children.

DARK MILD 3.3% ABV
BITTER 3.8% ABV
ROSSENDALE ALE 4.2% ABV
PORTER 5.0% ABV
SUNSHINE 5.3% ABV
Plus occasional and seasonal brews.

OPEN *All day, every day.*

LITTLE ECCLESTONE

The Cartford Hotel

Cartford Lane, Little Ecclestone, Preston PR3 0YP
☎ *(01995) 670166* Andrew Mellodew

The Hart Brewery operates from the premises producing a range of 16 beers for sale in the hotel and some local freehouses. Fuller's London Pride and Timothy Taylor Landlord are also regularly available plus a range of over 3,000 other beers so far served on a guest basis.

An award-winning, 400-year-old family pub. One large bar, large garden with children's play area. Quiet eating area with food available at lunchtime and evenings. Children allowed. Brewery tours by appointment. Car park. Games room. Accommodation.

SECOND COMING 3.8% ABV
Easter special. Light and sweet.
GOLD BEACH 3.8% ABV
A true summer session ale, light and hoppy.
GOLDEN SQUIRREL 3.9% ABV
A summer ale blending Squirrels Hoard and Gold Beach.
DISHY DEBBIE 4.0% ABV
A year-round session beer. Light and golden with a citrus flavour.
SQUIRRELS HOARD 4.0% ABV
Award-winning session beer. Intense nut taste.
AMBASSADOR 4.2% ABV
A relatively dry beer, red in colour.
NO BALLS 4.5% ABV
Christmas ale. Light and refreshing.
NEMESIS 4.5 % ABV
Golden premier bitter. Also known as The Goddess.
CRIMIN ALE PORTER 4.7% ABV
A true porter brewed once a year.
VAL.(ADDICTION) (4.8% ABV)
Dark, sweet, easy-drinking beer.
AMADEUS 5.0% ABV
Dark, rich winter warmer.
COBBLESTONE 5.0% ABV
A stout-style beer.
EXCALIBUR 5.0% ABV
A light lager-style beer with citrus taste and sweet finish.
OLD RAM 5.0% ABV
Bronze, full-bodied beer. Brewed more in the winter than summer.
CESTRIAN HART 5.2% ABV
Dark and sweet.
STEAMIN' JACK 5.5% ABV
A version of Nemesis.

OPEN *12–3pm and 6.30–11pm Mon–Sat; all day Sun.*

The Taps

Henry Street, Lytham FY8 5LE
☎ *(01253) 736226* Ian Rigg

 A Whitbread house with an extensive guest beer policy. Hook Norton Old Hooky, Wychwood The Dog's Bollocks, Orkney Dark Island and Moorhouse's Pendle Witches Brew regularly available, plus beers from breweries such as Black Sheep.

A town pub with yard, viewing cellar. Disabled facilities and toilets. Food served at lunchtime only. Children allowed only if dining.

All day, every day.

The Queen's Head

30 Moor Street, Ormskirk L39 2AQ
☎ *(01695) 574380* Gerry Fleming

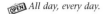 Up to four guest ales available including Fuller's London Pride, Shepherd Neame Bishop's Finger and Spitfire, Black Sheep Special or Wychwood The Dog's Bollocks.

A traditional one-bar pub with beer garden. Annual themed beer festival. Food served 12–2pm Mon–Sat. Well-behaved children allowed.

All day, every day.

The Stanley Arms

Lancaster Road, Preston PR1 1DA
☎ *(01772) 254004* Jim Ageros

Four guest beers, regularly including Charles Wells Bombardier or Morland Old Speckled Hen.

A traditional pub in a Grade II listed building. One bar and function room which will soon be turned into a dining room. Food available 11am–9pm Mon–Thurs; 11am–7pm Fri–Sat; 12–5pm Sun. Children allowed in the dining area only.

All day, every day.

Hinds Head

Mossy Lea Road, Wrightington, Nr Wigan WN6 9RN
☎ *(01257) 421168* Mr Ferro

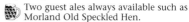 Two guest ales always available such as Morland Old Speckled Hen.

A big traditional pub with restaurant, beer garden and bowling green. Food available. Children allowed.

11am–2.30pm Tues–Thurs; 5.30–11pm Mon–Thurs; all day Fri–Sun.

★ *The Bay Horse Hotel,* Arkholme, Carnforth
★ *The Beacon Inn,* Beacon Lane, Dalton, Wigan
★ *The Blue Anchor,* South Road, Bretherton, Preston
★ *The Eagle & Child Inn,* Wharles, Preston
★ *The Hornby Hotel,* King Street, Blackburn
★ *Lane Ends Hotel,* Weeton Road, Wesham, Preston
★ *The Mayfield,* 22 County Road, Ormskirk
★ *The Old Black Bull,* 35 Friargate, Preston
★ *The Prince Albert,* 109 Wigan Road, Westhead
★ *The Queen's Head,* 412 Burnley Road, Cliviger
★ *The Saddle Inn,* Bartle
★ *The Strawberry Duck,* Overshores Road, Entwistle
★ *The Swan Hotel,* 62 King Street, Whalley, Clitheroe
★ *The Tap & Spile,* Fylde Road, Ashton-on-Ribble, Preston

Places Featured:

Barrowden	Medbourne
Frisby on the Wreake	Oadby
Glooston	Old Dalby
Hose	Shearsby
Kirby Muxloe	Somerby
Leicester	Sutton Bassett
Loughborough	Walcote

THE BREWERIES

BELVOIR BREWERY LTD

*Woodhill, Nottingham Lane, Old Dalby
LE14 3LX*
☎ *(01664) 823455*

 WHIPPLING GOLDEN BITTER 3.6% ABV
Light, refreshing and hoppy.
STAR BITTER 3.9% ABV
Citrus fruit and hoppy flavour.
PEACOCK'S GLORY 4.7% ABV
Golden, fruity and hoppy.
Plus occasional brews.

BREWSTERS BREWING CO. LTD

Penn Lane, Stathern, Melton Mowbray LE14 4JA
☎ *(01949) 81868*

EVERARDS BREWERY LTD

Castle Acres, Narborough LE9 5BY
☎ *(0116) 2014100*

 BEACON BITTER 3.8% ABV
Award-winning, fresh, clean taste.
TIGER BEST BITTER 4.2% ABV
Good body, dry hopped and long bitter finish.
OLD ORIGINAL 5.2% ABV
Copper-brown, smooth, malty and sweetish.
Plus seasonal beers.

FEATHERSTONE BREWERY,

Unit 3, King Street Buildings, Enderby LE9 5NT
☎ *(0116) 2750952*

 HOWS HOWLER 3.6% ABV
BEST BITTER 4.2% ABV
Plus occasional brews.

THE GRAINSTORE BREWERY

*Davis's Brewing Co. Ltd, Station Approach,
Oakham LE15 6QW*
☎ *(01572) 770065* (Brewery tours)

 COOKING 3.6 ABV
Golden and well-balanced.
TRIPLE B 4.2% ABV
Malty sweetness with balancing hop flavours.
TEN FIFTY 5.0 ABV
Easy-drinking sweet maltiness, with bitter finish.
Plus seasonal beers.

TOM HOSKINS BREWERY PLC

*Beaumanor Brewery, 133 Beaumanor Road,
Leicester LE4 5QE*
☎ *(0116) 2661122*

 BITTER 3.7% ABV
Powerful bitterness throughout.
TOM'S GOLD 4.4% ABV
Malty throughout.
CHURCHILL'S PRIDE 4.9% ABV
Sweet and malty.

HOSKINS & OLDFIELD BREWERY LTD

North Mills, Frog Island, Leicester LE3 5DH
☎ *(0116) 2510532*

 HOB BEST MILD 3.5% ABV
Dark, balanced, traditional mild.
BRIGADIER 3.6% ABV
Light, easy-drinking session beer.
HOB BITTER 4.0% ABV
Pale, with hop flavour.
LITTLE MATTY 4.0% ABV
Dark and full-flavoured.
WHITE DOLPHIN 4.0% ABV
Pale, tart wheat beer.
IPA 4.2% ABV
Traditional pale ale.
TOM KELLY STOUT 4.2% ABV
Dark and malty with hoppy bitterness.
SUPREME 4.4% ABV
Golden and refreshing.
PORTER 4.8% ABV
Dark, traditional-style porter.
EXS 5.0% ABV
Golden and well-balanced.
'04' ALE 5.2% ABV
Well-rounded.
OLD NAVIGATION 7.0% ABV
Dark, classic winter warmer.
CHRISTMAS NOGGIN 10.0% ABV
Smooth, sweet and rounded.
Plus occasional brews.

SHARDLOW BREWING CO. LTD

Old Stables, British Waterways Yard, Cavendish Bridge DE72 2HL

 CHANCELLOR'S REVENGE 3.6% ABV
BEST BITTER 4.1% ABV
GOLDEN HOP 4.1% ABV
NARROW BOAT 4.3% ABV
OLD STABLE BREW 4.4% ABV
CAVENDISH GOLD 4.5% ABV
REVEREND EATON'S ALE 4.5% ABV
WHISTLE STOP 5.0 ABV
Plus occasional brews.

THE PUBS

BARROWDEN

The Exeter Arms

Main Street, Barrowden, Oakham, Rutland LE15 8EQ
☎ *(01572) 747247* Mr Peter Blenco

A freehouse and home of the Blenco Brewing Company. A full range of brews is always available (and only sold here). Also various guests such as Fuller's London Pride, Wyre Piddle Piddle in the Wind or Bateman XB. The aim is only to repeat the guest beers a maximum of three times a year.

A very traditional country pub, situated off the beaten track. One bar, huge garden, plans for accommodation. Brewery tours by appointment only. Food available every lunchtime and Tues–Sat evenings. Children allowed. Ring for directions

BARROWDEN BOYS 3.6% ABV
A year-round session bitter
BEACH BOYS 3.8% ABV
Brewed mainly in summer
LOVER BOYS 3.8% ABV
Valentine's Day special
YOUNG BOYS 4.1% ABV
BIG BOYS 4.5% ABV
DANNY BOY 4.5% ABV
An autumn-winter stout
STRONG BOYS 5% ABV
Brewed mainly in Autumn and Winter

11am–2.30pm and 6–11pm (10.30pm Sun).

FRISBY ON THE WREAKE

The Bell Inn

2 Main Street, Frisby on the Wreake LE7 2NJ
☎ *(01664) 434237* Mr Simpson

A freehouse with Marston's Pedigree, Greene King Abbot and IPA among the beers permanently available plus occasional guests.

A 250-year-old village pub. One bar serves two rooms. Outside seating and conservatory. Food served at lunchtime and evenings. Children allowed in the conservatory only.

12–2.30pm and 6–11pm (10.30pm Sun).

GLOOSTON

The Old Barn Inn

Andrews Lane, Glooston, Nr Market Harborough LE16 7ST
☎ *(01858) 545215* Charles Edmondson-Jones

Four beers (30 per year) always available from brewers such as Adnams, Hook Norton, Fuller's, Wadworth, Oakhill, Nene Valley, Ridley, Bateman, Thwaite, Leatherbritches, Mauldons, Cotleigh, Greene King and Tolly Cobbold.

A sixteenth-century village pub in rural location with a log fire, no juke box or games machines. Bar and restaurant food available in evenings and Sunday lunchtime. Car park. Catering for parties, receptions and meetings. Well-behaved children and dogs welcome. Accommodation. On an old Roman road between Hallaton and Tur Langton.

12–2.30pm Tues–Sun; 7–11pm Mon–Sat.

HOSE

The Rose & Crown

43 Bolton Lane, Hose LE14 4JE
☎ *(01949) 860424*

Eight beers including a mild always available from a list that changes every week. Selected ales may vary in strength from 3.8 to 7% ABV.

Not easy to find at the back of the village, this modernised open-plan bar has a pool table and juke box. Bar and restaurant food is available at lunchtime and evenings. Car park, garden. Children allowed in the dining area.

12–2.30pm and 7–11pm.

KIRBY MUXLOE

The Royal Oak

Main Street, Kirby Muxloe, Leicester LE9 2AN
☎ *(0116) 239 3166* Mr Jackson

An Everards house with Tiger, Beacon and Old Original always available. Also two guest pumps serving beers such as Greene King Abbot Ale, Nethergate Old Growler or an Adnams brew.

A food-oriented village pub. Modern building with traditional decor. Function facilities. Disabled access. Garden. Food available at lunchtime and evenings. Children allowed.

11am–3pm and 5.30–11pm (10.30pm Sun).

The North Bridge Tavern

Frog Island, Leicester LE3 5AG
☎ *(0116) 251 2508* David Rochester

 A freehouse with Marston's Pedigree always available plus one guest, often from a small local brewery such as Tom Hoskins.

A food-oriented town pub. One bar, function room. Non-smoking dining area. Traditional building with disabled access. Food available all day. Children allowed.

OPEN *All day, every day.*

Rainbow & Dove Tap House

185 Charles Street, Leicester LE1 1LA
☎ *(0116) 255 5916* Nicola Turner

Up to nine real ales available including Banks's Bitter, Camerons Strong Arm and Marston's Pedigree plus two guests often including Timothy Taylor Landlord, Hop Back Summer Lightning, Fuller's ESB, Badger Tanglefoot, Wychwood The Dog's Bollocks or Orkney Dark Island.

A traditional town alehouse with one bar and function room. Food served at lunchtime and evenings. No children.

OPEN *All day, every day.*

Tom Hoskins

133 Beaumanor Road, Leicester LE4 5QE
☎ *(0116) 261 1008* Mr Watson

The Hoskins Brewery operates from the back of this pub, so Hoskins Bitter, Churchill's Pride and Tom's Gold are always available, plus seasonal specials.

A traditional community pub with garden and the oldest cottage tower brewery in Britain. Disabled access. Function room. Pub food available at lunchtime. Children allowed in the function room only.

OPEN *All day Mon–Sat; 12–3pm and 7–10.30pm Sun.*

The Vaults

1 Wellington Street, Leicester LE1 6HH
☎ *(0116) 255 5506* Mr Spencer

A freehouse offering Leatherbritches Steamin' Billy Bitter and Goldings plus a wide range of other real ales, constantly changing. More than 1,000 beers have been served in the past three years. Smaller breweries are supported whenever possible.

A traditional pub with cellar bar. One bar area. Music on Sundays with an admission charge. No food. No children.

OPEN *5–11pm Mon–Thurs; 12–11pm Fri–Sat; 12–3pm and 7–10.30pm Sun.*

The Albion Inn

Canal Bank, Loughborough LE11 1QA
☎ *(01509) 213952* Mr Hartley

Samuel Smith OBB and Mansfield Riding Mild always available plus guests such as Shepherd Neame Spitfire and Early Bird, Black Sheep Special or brews from Morrells or Morland.

A traditional two-bar pub with garden, situated on the canal bank. Disabled access. Food available at lunchtime and evenings. No children.

OPEN *11am–3pm and 6–11pm (10.30pm Sun).*

The Garden Inn

Bedford Square, Loughborough LE11 2TP
☎ *(01509) 239120* Emma Chouhan

A Tap & Spile pub serving up to six real ales. Morland Old Speckled Hen, Marston's Pedigree, Fuller's London Pride, Wadworth 6X, Highgate Fox's Nob and a Bateman brew all regularly stocked.

A refurbished contemporary pub with traditional atmosphere. One open bar, skittle alley, garden with petanque pitch. Food served at lunchtime and evenings. Children allowed if eating.

OPEN *All day, every day.*

The Swan in the Rushes

21 The Rushes, Loughborough
☎ *(01509) 217014* Andrew Hambleton

Springhead Roaring Meg, Leatherbritches Belter, Archers Golden and Marston's Pedigree always available plus six guest beers (300 per year) at any one time, to include absolutely anything.

A cosmopolitan town-centre alehouse, smart yet down to earth, with a friendly atmosphere. Bar and restaurant food is available at lunchtime and evenings. Car park and accommodation. Children allowed. On the A6, behind Sainsbury's.

OPEN *12–2.30pm and 5–11pm Sun–Thurs; all day Fri–Sat.*

MEDBOURNE

The Nevill Arms

Medbourne, Market Harborough, LE16 8EE
☎ *(01858) 565288* Mrs Hall

 A freehouse with Adnams Bitter always available plus two guests changing twice-monthly. Fuller's London Pride and Timothy Taylor Landlord are popular but beers from many other breweries are also stocked.

A traditional, two-bar country pub. Outside seating on benches near a brook. Accommodation. Bar food served at lunchtime and evenings. Well-behaved children allowed.

[OPEN] *12–2.30pm and 6–11pm Mon–Sat; 12–3pm and 7–10.30pm Sun.*

OADBY

The Cow & Plough

Stoughton Farm Park, Gartree Road, Oadby LE2 5JB
☎ *(0116) 272 0852*

HOB Bitter (Hoskins & Oldfield), Fuller's London Pride and Steaming Billy Bitter and Mild always available, plus rotating guest beers (150 per year) mainly from micro-breweries.

A converted barn on a leisure park, open as part of the park during the day and as a pub from 5pm daily. The vaults are full of brewing memorabilia with a Victorian bar at the back. Adjoining car park, garden, children's room. CAMRA East Midlands Pub of the Year 1995 and 1998. Signposted on the A6 as Farmworld.

[OPEN] *5–9pm daily.*

OLD DALBY

The Crown Inn

Debdale Hill, Old Dalby, Nr Melton Mowbray LE14 3LF
☎ *(01664) 823134* Miss Lynn Bryan

Marston's Best and Pedigree plus brews from Hardys & Hansons, Black Sheep, Timothy Taylor and Bateman always available plus eight guests including Greene King Abbot, Wadworth 6X, Woodforde's Wherry Best, JW Lees Moonraker, Fuller's London Pride, Exmoor Gold, Marston's Owd Rodger, Mauldons Black Adder and Brains, Smiles, Thwaites and Adnams ales.

Built in 1590, a pub with six small rooms, oak beams, open fires, antique furniture, fresh flowers and prints. Large patio and terrace with orchard at bottom of the garden. Beer served from cellar near back door. Bar and restaurant food served at lunchtime and evenings. Car park, children's room, petanque pitch, ballooning and riding arranged. Take the A46 Nottingham to Leicester road. Turn off at Willougby Hotel, left for Upper Broughton, right for Old Dalby.

[OPEN] *12–3pm and 6–11pm.*

SHEARSBY

Chandler's Arms

Village Green, Shearsby, Nr Lutterworth LE17 6PL
☎ *(0116) 247 8384* Mr Ward

Fuller's London Pride and Marston's Pedigree and Bitter always available plus four guests. Beers featured include Greene King Abbot, Wadworth 6X, Exmoor Gold or brews from Timothy Taylor or Jennings.

A seventeenth-century red-brick pub overlooking the village green, with a three-tier prize-winning garden. Two lounges. AA recommended. International cuisine served at lunchtime and evenings. Children allowed.

[OPEN] *12–2.30pm and 6.30–11pm (10.30pm Sun).*

SOMERBY

The Old Brewery Inn

High Street, Somerby, Leicester LE14 2PZ
☎ *(01664) 454777* Celia Frew

Home of the John o'Gaunt Brewing Company and the Parish Brewery. Robin a Tiptoe, Cropped Oak and Coat o'Red always available plus a good range of Parish bitters such as Somerby Premium, Poachers Ale and Special. Other celebration ales, as appropriate, for instance Life Sentence, which was brewed for the landlady's wedding!

Three bars, restaurant, function room and beer garden. Disabled access. Brewery visits permitted if quiet or pre-arranged. Food served at lunchtime and evenings Tues–Sun. Children allowed.

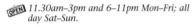

JOHN O'GAUNT:
ROBIN A TIPTOE 3.9% ABV
CROPPED OAK 4.4% ABV
COAT O'RED
PARISH:
MILD 3.5% ABV
SPECIAL BITTER 3.8% ABV
FARM GOLD 4% ABV
SOMERBY PREMIUM 4% ABV
PORTER 4.8% ABV
POACHERS ALE 6% ABV
BAZ'S BONCE BLOWER 11% ABV
BAZ'S SUPER BREW 23% ABV

OPEN *11.30am–3pm and 6–11pm Mon–Fri; all day Sat–Sun.*

SUTTON BASSETT

The Queen's Head

Sutton Bassett, Market Harborough LE16 8HP
☎ *(01858) 463530* Mario Cancelliere

A freehouse with up to eight real ales including Timothy Taylor Landlord and Adnams Bitter plus a selection of guests including Fuller's London Pride, Morland's Old Speckled Hen and Ward's Waggle Dance.

A friendly country pub with traditional decor, real fires, front and back bars. Disabled facilities on ground floor. Patio and petanque court. Food served at lunchtime and evenings (pub food in the bar and Italian food in restaurant upstairs). Large parties and functions catered for. Children allowed. Prettily situated with views of the Welland valley.

OPEN *11.45am–3pm and 6.30–11pm Mon–Sat; 12–3pm and 7–10.30pm Sun.*

WALCOTE

The Black Horse

Littleworld Road, Walcote LE17 4JU
☎ *(01455) 552684* Mrs Tinker

HOB Bitter (Hoskins & Oldfield), Timothy Taylor Landlord and Hook Norton Old Hooky always available plus two guest beers (75 per year) always from independent breweries.

A one-bar village pub. Bar and restaurant food available at lunchtime and evenings. Authentic Thai cooking. Car park, garden and children's room. One mile east of M1 junction 20.

OPEN *12–2pm and 7–11pm. Closed Mon and Tues lunchtime.*

YOU TELL US

★ *The Crown & Anchor,* Oadby
★ *The Hat and Beaver,* Highcross Street, Leicester
★ *The Jolly Sailor,* 21 Main Street, Hemington
★ *The Old Crown,* Cavendish Bridge
★ *The Tap & Mallet,* 36 Nottingham Road, Loughborough
★ *The Three Cranes Hotel,* 82 Humberstone Gate, Leicester
★ *The Queens Head,* Main Street, Saddington, Leicester
★ *The White Swan,* Main Street, Shawell, Lutterworth

Places Featured:

Allington
Aslackby
Aubourn
Boston
Caythorpe
Gainsborough
Grainthorpe
Grantham
Harmston

Laughterton
Lincoln
Louth
North Kelsey
Rothwell
Scamblesby
Spalding
Woolsthorpe-by-Belvoir

THE BREWERIES

GEORGE BATEMAN & SON LTD

*Salem Bridge Brewery, Mill Lane, Wainfleet,
Skegness PE24 4JE*
☎ *(01754) 880317*

 DARK MILD 3.0% ABV
Dark and fruity, some roast malt, hoppy finish.
XB 3.7% ABV
Distinctive, refreshing dry bitterness.
VALIANT 4.3% ABV
Golden, complex, well-balanced. Clean finish.
SALEM PORTER 4.7% ABV
Dry, nutty, rich malt and superb hop flavours.
XXXB 4.8% ABV
Multi-faceted malt and fruit character.
VICTORY ALE 7.0% ABV
Full-flavoured, surprisingly delicate palate.
Plus seasonal and monthly brews.

BIGFOOT BREWERY

New Farm, Blyton Carr, Gainsborough DN21 3EN
☎ *(01427) 628563*

BLYTON BEST 3.6% ABV
GENESIS 3.8% ABV
GAINSBOROUGH GOLD 4.5% ABV
EXTRA 4.9% ABV
Plus seasonal and occasional brews.

DARK TRIBE BREWERY

*25 Doncaster Road, Gunness, Scunthorpe
DN15 8TG*
☎ *(01724) 782324*

MILD 3.6% ABV
FULL AHEAD 3.8% ABV
FUTTOCKS 4.2% ABV
GALLEON 4.7% ABV
TWIN SCREW 5.1% ABV
Plus occasional brews.

HIGHWOOD BREWERY LTD

Melton Highwood, Barnetby DN38 6AA
☎ *(01652) 680020*

BEST BITTER 3.5% ABV
Well-hopped and refreshing.
SHEPHERD'S DELIGHT 4.0% ABV
Easy-quaffing and full-flavoured.
LINCOLNSHIRE LEGEND 4.2% ABV
Good, hoppy bitterness throughout.
HARVEST 4.3% ABV
Soft and well-balanced.
OLD TIMBER 4.5% ABV
Smooth and full-flavoured.
BOMBER COUNTY 4.8% ABV
Red, with good hoppy flavour.

NEWBY WYKE BREWERY

13 Calder Close, Grantham NG31 7QT
☎ *(01476) 402167*

SIDEWINDER 3.8% ABV
SKIPPER EDDIES ALE 4.0% ABV
WHITE SQUALL 4.8% ABV

OLDERSHAW BREWERY

12 Harrowby Hall Estate, Grantham NG31 9HB
☎ *(01476) 572135*

HARROWBY BITTER 3.6% ABV
NEWTON'S DROP 4.1% ABV
ERMINE ALE 4.2% ABV
REGAL BLONDE 4.4% ABV
OLD BOY 4.8% ABV
Plus seasonal brews.

THE PUBS

ALLINGTON

The Welby Arms
The Green, Allington, Grantham NG32 2EA
☎ *(01400) 281361* Mr Dyer

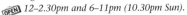 Timothy Taylor Landlord is one of three brews always available, plus three guests perhaps including Wadworth 6X, Phoenix Wobbly Bob or Greene King Abbot.

A traditional village pub with log fires and terrace. Disabled access. Baguettes or soup available at lunchtime in the bar, plus restaurant food at both lunchtime and evenings. Well-behaved children allowed.

OPEN *12–2.30pm and 6–11pm (10.30pm Sun).*

ASLACKBY

Robin Hood & Little John
Aslackby, Sleaford NG34 0HL
☎ *(01778) 440681* Mike Wickens

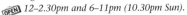 A freehouse with Greene King Abbot always available, plus one guest pump serving a real ale such as, perhaps, Adnams Broadside or a Wood or Oldershaw ale.

A traditional country pub, one bar, function room, restaurant. Food available at lunchtime and evenings. Children's garden with sheep next door, children allowed in designated area only.

OPEN *11am–3pm and 5.30–11pm (10.30pm Sun).*

AUBOURN

The Royal Oak
Royal Oak Lane, Aubourn LN5 9DT
☎ *(01522) 788291*

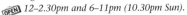 Bateman XB and XXXB and Samuel Smith OBB always available plus three guest beers from breweries stretching from the Orkneys to Cornwall.

A traditional village pub with character. Bar food available at lunchtime and evenings. Car park and garden. Children welcome at lunchtime and evenings in the function room until 8.30pm. South of Lincoln, off the A46.

OPEN *12–2.30pm and 7–11pm (10.30pm Sun).*

BOSTON

The Carpenter's Arms
Witham Street, Boston PE21 6PU
☎ *(01205) 362840* John Blakeborough

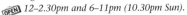 A Bateman house with XB always available plus two changing guests which are often other Bateman brews but also sometimes Marston's Pedigree, Morland Old Speckled Hen or Fuller's London Pride. A wider selection of real ales is available in the summer than during the winter.

A traditional one-bar town pub. Games room, real fires, outside seating. No food. Well-behaved children allowed.

OPEN *11am–3pm and 7–11pm Mon–Thurs; all day Fri–Sun.*

The Eagle
144 West Street, Boston PE21 8RE
☎ *(01205) 361116* Mr Watson

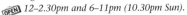 Timothy Taylor Landlord, Adnams Broadside and Everards Beacon always available, plus up to three guests such as Exmoor Gold, Hop Back Summer Lightning or Bateman special brews. May operate up to five real ales during special events.

A traditional local on the outskirts of Boston town centre. Two bars, real fires, garden. Regular annual beer festival held at the end of July, plus several others during the year. Kitchen under refurbishment but food will be available again towards the end of 1999. Children allowed in the garden only.

OPEN *11am–2.30pm Mon–Thurs; 6–11pm Mon–Wed; 5–11pm Thurs; all day Fri–Sun.*

CAYTHORPE

The Red Lion Inn
62 High Street, Caythorpe, Grantham NG32 3DN
☎ *(01400) 272632* Ann Roberts

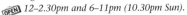 A freehouse serving Adnams Best plus up to three guests from every possible brewery. Glentworth and Slaters (Eccleshall) brews are particular favourites.

A seventeenth-century traditional country inn with two gardens and two bars. No music or games machines. Disabled access. Food available at lunchtime and evenings in a separate restaurant. Children allowed in the restaurant and one of the bars only.

OPEN *11am–2.30pm and 6–11pm (10.30pm Sun).*

GAINSBOROUGH

The Eight Jolly Brewers
Ship Court, Caskgate Street, Gainsborough DN21 2DL
☎ *(01427) 677128* Alex Craig

Timothy Taylor Landlord and Black Sheep Best always available plus a varied range of guest ales. No national beers served, micro-breweries favoured. Examples include Highwood Lincolnshire Legend and Glentworth Little Gem.

A 300-year-old town-centre freehouse with two bars in a traditional building. Small outdoor area and patio. Sandwiches available at lunchtime only. No children. Located near the Guildhall.

11am–4pm and 7–11pm Mon–Thurs; all day Fri–Sun.

GRAINTHORPE

The Black Horse Inn
Mill Lane, Grainthorpe, Louth LN11 78U
☎ *(01472) 388229* Mrs Donaghue

A freehouse serving Bateman ales plus a guest such as Timothy Taylor Landlord or Ward's Waggle Dance. Plans to start home brewing.

A cosy country village pub with a real ale theme. Open fires, beer garden with children's area. Food served every evening and at lunchtime at weekends and during the summer. Children allowed, if eating.

7–11pm and lunchtime at weekends and during the summer.

GRANTHAM

The Blue Bull
64 Westgate, Grantham NG31 6LA
☎ *(01476) 70929*

Bateman XB and Wadworth 6X always available plus three guest beers (100 per year) perhaps from Enville, Hampshire, Greene King, Clark's, Rooster's and Kelham Island.

CAMRA Lincolnshire Pub of the Year 1995. Dates from the 1850s. Bar and restaurant food available at lunchtime and evenings. Car park. Children allowed in the restaurant. Three minutes from the main line BR railway station.

11am–3pm and 7–11pm.

HARMSTON

The Thorold Arms
High Street, Harmston, Lincoln LN5 9SN
☎ *(01522) 720358* Mr Duffield

The tiny Duffield Brewery operates from the cellar of this freehouse and a home brew is usually available. Also something from Greene King and perhaps a celebration or seasonal ale from an independent brewery.

A rural pub with traditional decor and two log fires. Disabled access and toilets. Food available at lunchtime and evenings in a separate dining area. No children.

BITTER 3.6% ABV
SPECIAL 4.3% ABV
MULLEY'S IRISH STOUT 4.4% ABV
EXTRA SPECIAL BITTER 4.8% ABV

11am–3pm and 6–11pm (10.30pm Sun).

LAUGHTERTON

The Friendship Inn
Main Road, Laugherton, Lincoln LN21 2JZ
☎ *(01427) 718681* Diane Humphries

A freehouse with Ward's Best, Marston's Pedigree and Mansfield Old Bailey always available plus one guest, which may well be something from Brewsters, Slaters (Eccleshall) or another micro-brewery.

A traditional, friendly one-bar village pub. Log fires, garden, disabled access. Food available at lunchtime and evenings (except Sun evening) in a designated dining area. Children allowed.

11.30am–2.30pm and 6–11pm Mon–Sat; 12–3pm and 7–10.30pm Sun.

LINCOLN

The Golden Eagle
21 High Street, Lincoln LN5 8BD
☎ *(01522) 521058* Mr and Mrs Fairclough

A freehouse with Everards Beacon, Bateman XB and Timothy Taylor Landlord always available plus one mild and one real cider. Three guest ales, rotating continually.

A locals' pub with two bars, one with no music or games machines, half a mile from the city centre. No food. Car park and garden. Children not allowed in the pub.

11am–3pm and 5.30–11pm Mon–Thur; all day Fri–Sun.

The Tap & Spile
21 Hungate, Lincoln LN1 1ES
☎ *(01522) 534015* Mr and Mrs Cay

Eight beers always available but the range changes daily. Approx 150 brews per year including Charles Wells Fargo, Thwaites Craftsman and Greene King IPA etc.

F ormerly the White Horse, a city-centre pub with stone and wood floors, bare brick and plaster walls. Bar food available at lunchtime. Pay and display car park opposite. Children not allowed. At the top of the high street turn left, then 200 yards on the left near the police station.

OPEN *11am–11pm Mon–Sat; 12–3pm and 7–10.30pm Sun.*

The Victoria
6 Union Road, Lincoln LN1 3BJ
☎ *(01522) 536048* Mr Renshaw

Up to ten beers always available including Everards Tiger and Old Original, Timothy Taylor Landlord, Bateman XB and Oldershaw Regal Blonde. Plus four guests (up to 1,000 per year) including Orkney Raven Ale, Brains Bitter, Exmoor Gold, Hop Back Summer Lightning and Adnams brews.

A traditional, two-bar Victorian terraced pub with a small patio, in the city by the west gate of the castle. Bar food available at lunchtime. Regular beer festivals and brewery feature nights.

OPEN *11am–11pm Mon–Sat; 12–10.30pm Sun.*

The Woodman Inn
134 Eastgate, Louth LN11 9AA
☎ *(01507) 602100* Dave Kilgour

Greene King Abbot always available plus two guests. Among those recently featured are Wadworth 6X, Charles Wells Bombardier and brews from Cotleigh and Abbeydale. Other specials from micro-breweries stocked when possible.

S ituated on the edge of town, this pub has a film theme. Two bars, one a live rock and blues music venue. Food available at lunchtime only. Children allowed.

OPEN *11am–4pm and 7–11pm Mon–Fri; all day Sat; 12–3.30pm and 7–10.30pm Sun.*

The Butchers Arms
Middle Street, North Kelsey, Market Rasen LN7 6EH
☎ *(01652) 678002* Steve Cooper

A Highwood Brewery tied house serving the range of Highwood beers, such as Tom Wood Best, Shepherd's Delight and Bomber County. One constantly changing guest.

A small, old-style village pub. One bar. No music or games. Outside seating. Sandwiches, salads and ploughmans available at weekends. Children allowed.

OPEN *4–11pm Mon; 12–2pm and 4–11pm Tues–Fri; all day Sat–Sun.*

The Nickerson Arms
Hillrise, Rothwell LN7 6AZ
☎ *(01472) 371300* Peter Wright

Mansfield Smooth, Old Bailey, Marston's Pedigree and Charles Wells Bombardier always available, plus guests.

A 400-year-old haunted pub, formerly a blacksmiths, with oak beams, real fires and candles. Bar and restaurant food available at lunchtime and evenings. Car park, garden, children's room and function room. Free sausage and chips on Tuesday nights, from 7–9pm. Three miles off the A46 between Grimsby and Caistor.

OPEN *12–3pm and 7–11pm Mon–Sat; 12–4pm and 7–10.30pm Sun.*

The Green Man
Old Main Road, Scamblesby, Louth LN11 9XG
☎ *(01507) 343282*
Michael Jones and Margaret Barnard

A freehouse with three pumps serving a constantly changing range of real ales. Charles Wells Bombardier and Highwood Tom Wood Best are popular. Independent breweries favoured.

A country pub with lounge and public bar. Food available at lunchtime and evenings. Children allowed.

OPEN *12–2pm and 7–11pm (in summer, closed Tues–Wed lunch).*

LINCOLNSHIRE

SPALDING

The Lincolnshire Poacher
11 Double Street, Spalding PE11 2AA
☎ *(01775) 766490* Pauline Broderick

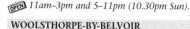 A Tom Hoskins tied house with Hoskins Bitter and Churchill's Pride always available. Three guest pumps serve a range of real ales including Morland Old Speckled Hen.

A food-oriented pub, situtated near the river, with two bars, garden and non-smoking dining area. Disabled access. Food available at lunchtime only. Children allowed.

OPEN *11am–3pm and 5–11pm (10.30pm Sun).*

WOOLSTHORPE-BY-BELVOIR

The Chequers
Main Street, Woolsthorpe-by-Belvoir, Grantham NG32 1LV
☎ *(01476) 870701* Mr Potter

A freehouse with Marston's Bitter and Pedigree always available plus two guest ales such as Timothy Taylor Landlord or Greene King Abbot plus beers from local breweries such as Brewsters.

A country pub with traditional decor. Five-acre garden, disabled access, function room. Accommodation. Restaurant food available at lunchtime and evenings. Children allowed.

OPEN *12–3pm and 7–11pm (10.30pm Sun).*

YOU TELL US

★ *Ebrington Arms,* Main Street, Kirkby on Bain, Woodhall Spa, Lincolnshire
★ *New Inn,* Hill Road, Springthorpe, Gainsborough
★ *The Portland Arms,* 50 Portland Street, Lincoln
★ *Sippers,* 26 Melville Street, Lincoln
★ *The Wishing Well Inn,* Main Road, Dyke, Bourne
★ *Yarborough Hotel,* 18 Bridge Road, Gainsborough

Places Featured:

LONDON CENTRAL
EC1: Clerkenwell
EC2: Barbican
EC4: Fleet Street
WC1: Bloomsbury/Holborn

LONDON EAST
E2: Bethnal Green
E3: Bow
E5: Clapton
E7: Forest Gate
E11: Leytonstone
E14: Limehouse
E15: Stratford
E17: Walthamstow

LONDON NORTH
N1: Hoxton
N2: East Finchley
N8: Crouch End
N9: Lower Edmonton
N16: Stoke Newington
N17: Tottenham

LONDON NORTHWEST
NW2: Cricklewood
NW8: St John's Wood

LONDON SOUTHEAST
SE1: Borough
SE5: Camberwell
SE8: Deptford
SE13: Lewisham
SE20: Penge
SE25: South Norwood

LONDON SOUTHWEST
SW1: Whitehall
SW2: Brixton
SW4: Clapham
SW6: Fulham
SW7: Chelsea
SW8: Stockwell
SW9: Brixton
SW18: Wandsworth

LONDON WEST
W1: Soho
W2: Lancaster Gate

THE BREWERIES

FULLER, SMITH & TURNER PLC

*Griffin Brewery, Chiswick Lane South, Chiswick
W4 2QB*
☎ *(0181) 996 2000*

 CHISWICK BITTER 3.5% ABV
Quenching, with flowery hop character.
SUMMER ALE 3.9% ABV
Seasonal. Lager-style beer.
LONDON PRIDE 4.1% ABV
Smooth and rounded, with excellent balance.
HONEY DEW 4.3% ABV
Seasonal. Golden smooth and honeyed
sweetness.
RED FOX 4.3% ABV
Seasonal. Tawny, mellow and well-rounded.
OLD WINTER ALE 4.8% ABV
Seasonal. Amber, sweet and nutty.
ESB 5.5% ABV
Powerful, rounded and well-balanced.
GOLDEN PRIDE 8.5% ABV
Rare in cask form.

MASH LONDON BREWERY LTD

19–21 Great Portland Street W1M 5DG

O'HANLON'S BREWING CO.

114 Randall Road, Vauxhall SE11 5JR
☎ *(0171) 793 0803*

FIREFLY 3.7% ABV
WHEATBEER 4.0% ABV
DRY STOUT 4.2% ABV
BLAKELEY'S BEST NO.1 4.4% ABV
MYRICA ALE 4.5% ABV
PORT STOUT 4.8% ABV
Plus seasonal brews.

PITFIELD BREWERY

*The Beer Shop, 14 Pitfield Street, Hoxton
N1 6EY*
☎ *(0171) 739 3701*

ORIGINAL BITTER 3.7% ABV
EAST KENT GOLDINGS 4.2% ABV
ECO WARRIOR 4.5% ABV
HOXTON HEAVY 4.8% ABV
BLACK EAGLE 5.0% ABV
Plus seasonal and occasional brews.

SOHO BREWING CO.
41 Earlham Street, Covent Garden WC2
☎ *(0171) 240 0606*

 PALE 4.5% ABV
RED 4.6% ABV
WHEAT 5.0% ABV
SPECIAL 5.5% ABV

YOUNG & CO. BREWERY
The Ram Brewery, Wandsworth SW18 4JD
☎ *(0181) 875 7000*

BITTER 3.7% ABV
Pale and bitter throughout.
FIRST GOLD 4.0% ABV
Seasonal, pale and refreshing.
OREGON AMBER 4.0% ABV
Seasonal lager-style beer.
DIRTY DICK'S 4.1% ABV
Seasonal beer.
SPECIAL 4.6% ABV
Excellent malt and hop balance.
WINTER WARMER 5.0% ABV
Rich, smooth and sweet seasonal brew.

THE PUBS

LONDON CENTRAL

EC1: CLERKENWELL

The Jerusalem Tavern
55 Britton Street, Clerkenwell EC1M 5NA
☎ *(0171) 490 4281*
Bruce Patterson (Manager)

A St Peter's Brewery tied house serving the range of St Peter's brews such as Best Bitter, Strong Bitter, Wheat Beer, Golden Ale, Fruit Beer (elderberry), Summer Ale and Winter Ale.

A small, old-fashioned pub with no music or machines. Outside seating. Food available at lunchtime from 12–2.30pm and toasted sandwiches in the evenings. Children allowed.

9am (for coffee)–11pm Mon–Fri; closed Sat–Sun.

The Leopard
33 Seward Street, Clerkenwell EC1V 3PA
☎ *(0171) 253 3587* Malcolm Jones

A freehouse with Gibbs Mew (Ushers) Salisbury always available, plus three guests such as Greene King Abbot and brews from O'Hanlon's, Nethergate, Eccleshall and Cottage. Guests changed daily.

A one-bar pub, a mixture of modern and traditional, with wooden floors, conservatory, dining area, disabled facilities and small outside seating area. Food available from 12.30–9pm. Children allowed in conservatory.

11am–11pm Mon–Fri; closed Sat–Sun.

EC2: BARBICAN

Crowders Well
185 Fore Street, Barbican EC2Y 5EJ
☎ *(0171) 628 8574* John Lowe

A Greene King pub with a range of Greene King ales always available.

An old, traditional city-centre pub. Food available at lunchtime only. No children.

All day Mon–Fri; closed Sat–Sun.

EC4: FLEET STREET

The Old Bank of England
194 Fleet Street EC4 2LT
☎ *(0171) 430 2255* Natasha Percival

The Fuller's flagship alehouse with London Pride, Chiswick and ESB always available plus a guest seasonal Fuller's beer and one other real ale such as Timothy Taylor Landlord. Guests changed monthly.

An impressive old pub which was once annexed to the law courts. Styled in brass and wood. Two seperate rooms for dining (smoking and non-smoking) in which food is available 12–8pm. Full bar menu, but the pub is famous for its pies. Children allowed

11am–11pm Mon–Fri; closed Sat–Sun.

WC1: BLOOMSBURY/HOLBORN

The King's Arms
11a Northington Street, Bloomsbury WC1N 2JF
☎ *(0171) 405 9107* Clive Gilbert

Greene King IPA, Marston's Pedigree and Wadworth 6X usually available, plus occasional guests but no very strong ales.

An office workers' pub in the midst of a legal and media professional area. Food available at lunchtime only. No children.

11am–11pm Mon–Fri; closed Sat–Sun.

The Yorkshire Grey
2–6 Theobald's Road, Holborn, WC1X 8PN
☎ *(0171) 405 2519* Marianne & Chris Bee

A Scottish & Newcastle tied pub which is home to the Yorkshire Grey Brewery in the cellar. Barristers and QC are brewed and served on the premises. One other pump used for occasional specials. Also guests changed every three weeks.

Traditional city pub with wooden floors and beams. One bar on ground-floor level and function room for hire. Hot and cold food available 11am–11pm. Brewery tours.

BARRISTERS BITTER% ABV
QC BITTER 4.5% ABV

11am–11pm Mon–Fri; closed Sat–Sun unless pre-booked.

LONDON EAST

E2: BETHNAL GREEN

The Approach Tavern
47 Approach Road, Bethnal Green E2 9LY
☎ *(0181) 980 2321* Caroline Apperley

 A freehouse with Morland Old Speckled Hen, Fuller's London Pride, Wadworth 6X and Marston's Pedigree always available. Guests stocked occasionally.

A friendly pub with good atmosphere, decorated with photographs. Gallery, beer garden. Famous local chef who featured in Time Out's top 100 chefs and in Marie Claire – food available 1–2.30pm and 7–10pm Tues–Sun. Children and dogs on lead welcome.

OPEN *12pm–close.*

E3: BOW

The Coborn Arms
8 Coborn Road, Bow E3 2DA
☎ *(0181) 980 3793* Colin Shipley

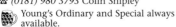 Young's Ordinary and Special always available.

A busy one-bar locals' pub. Food available at lunchtime and evenings. No children.

OPEN *11am–11pm Mon–Sat; 12–10.30pm Sun.*

E5: CLAPTON

The Anchor & Hope
15 High Hill Ferry, Clapton E5 9HG
☎ *(0181) 806 1730* Mr Heath

A Fuller's pub serving ESB and London Pride.

A small, single-bar pub by the river. No food. Children allowed outside only.

OPEN *11am–3pm and 5.30–11pm (10.30pm Sun).*

E7: FOREST GATE

The Old Spotted Dog
212 Upton Lane, Forest Gate E7 9NP
☎ *(0181) 472 1794* Mark Dipple

Marston's Pedigree and Morland Old Speckled Hen always available, plus two guests such as Everards Tiger and Old Original, changing weekly.

A Tudor pub with two large bars, restaurant, family room and children's play area. Bar snacks available at lunchtime, restaurant food available all day. Children allowed.

OPEN *11am–3.30pm and 5–11pm (10.30pm Sun).*

E11: LEYTONSTONE

The Birkbeck Tavern
45 Langthorne Road, Leytonstone E11 4HL
☎ *(0181) 539 2584* Mr Delaney

A freehouse with a house brew (Rita's Special 4%) named after the landlady among the beers always available. Two guests such as Barnsley Bitter or brews from Nethergate and Mighty Oak. Guests changed at least twice a week.

A friendly back-street community pub in a late Victorian building. Two bars, function room and garden. Sandwiches only available. Children allowed in the garden. Near Leyton tube on the Central Line.

OPEN *All day every day*

E14: LIMEHOUSE

The Oporto Tavern
43 West India Dock Road, Limehouse E14 8EZ
☎ *(0171) 987 1530* Steve Baldwin

Three guest beers. Wadworth 6X, Greene King IPA and a Brains brew regularly available. Other guests changed monthly.

A traditional male-dominated boozer set in a Victorian building retaining some original features. One bar, TV, darts, pool, and racing club. Hot food, including specials, and baguettes available 12–3pm. Children allowed in the paved area at front with bench seating.

OPEN *All day, every day.*

E15: STRATFORD

The Golden Grove
146–8 The Grove, Stratford E15 1NS
☎ *(0181) 519 0750* Sue Guyatt

Greene King Abbot Ale and Shepherd Neame Spitfire always available plus three guests such as Hop Back Summer Lightning.

A large Wetherspoon's pub with one bar, non-smoking dining area, no music, disabled access and beer garden. Food available all day. No children.

OPEN *All day, every day.*

E17: WALTHAMSTOW

The Village
31 Orford Road, Walthamstow E17 9NL
☎ *(0181) 521 9982* Gary Leader

Guest ales always available on two hand pumps. Favourites include Adnams Broadside, King and Barnes Sussex, Young's IPA, Sharp's Cornish Coaster, Wolf Golden Jackal and Oakham JHB. Beers changed daily during the winter, two or three times a week in the summer.

A newly refurbished residential pub with one bar and one snug. Large garden. Food available Mon–Fri lunchtimes and some evenings. Children allowed in the snug and the garden. Located near the railway station.

OPEN *11am–11pm (10.30pm Sun).*

LONDON NORTH

N1: HOXTON

The Wenlock Arms
26 Wenlock Road, Hoxton N1 7TA
☎ *(0171) 608 3406* Steven Barnes

A freehouse with Adnams Best and Broadside and Mighty Oak brews regularly available. Plus up to six other guests usually including something from the nearby Pitfield Brewery. Guest beers changed every couple of days.

A one-bar town pub. Sandwiches only available. No children.

OPEN *12–11pm (10.30pm Sun).*

N2: EAST FINCHLEY

Madden's Ale House
130 High Road, East Finchley N2 7ED

Greene King Abbot, Wadworth 6X, Fuller's London Pride and Adnams Broadside always available plus up to eight guests (300 per year) including Ridleys Witchfinder Porter, Ward's Waggle Dance, Gibbs Mew The Bishop's Tipple, Ringwood Old Thumper and Fortyniner etc. Also country wines.

A converted shop on the High Road, not far from East Finchley tube. Bar food available at lunchtime. Children allowed.

OPEN *11am–11pm Mon–Fri; 12–10.30pm Sun.*

N8: CROUCH END

The Hogshead
33–5 Crouch End Hill, Crouch End N8 8DH
☎ *(0181) 342 8465* Clare Gardner

Wadworth 6X, Marston's Pedigree, Fuller's London Pride and an Adnams brew always available, plus up to nine guests, regularly including Young's Special.

A town pub with one bar. Disabled access, no music, two fruit machines. Food available 12–9pm. No children.

OPEN *All day, every day.*

N9: LOWER EDMONTON

The Lamb Inn
52–4 Church Street, Lower Edmonton N9 9PA
☎ *(0181) 887 0128*
Dave and Brenda Andrews

A freehouse with Greene King IPA and Fuller's London Pride among the brews always available, plus up to five guests including, perhaps, Greene King Abbot Ale and Fuller's ESB.

A modern community pub with one large bar, non-smoking dining area and disabled access. Food available all day. Children allowed.

OPEN *All day, every day.*

N16: STOKE NEWINGTON

The Rochester Castle
145 Stoke Newington High Street, Stoke Newington N16 0NY
☎ *(0171) 249 6016* Richard Scrivens

Greene King Abbot and Shepherd Neame Spitfire always available plus six guests each week, rotated on three hand pumps. Regulars include Hop Back Summer Lightning and Fuller's London Pride.

A huge Wetherspoon's pub with one big bar, patio, disabled access and facilities. No music. Board games – chess, backgammon etc. Non-smoking dining area. Food available all day. No children.

OPEN *All day, every day.*

N17: TOTTENHAM

The New Moon
413 Lordship Lane, Tottenham N17 6AG
☎ *(0181) 801 3496* Tom Connelly

A freehouse with Wyre Piddle Piddle in the Wind permanently available, plus three guests stocked to customer order. Customers tick a list of suggested ales each month and the ones with the most ticks win! Badger Tanglefoot is popular.

A large town pub with three bars, dining area, patio, disabled access and facilities. Food available lunchtimes and evenings. Children allowed.

OPEN *All day, every day.*

LONDON NORTHWEST

NW2: CRICKLEWOOD

The Beaten Docket
55–6 Cricklewood Broadway, Cricklewood NW2 3ET
☎ *(0181) 450 2972* Nick Hand

Shepherd Neame Spitfire and Greene King Abbot always available, plus two constantly changing guests.

A two-bar pub with dining area and patio. Music, but no games. Food available all day. No children.

OPEN *All day, every day.*

NW8: ST JOHN'S WOOD

The Clifton Hotel
96 Clifton Hill, St John's Wood NW8 9JT
☎ *(0171) 624 5233* Sheila Hale

Adnams Best and Marston's Pedigree always available, plus two weekly changing guests such as Timothy Taylor Landlord.

A converted house in St John's Wood with a garden at the front and a patio at the back. Mainly a business clientele (average age 25–35ish). Food available 12–10pm with traditional roasts on Sun. Children allowed if eating, but not at the bar. Situated off Abbey Road.

OPEN *All day, every day.*

LONDON SOUTHEAST

SE1: BOROUGH

The George Inn
77 Borough High Street, Borough SE1 1NH
☎ *(0171) 407 2056* George Cunningham

Fuller's London Pride, Morland Old Speckled Hen and Greene King Abbot among the brews always available, plus at least one guest (often seasonal).

A famous galleried sixteenth-century pub, owned by the National Trust. Large courtyard, one bar, servery, courtyard and function room. Food available Mon–Fri lunchtime and Mon–Sat evenings in restaurant. Children allowed.

OPEN *All day, every day.*

The Glove Tavern
8 Bedale Street, Borough SE1 9AL
☎ *(0171) 407 0043*

An Adnams and Young's brew always available, plus four guests such as Greene King Abbot, Morland Old Speckled Hen and Marston's Pedigree.

A traditional town pub with one bar. Background music, bar billiards, game machines. Disabled access. No food. No children.

OPEN *11am–11pm Mon–Fri; closed Sat–Sun but available for private hire.*

The Market Porter
9 Stoney Street, Borough SE1 9AA
☎ *(0171) 407 2495* Tony Hedigan

Harveys Best and Fuller's London Pride always available, plus between five and 15 guests which vary each week.

An old, traditional pub within Borough Market. Food available at lunchtime. Children welcome in the restaurant. Function room available seven days per week for private functions, meetings, etc.

OPEN *11am–11pm Mon–Sat; 12–10.30pm Sun.*

SE5: CAMBERWELL

Fox in the Hill
149 Denmark Hill, Camberwell SE5 8EH
☎ *(0171) 738 4756* Mark Gardner

Shepherd Neame Spitfire and Hop Back Summer Lightning among the brews always available plus a wide range of guests.

A large, modern Wetherspoon's pub with one bar, non-smoking dining area, garden and disabled facilities. Food available all day. Children allowed in the non-smoking area only.

OPEN *All day, every day.*

Hermit's Cave
*28 Camberwell Church Street, Camberwell
SE5 8QU*
☎ *(0171) 703 3188*

Twelve beers available including Morland Old Speckled Hen, Marston's Pedigree, Gales HSB, Fuller's London Pride and Adnams Best. Micro-brewers provide the guest beers.

B uilt in 1902, this beamed pub serves bar food at lunchtime and evenings. Street parking. Children not allowed.

OPEN *11am–11pm Mon–Sat; 12–10.30pm Sun.*

SE8: DEPTFORD

The Dog & Bell
116 Prince Street, Deptford SE8 3JD
☎ *(0181) 692 5664*

Five beers always available. Brews might include Fuller's London Pride and ESB, Shepherd Neame Spitfire, Nethergate Bitter and something from Larkins or Archers.

B uilt in 1850 and recently extended. Bar food available. Street parking, garden. Children aged 14 and over allowed. Tucked away, not far from the railway station.

OPEN *11am–11pm Mon–Sat; 12–5pm and 7–10.30pm Sun.*

SE13: LEWISHAM

The Watch House
*198–204 Lewisham High Street, Lewisham
SE13 6JP*
☎ *(0181) 318 3136* Steve Asprey

Shepherd Neame Spitfire and Hop Back Summer Lightning among the brews always available plus up to five guests from breweries such as Bateman, Ash Vine, JW Lees, Nethergate and Cotleigh.

A town-centre pub with a mature clientele. No music. Patio, non-smoking area, disabled facilities. Food available all day. No children.

OPEN *All day, every day.*

SE20: PENGE

Moon & Stars
164–6 High Street, Penge SE20 7QS
☎ *(0181) 776 5680* Lenny Bignall

Shepherd Neame Spitfire, Greene King IPA and Abbot and Hop Back Summer Lightning among the beers always available, plus up to six guests.

A large Wetherspoon's pub. Disabled facilities. Non-smoking dining area, beer garden. Food available all day. No children.

OPEN *All day, every day.*

SE25: SOUTH NORWOOD

The Alliance
91 High Street, South Norwood SE25 6EA
☎ *(0181) 653 3604* Mr Goodridge

Wadworth 6X and Marston's Pedigree always available, plus one guest such as Timothy Taylor Landlord, Hook Norton Old Hooky, Hop Back Summer Lightning or Cotleigh Barn Owl.

A traditional pub with bar snacks available at lunchtime. Children allowed

OPEN *11am–11pm Mon–Sat; 12–10.30pm Sun.*

LONDON SOUTHWEST

SW1: WHITEHALL

Lord Moon of the Mall
16–18 Whitehall, Trafalgar Square SW1A 2DY
☎ *(0171) 839 7701* James Langan

Fuller's London Pride and Shepherd Neame Spitfire always available, plus four guests such as Ridleys Rumpus, Hop Back Summer Lightning, Everards Tiger, Exmoor Gold, Smiles Golden and Batemans XXXB.

A city pub with high ceilings, arches and oak fittings. Non-smoking area, disabled facilities. Food available all day. No children.

OPEN *All day, every day.*

SW2: BRIXTON

The Crown & Sceptre
2a Streatham Hill, Brixton SW2 4AH
☎ *(0181) 671 0843*

Shepherd Neame Spitfire among the brews always available plus two guests such as Hop Back Summer Lightning and ales from Adnams or Cotleigh.

O ne big bar, non-smoking dining area, front and rear patios. Food available all day. Children allowed in the garden only.

OPEN *All day, every day.*

SW4: CLAPHAM

The Bread & Roses
68 Clapham Manor Street, Clapham SW4 6DZ
☎ *(0181) 498 1779* Peter Dawson

A freehouse with Adnams Best and Workers Ale (a house ale brewed by Smiles) always available, plus two guests, perhaps Adnams Regatta, Old Ale or Broadside, Oakhill Mendip Gold or O'Hanlon's Red Ale.

A bright, modern town pub. Bar and function room, front and rear garden, disabled access and toilets. Food available at lunchtime and evenings. Children allowed during the day in the non-smoking area only.

OPEN *11am–11pm Mon–Sat; 12–10.30pm Sun.*

SW6: FULHAM

The White Horse
1 Parsons Green, Fulham SW6 44L
☎ *(0171) 736 2115*
Mark Dorber and Rupert Reeves

Harveys Sussex, Adnams Extra and Highgate Mild always available plus guests including Adnams Tally Ho, Barley Mow, Old and Summer Ale, Archers Golden, Bateman Strawberry Fields and Salem Porter, Cains Traditional, Formidable, Stout and Mild, also Rooster's, Lees, Robinson's, Shepherd Neame and Young's.

A large, comfortable Victorian pub overlooking Parsons Green, with a big reputation for good cask and bottled beers, flavoursome wines and food served at lunchtime and evenings. Regular beer festivals. Parking, terrace/garden. Children allowed. Just 100 yards from Parsons Green tube station.

OPEN *All day, every day.*

SW7: CHELSEA

The Anglesea Arms
15 Selwood Terrace, Chelsea SW7 3GG
☎ *(0171) 373 7960*

Seven beers always available including Adnams Best, Marston's Pedigree, Greene King Abbot, Fuller's London Pride and Young's Special. Guest beers are rotated monthly.

A lively, easy-to-find, 200-year-old pub with bar food available at lunchtime. Patio garden. Children over 14 allowed. Just off the Fulham Road.

OPEN *11am–11pm Mon–Sat; 12–4pm and 7–10.30pm Sun.*

SW8: STOCKWELL

The Priory Arms
83 Lansdowne Way, Stockwell SW8 2PB
☎ *(0171) 622 1884* Gary Morris

Young's Bitter and Special always available plus four guests (350 per year) from breweries such as Woodforde's, Hop Back, Hogs Back, Jennings and Goddards.

R ecently refurbished. Bar food available at lunchtime. CAMRA pub of the year. Near Stockwell tube station.

OPEN *11am–11pm Mon–Fri; 12–3pm and 7–10.30pm Sun.*

SW9: BRIXTON

The Beehive
409 Brixton Road, Brixton SW9 7DG
☎ *(0171) 738 3643* Peter Martin

Shepherd Neame Spitfire permanently available, plus three guests such as Hop Back Summer Lightning, Greene King Abbot or Strawberry Blonde.

One bar, non-smoking dining area, disabled access. Food available all day. No children.

OPEN *All day, every day.*

SW18: WANDSWORTH

The Spotted Dog
72 Garratt Lane, Wandsworth SW18 4DJ
☎ *(0181) 875 9531* Colin Daniels

Fuller's London Pride and ESB and Greene King IPA and Abbot always available, plus two guests such as Jennings Cocker Hoop, Fuller's Summer Ale and Greene King Centenary. Beers changed weekly.

A traditional one-bar town pub with food available 12–4pm. Disabled facilities. Patio. Children allowed if dining.

OPEN *All day, every day.*

W1: SOHO

The Argyll Arms

18 Argyll Street, Soho W1 1AA
☎ *(0171) 734 6117* Mike Tayara

Seven beers always available including Wadworth 6X and an ever-changing selection that might feature Everards Daredevil, Hop Back Summer Lightning, Felinfoel Double Dragon, Charles Wells Bombardier and brews from Jennings, Ringwood, Tomintoul etc.

A 300-year-old pub just off Oxford Circus owned by the Duke of Argyll. Air-conditioned. Bar and restaurant food available at lunchtime and evenings. Function room, non-smoking area. Children allowed in play area.

[OPEN] *11am–11pm Mon–Sat; 12–10.30pm Sun.*

The Blue Posts

18 Kingley Street, Soho W1R 5LB
☎ *(0171) 734 1170* Trevor Mayer

Marston's Pedigree, Fuller's London Pride and Greene King Abbot always available, plus one fortnightly changing guest such as Morland Old Speckled Hen and Wadworth 6X.

A traditional English tavern with two bars, wooden floors, beams, dining area, juke box and front patio. Food served 11am–3pm daily. Live jazz festival with bands every 2–3 months. Children allowed. Located behind Hamley's.

[OPEN] *11am–11pm (10.30pm Sun).*

W2: LANCASTER GATE

Archery Tavern

4 Bathurst Street, Lancaster Gate W2 2SD
☎ *(0171) 402 4916* Tony O'Neil

A Hall & Woodhouse tied pub with Badger Dorset Best, Tanglefoot and IPA always available, plus two guests such as Gribble Black Adder II or Golden Champion Ale.

A one-bar traditional pub. Fruit machines, quiz machine, darts. Food available 12–10pm. Well-behaved children allowed.

[OPEN] *All day, every day.*

YOU TELL US

★ *Ain't Nothing But,* 20 Kingly Street, W1
★ *The Britannia,* Allen Street, Kensington
★ *The Blue Eyed Maid,* 173 Borough High Street, SE1
★ *The Carpenter's Arms,* 12 Seymour Place, Marylebone, W1
★ *The Clifton Arms,* 21 Clifton Road, SE25
★ *The Cock & Woolpack,* 6 Finch Lane, EC3
★ *The Cross Keys,* 57 Black Lion Lane, Hammersmith, W6
★ *The Crown,* Dovehouse Street, SW3
★ *Crystal Palace Tavern,* 105 Tanner's Hill, SE8
★ *The Flask,* 77 Highgate West Hill, Highgate
★ *The George,* High Street, Wanstead, E11
★ *Haggards,* 577 Kings Road, London (brewpub)
★ *The Head of Steam,* Euston Station, NW1
★ *The Hedgehog & Hogshead,* 259 Upper Street, Highbury Corner, N1
★ *The King Edward VII,* 47 The Broadway, E15
★ *Kings Ford,* 250 Chingford Mount Road, Chingford, E4
★ *The Lord Rodney's Head,* 285 Whitechapel Road, E1
★ *O'Hanlon's,* 8 Tysoe Street, EC1
★ *The Orange Tree,* 18 Highfield Road, Winchmore Hill, N21
★ *Pacific Oriental Bar,* 1 Bishopsgate EC2 (brewpub)
★ *Parisa Café Bar,* 146 Putney High Street, SW15 (brewpub)
★ *Portmanor,* 1 Portland Road, SE26
★ *The Pride of Spitalfields,* 3 Heneage Street, Spitalfields, E1
★ *The Prince Albert,* 49 Hare Street, Woolwich, SE18
★ *The Prince Arthur,* 95 Forest Road, Dalston, E8
★ *The Railway,* Crouch End Broadway, N4
★ *The Red Lion,* 13 St Mary's Road, Ealing, W5
★ *The Shipwright's Arms,* 88 Tookley Street, Borough SE1
★ *The Spread Eagle,* 141 Albert Street, Camden Town, NW1
★ *Tally Ho,* 749 High Road, North Finchley
★ *The Tap & Spile,* 29 Crouch Hill, N4
★ *The Tappit Hen,* 295 Holloway Road, N7
★ *The Trinity Arms,* 29 Swan Street, SE1
★ *The Truscott Arms,* 55 Shirland Road, Maida Vale, W9
★ *Warrington Hotel,* 93 Warrington Crescent, Maida Vale, W9
★ *The Wheatsheaf,* 6 Stoney Street, Borough, SE1
★ *The William IV,* 816 High Road, Leyton, E10

Places Featured:

Barking	Ilford
Barnet	Isleworth
Bexleyheath	Kingston-upon-Thames
Brentford	North Cheam
Bromley	Petts Wood
Carshalton	Romford
Feltham	Staines
Hampton	Stanmore
Harefield	Surbiton
Heathrow	Uxbridge
Hounslow	Woodford Green

BARKING

The Britannia
1 Church Road, Barking, Essex IG11 8PR
☎ *(0181) 594 1305* Mrs Pells

A Young's pub with Special and Bitter always available, plus a winter warmer from October and various specials in summer.

An old-fashioned community alehouse with public bar, saloon/lounge bar and snug. Patio. Food available at lunchtime and evenings. No children. Can be extremely difficult to find – ring if need be.

OPEN *11am–3pm and 5–11.30pm Mon–Fri; all day Sat–Sun.*

BARNET

Moon Under Water
148 High Street, Barnet, Hertfordshire EN5 5XP
☎ *(0181) 441 9476* Gareth Fleming

A Wetherspoon's pub with Greene King IPA and Abbot plus Shepherd Neame Spitfire always available. Also three guests such as Hop Back Summer Lightning which are changed on a weekly basis.

An olde-worlde town pub with one large bar, a non-smoking dining area and big beer garden. Food available from 11am–10pm. No children.

OPEN *All day, every day.*

BEXLEYHEATH

Robin Hood & Little John
78 Lion Road, Bexleyheath, Kent DA6 8PF
☎ *(0181) 303 1128* Mr Johnson

A freehouse with Shepherd Neame Spitfire and Golding, Burtonwood Bitter, plus Flagship Destroyer & Futtock, Timothy Taylor Landlord and others regularly available. The least popular brew is dropped each month to try something different. Up to eight pumps in operation.

A one-bar, village-type pub with wood panel walls and old Singer sewing machine tables. Beer garden. Food available at lunchtime only, Mon–Sat. No children.

OPEN *11am–3.30pm and 6–11pm; 7–11pm weekends.*

BRENTFORD

The Magpie & Crown
128 High Street, Brentford, Middlesex TW8 8EW
☎ *(0181) 560 5658* Charlie and Steve Bolton

A freehouse with four pumps serving a range of ales such as Brakspear Bitter, Greene King IPA, something from Cottage and many, many more.

A mock-Tudor pub. One bar. No food. No children.

OPEN *11am–11pm (10.30pm Sun).*

The Red Lion
10 North Road, Bromley, Kent BR1 3LG
☎ *(0181) 460 2691* Mr and Mrs Humphrey

 Beers from Beards and Harveys, plus Greene King Abbot always available with two guest pumps regularly serving Shepherd Neame Golding among others. Guests changed twice weekly

A locals' pub, with food available at lunchtime and evenings. Children allowed.

OPEN *All day, every day.*

The Racehorse
17 West Street, Carshalton, Surrey SM5 2PT
☎ *(0181) 647 6818* Julian Norton

 A freehouse with King and Barnes Sussex among the brews always on sale, plus usually three guests such as Fuller's London Pride and ESB and beers from Gales and Morland. Guests changed every few days.

A locals' pub with two bars, dining area, disabled access and patio. Food available at lunchtime and evenings (not Sunday pm).

OPEN *11am–11pm Mon–Sat; 12–4pm and 7–10.30pm Sun.*

Moon on the Square
30 The Centre, Feltham, Middlesex TW13 4AU
☎ *(0181) 893 1293* Phil Cripps

Fuller's London Pride and Marston's Pedigree always available, plus four guests changing all the time, from breweries such as Brakspear, Cotleigh, Hook Norton and Exmoor.

One big bar plus non-smoking dining area in which food is available all day. No children.

OPEN *All day, every day.*

The White Hart
70 High Street, Hampton, Middlesex TW12 2SW
☎ *(0181) 979 5352* Mrs Macintosh

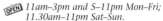 Greene King Abbot is among those beers always available plus six guest beers (hundreds per year) including ales from Ringwood, Pilgrim, Nethergate, Hop Back, Archers, Hogs Back, Brakspear, Gales, Shepherd Neame, Charles Wells, Titanic, Woodforde's and Harviestoun breweries.

Mock-Tudor pub in an historical area with a log fire in winter and large patio area. No darts or pool. Home-made bar food served at lunchtime and a Thai restaurant in the evenings. Car park, garden and function room with bar. Close to Hampton BR station. Easy access from the M3 and A316. On main bus routes from Richmond, Heathrow and Wimbledon.

OPEN *11am–3pm and 5–11pm Mon–Fri; 11.30am–11pm Sat–Sun.*

The Plough
Hill End Road, Harefield, Middlesex UB9 6LQ
☎ *(01895) 822129* Mr and Mrs Knight

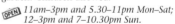 Ruddles Best, Fuller's London Pride and Brakspear ales always available up to six guests including Chiltern Beechwood and Black Sheep Bitter. Half a mile past the main entrance to Harefield Hospital.

A country-style family pub. Bar food available at lunchtime. Car park and garden. Children allowed.

OPEN *11am–3pm and 5.30–11pm Mon–Sat; 12–3pm and 7–10.30pm Sun.*

The Tap & Spile
Upper Concourse, Terminal One, Heathrow Airport, Middlesex UB5 4PX
☎ *(0181) 897 8418* John Heaphy

Marston's Pedigree always available plus up to nine guest beers (50 per year) including Rooster's Bitter, Charles Wells Eagle, Brains SA, Nethergate IPA and Adnams Best.

Cosy and relaxing refuge with a 1930s feel overlooking the anarchy of the check-in area. Bar food available at lunchtime and evenings. Car park and children's room. On the catering balcony at departure level in terminal one.

OPEN *9–11am for breakfast, then 11am–11pm.*

HOUNSLOW

Moon Under Water

84–6 Staines Road, Hounslow, Middlesex
TW3 3LF
☎ *(0181) 572 7506* Gary Hancock

Fuller's London Pride and Shepherd Neame Spitfire always available plus two guests such as Hop Back Summer Lightning.

A Wetherspoon's pub with non-smoking area, beer garden, patio, disabled facilities. Food available all day from 11am–10pm. No children.

OPEN *All day, every day.*

ILFORD

The Rose & Crown

16 Ilford Hill, Ilford, Essex IG1 2DA
☎ *(0181 0 478 7104* Neil Smith

Marston's Pedigree and Adnams Best always available along with a monthly selection which might include Shepherd Neame Spitfire or a special brew. Five guest pumps, two changed daily.

A town pub just off the high street with beams and log fires. One bar with dining area and a small terrace. Food available 12–2.30pm Mon–Fri. Children allowed if eating.

OPEN *12–11pm Mon–Sat; 10am–12.30pm Sun.*

ISLEWORTH

The Red Lion

94 Linkfield Road, Isleworth, Middlesex
TW7 6QJ
☎ *(0181) 560 1457* Nicky Redding

A freehouse with up to seven beers available each week. These regularly include Cottage Golden Arrow and other Cottage brews. Guests changed every two days.

A large, friendly, locals' pub in a back street near the station, with live music and a relaxed atmosphere. Two bars and a large garden with BBQs on weekdays and all day Friday, sometimes weekends. Food available 12–3pm Mon–Fri. Children allowed in the garden only.

OPEN *11am–11pm.*

KINGSTON-UPON-THAMES

The Fighting Cocks

56 London Road, Kingston-upon-Thames, Surrey
KT2 6QA
☎ *(0181) 546 5174* Natalie Salt

Wadworth 6X among the brews always available plus two guests such as Marston's Pedigree.

A town pub with wooden floors and panelled walls. Two bars and courtyard. No food. Children allowed.

OPEN *11am–11pm.*

The Kelly Arms

2 Glenthorne Road, Kingston-upon-Thames,
Surrey KT1 2UB
☎ *(0181) 296 9815* Vanessa McConnon

Two guests always available. Marston's Pedigree and beers from Wychwood Brewery appear regularly, plus others such as Hop Back Summer Lightning and Timothy Taylor Landlord.

A back-street, locals' pub, with one big bar, pool tables, darts, pinball and skittles. Garden with BBQ. Food available all day. Children allowed if eating or in garden. Situated off the beaten track, near Alfred Road.

OPEN *11am–11pm Mon–Sat; 12–10.30pm Sun.*

NORTH CHEAM

Wetherspoons

552–6 London Road, North Cheam, Surrey
SM3 9AA
☎ *(0181) 644 1808* Dean Kelly

A Wetherspoon's pub with Fuller's London Pride always available plus two guests such as Shepherd Neame Spitfire. Guests changed every three days

One large bar and non-smoking dining area. Food available all day. Disabled facilities. No children.

OPEN *All day, every day.*

PETTS WOOD

Sovereign of the Seas

109 Queensway, Petts Wood, Orpington, Kent
BR5 1DG
☎ *(01689) 891606* Robert Barfoot

A Wetherspoon's pub with Shepherd Neame Spitfire among the brews always available. Two guests might include Hop Back Summer Lightning, or Timothy Taylor Landlord. Guests changed weekly.

A community pub with one big bar, a non-smoking dining area and disabled facilities. Outside patios in summer. Food available all day. No children.

OPEN *All day, every day.*

ROMFORD

The Moon & Stars

103 South Street, Romford, Essex RM1 1NX
☎ *(01708) 730117* Sarah Saye

A Wetherspoon's pub with Greene King Abbot and Shepherd Neame Spitfire among the beers always available. Four guest ales change on a weekly basis.

L arge bar, non-smoking dining area, outside seating, disabled facilities. Food available all day. Children allowed outside only.

[OPEN] *All day, every day.*

STAINES

The Angel Hotel

Angel Mews, High Street, Staines, Middlesex TW18 4EE
☎ *(01784) 452509* John Mortimer

A freehouse with Hogs Back Hair of the Hog and an Adnams brew regularly available. Five guest pumps are varied as much as possible and changed twice a week.

A town pub and restaurant with patio garden and 11 bedrooms. Food available at lunchtime and evenings. Children allowed.

[OPEN] *11am–11pm.*

The George

2–8 High Street, Staines, Middlesex TW18 4EE
☎ *(01784) 462181* Jim Conlin

Fuller's London Pride and Greene King Abbot among the beers always available plus four guests such as Marston's Pedigree, Shepherd Neame Spitfire and Morland Old Speckled Hen. Always a good selection of brews from all over the UK. Guests changed monthly

A large, two-level Wetherspoon's pub. No music, non-smoking dining areas upstairs and down, disabled access and toilets. Food available all day. No children.

[OPEN] *All day, every day.*

The Hobgoblin

14–16 Church Street, Staines, Middlesex TW18 4EP
☎ *(01784)452012* Del Woolsgrove

Wychwood Special, Shires XXX and Hobgoblin always available. Three guests could include Marston's Pedigree, Charles Wells Bombardier and beers from Hampshire and Rebellion breweries.

A town-centre, regulars' pub, frequented by the 23–35 age group in evenings, with an older clientele at lunchtimes. An old building with wooden floors and beams, one bar and courtyard. Food available 12–2.30pm. Children allowed in courtyard if open.

[OPEN] *12–11pm Mon–Sat (10.30pm) Sun.*

STANMORE

The Malthouse

7 Stanmore Hill, Stanmore, Middlesex HA7 3DP
☎ *(0181) 420 7265* Charles Begley

A freehouse serving a range of four constantly changing real ales. Favourites include Wadworth 6X and beers from breweries such as Rebellion, Slaters, Ringwood, Cottage and Greene King.

A modern pub decorated in an old-style. Late licence. Garden, disabled access. Food available lunchtimes only. Children allowed.

[OPEN] *11am–11pm Mon–Tues; 11am–12pm Wed–Thurs; 11am–1am Fri–Sat; 11am–10.30pm Sun.*

SURBITON

Coronation Hall

St Mark's Hill, Surbiton, Surrey KT6 4TB
☎ *(0181) 390 6164* Emma Wales

A Wetherspoon's pub with Shepherd Neame Spitfire and Fuller's London Pride always available. Three guest pumps changed twice a week, which might include Hop Back Summer Lightning.

L arge bar area, non-smoking dining area and disabled facilities. Food available all day. No children.

[OPEN] *All day, every day.*

UXBRIDGE

The Load of Hay

Villier Street, Uxbridge, Middlesex UB8 2PU
☎ *(01895) 234676* Heather Winsbottom

A freehouse with Buckley's Best always available plus three guests from breweries such as Wye Valley, Everards, Rebellion and Cottage – a different one appears each week. Local breweries, micros and small independents favoured.

S ituated on the outskirts of town, near the university. University clientele during the daytime, and locals in the evenings. Two bars. Beer garden. Food available every lunchtime and Mon–Sat evenings. Children allowed in the smaller bar area and the garden. In a secluded location – ring for directions if necessary.

[OPEN] *11am–3pm and 5.30–11pm Mon–Fri; 11am–3pm and 7–close Sat–Sun.*

The Cricketers

*299–301 High Road, Woodford Green, Essex
IG8 9EG*

☎ *(0181) 504 2734* Mr and Mrs Woolridge

Owned by McMullen, so AK Original, Gladstone and Country Best Bitter always served, with specials and seasonals when available.

A semi-rural pub with lounge and public bars and beer garden. Food available 12–2pm Mon–Sat, with OAP specials Mon–Thurs. Children allowed till 7.30pm. Situated near the statue of Winston Churchill.

*11am–3.30pm and 5.30–11pm
Mon–Thurs; all day Fri–Sun.*

★ *The Albany*, Station Yard, Twickenham
★ *The Beaconsfield Arms*, 63 West End Road, Southall
★ *The Canford Arms*, Canford Park Road, Kingston-upon-Thames
★ *Claret Free House*, 5A Bingham Corner, Lower Addiscombe Road, Addiscombe
★ *The Cricketer's Arms*, 21 Southbridge Place, Croydon
★ *The Cricketers*, 93 Chislehurst Road, Orpington
★ *The Dolphin*, 13 Lower Boston Road, Hanwell
★ *The Eel Pie Pub*, 11 Church Street, Twickenham, Middlesex
★ *The Five Bells*, Church Road, Chelsfield
★ *The George*, 17 George Street, Croydon
★ *The Greyhound*, 82 Kew Green, Kew
★ *Hedgehog & Hogshead*, 2 High Street, Sutton
★ *Hogshead*, 35 York Street, Twickenham
★ *The Moon under Water*, 194 Balham High Road, Balham
★ *The Pit Bar*, Billet Lane, Hornchurch
★ *The Royal Standard*, 39 Nuxley Road, Upper Belvedere
★ *The Windsor Castle*, 378 Carshalton Road, Carshalton
★ *The Woodman*, 50 High Street, Farnborough Village
★ *The Wrong 'un*, 234 Broadway, Bexleyheath

Places Featured:

Ashton-under-Lyne
Atherton
Bolton
Bury
Castleton
Cheetham
Delph
Failsworth
Hawkshaw

Heywood
Hindley
Hyde
Manchester
Oldham
Rochdale
Salford
Stalybridge (*see* Cheshire)
Wigan

THE BREWERIES

BANK TOP BREWERY

*Unit 1, Back Lane, Vernon Street, Bolton
BL1 2LD*
☎ *(01204) 528865*

 BRIDGE BITTER 3.8% ABV
FRED'S CAP 4.0% ABV
GOLD DIGGER 4.0% ABV
SAMUEL CROMPTON'S ALE 4.2% ABV
CLIFFHANGER 4.5% ABV
SMOKESTACK LIGHTNIN' 5.0% ABV
Plus seasonal brews

BRIDGEWATER ALES LTD

42 Chapel Street, Salford M3 6AF
☎ *(0161) 831 9090*

 NAVIGATOR 3.7% ABV
BARTON ALE 4.3% ABV
DELPH PORTER 4.5% ABV

J W LEES & CO.

*Greengate Brewery, Middleton Junction,
Manchester M24 2AX*
☎ *(0161) 643 2487*

GB MILD 3.5% ABV
Smooth and sweet, with a malt flavour
and a dry finish.
BITTER 4.0% ABV
Refreshing maltiness, with a bitter finish.
MOONRAKER 7.5% ABV
Rounded sweetness, with balancing bitterness.
Plus seasonal brews.

JOSEPH HOLT PLC

*Derby Brewery, Empire Street, Cheetham,
Manchester M3 1JD*
☎ *(0161) 834 3285*

 MILD 3.2% ABV
Malty with good hoppiness.
BITTER 4.0% ABV
Powerful, hoppy and bitter throughout.
DBA 4.5% ABV
150th Anniversary Ale.

HYDES' ANVIL BREWERY LTD

46 Moss Lane West, Manchester M15 5PH
☎ *(0161) 226 1317*

 BITTER 3.8% ABV
CENTENARY ALE

PHOENIX BREWERY

*Oak Brewing Co., Green Lane, Heywood, Greater
Manchester OL10 2EP*
☎ *(01706) 627009*

 BANTAM BITTER 3.5% ABV
OAK BEST BITTER 3.9% ABV
HOPWOOD BITTER 4.3% ABV
OLD OAK ALE 4.5% ABV
THIRSTY MOON 4.6% ABV
BONNEVILLE 4.8% ABV
WOBBLY BOB 6.0% ABV
Plus seasonal brews

THE PUBS

ASHTON-UNDER-LYNE

The Station

2 Warrington Street, Ashton-under-Lyne
OL6 6XB
☎ *(0161) 330 6776* Susan Watson

Marston's Pedigree and Station Bitter (a special brew) among the beers always available, plus up to six guests, perhaps including Timothy Taylor Landlord and Hydes' Anvil Bitter.

A traditional Victorian freehouse filled with railway memorabilia. Beer garden, happy hours on weekdays from 3–8pm, 4–8pm (Sat) and 12–5pm (Sun). Entertainment on Friday and Saturday nights. Food served at lunchtime and evenings. Children allowed.

12–11pm (10.30pm Sun).

The Witchwood

152 Old Street, Ashton-under-Lyne OL6 7SF
☎ *(0161) 344 0321* Pauline Town

Marston's Pedigree and Moorhouse's Pendle Witches Brew among the beers always available, plus four guests from a range of 15 independent brewers.

A real ale bar and live music venue six days a week. Two bars, beer garden. Food available. No children.

12–11pm (10.30pm Sun).

ATHERTON

The Pendle Witch

2–4 Warburton Place, Atherton, Manchester M46 0EQ
☎ *(01942) 884537* Joan Houghton

Tied to Moorhouse's with Premier and Pendle Witches Brew always available plus a couple of others, perhaps Moorhouse's seasonal ales or specials such as Bursting Bitter, Black Witch, Black Panther, Thunder Struck, Black Cat or Easter Ale.

A 100-year-old cottage pub. Light snacks only available. Beer garden. Children allowed inside in the afternoons, or in the garden. Situated off Market Street.

All day, every day.

BOLTON

The Clifton Arms

94 Newport Street, Bolton, BL3 6AB
☎ *(01204) 392738* Peter Morris

Moorhouse's Bitter and Jennings Bitter among the beers always available, plus a good range (up to four new ones per week) available on a guest basis. Regular breweries featured are Black Sheep, Broughton and Caledonian. Three beer festivals held each year with 20 different beers served over 14 days.

A traditional local situated opposite the railway station. Food available during the daytime only. No children.

11am–11pm Mon–Sat; 7–10.30pm Sun.

The Hen & Chickens

Deansgate, Bolton BL1 1EX
☎ *(01204) 389836* Anthony Coyne

Greenalls Bitter and Mild always available, plus three constantly changing guests such as Wadworth 6X, Timothy Taylor Landlord, Robinson's Best, Marston's Pedigree or Young's Special.

A traditional pub situated near the post office. Home-made food served at lunchtime only. Children allowed at lunchtime only.

11.30am–11pm Mon–Sat; 7–10.30pm Sun.

Howcroft Inn

36 Pool Street, Bolton BL1 2JU
☎ *(01204) 526814* Clive Knightingale

Walkers Best and Dark Mild and Timothy Taylor Landlord always available plus three guests, often from Bank Top Brewery, such as Samuel Crompton's Ale and Gold Digger or from Hart, Phoenix or Moorhouse's. Micro-breweries favoured.

A traditional pub with a broad clientele. Beer garden and bowling green. Food served every lunchtime, including Sundays. Children allowed.

12–11pm.

Dusty Miller

87 Crostons Road, Bury BL8 1AL
☎ *(0161) 764 1124* Sue Johnson

A Moorhouse's pub with Premier, Pendle Witches Brew and Black Cat Mild always available. Three guests served including, perhaps, Everards Old Original, Ridleys Rumpus, Charles Wells Eagle IPA, Gales Anniversary, Mansfield Old Baily, Cotleigh Old Buzzard or a Crown Buckley brew.

A traditional local pub. No food. No car park. Children allowed in the conservatory only. Located between Walshaw and Toddington.

OPEN *2–11pm Mon–Thurs; 12–11pm Fri–Sun.*

Midland Beer Company

826 Manchester Road, Castleton, Rochdale OL11 3AW
☎ *(01706) 750873* Mr Welsby

A freehouse with Thwaites Bitter and Webster's Green Label available, plus two guests such as Timothy Taylor Best and Landlord, Mallard IPA or a Cottage Brewery ale.

A traditional pub in an old bank building with beer garden. Food available. Children allowed. Opposite Castleton railway station.

OPEN *All day, every day.*

The Queen's Arms

Honey Street, Cheetham M8 8RG
☎ *(0161) 834 4239*

Eight beers always available, usually including Timothy Taylor Landlord and Phoenix Bantam. Others change constantly. Also a wide range of Belgian beers.

A traditional town pub built in the 1800s and subsequently extended. Bar food available at lunchtime and until 8pm. Street parking, children's play area and garden.

OPEN *12–11pm (10.30pm Sun)*

Royal Oak Inn

Broad Lane Heights, Delph, Saddleworth OL3 5TX
☎ *(01457) 874460* Michael and Sheila Fancy

A freehouse with Moorhouse's Black Cat Mild and Bitter always available plus four guest ales often including Fuller's London Pride or brews from Black Sheep or Jennings.

B uilt in 1767 this is an unspoilt pub with low beams, open fires and dining area. Situated in a remote setting off the Delph–Denshaw road, with good views over Saddleworth Moor. Food available Fri–Sun only. Children allowed.

OPEN *7–11pm Mon–Fri (closed lunchtime); 12–3pm and 7–11pm Sat–Sun.*

The Millgate

Ashton Road West, Failsworth M35 0ES
☎ *(0161) 681 8284* David McConvile

A freehouse with Joseph Holt Bitter and Willy Booth's Best (a house beer supplied by Bridgewater Ales) plus two guests such as Liverpool Blondie.

A family-oriented pub with log fires, restaurant, beer garden and children's play area. Food available. Children allowed.

OPEN *11am–11pm (10.30pm Sun).*

The Red Lion Hotel

81 Ramsbottom Road, Hawkshaw, Bury BL8 4JS
☎ *(01204) 856600* Carl Owen

A Jennings brewery house with a range of Jennings brews always available. Two guest pumps, often serving a Bank Top beer.

A traditional pub and restaurant. Bar and restaurant food available. Children allowed.

OPEN *12–3pm and 6–11pm Mon–Sat; all day Sun.*

HEYWOOD

The Wishing Well
89 York Street, Heywood OL10 4NS
☎ *(01706) 620923 Mr TM Huck*

A freehouse with Moorhouse's Pendle Witches Brew and Premier, Phoenix Hopwood, Jennings Cumberland and Timothy Taylor Landlord usually available, plus two rotating guests from a vast range of independent and micro-breweries.

A traditional pub with dining area. Food available at lunchtime and evenings. Children allowed.

OPEN *All day, every day.*

HINDLEY

The Edington Arms
186 Ladies Lane, Hindley
☎ *(01942) 259229*

Holt Mild and Bitter always available plus up to nine guests (200 per year).

An old coaching house with two large, comfortable rooms. No food. Parking and garden. Children allowed. A CAMRA pub of the year. Function room upstairs. Next to Hindley railway station.

OPEN *All day, every day.*

HYDE

The Sportsman
58 Mottram Road, Hyde SK14 2NN
☎ *(0161) 368 5000 Geoff Oliver*

A freehouse with Plassey Bitter and Hartington Bitter always available, plus two guests from an ever-changing list including Timothy Taylor Landlord, Whim Magic Mushroom Mild or a Robinson's brew.

A traditional alehouse with open fires. Bar food available at lunchtime. Well-supervised children allowed. Near the railway station at Newton St Hyde Central.

OPEN *All day, every day.*

MANCHESTER

The Beerhouse
Angel Street, Manchester
☎ *(0161) 839 7019*

Moorhouse's Pendle Witches Brew and Burtonwood Bitter always available plus up to ten other real ales (up to 300 per year) from a wide range of breweries.

A popular, recently refurbished traditional alehouse off the Rochdale Road, just beyond Mill Street. Bar food is available at lunchtime and Wednesday to Friday evenings. Garden, bar billiards, family room, function room. Children over 14 years allowed before 7pm.

OPEN *11am–11pm Mon–Sat; 12–10.30pm Sun.*

The Lass o'Gowrie
36 Charles Street, Manchester M1 7DB
☎ *(0161) 273 6932 Joe Fylan*

Two house brews always available plus three guests from a range of 150 per year to include Morland Old Speckled Hen, Timothy Taylor Landlord and Marston's Pedigree.

A Victorian tiled pub with an open view to the cellar and gas lighting. Bar food available at lunchtime. Close to BBC North. Parking nearby. Children allowed.

OPEN *11am–11pm Mon–Sat; 12–10.30pm Sun.*

Marble Arch Inn
73 Rochdale Road, Manchester M4 4HY
☎ *(0161) 832 5914 Mr Dade*

Home of the Marble Brewery, with a range of up to ten beers produced and served on the premises.

A Victorian pub dating from 1880, with mosaic floor, brick ceiling with ornate frieze made of marble. The micro-brewery was installed in December 1998. No food. No children.

DADES BITTER 3.8% ABV
SPOOKY MARBLE 3.8% ABV
Halloween brew.
MARBLE BITTER 4% ABV
LIBERTY IPA 4.6% ABV
SUMMER MARBLE 4.7% ABV
MCKENNA'S REVENGE PORTER 5% ABV
TOTALLY MARBLED 5.9% ABV
GINGER MARBLE 6% ABV
Summer brew.
DOBBER 6.5% ABV
WEE STAR 8.6% ABV
Christmas special.

OPEN *All day Mon–Sat; closed Sun.*

Sand Bar

*120 Grosvenor Street, All Saints, Manchester
M1 7HL*
☎ *(0161) 273 3141* Rob Loyeau

A freehouse with Phoenix Bantam and Charles Wells Bombardier always available, plus three guests from breweries such as Abbeydale, Goose Eye, Kelham Island, Eccleshall, Burton Bridge and Phoenix. Also selling the biggest range of bottled beers in Manchester (70 in total, mainly German and Belgian).

A city café bar in an old Georgian building. One main bar and benches outside. Food available 12–3pm Mon–Fri. Children allowed. Located off the A34 by the University.

OPEN *11am–11pm Mon–Fri; 12.30–11pm Sat; 5–10.30pm Sun.*

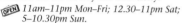
OLDHAM

Hark to Topper

Bow Street, Oldham OL1 1SJ
☎ *(0161) 624 7950* Harry Hurn

A Samuel Smiths pub with two hand pumps, always serving the brewery's ale.

A small, refurbished country-style pub located near the town centre. Open fires. Food available at lunchtime and evenings. Children allowed.

OPEN *All day, every day.*

ROCHDALE

Cask and Feather

1 Oldham Road, Rochdale, OL16 1UA
☎ *(01706) 711476* Jackie Grimes

Home of the Thomas McGuinness Brewery, so beers from the range of own brews always available on five hand pumps.

A small brewery founded in 1991 by Thomas McGuinness, who died in early 1993. Expansion plans are in hand. An old-style castle-fronted pub dating from 1814 and close to the town centre. Bar and restaurant food available at lunchtime and evenings. Parking. Children allowed. Located on the main road near the station.

FEATHER PLUCKER MILD 3.4% ABV
Dark in colour, rich maltiness throughout.
BEST BITTER 3.8% ABV
Well-hopped and quenching, with some fruitiness.
SPECIAL RESERVE BITTER 4.0% ABV
Malt flavour, with sweetness and some fruitiness.
JUNCTION BITTER 4.2% ABV
Strong malt flavours.
AUTUMN GLORY 4.6% ABV
Seasonal brew.
WINTER'S REVENGE 4.6% ABV
Seasonal brew.
SUMMER TIPPLE 4.6% ABV
Seasonal brew.
CHRISTMAS CHEER 4.6% ABV
Seasonal brew.
TOMMY TODD PORTER 5.0% ABV
A warming winter brew.
OPEN *All day, every day.*

Cemetery Inn

470 Bury Road, Rochdale OL11 5EU
☎ *(01706) 645635* Kevin Robinson

A freehouse serving Timothy Taylor Best, Landlord and Dark Mild and a Moorhouse's brew plus three guests from breweries such as Phoenix, Wye Valley or Rooster's.

A Victorian pub with log fires, dating from 1865. Food currently available at weekends and for functions only. Children allowed.

OPEN *All day, every day.*

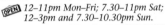

SALFORD

WIGAN

The Crescent

20 The Crescent, Salford M5 4PF
☎ *(0161) 736 5600* Mrs J Davies

Crescent Bitter (house beer) always available plus up to ten others (150 per year) primarily from local breweries, including Oak, Moorhouse's, Titanic and Marston's. Other guests from all around the country. Occasional beer festivals.

A sprawling pub with a comfortable atmosphere, frequented by students and locals alike. Bar food available at lunchtime. Car park. Traditional pub games. Opposite Salford University. The nearest station is Salford Crescent, on the main A6.

12–11pm Mon–Fri; 7.30–11pm Sat; 12–3pm and 7.30–10.30pm Sun.

The Old Pint Pot

2 Adelphi Street, Salford M3 6EN
☎ *(0161) 939 1514* Thomas and Peter Morrison

A freehouse with small micro-brewery producing Bridgewater. Plus two guest ales such as Liverpool's Blondie or Greene King Abbot.

A riverside pub in a converted convent, with a largely student clientele. Food available. Children allowed. Beer garden. Situated next to Salford University, below road level.

 BRIDGEWATER % ABV varies

All day, every day.

The Beer Engine

69 Poolstock Road, Wigan, WN3 5DF
☎ *(01942) 321820* John Moran

Moorhouse's Pendle Witches Brew and Ruddles brews always available plus up to five guest beers (186 per year) with the emphasis on supporting the smaller brewer.

F ood available on Saturday and Sunday. Function room with a capacity of 250 for hire. Three full-size snooker tables. Crown green bowling alley. Annual beer, pie and music festival in September. Twice winner of CAMRA Pub of the Year. Children allowed. Well known in Wigan, five minutes' walk from the railway station and town centre.

11am–11pm Mon–Sat; 12–10.30pm Sun.

Moon Under Water

Market Place, Wigan WN1 1PE
☎ *(01942) 323437* Paul Hammonds

A Wetherspoon's pub with Cains Mild among the beers always available, plus two guests often from East–West Ales, perhaps Brakspear Bee Sting. Two annual beer festivals.

A quiet town-centre pub with no music. Food available. No children.

All day, every day.

The Orwell

Wigan Pier, Wallgate, Wigan WN3 4EU
☎ *(01942) 323034* Dean McDonald

A freehouse. Three guest beers always available from micro-breweries whenever possible. Coach House, Titanic and Rooster's brews are recent examples.

A tourists' pub on the edge of town on the pier. Styled as a traditional Victorian cotton warehouse. Three bars, non-smoking dining area, baby changing facilities, disabled toilets, passenger lift to all floors. Benches outside. Food available lunchtimes only. Children allowed.

All day, every day.

The Tudor House Hotel

New Market Street, Wigan
☎ *(01942) 700296* Mr Miller

A freehouse with Moorhouse's Pendle Witches Brew among the beers always available plus up to four guests including Everards Tiger, Hop Back Summer Lightning, Wychwood Hobgoblin, O'Hanlon's Summer Gold and Phoenix Wobbly Bob.

A predominantly student pub with open fires, a beer garden and accommodation. Food available at lunchtime and evenings, children allowed during the day.

All day, every day.

Places Featured:

Bebington
Birkenhead
Irby

Liverpool
Rainhill
Southport

THE BREWERIES

ROBERT CAIN & CO. LTD
The Robert Cain Brewery, Stanhope Street,
Liverpool L8 5XJ
☎ *(0151) 709 8734*

DARK MILD 3.2% ABV
Very dark and distinctive.
BREWERY BITTER 3.5% ABV
Light with malt flavours.
TRADITIONAL BITTER 4.0% ABV
SUNDOWNER 4.5% ABV
FORMIDABLE 5.0% ABV
Pale, well-rounded and balanced with malt and
hop flavours.
Plus seasonal brews.

THE LIVERPOOL BREWING CO.
21–3 Berry Street, Liverpool L1 9DF
☎ *(0151) 709 5055*

BERRY STREET MILD 3.4% ABV
YOUNG STALLION 3.6% ABV
RED 3.8% ABV
BLONDIE 4.1% ABV
FIRST GOLD 4.2% ABV
BITTER 4.3% ABV
ROCKET 4.3% ABV
CELEBRATION 4.8% ABV

THE PASSAGEWAY BREWING CO.
Unit G8, Queen's Dock Commercial Centre,
Norfolk Street, Liverpool L1 0BG
☎ *(0151) 708 0730*

THE PUBS

BEBINGTON

Traveller's Rest Hotel
169 Mount Road, Bebington, Wirral L63 8PJ
☎ *(0151) 608 2988* Alan Irving

Greene King Abbot and Cains
Traditional always available, plus two
guests from breweries such as Timothy
Taylor, Enville, Wye Valley, Hart,
Cumberland and Morland.

A rural village pub bordering fields with a
view of Wales. Open fires, non-smoking
lounge. Food available. No children.

All day, every day.

BIRKENHEAD

The Crown & Cushion
60 Market Street, Birkenhead L41 5BT
☎ *(0151) 647 8870* Linda Chesters

Three guest ales available, perhaps
Highgate Dark Mild, Morland Old
Speckled Hen or a Cains brew.

A traditional town-centre pub. No food.
Children allowed until 7pm.

All day, every day.

The Crown Hotel
128 Conway Street, Birkenhead L41 6JE
☎ *(0151) 647 9108* Steve Eldon

Jennings Sneck Lifter and Dark Mild,
Cains Traditional and Mild always
available plus up to six guests. Also cask
ciders.

A typical old alehouse under new
management. Bar food available.
Parking, darts/meeting room. Children
allowed. Head for Birkenhead town centre,
not far from the Birkenhead tunnel (Europa
Park).

11.30am–11pm Mon–Sat; 12–3pm and
7–10.30pm Sun.

The Dispensary

20 Chester Street, Birkenhead CH41 5DQ
☎ *(0151) 649 8259* Dean Hornby

A Cains tied house, with Traditional and Dark Mild always available, plus a selection of seasonal and special ales with at least one new one each month.

A modern, refurbished building with raised glass ceiling. Formerly a chemist, hence the new name. Used to be known as The Chester Arms. Food available at lunchtime only. Children allowed only if eating.

[OPEN] *All day, every day.*

IRBY

Shippons Inn

Thingwall Road, Irby, Wirral CH61 3UA
☎ *(0151) 648 0449* Stephen Thompson

A freehouse serving Banks's Mild and Bitter, Cameron Strongarm and Marston's Pedigree, plus two guests, maybe a Banks's seasonal ale or a brew from Bateman, Jennings or Shepherd Neame among others.

A rustic pub with beams and stone floor. Food available 12–2.30pm. No children.

[OPEN] *All day, every day.*

LIVERPOOL

The Brewery

21–3 Berry Street, Liverpool L1 9DF
☎ *(0151) 709 5055*

Home of the Liverpool Brewing Company. At least six beers available from the six-barrel plant. Plus occasional seasonal brews

The Brewery, previously called The Black Horse & Rainbow, was renamed when it was sold in 1996. It is still a student-based brewpub, serving real ales brewed on the premises. Bar food available.

YOUNG STALLION 3.6% ABV
RED 3.8% ABV
BLONDIE 4.1% ABV
FIRST GOLD 4.2% ABV
ROCKET 4.3% ABV
CELEBRATION 4.8% ABV

[OPEN] *12pm–2am.*

The Brewery Tap

Stanhope Street, Liverpool L8 5XJ
☎ *(0151) 709 2129* John Wright

Tied to the Robert Cain brewery, so Cains Bitter, Dark Mild and Formidable Ale (FA) always available, plus seasonal and special brews such as Sundowner and Dr Duncans. Also four guests, perhaps Timothy Taylor Landlord, Bateman XB and XXXB, Derwent Bitter or Exmoor Gold and Stag.

B uilt in 1869, winner of CAMRA's New Heritage Award 1994. Food available. Children allowed if eating.

[OPEN] *All day, every day.*

The Cambridge Pub

28 Picton Road, Liverpool L15 4LH
☎ *(0151) 280 5126* Joan Adali

A freehouse with Chester's Mild among the brews always available, plus two twice-monthly changing guests.

A modern pub with music. No food. No children.

[OPEN] *All day, every day.*

Coopers Bar

Lime Street, Liverpool L1 1JD
☎ *(0151) 709 0076* Karen Lee

A good range of real ales available.

A modern pub refurbished in summer 1999. Serving food. No children.

[OPEN] *7am (for breakfast) –11pm daily.*

Everyman Bistro

9–11 Hope Street, Liverpool L1 9BH
☎ *(0151) 708 9545* Jeff Hale

A freehouse with Marston's Pedigree, Timothy Taylor Landlord and a Cains beer always available, plus two guests such as Rooster's Yankee and Ringo or a Hanby Ales brew.

A traditional pub with restaurant. Food served all day. Children allowed.

[OPEN] *12pm–12am Mon–Sat; closed Sun.*

The Ship & Mitre
133 Dale Street, Liverpool L2 2JH
☎ *(0151) 236 0859* David Stevenson

 Holt Bitter and Cains Mild and Bitter always available plus eight guest beers of all shapes and sizes. Two ciders.

A town-centre CAMRA pub of the year popular with students and council staff. Food served at lunchtime. Pay and display car park opposite. Children not allowed. Near the Mersey tunnel entrance, five minutes' walk from Lime Street station and Moorfields station.

11.30am–11pm Mon–Fri; 12.30–11pm Sat; closed Sun.

The Swan Inn
86 Wood Street, Liverpool L1 4DQ
☎ *(0151) 709 5281* Clive Briggs

A freehouse with Marston's Pedigree, Phoenix Wobbly Bob and a Cains brew always available, plus three constantly changing guests from breweries such as Hanby Ales, Durham, Cottage, Wye Valley (Dorothy Goodbody's) or Belhaven.

A traditional back-street pub with wooden floors. Food served in separate dining area. No children. Located off Berry Street at the back of Bold Street

All day, every day.

Ye Cracke
13 Rice Street, Liverpool L1 9BB
☎ *(0151) 709 4171* Del Pritchard

Oak Best, Phoenix Wobbly Bob, a Cains brew and a Marston's brew always available, plus two guests from independent and micro-breweries whenever possible. Examples include Tomintoul brews, Phoenix Sticky Wicket, Cottage IPA, Brakspear Bee Sting and Rebellion Red October.

A traditional local with beer garden. Food available. Children allowed in the garden only. Located in a back street off Hope Street.

All day, every day.

The Manor Farm
Mill Lane, Rainhill, Prescot L35 6NE
☎ *(0151) 430 0335* Brian Maguire

A Burtonwood tied house always serving Burtonwood brews. Two other guests from a range including Wyre Piddle Piddle in the Hole.

A traditional seventeenth-century pub with restaurant and beer garden. No juke boxes. Food available. Children allowed.

All day, every day.

Barons Bar in The Scarisbrick Hotel
Lord Street, Southport PR8 1NZ
☎ *(01704) 543000* Sharon Morgan

A freehouse always serving Morland Old Speckled Hen plus brews such as Cains' Traditional, Fuller's London Pride, Timothy Taylor Landlord and Shepherd Neame The Bishop's Finger on a guest basis.

A recently refurbished pub with open fire. Bar snacks only in the pub, but there is a restaurant in the adjoining hotel. Children not allowed in the bar.

All day, every day.

Blakes Hotel and Pizza Pub
19 Queens Road, Southport PR9 9HN
☎ *(01704) 500811* Philip Ball

Marston's Bitter, Adnams Best, Fuller's London Pride, Moorhouse's Black Cat Mild and Pendle Witches Brew and Timothy Taylor Landlord always available, plus three constantly rotating guests including, perhaps, Banks's Bitter, another Moorhouse's ale or a Bateman brew.

A family-run freehouse just outside the town centre, anxious to promote the real ale cause, with an extended bar. Music. Pizzas served from 5–11pm. Children allowed. Car park and accommodation. Look behind the fire station.

4–11pm Mon–Fri; 12–11pm Sat–Sun.

Wetherspoons

93 Lord Street, Southport PR8 1RH
☎ *(01704) 530217* Dave and Donna Pagett

A Wetherspoon's pub. Regular guest beers served on three pumps include Cotleigh Osprey, Hop Back Summer Lightning and brews from Burton Bridge, Spinnaker (Brewery on Sea), Hook Norton, Everards, Ash Vine and Banks and Taylor.

A n old-fashioned, quiet, drinker's pub. Food available. No children.

All day, every day.

Places Featured:

Attleborough
Blickling
Burnham Thorpe
Cantley
Downham Market
Erpingham
Fakenham
Foulden
Great Yarmouth
Gressenhall
Hilborough
Hingham
Hockwold
Kenninghall
Little Dunham
Lynford
Mundford
Northwold
Norwich

Pulham St Mary
Reedham
Reepham
Ringstead
Sheringham
Stiffkey
Stowbridge
Swanton Morley
Thornham
Walsingham
Warham
West Rudham
Whinburgh
Winterton-on-Sea
Wiveton
Woodbastwick
Wreningham
Wymondham

THE BREWERIES

BUFFY'S BREWERY

Mardle Hall, Rectory Road, Tivetshall St Mary MR15 2DD
☎ *(01379) 676523*

NORWICH TERRIER 3.6% ABV
BITTER 3.9% ABV
Easy-drinking, well-hopped brew.
MILD 4.2% ABV
Smooth, dark mild.
POLLY'S FOLLY 4.3% ABV
Traditional bitter.
IPA 4.7% ABV
Superb, genuine IPA.
POLLY'S EXTRA FOLLY 4.9% ABV
Stronger version of Polly's Folly.
ALE 5.5% ABV
Well-rounded and hoppy.
FESTIVAL 9X 9.0% ABV

CHALK HILL BREWERY

Rosary Road, Thorpe Hamlet, Norwich NR1 4DA
☎ *(01603) 477077*

TAP BITTER 3.6% ABV
CHB 4.2% ABV
DREADNOUGHT 4.9% ABV
FLINTKNAPPER'S MILD 5.0% ABV
IPA 5.3% ABV
OLD TACKLE 5.6% ABV

HUMPTY DUMPTY BREWERY

17 The Havaker, Reedham NR13 3HG
☎ *(01493) 701818*

HOW MUCH 4.1% ABV
HOP ON THE TRAIN 4.1% ABV
BUTT JUMPER 4.8% ABV

THE ICENI BREWERY

3 Foulden Road, Ickburgh IP26 5GJ
☎ *(01842) 878922*

BOADICEA 3.8% ABV
Full-flavoured and hoppy with some fruit.
CELTIC QUEEN 4.0% ABV
Flavoursome easy drinker.
FINE SOFT DAY 4.0% ABV
Maple syrup and hops give bittersweet flavour.
FEN TIGER 4.2% ABV
Malty with coriander.
FOUR GRAINS 4.2% ABV
Rounded, fruity flavour.
CU CHULAINN 4.3% ABV
Full-bodied with slight toffee sweetness.
DEIRDRE OF THE SORROWS 4.4% ABV
Amber and complex.
ROISIN DUBH 4.4% ABV
Dark and sweet.
KIWI 4.5% ABV
Smooth and easy-drinking, with kiwi fruit.
ICENI GOLD 5.0% ABV
Golden and refreshing.
WINTER LIGHTNING 5.0% ABV
Light, smooth and refreshing.

OLD CHIMNEYS BREWERY

The Street, Market Weston, Diss IP22 2NZ
☎ *(01359) 221411*

REEPHAM BREWERY

Unit 1, Collers Way, Reepham NR10 4SW
☎ *(01603) 871091*

GRANARY BITTER 3.8% ABV
RAPIER PALE ALE 4.3% ABV
NORFOLK WHEATEN 4.5% ABV
VELVET STOUT 4.5% ABV
Plus seasonal brews.

WOLF BREWERY

Attleborough

WOLF IN SHEEPS CLOTHING 3.8% ABV
Smooth and malty.
BEST BITTER 3.9% ABV
Rounded with good hoppiness.
COYOTE 4.3% ABV
Golden with floral hoppiness.
GRANNY WOULDN'T LIKE IT 4.8% ABV
Complex, malty flavour.
WOILD MOILD 4.8% ABV
Dark, smooth and fruity.

WOODFORDE'S NORFOLK ALES

*Broadland Brewery, Woodbastwick, Norwich
NR13 6SW*
☎ *(01603) 720353*

BROADSMAN BITTER 3.5% ABV
Well-balanced fruit and hop flavours
MARDLER'S MILD 3.5% ABV
Light, mid-coloured mild.
WHERRY 3.8% ABV
Superb, well-hopped session ale.
GREAT EASTERN ALE 4.3% ABV
Golden with malt flavour.
NELSON'S REVENGE 4.5% ABV
Flavoursome throughout.
NORFOLK NOG 4.6% ABV
Smooth chocolate malt flavour.
HEADCRACKER 7.0% ABV
Fruity and easy to drink for gravity.

THE PUBS

ATTLEBOROUGH

The Griffin Hotel

Attleborough, NR17 2AH
☎ *(01953) 452149* Richard Ashbourne

Wolf Best, Coyote and Granny Wouldn't Like It plus Greene King Abbot always available. Also one hand pump serving a guest ale from a range of small breweries.

A sixteenth-century freehouse in the centre of town. Beams, log fires, dining area, accommodation. Food available at lunchtime and evenings. Children allowed.

OPEN *10.30am–3.30pm and 5.30–11pm.*

BLICKLING

The Buckinghamshire Arms

Blickling, Nr Aylsham NR11 6NF
☎ *(01263) 732133* Mark Stubley

Woodforde's Wherry and Blickling (house beer from Woodforde's) plus Adnams brews usually available.

An olde-English, food-oriented freehouse with small bar, log fires and beer garden. Food available at lunchtime and evenings in separate restaurant. Children allowed.

OPEN *11.30am–3pm and 6–11pm.*

BURNHAM THORPE

The Lord Nelson

*Walsingham Road, Burnham Thorpe, King's
Lynn PE31 8HN*
☎ *(01328) 738241* Miss L Stafford

A Greene King house with Abbot, IPA and XX Mild always available, plus Woodforde's Wherry.

A 355-year-old village pub in the birthplace of Nelson. Log fires, beer garden. Food available at lunchtime and evenings. Children allowed.

OPEN *11am–3pm and 6–11pm Mon–Sat;
12–3pm and 7–10.30pm Sun.*

CANTLEY

The Cock Tavern

Manor Road, Cantley NR13 3JQ
☎ *(01493) 700895* Mr and Mrs Johnson

 Samuel Smith OBB always available plus four guest beers (100+ per year) including Wild's Wild Blonde, Nethergate Old Growler, Burton Bridge, Woodforde's and Nene Valley brews.

A traditional country pub not far from Norwich with many separate areas, a beamed ceiling and two open fires. Bar food is available at lunchtime and evenings. Car park, garden and children's room. Caravan Club campsite nearby. Turn right off the A47 (Norwich to Yarmouth road) near Acle, then signposted Cantley. Approx four miles from the turn.

OPEN *11am–3.30pm and 6–11pm Mon–Fri; 7–11pm Sat; 12–10.30pm Sun.*

DOWNHAM MARKET

The Crown Hotel

Bridge Street, Downham Market PE38 9DH
☎ *(01366) 382322* Mrs N Hayes

 A freehouse with Bateman XB and Charles Wells Bombardier always available, plus a guest which might be Wyre Piddle Piddle in the Wind, Sheperd Neame Spitfire or Charles Wells' Summer Solstice.

An olde-worlde pub with open fires. Food available at lunchtime and evenings in two restaurants. No children.

OPEN *11am–2.30pm and 5–11pm Mon–Thurs; all day Fri–Sat; 12–3pm and 7–10.30pm Sun.*

ERPINGHAM

The Spread Eagle

Erpingham, Norwich NR11 7QA
☎ *(01263) 761591* Billie Carder

Woodforde's Wherry, Adnams Regatta and Greene King Abbot always on offer. Also two guests which could be something like Morland Old Speckled Hen or another Woodforde's brew such as Headcracker.

A traditional pub with open fires, dining area and beer garden. Food available at lunchtime and evenings. Children allowed.

OPEN *11am–3pm and 6.30–11pm Mon–Sat; 12–3pm and 7–10.30pm Sun.*

FAKENHAM

The Bull

Bridge Street, Fakenham NR21 9AG
☎ *(01325) 862560* Graham Blanchfield

Home of Blanchfields Brewery. At least three beers brewed and served on the premises. Other seasonal ales as available.

A nineteenth-century pub with two small bar rooms and a dining area. Food available at lunchtime only. Children allowed. Brewery viewing by arrangement.

BLACK BULL MILD 3.6% ABV
A traditional dark mild.
BULL BEST BITTER 3.9% ABV
Hoppy bitter.
THE WHITE BULL 4.4% ABV
A seasonal wheat beer available in summer only.
RAGING BULL 4.9% ABV
Strong malty flavoured bitter. Also available in bottles.

OPEN *11am–3pm and 7–11pm Mon–Wed; 11am–11pm Thurs–Sat; 12–10.30pm Sun.*

FOULDEN

The White Hart Inn

White Hart Street, Foulden, Thetford IP26 5AW
☎ *(01366) 328638* Sylvia Chisholm

A freehouse serving Greene King IPA, Mild, XS and Abbot plus two guests such as Shepherd Neame Spitfire or other customer requests.

A traditional pub with dining area, fires and beer garden. Live music on Friday or Saturday. Biker-friendly. Food available at lunchtime and evenings. Children allowed.

OPEN *11am–3.30pm and 6–11pm.*

GREAT YARMOUTH

The Mariner's Tavern

69 Howard Street South, Great Yarmouth NE30 1LN
☎ *(01493) 332299* Mr Munro

Fuller's London Pride, Highgate Dark, Greene King Abbot and beers from Adnams always available. One guest changed each weekend. Recent brews have included Thwaites Bloomin Ale and Greene King Triumph.

A small traditional pub with log fires. Snacks only. Children allowed. Ring for directions.

OPEN *11am–3pm and 7–11pm Mon–Sat; closed Sun.*

The Red Herring

24–5 Havelock Road, Great Yarmouth
NR30 3HQ
☎ *(01493) 853384*
Audrey and Graham Bould

 A freehouse with Adnams Best and Elgood's Black Dog Mild always available. Four constantly changing guests such as Greene King Triumph, Woodforde's Wherry, Buffy's Bitter, Mauldons White Adder and Suffolk Pride or Nethergate and Green Jack brews.

A n old-fashioned, country-style pub in a town location. Home-made bar food available. Children allowed. Ring for directions.

 11am–3pm and 6–11pm Mon–Sat;
12–3pm and 7–10.30pm Sun.

The Swan

The Green, Gressenhall, Dereham NR20 4DU
☎ *(01632) 860340* Mr Mansfield

 Greene King IPA always available, plus two guests such as Marston's Pedigree or Young's Bitter.

A family-oriented country pub with dining area, log fires and beer garden. Food available at lunchtime and evenings. Children allowed.

 12–2.30pm and 6–11pm Mon–Sat;
12–3pm and 7–10.30pm Sun.

The Swan

Hilborough, Thetford IP26 5BW
☎ *(01760) 756380* Mr Wallis

 Greene King Abbot and IPA, Bateman Mild and an Adnams beer always available, plus a guest which changes once a fortnight and may well be a Greene King seasonal or special brew.

A n olde-worlde pub with log fires, beer garden and accommodation. Smallholding with animals. Food available at lunchtime and evenings. Children allowed.

 11am–3.30pm and 6–11pm.

The White Hart Hotel

3 Market Place, Hingham, Norwich NR9 4AF
☎ *(01953) 850214* Mr Jackson

 Greene King IPA and Abbot always available plus two guests.

T he only pub in Hingham, this is a family-oriented pub and restaurant with beer garden and accommodation. Food available at lunchtime and evenings. Children allowed.

 12–3pm and 6–11pm Mon–Fri;
11am–11pm Sat; 12–5pm and 7–10.30pm
Sun.

The Red Lion

Main Street, Hockwold IP26 4NB
☎ *(01842) 828875* Mrs Miles

 Greene King IPA always available plus two guests which change fortnightly. A beer festival is held each August bank holiday.

A village pub and restaurant. Children allowed.

 12–2.30pm and 6–11pm Sun–Fri;
12–11pm Sat.

The Red Lion

East Church Street, Kenninghall, Diss NR16 2EP
☎ *(01953) 887849* Mandy and Bruce Berry

 A freehouse with Greene King IPA, Abbot, Triumph and Mild always available, plus two guests such as Fuller's London Pride or brews from local breweries such as Wolf or Elgood's.

A one-bar village pub with beams, open fires, bare stone floors and floorboards. The snug is part of a listed building. Bar food available at lunchtime only but the restaurant is open all day. Beer garden. Children allowed, but not in the bar area.

 12–3pm and 6.30–11pm Mon–Fri; all day
Sat–Sun.

LITTLE DUNHAM

The Black Swan

The Street, Little Dunham, King's Lynn
PE32 2DG
☎ *(01760) 722200* Mr Budd

A freehouse with Adnams Bitter and IPA always available, plus a guest. Morland Old Speckled Hen, Shepherd Neame The Bishop's Finger and Cottage brews are all popular.

A country pub with log fires, dining area and beer garden. Food available lunchtimes and evenings. Children allowed. Located off the A47.

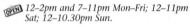 *12–2pm and 7–11pm Mon–Fri; 12–11pm Sat; 12–10.30pm Sun.*

LYNFORD

Lynford Hall

Lynford, Thetford IP26 5HW
☎ *(01842) 878351* Peter Scopes

Adnams Best and Woodforde's Wherry available.

P ub located within Lynford Hall, a stately home and tourist attraction open to the public. Separate restaurant and beer garden. Food available. Children allowed.

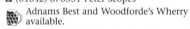 *11am–11pm.*

MUNDFORD

The Crown Hotel

Crown Street, Mundford, Nr Thetford IP26 5HQ
☎ *(01362) 637647* Barry Walker

Seven beers always available including Samuel Smith OBB, Woodforde's Norfolk Wherry and Marston's Pedigree plus more than 100 guests per year including all Iceni brews, Morland Old Speckled Hen, Woodforde's Nelson's Revenge and Mauldons brews.

A sixteenth-century beamed pub with open fires in winter. Bar and restaurant food available at lunchtime and evenings. Pool and darts, car park, garden, function room, accommodation. Children allowed.

 11am–11pm Mon–Sat; 12–10.30pm Sun.

NORTHWOLD

The Crown Inn

High Street, Northwold, Thetford IP26 5LA
☎ *(01366) 727317* Rona Bryan

A freehouse. Greene King IPA and Abbot always available plus two local beers available as guests. Breweries favoured include Iceni, Nethergate and Burton Bridge.

A village pub with log fires and beer garden. Food available at lunchtime and evenings. Children allowed.

12–3pm and 6–11pm Mon–Fri; all day Sat; 12–3pm and 7–10.30pm Sun.

NORWICH

Alexandra Tavern

Stafford Street, Norwich NR2 3BB
☎ *(01603) 627772* JL Little

A freehouse with Chalk Hill Best, Flintknapper's Mild, IPA and Dreadnought, Marston's Pedigree and Adnams Best always available. Guests on two hand pumps tend to be local brews such as Green Jack Summer Dream.

A traditional local with log fires in winter. Snacks only. Children allowed until 7pm.

All day, every day.

Coach & Horses

82 Thorpe Road, Norwich NR1 1BA
☎ *(01603) 477077* Bob Cameron

Up to nine beers available at any one time including Chalk Hill Tap, Best, Dreadnought and Old Tackle plus Timothy Taylor Landlord. Guests include Hop Back Summer Lightning, Cheriton Digger's Gold, Otter Bright and Coach House Gunpowder Mild.

B usy old-style pub with open fires. Bar food available at lunchtime and evenings. Children allowed.

11am–11pm Mon–Sat; 12–10.30pm Sun.

Eaton Cottage

75 Mount Pleasant, Norwich NR2 2DQ
☎ *(01603) 453048* Mr M Howard

Marston's Pedigree, Adnams Best, Scott's Blues and Bloater always available. Four other guests such as Adnams Regatta, Woodforde's Broadman, Morland Old Speckled Hen, Elgood's Golden Newt and Fuller's London Pride.

A basic traditional corner freehouse. No food. No children.

11am–11pm (10.30pm Sun).

The Fat Cat

49 West End Street, Norwich NR2 4NA
☎ *(01603) 624364*

Up to 25 beers available at any one time. Regulars include Adnams Best, Woodforde's Nelson's Revenge, Kelham Island Pale Rider, Greene King Abbot and a guest list that now runs into thousands.

A traditional Victorian pub decorated with breweriana and pub signs. Bar food available at lunchtime. Street parking. Children not allowed.

11am–11pm Mon–Sat; 12–10.30pm Sun.

The Jubilee
26 St Leonards Road, Norwich NR11 4BL
☎ *(01603) 618734*
Tim Wood and Teresa Santos

Wadworth 6X, Fuller's London Pride, Greene King Abbot, Jubilee Ale and Triumph always available, plus three other guests including, perhaps, Hop Back Summer Lightning.

A traditional freehouse with beer garden and adults' games room. Food available at lunchtime only. Children allowed until 5pm.

All day, every day.

The Mustard Pot
101 Thorpe Road, Norwich NR1 1TR
☎ *(01603) 432393* Jason Bates

An Adnams house with Best, Broadside and Extra always available, plus Regatta when in season. A range of guest ales such as Charles Wells Summer Solstice or Fuller's London Pride is also served.

A drinkers' pub with beer garden and food available at lunchtime and evenings. No children.

All day, every day.

The Ribs of Beef
24 Wensum Street, Norwich NR3 1HY
☎ *(01603) 619517* Julia Cawdron

A freehouse with Marston's Pedigree, Woodforde's Wherry and Headcracker, Fuller's London Pride and an Adnams brew among the beers always available, plus two guests changing twice-weekly. These might be something like Brakspear Bee Sting or Adnams Regatta.

A popular local situated near the river with private jetty. Food available at lunchtime and evenings. Children allowed.

All day, every day.

Rosary Tavern
95 Rosary Road, Norwich
☎ *(01603) 666287* Jenny Watt

Seven real ales always available. Adnams Best and Aylesbury Bitter on permanently plus five constantly changing guests. Also sells real Norfolk cider.

A small town pub with a friendly atmosphere. Bar food available at lunchtime (not Sun). Car park, beer garden and function room. Easy to find, near the yacht and railway station.

11.30am–11pm Mon–Sat; 12–10.30pm Sun.

St Andrew's Tavern
4 St Andrews Street, Norwich NR2 4AT
☎ *(01603) 614858* John Croft

Adnams Best and Broadside plus Charles Wells Bombardier always available. Eight guest beers (400 per year) may include K&B Festive, Arkell's Kingsdown, Wadworth Farmer's Glory, Mansfield Old Baily and Hop Back Summer Lightning.

A friendly city-centre pub with two bars. Bar food available at lunchtime and all day Saturday. Garden and cellar bar. Children not allowed. At the junction of Duke Street and St John Madmarket opposite St Andrews car park.

11am–11pm Mon–Sat; closed Sun.

Seamus O'Rourke's
92 Pottergate, Norwich NR2 1DZ
☎ *(01603) 626627* Phil Adams

A freehouse with Adnams Best and O'Rourke's Revenge (house beer) always available, plus up to eight guests including Charles Wells Bombardier, Wolf Coyote, Iceni Fine Soft Day, Scott's Blues and Boater or a Burton Bridge beer.

Irish sports themed pub with open fires and food available at lunchtime. No children.

All day, every day (except Christmas Day 12–3.30pm).

The Steam Packet
39 Crown Road, Norwich NR1 3DT
☎ *(01603) 441545* Michael Blackmore

An Adnams house with Best, Broadside and Regatta always available. Two guests such as Badger Tanglefoot, Oak Hill Best, Wadworth Valentine or Bateman XXXB.

A 200-year-old traditional local. Food available at lunchtime only. No children.

All day, every day.

The Tap & Spile
73 Oak Street, Norwich NR3 3AR
☎ *(01603) 620630* Mr and Mrs Royle

Ushers Founder's Ale and Bateman beers always available plus approx 12 guest beers (300+ per year) including Rooster's Yankee and B&T Dragonslayer.

A 450-year-old pub with old beams, slate floors, loads of wood, brass and pot plants. Candles every evening. Live music three times a week. Bar food available at lunchtime and evenings. Parking and children's room. On the inner ring road going anti-clockwise, first left before the river on the east side.

11am–3.30pm and 5.30–11pm Mon–Thurs; 11am–11pm Fri–Sat; 12–3pm and 7–10.30pm Sun.

The York Tavern

1 Leicester Street, Norwich NR22 2AS
☎ *(01603) 620918* Mr Verret

Adnams ales usually available, plus guests such as Wadworth 6X, Marston's Pedigree or Morland Old Speckled Hen.

A n old-fashioned London-style pub with open fires, restaurant and beer garden. Food available at lunchtime and evenings. Children allowed in the restaurant only.

OPEN *11am–11pm.*

PULHAM ST MARY

The King's Head

The Street, Pulham St Mary IP21 4RD
☎ *(01379) 676318* Graham Scott

Adnams Best always available plus three guests (150 per year) including Marston's Pedigree, Wadworth 6X, Shepherd Neame Spitfire, Woodforde's Wherry Best and brews from Buffy's, Brains, Robinson's and Scott's.

B uilt in the 1600s, this pub has an old oak timber frame with exposed beams. Bar and restaurant food available at lunchtime and evenings. Non-smoking dining area, bowling green, paddock, car park, garden, children's area, accommodation. Off the A140 to Harlesdon, on the B1134.

OPEN *11.30am–3pm and 5.30–11pm Mon–Fri; all day Sat–Sun.*

REEDHAM

The Railway Tavern

17 The Havaker, Reedham NR13 3HG
☎ *(01493) 700340*
Mrs Cathy Swan and Mr Ivor Cuders

Woodforde's and Adnams ales always available plus many guest beers including those from Scott's, Chalk Hill and Elgood's breweries. Four beer festivals held so far.

A listed Victorian railway hotel freehouse. CAMRA award. No fruit machines. Bar and restaurant food is available at lunchtime and evenings. Car park, garden and children's room. Take the A47 south of Acle, then six miles on the B1140. By rail from Norwich, Gt Yarmouth or Lowestoft.

OPEN *12–3pm and 6.30–11pm Mon–Thurs; all day Fri–Sat; normal Sun hours.*

REEPHAM

The Crown

Ollands Road, Reepham, Norwich NR10 4EJ
☎ *(01603) 870964* Mr Good

Marston's Pedigree and Greene King Abbot among the beers always available.

A village pub with dining area and beer garden. Food available at lunchtime and evenings. Children allowed.

OPEN *12–3pm and 7–11pm Mon–Sat; 12–5pm and 7–10.30pm Sun.*

The Old Brewery House Hotel

Market Place, Reepham, Norwich NR10 4JJ
☎ *(01603) 870881* Sarah Gardener

A freehouse with Greene King Abbot, Adnams beers and a house bitter always available, plus one changing guest which will be something like Morland Old Speckled Hen, Adnams Regatta or another local brew.

A n olde-worlde pub with beams, log fires, restaurant, beer garden and accommodation. Food available at lunchtime and evenings. Children allowed.

OPEN *11am–11pm.*

RINGSTEAD

The Gin Trap Inn

Ringstead, Nr Hunstanton PO36 5JU
☎ *(01485) 525264*
Brian and Margaret Harmes

A freehouse with a house beer brewed by Woodforde's called Gin Trap always available, plus Norfolk Nog, Greene King Abbot and an Adnams ale. One other guest served.

A 350-year-old traditional English pub. Dining area, beer garden, self-catering accommodation. Food available at lunchtime and evenings. Children allowed. Ring for directions.

OPEN *11.30am–2.30pm and 6.30–11pm Mon–Sat; 12–2.30pm and 6.45–10.30pm Sun.*

SHERINGHAM

The Windham Arms

15 Wyndham Street, Sheringham NR26 8BA
☎ *(01263) 822609* Mr Thomas

Woodforde's Wherry and Mardler's Ale and Greene King Abbot and IPA always available, plus a wide selection of guest ales served on three hand pumps (never the same beer twice). An annual beer festival is held on the first weekend in July with 20 different guest beers on offer.

A large pub with restaurant, log fires, beer garden. Food available at lunchtime and evenings. Children allowed.

OPEN *All day, every day.*

The Red Lion

*44 Wells Road, Stiffkey, Wells-next-the-Sea
NR23 1AJ*
☎ *(01328) 830552* Matthew Rees

A freehouse with Woodforde's Wherry, Adnams Best and Greene King Abbot always available, plus two guests, perhaps seasonal Woodforde's ales such as Great Eastern in Summer or Norfolk Nog in Winter, or Elgood's Black Dog Mild, Wolf Best, or something from Nethergate, Green Jack or other local breweries.

A n old, rustic pub with tiled floor, log fires and beer garden. Food available at lunchtime and evenings. Children and dogs welcome. Located on the main A149.

OPEN *11am–3pm and 6–11pm.*

The Heron

Station Road, Stowbridge, King's Lynn PE34 3PH
☎ *(01366) 384147* Nick and Brenda Frost

A freehouse with Greene King IPA and Abbot plus Adnams Best always available. Also three guests including, perhaps, Woodforde's Wherry, Charles Wells Bombardier or Morland Old Speckled Hen.

A 150-year-old traditional pub with log fires, beer garden and accommodation. Food available at lunchtime and evenings. Children allowed. Situated between two rivers, ring for directions if necessary.

OPEN *11am–2pm and 7–11pm Mon–Thurs and Sat; 11am–2pm and 5–11pm Fri; 12–4pm and 7–10pm Sun.*

The Angel Inn

Greengate, Swanton Morley, Norwich NR20 4LX
☎ *(01362) 637407* David Ashford

A freehouse with Samuel Smith Old Brewery Bitter always available. Two guests such as Greene King Abbot.

A country village pub dating from 1609 with log fires, beer garden and bowling green. No food. Children allowed.

OPEN *12–11pm Mon–Sat; 12–3pm and 7–10.30pm Sun.*

Darby's Freehouse

*1 Elsing Road, Swanton Morley, Dereham
NR20 4JU*
☎ *(01362) 637647* John Carrick

Eight real ales including Adnams Best and Broadside, Woodforde's Wherry and Badger Tanglefoot always available plus a couple of guest beers (100 per year) from just about everywhere.

A genuine, family-owned and -run freehouse converted from two derelict farm cottages. Traditional English and Thai cuisine available at lunchtime and evenings. Hunter's Hall function room opened in 1999, ideal for dinner dances and conferences. Accommodation. Fishing and farm trails. Car park, garden and children's room and playground. Regular summer barbecues. Take the B1147 from Dereham to Bawdeswell, turn right on to Elsing Road at Swanton Morley.

OPEN *11am–11pm Mon–Sat; 12–3pm and 7–10.30pm Sun.*

The Lifeboat Inn

Ship Lane, Thornham, Hunstanton PE36 6LT
☎ *(01485) 512236* Mr and Mrs Coker

Adnams, Greene King and Woodforde's ales always available plus a couple of guest beers, mainly from small independents including Tolly Cobbold.

A sixteenth-century smugglers' alehouse with wood beams, hanging paraffin lamps and open fires overlooking salt marshes. Bar and restaurant food available at lunchtime and evenings. Car park, garden and accommodation. Children allowed. Turn first left when entering the village from Hunstanton.

OPEN *All day, every day.*

The Bull Inn

*Common Place, Shire Hall Plain, Walsingham
NR22 6BP*
☎ *(01328) 820333* Philip Horan

Tolly Original and Marston's Pedigree among the beers always available.

A 600-year-old olde-worlde pub with open fires, restaurant, beer garden and accommodation. Food available at lunchtime and evenings. Children allowed.

OPEN *11am–3pm and 6–11pm Mon–Sat; 12–3pm and 7–10.30pm Sun.*

WARHAM

The Three Horseshoes

*Bridge Street, Warham, Wells-next-the-Sea
NR23 1NL*
☎ *(01328) 710547* Mr Salmon

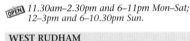 Woodforde's Wherry and Greene King IPA always available plus a guest (changed each week) such as Greene King Abbot, Morland Old Speckled Hen, Woodforde's Nelson's Revenge and Wadworth 6X.

T raditional cottage pub in the centre of the village with gas lighting and open fires. Bar food available at lunchtime and evenings. Car park, garden, function room, non-smoking room, accommodation. Children allowed.

11.30am–2.30pm and 6–11pm Mon–Sat; 12–3pm and 6–10.30pm Sun.

WEST RUDHAM

The Duke's Head

West Rudham, King's Lynn PE31 8RW
☎ *(01485) 528540* Mr Feltham

A freehouse with a good selection of Woodforde's and Shepherd Neame ales always available.

A fifteenth-century coaching inn. Food oriented with separate dining area and food available at lunchtime and evenings. Children allowed.

11am–3pm and 7–11pm Mon–Sat; 12–2.30pm and 7–10.30pm Sun.

WHINBURGH

The Mustard Pot

Dereham Road, Whinburgh, Dereham NR19
☎ *(01362) 692179* Mr Tullett

A freehouse with Woodforde's Wherry among the brews usually available. One guest changing every fortnight might be Shepherd Neame Spitfire or Woodforde's Great Eastern.

A n old pub with beams, log fires and a beer garden. Food available at lunchtime and evenings. Children allowed.

11.30am–3pm and 6.30–11pm.

WINTERTON-ON-SEA

The Fisherman's Return

*The Lane, Winterton-on-Sea, Great Yarmouth
NR29 4BN*
☎ *(01493) 393305* Kate and John Findlay

A freehouse with Woodforde's Wherry, Great Eastern and Norfolk Nog always available, plus two guests changing at least twice a week. These will include something like Mauldons Cuckoo, Buffy's Mild, Cottage Our Ken or Woodforde's Nelson's Revenge.

A 300-year-old brick and flint pub with open fires and beer garden. Food available at lunchtime and evenings. No children.

11am–2.30pm and 6.30–11pm Mon–Fri; all day Sat–Sun.

WIVETON

The Wiveton Bell

The Green, Wiveton, Blakeney NR25 7TL
☎ *(01263) 40101* Dennis Clark

A freehouse with a range of beers brewed especially for the pub by the Cambridge Brewery: Standard (3.8% ABV), Swift (4.2% ABV – summer), Swallow (5.3% ABV – winter). Other special brews served as guests plus occasional guests from other breweries.

A classic car themed pub. 1997 and 1998 North Norfolk Tourism Award winner for food and drink. Dining area, children's playhouse, beer garden, accommodation. Food available at lunchtime and evenings.

11am–3pm and 6–11pm.

WOODBASTWICK

The Fur & Feather Inn

Woodbastwick, Norwich, NR13 6HQ
☎ *(01603) 720003* Mr Marjoram

A freehouse situtated next door to Woodforde's brewery. Therefore the pub specialises in the range of Woodforde's ales: Wherry, Broadsman Bitter, Wherry Best, Mardler's Mild, Great Eastern, Nelson's Revenge, Norkie and Headcracker.

A thatched pub/restaurant with beer garden. Food available at lunchtime and evenings. Children allowed.

12–2.30pm and 6–11pm Mon–Sat; 12–3pm and 7–10.30pm Sun.

WRENINGHAM

Bird in Hand

Church Road, Wreningham NR16 1BH
☎ *(01508) 489438* Mrs Carol Turner

 A freehouse with Woodforde's Wherry, Fuller's London Pride and an Adnams brew always available, plus one guest, perhaps Greene King Abbot.

A traditional pub with wood burners, restaurant and beer garden. Food available at lunchtime and evenings. Children allowed if eating. Ring for directions.

11.30am–3pm and 6–11pm Mon–Sat; 12–3pm and 6–10.30pm Sun.

WYMONDHAM

The Feathers Inn

Town Green, Wymondham NR18 0PN
☎ *(01953) 605675* Eddie Aldours

Adnams Best, Marston's Pedigree and Greene King Abbot among the brews always available, plus two guests such as Fuller's London Pride, Adnams Regatta, Elgood's Greyhound, Brakspear Bee Sting or Adnams Broadside.

A town freehouse with open fires and beer garden. Food available at lunchtime and evenings. Children allowed.

11am–2.30pm and 7–11pm Mon–Sat; 12–2.30pm and 7–10.30pm Sun.

YOU TELL US

★ *The Angel Inn,* Larling
★ *The Billy Bluelight,* 27 Hall Road, Norwich
★ *The Cliff Hotel,* Gorleston-on-Sea
★ *The Crown Inn,* Crown Green, Burston
★ *Dock Tavern,* Dock Tavern Lane, Gorleston, Great Yarmouth
★ *The Greyhound,* The Street, Tibenham
★ *Hill House,* Happisburgh
★ *The Lion,* West Summerton
★ *The Red Lion,* Church Street, Coltishall, Norwich
★ *The Short Blue,* 47 High Street, Gorleston-on-Sea
★ *Stuart House Hotel,* 35 Goodwins Road, King's Lynn
★ *The Toft Lion,* Beccles Road, Toft Monks
★ *The Trafford Arms,* Norwich
★ *The Ugly Bug Inn,* High House, Farm Lane, Colton
★ *The White Horse,* Brandon
★ *The White Horse,* 17 Chapel Road, Upton
★ *The Windmill Inn,* Water End, Great Cressingham

Places Featured:

Ashby St Ledgers
Brackley
Corby
Daventry
Eastcote
Finedon
Geddington
Great Brington
Great Houghton
Higham Ferrers
Holcot

Kettering
Litchborough
Little Brington
Little Harrowden
Mears Ashby
Northampton
Orlingbury
Ravensthorpe
Sudborough
Wellingborough

THE BREWERIES

FROG ISLAND BREWERY
The Maltings, Westbridge, St James Road,
Northampton
☎ (01604) 587772

 BEST BITTER 3.8% ABV
Golden, quenching and well-hopped.
Malty finish.
SHOEMAKER 4.2% ABV
Malty with delicate hoppiness and bitter finish.
FIRE-BELLIED TOAD 4.4% ABV
Pale gold, single hop award winner.
NATTERJACK 4.8% ABV
Sweet and malty, pale and dangerously
drinkable.
Plus seasonal brews.

THE PUBS

ASHBY ST LEDGERS

The Olde Coach House Inn
Ashby St Ledgers, Nr Rugby CV23 8UN
☎ *(01788) 890349* Mr and Mrs McCabe

 St Ledger Ale (house brew) and Everards
Old Original always available plus five
guest ales (200 per year) including Jennings
Cumberland, Mansfield Red Admiral, Hop
Back Summer Lightning, Hook Norton
Haymaker, Frog Island Natterjack and
Adnams Broadside.

A n olde-English converted farmhouse in
the middle of an historic village. Lots of
family tables and small intimate nooks and
crannies. Large secure garden for children
and plenty of parking space. Bar and
restaurant food available at lunchtime and
evenings. Car park. Accommodation. Three
miles from M1 junction 18, close to M6 and
M40 and adjacent to A5. Daventry three
miles to the south, Rugby four miles to the
north.

OPEN *12–2.30pm and 6–11pm Mon–Fri;*
12–11pm Sat; 12–2.30pm and 7–10.30pm
Sun.

BRACKLEY

The Greyhound Inn
Milton Malsor, Brackley, Borthampton, NN7 3AP
☎ *(01604) 858449* Mr and Mrs Rush

At least six beers always available, with
Morland's Old Speckled Hen among
them.

A fifteenth-century inn, cosy atmosphere
wth real fires. Large beer garden. Food
available. Children allowed. Situated on the
main road into the village.

OPEN *All day, every day.*

Knight's Lodge

Towerhill Road, Corby NN18 0TH
☎ *(01536) 742602* Fred Hope

An Everards house with Tiger, Beacon and Old Original always available. Two other guests including, perhaps, Morland Old Speckled Hen, Wadworth Farmers Glory or Perfick, Nethergate Old Growler, Everards Equinox, Charles Wells Fargo or Wood Shropshire Lad.

A traditional seventeenth-century inn linked to Rockingham Castle by a network of tunnels. Food available in dining area Fri–Sun. Garden. Children allowed in the dining area if eating, and in the garden.

OPEN *12–3pm and 6–11pm Mon–Thurs; 12–4pm and 6–11pm Fri–Sat; 12–3.30pm and 6–10.30pm Sun.*

The Eastcote Arms

6 Gayton Road, Eastcote, Towcester NN12 8NG
☎ *(01327) 830731* John and Wendy Hadley

Fuller's London Pride, an Adnams ale and a Hook Norton brew always available, plus one guest, constantly changing. Beers sold have included Shardlow Whistle Stop. An annual beer festival takes place over the Whitsun bank holiday.

A 330-year-old freehouse with dining area and beer garden. Food served at lunchtime and evenings. Children allowed in the dining area only. Ring for directions.

OPEN *6–11pm only Mon; 12–2.30pm and 6–11pm Tues–Sat; 12–3pm and 7–10.30pm Sun.*

The Bell Inn

Bell Hill, Finedon, Nr Wellingborough NN9 5ND
☎ *(01933) 680332* Denise Willmott

A freehouse with Fuller's London Pride always available, plus three guests perhaps from Woodforde's, Cottage, York or Frog Island.

An ancient pub, apparently dating from 1042. Food served at lunchtime and evenings in dining area. Children allowed.

OPEN *11.30am–3pm and 5.30–11pm Mon–Sat; 12–3pm and 7–10.30pm Sun.*

The Star Inn

2 Bridge Street, Geddington, Kettering NN14 1AD
☎ *(01536) 742386*
Ann Carey and Peter Smart

A freehouse with Marston's Pedigree among the brews always available, plus four guests such as Wadworth 6X, Greene King Abbot, Charles Wells Bombardier and others from local breweries.

A traditional pub. Food available in separate smoking and non-smoking dining areas. Children allowed. Located off the A43 between Kettering and Corby, near the ancient monument.

OPEN *All day, every day.*

The Fox & Hounds

Althorp Coaching Inn, Great Brington, Northampton NN7 4JA
☎ *(01604) 770651* Peter Cramples

A freehouse with Greene King IPA and Abbot plus an Adnams beer always available, also a good selection of guests such as Lloyds Wolf, Adnams Regatta, Marston's Pedigree or an Eccleshall brew. Local beers favoured when possible.

A sixteenth-century coaching inn with log fires, exposed beams and stone/wood floors. Dining area and beer garden. Food served at lunchtime. Children allowed. Take the A428 from Northampton past Althorp House, then first left turn before railway bridge.

OPEN *11.30am–11pm Mon–Sat; 12–10.30pm Sun.*

GREAT HOUGHTON

The Old Cherry Tree

Cherry Tree Lane, Great Houghton, Northampton NN4 7AT

☎ *(01604) 761399* Mr Carr

🍺 A Charles Wells house with Bombardier and Eagle always available, plus one other guest such as Adnams Broadside

A pub and restaurant. Children allowed in the restaurant only. Located off the A428 from Northampton to Bedford. Three miles out of Northampton. Turn right into the village, then first left.

🍺 *12–3pm and 6–11.30pm (10.30pm Sun).*

HIGHAM FERRERS

The Green Dragon

College Street, Higham Ferrers, Rushden NN10 8DZ

☎ *(01933) 312088* Graham Sharp

🍺 A freehouse with Fuller's London Pride and Shepherd Neame Spitfire always available. Guests are numerous and varied and come mostly from small local breweries.

A seventeenth-century coaching inn with open fires, restaurant, beer garden, accommodation. Food served lunchtimes and evenings. Children allowed.

🍺 *All day, every day.*

The Griffin Inn

High Street, Higham Ferrers, Rushden NN10 8BW

☎ *(01933) 312612* Ray Gilbert

🍺 Charles Wells Eagle, Greene King Abbot, Fuller's London Pride and Wadworth 6X always available, plus a range of guests constantly changing but often including Marston's Pedigree and Morland Old Speckled Hen.

A luxurious seventeenth-century freehouse with leather Chesterfield, inglenook fireplace and conservatory. Patio. Food served at lunchtime and evenings in a 50-seater restaurant. Children allowed in the restaurant only.

🍺 *11am–3pm and 5.30–11pm.*

HOLCOT

The White Swan Inn

Main Street, Holcot, Northampton NN6 9SP

☎ *(01604) 781263* Mr Hodgson

🍺 A freehouse with Greene King IPA and a Hook Norton brew always available plus occasional guests which have included Charles Wells Fargo, Shepherd Neame Spitfire and beers from Jennings.

A thatched country pub with two bars, games room and small garden. B&B. Food available at lunchtime and evenings. Children allowed.

🍺 *12–2.30pm and 5.30–11pm Mon–Fri; all day Sat–Sun.*

KETTERING

Park House/The Milestone Restaurant

Kettering Venture Park, Kettering NN15 6XE

☎ *(01536) 523377* Rachel Early

🍺 Banks's Bitter and Original and Marston's Pedigree always available.

A traditional pub and restaurant. Children allowed.

🍺 *11am–11pm.*

LITCHBOROUGH

The Old Red Lion

Banbury Road, Litchborough, Towcester NN12 8HF

☎ *(01327) 830250* Mr and Mrs O'Shey

🍺 Banks's Bitter and a Marston's ale always available.

A small, 300-year-old pub with log fires and beer garden. Food available Tues–Sat, lunchtime and evenings. Children allowed.

🍺 *11.30am–2.30pm and 6.30–11pm Mon–Sat; 12–3pm and 7–10.30pm Sun.*

LITTLE BRINGTON

The Saracen's Head

Little Brington, Northampton, NN7 4HS

☎ *(01604) 770640*

Colin Boyson and Derek Lowd

🍺 A freehouse with Fuller's London Pride always available, plus guests on three pumps. Beers featured recently include Frog Island Best, Shepherd Neame Spitfire and a Hook Norton brew.

T he only pub in Little Brington. Open fires and beer garden. Food available in two restaurants. Children allowed in the restaurants and garden only.

🍺 *12–2.30pm and 5.30–11pm Mon–Fri; 12–3pm and 5.30–11pm Sat; 12–3pm and 7–10.30pm Sun.*

LITTLE HARROWDEN

The Lamb Inn
Orlingbury Road, Little Harrowden,
Wellingborough NN9 5BH
☎ *(01933) 673300* John Bevis

 A Charles Wells house with Eagle and Bombardier always available, as well as Adnams Broadside, Badger Dorset Best and one guest, regularly changing. Marston's Pedigree, Morland Old Speckled Hen, Charles Wells Summer Solstice, Ward's Waggle Dance and Young's ales are all popular.

A traditional seventeenth-century Northampton inn. Skittles table. Garden. Food available in separate dining area, Children allowed in the garden or in the dining area if eating.

🍺 *11am–2.30pm and 7–11pm Mon–Sat;*
12–3pm and 7–10.30pm Sun.

MEARS ASHBY

The Griffin's Head
Wilby Road, Mears Ashby, Northampton
NN6 0DX
☎ *(01604) 812945* Philip Tompkins

Marston's Pedigree, Charles Wells Eagle and Everards Beacon always available, plus two guests including, perhaps, Everards Tiger or an Adnams brew. Also seasonal ales.

A cosy freehouse with log fires, restaurant and beer garden. Food served at lunchtime and evenings. Children allowed if eating. Can be difficult to find (ring for directions).

🍺 *11.30am–3pm and 5.30–11pm Mon–Fri;*
12–3pm and 6–11pm Sat;
11.30am–10.30pm Sun.

NORTHAMPTON

The Malt Shovel
121 Bridge Street, Northampton, NN1 1QF
☎ *(01604) 234212* Malcolm Mackenzie

A freehouse with Castle Eden Ale and Frog Island Natterjack among the brews always available, plus many other constantly changing guests, such as Hop Back Summer Lightning, Kelham Island Pale Rider, Fuller's London Pride or an Oakham ale.

A traditional pub with beer garden. Food served at lunchtime and early evenings. Children allowed in the garden only. Located opposite the Carlsberg Brewery.

🍺 *11–30am–3pm and 5–11pm Mon–Sat;*
12–4pm and 7–10.30pm Sun.

ORLINGBURY

The Queen's Arms
11 Isham Road, Orlingbury NN14 1JD
☎ *(01933) 678258* David Myacn

Up to six guest ales available, perhaps including Exmoor Gold, Young's Special or a Burton Bridge brew. The selection changes every week.

A country freehouse and restaurant with beer garden. Food served at lunchtime and evenings. Children allowed. CAMRA pub of the year 1994.

🍺 *12–2.30pm and 6–11pm Mon–Fri; all day Sat–Sun.*

RAVENSTHORPE

The Chequers
Church Lane, Ravensthorpe NN6 8ER
☎ *(01604) 770379* Gordon Walker

A freehouse serving Fuller's London Pride and a Mansfield ale on a regular basis, plus two guests including, perhaps, Greene King Abbot or something from Leatherbritches or Bateman.

A cosy village pub with open fires. Food garden. Children allowed.

🍺 *12–3pm and 6–11pm Mon–Fri; all day Sat; 12–3pm and 7–10.30pm Sun.*

SUDBOROUGH

The Vane Arms
Main Street, Sudborough NN14 3BX
☎ *(01832) 733223* Tom Tookey

Nine different beers changed regularly (150 per year) including Hoskins & Oldfield Ginger Tom, Hop Back Summer Lightning, Woodforde's Headcracker, Adnams Broadside and Oakham Old Tosspot.

A centuries-old listed thatched village inn. Bar and restaurant food available at lunchtime and evenings. Mexican specials. Car park, garden, games room. Children allowed. Accommodation. Just off the A6116 between Thrapston and Corby.

🍺 *11.30am–3pm and 5.30–11pm.*

Red Well

16 Silver Street, Wellingborough, NN14 1PA
☎ *(01933) 440845*
Steve Frost and Tina Garner

A freehouse with five guest ales always available, More than 50 different beers have been served in the past three months. Regulars include Hop Back Summer Lightning, Nethergate Old Growler, Morland Old Speckled Hen, Cotleigh Osprey, Ash Vine Frying Tonight and Adnams Regatta. Beer festivals held three times a year.

A new-age pub, no music, no games. Separate non-smoking area, disabled access, garden. Food available all day, every day. Children allowed in the garden only.

All day, every day.

YOU TELL US

★ *The Duke's Arms*, The Green, Woodford, Kettering
★ *The Exeter Arms,* Main Street, Wakerley
★ *Eykyn Arms,* 20 High Street, Gayton, Northampton
★ *Half Moon,* Main Road, Grendon, Northampton
★ *The Inn,* Chapel Road, Greatworth
★ *The Montagu Arms,* Barnwell
★ *The Marston Inn,* Marston St Lawrence
★ *The Moon on the Square,* The Parade, Northampton
★ *The Navigation Inn,* Thrupp Wharf, Castlethorpe Road, Crossgrove
★ *The Old Plough Inn,* 82 High Street, Braunston, Daventry
★ *The Plough Inn,* Market Square, Towcester
★ *The Shuckburgh Arms,* Main Street, Southwick
★ *The Star Inn,* Manor Road, Sulgrave
★ *The White Swan,* Main Street, Woodnewton

Places Featured:

Acomb
Allendale
Alnwick
Ashington
Berwick-upon-Tweed
Cramlington

Haltwhistle
Hedley on the Hill
Hexham
High Horton
Morpeth
Shotley Bridge

THE BREWERIES

BORDER BREWERY CO.

The Old Kiln, Brewery Lane, Berwick-upon-Tweed TD15 2AH
☎ *(01289) 303303*

 SPECIAL BITTER 3.8% ABV
Light, golden and hoppy.
FARNE ISLAND 4.0% ABV
Refreshing, amber brew.
OLD KILN ALE 4.0% ABV
Fruit, malt and hops combine in this flavoursome ale.
NOGGINS NOG 4.2% ABV
Dark, with powerful chocolate malt flavour.
RAMPART 4.8% ABV
Golden, clean and refreshing.
SOB 5.0% ABV
Red and distinctive, with malt flavours.
Plus seasonal and occasional brews.

HEXAMSHIRE BREWERY

The Brewery, Leafields, Hexham NE45 1SX
☎ *(01434) 606577*

 DEVIL'S ELBOW 3.6% ABV
SHIRE BITTER 3.8% ABV
DEVIL'S WATER 4.1% ABV
WHAPWEASEL 4.8% ABV
Plus seasonal:
OLD HUMBUG 5.5% ABV

THE NORTHUMBERLAND BREWERY

Earth Balance, West Sleekburn Farm, Bomarsund, Bedlington NE22 7AD
☎ *(01670) 822122*

 CASTLES 3.8% ABV
Hoppy session bitter.
COUNTY 4.0% ABV
Well-balanced, easy-drinking brew.
BALANCE 4.2% ABV
As the name suggests ... well-balanced!
SECRET KINGDOM ALE 4.3% ABV
Smooth and rich.
BEST 4.5% ABV
Rounded and full-flavoured.
BOMAR 5.0% ABV
Pale and refreshing.

THE PUBS

ACOMB

The Miner's Arms

Main Street, Acomb, Hexham NE46 4PW
☎ *(01434) 603909* Tom Stokoe

A freehouse serving Miners Lamp (brewed especially by the Big Lamp Brewery) and five guests which may include Durham White Velvet, Mansfield Four Seasons, Northumberland Secret Kingdom, or a Yates or Black Sheep brew.

An unspoilt old-style stone pub, dating from 1750. Two bar areas, outside garden and barbecue. Bar meals served at lunchtime and evenings (not Mondays). Children allowed until 9pm.

12–3pm and 5–11pm Mon–Fri; all day Sat–Sun.

ALLENDALE

The King's Head Hotel

Market Place, Allendale, Hexham NE47 9BD
☎ *(01434) 683681* Margaret Taylor

A freehouse with Jennings Cumberland Ale and Greene King Abbot always available, plus three guests such as Timothy Taylor Landlord, Mordue Workie Ticket, Morland Old Speckled Hen, Marston's Pedigree, Northumberland Cat 'n' Sawdust or one of many Durham Brewery ales.

A cosy quiet pub with two bars, fires and a function room. No music or games. Food served at lunchtime and evenings. Children allowed.

All day, every day.

ALNWICK

The Market Tavern
Fenkle Street, Alnwick NE66 1HW
☎ *(01665) 602759* Ken Hodgson

Ward's Waggle Dance among the beers always available, plus a rotating guest including, perhaps, Morland Old Speckled Hen or Charles Wells Bombardier. Other seasonal guests such as Wye Valley Winter Tipple when appropriate.

A traditional town-centre pub with one bar, restaurant, disabled access and accommodation. Food available at lunchtime and evenings. Children allowed.

OPEN *All day, every day.*

ASHINGTON

Bubbles Wine Bar
58a Station Road, Ashington, NE63 9UJ
☎ *(01670) 850800* David Langdown

A freehouse with three pumps serving a range of real ales. Too many to list; all breweries stocked as and when available.

A town-centre pub for all ages. One bar, back yard area, entertainment and discos. Food served at lunchtime only. Children allowed.

OPEN *11am–3pm and 6–11pm Mon–Thurs; all day Fri–Sat; 7–10.30pm Sun.*

BERWICK-UPON-TWEED

Barrels Ale House
Bridge Street, Berwick-upon-Tweed TD15 1ES
☎ *(01289) 308013* Mark Dixon

A freehouse with a house beer (Barrels Best) brewed especially by the Border Brewery, plus three beers, often including another Border ale plus beers from other smaller brewers such as The Kitchen Brewery.

A traditional two-bar pub, one up, one down. Dining area, real fires. Food served at lunchtime and evenings. Children allowed in certain areas.

OPEN *All day, every day.*

CRAMLINGTON

The Plough
Middle Farm, Cramlington NE23 9DN
☎ *(01670) 737633* Sir John Fitzgerald

Four pumps serving a range of cask ales such as Fuller's London Pride and any of the Black Sheep brews.

A two-bar village freehouse with dining area, beer garden and conservatory. Food served every lunchtime, including traditional Sunday roasts. Children allowed only if eating.

OPEN *11am–3pm and 6–11pm Mon–Wed; all day Thurs–Sun.*

HALTWHISTLE

The Black Bull
Market Square, Haltwhistle NE49 0BL
☎ *(01434) 320463* Mr Sandford

Jennings Cumberland Ale and Marston's Pedigree always available plus a good range of guests on two pumps, plus extra barrels at weekends. Plans for micro-brewing in the near future.

A small, quiet freehouse with one main bar and a small side room. No music or machines. No food. Children allowed at lunchtime only in the smaller area.

OPEN *12–3pm and 7–11pm Thurs–Sun (12–4pm Sat).*

HEDLEY ON THE HILL

The Feathers Inn
Hedley on the Hill, Stocksfield NE43 7SW
☎ *(01661) 843607* Marina Atkinson

Mordue Workie Ticket among the beers always available, plus a range of guests from local breweries such as Big Lamp and Northumberland whenever possible. Otherwise Fuller's London Pride and Chiswick or beers from Yates or Barnsley breweries.

A traditional, attractive pub with log fires, beams and stone walls. No music or games. Outside tables. Food served Tues–Sun evenings and lunchtime at weekends. Children allowed.

OPEN *6–11pm Mon–Fri; 12–3pm and 6–11pm Sat; 12–3pm and 7–10.30pm Sun.*

HEXHAM

The Dipton Mill Inn
Dipton Mill Road, Hexham NE46 1YA
☎ *(01434) 606577* Mr Brooker

A freehouse not far from the Hexhamshire brewery, so Hexhamshire beers such as Shire Bitter, Devil's Water and Whapweasel usually available. Four guest pumps serving guests such as Hart Brewery's Gold Beach.

An old-fashioned country pub. No music or games. One bar, beer garden, disabled access. Food served at lunchtime and evenings. Children allowed.

OPEN *12–2.30pm and 6–11pm Mon–Sat; 12–4.30pm and 7–10.30pm Sun.*

The Three Horseshoes

Hathery Lane, High Horton, Blyth NE24 4HF
☎ *(01670) 822410* Malolm Farmer

 A freehouse serving a good range of real ales from breweries such as Shepherd Neame, Bateman, Greene King, Fuller's, Adnams or Morland.

A large open-plan country pub. Dining room, garden, children's area. Disabled access. Food served at lunchtime and evenings. Children allowed.

All day, every day.

Tap & Spile

Manchester Street, Morpeth NE61 1BH
☎ *(01670) 513894* Mrs Boyle

Beers from breweries such as Cumberland, Adnams, Black Sheep, Jennings, Bateman and Fuller's. Also celebration and seasonal ales when available.

A n old-fashioned pub with small lounge and bar area. Open fires. Food served at lunchtime. Children allowed in the lounge only.

12–2.30pm and 4.30–11pm Mon–Thurs; all day Fri–Sun.

The Manor House Inn

Carterway Heads, Shotley Bridge, Nr Consett DH8 9LX
☎ *(01207) 255268* Mr and Mrs C Brown

Four beers at any one time with an emphasis on a rolling guest ale programme. Beers from all the local brewers (Mordue, Durham, Northumberland, North Yorkshire, Castle Eden) plus a wide range from all over the country, including Hampshire, Morland and many others.

A converted farmhouse, with open log fires in winter. Stunning views over the Derwent Valley. Bar and restaurant food available at lunchtime and evenings. Large car park, garden, accommodation. Children welcome.

11am–3pm and 6–11pm Mon–Sat; 12–3pm and 7–10.30pm Sun; all day Sat and Sun in school summer holidays.

★ *The Angel Inn,* 11 Brewery Bank, Tweedmouth, Berwick-upon-Tweed
★ *The Boathouse Inn,* Station Road, Wylam
★ *The Joiners Arms,* Coomassie Road, Blyth
★ *Northumberland Arms,* 112 Front Street East, Bedlington
★ *The Queen's Head Inn,* Great Whittington
★ *The Wallace Arms,* Bowfoot, Featherstone Park, Haltwhistle

Places Featured:

Basford
Beeston
Carlton on Trent
Caythorpe
Colston Bassett
Dunham on Trent
Kimberley

Nottingham
Ollerton
Radcliffe on Trent
Retford
Upton
Worksop

THE BREWERIES

CAYTHORPE BREWERY

3 Gonalston Lane, Hoveringham NG14 7JH
☎ *(0115) 966 4376*

DOVER BECK BITTER 4.0% ABV
**OLD NOTTINGHAM EXTRA PALE ALE
4.2% ABV**
BIRTHDAY BREW 4.5% ABV
Plus seasonal and occasional brews.

HARDYS & HANSONS PLC

Kimberley Brewery, Nottingham NG16 2NS
☎ *(0115) 938 3611*

KIMBERLEY BEST MILD 3.1% ABV
Dark red and nutty with good roast malt
flavour.
KIMBERLEY BEST BITTER 3.9% ABV
Golden and well-balanced with pleasing bitter
flavour.
KIMBERLEY CLASSIC 4.8% ABV
Overflowing with malt, fruit and hop flavours.
Plus seasonal brews.

LEADMILL BREWERY

118 Nottingham Road, Selston NG16 6BX
☎ *(01773) 810802*

WILD WEASEL 3.9% ABV
ROLLING THUNDER 4.5% ABV
APOCALYPSE NOW 5.2% ABV

MALLARD BREWERY

15 Hartington Avenue, Carlton NG4 3NR
☎ *(0115) 952 1289*

DUCK AND DIVE 3.7% ABV
WADDLERS MILD 3.7% ABV
BEST BITTER 4.0% ABV
DUCKLING 4.2% ABV
SPITTING FEATHERS 4.4% ABV
DRAKE 4.5% ABV
OWD DUCK 4.8% ABV
FRIAR DUCK 5.0% ABV
Plus seasonal brews.

MANSFIELD BREWERY PLC

Littleworth, Mansfield NG18 1AB
☎ *(01623) 625691*

MAYPOLE BREWERY

*North Laithes Farm, Wellow Road, Eakring
NG22 0AN*
☎ *(01623) 871690*

MAYFAIR 3.8% ABV
CELEBRATION 4.0% ABV
CENTENARY ALE 4.2% ABV
MAE WEST 4.6% ABV
Plus occasional brews.

SPRINGHEAD BREWERY

*Sutton Workshops, Old Great North Road, Sutton
on Trent, Newark NG23 6QS*
☎ *(01636) 821000*

HERSBRUCKER WEIZENBIER 3.6% ABV
Wheat beer. Available March to
September.
SURRENDER 1646 3.6% ABV
Full-flavoured for gravity. Fruity and bitter.
PURITAN'S PORTER 4.0% ABV
Dark and easy-drinking.
SPRINGHEAD BITTER 4.0% ABV
Refreshing and well-hopped session beer.
ROUNDHEAD'S GOLD 4.2% ABV
Quenching and moreish.
GOODRICH CASTLE 4.4% ABV
Pale ale with rosemary.
THE LEVELLER 4.8% ABV
Rich and rounded.
ROARING MEG 5.5% ABV
Pale and sweet with balancing hoppy, dry
aftertaste.
CROMWELL'S HAT 6.0% ABV
October–March. Herby flavours.

THE PUBS

BASFORD

The Lion Inn

Mosley Street, Basford, Nottingham NG7 7FG
☎ *(0115) 970 3506* Simon Ronstance

A freehouse with Lion's Mane (house brew produced especially by the Castle Rock brewery) always available, plus numerous guests such as Charles Wells Bombardier, Kelham Island Pale Rider, Castle Rock Elsie Mo, Everards Tiger and Bateman XXXB. Other seasonal celebration beers on bank holidays, at Christmas and Easter etc.

A traditional pub with wooden floorboards, open fires, beer garden and play area. A broad clientele. Live music (Blues, Blue Grass or Jazz) four or five times per week. An extensive menu served at lunchtime only. Children allowed.

All day, every day.

BEESTON

The Victoria Hotel

85 Dovecote Lane, Beeston, Nr Nottingham NG9 1JG
☎ *(0115) 925 4049*

A constantly changing range of ten beers always available from a list of 500 per year including Morland Old Speckled Hen, Woodforde's Wherry, Whim Hartington Bitter, Samuel Smith Old Brewery Bitter, Hop Back and Enville ales. Also 120 whiskies and extensive wine list.

Refurbished and redecorated Victorian railway pub with high ceilings. Bar and restaurant food is available at lunchtime and evenings. Car park, garden, conference room. Accompanied children allowed in the restaurant and outside. Off Queens Road, behind Beeston railway station.

11am–11pm (10.30pm) Sun.

CARLTON ON TRENT

The Great Northern Inn

Ossington Road, Carlton on Trent, Newark NG23 6NT
☎ *(01636) 821348* Ken and Fran Munro

A freehouse with four pumps serving a range of real ales. No permanent beers but guests might include Timothy Taylor Landlord, Marston's Pedigree or a Bateman ale.

A family-oriented pub with two bars, family room, restaurant, outside playground and large car park. Food served at lunchtime and evenings, including a children's menu.

12–2.30pm and 5–11pm Mon–Thurs; all day Fri–Sun and bank holidays.

CAYTHORPE

The Black Horse

29 Main Street, Caythorpe, Nottingham NG14 7ED
☎ *(0115) 966 3520* Miss Sharon Andrews

A freehouse and brewpub with a home-brewed ale, Dover Beck, plus brews from Adnams, Timothy Taylor and Black Sheep always available. Other guests include beers from micro-breweries such as Brewsters or Lloyds.

A traditional village pub with two beamed bar areas, garden and function room. Food served at lunchtime and evenings (booking necessary for evenings). No children.

 DOVER BECK BITTER 4% ABV

12–2.30pm and 5.30–11pm Tues–Sat (closed Mon lunch); 5.30–11pm Mon–Fri; 6–11pm Sat; 7–10.30pm Sun.

COLSTON BASSETT

The Martins Arms Inn

School Lane, Colston Bassett NG12 3FN
☎ *(01949) 81361* Miss L Bryan

Seven beers always available (200 per year), among them Bateman XB and XXXB, Marston's Best and Pedigree, Morland Old Speckled Hen, Greene King Abbot, Timothy Taylor Landlord, Wadworth 6X, Adnams Broadside, Robinson's etc.

This village freehouse was built in 1700 as a farmhouse set in 100 acres owned by the local squire. Now set in one acre with original stables surrounded by National Trust parkland. Antique furniture, prints, old beams, Jacobean fireplace and bar. Bar and restaurant food available at lunchtime and most evenings. Car park, large garden with croquet, children's room. Accommodation. On the A46 Newark to Leicester road.

12–3pm and 6–11pm.

DUNHAM ON TRENT

The Bridge Inn

Main Street, Dunham on Trent, Newark, NG22 0TY
☎ *(01777) 228385* David Ollerenshaw

A freehouse with three pumps serving a range of ales, with local breweries featured when possible.

A traditional village pub with two bars, non-smoking restaurant and beer garden. Disabled access. Food available at lunchtime and evenings. No children.

12–3pm and 5–11pm Mon–Fri; all day Sat–Sun.

The Nelson & Railway
Station Road, Kimberley NG16 2NR
☎ *(0115) 938 2177* Harry Burton

 Four beers always available including Hardys & Hansons Kimberley Best and Classic. Also an interesting guest from a range of six per year.

O pposite the Hardys & Hansons brewery. A Victorian, family-run village pub with dining area. Bar food available at lunchtime and evenings. Car park, garden, skittle alley and games. Accommodation. Children allowed in dining area for meals. One mile north of M1 junction 26.

OPEN *11am–3pm and 5–11pm Mon–Wed; 11am–11pm Thurs–Sat; 12–10.30pm Sun.*

Fellows
54 Canal Street, Nottingham NG1 7EH
☎ *(0115) 950 6795* Les Howard

 Home of the Fellows, Morton and Clayton Brewhouse Company, with Fellows Bitter and Posthaste always available, plus Timothy Taylor Landlord, Wadworth 6X or a Castle Eden brew. Other guests on four pumps, such as Fuller's London Pride, Burtonwood Top Hat or brews from Cains or local breweries such as Mallard and Castle Rock.

A traditional pub leased from Whitbread with a brewery on the premises. One bar, garden area and restaurant. Food served 12–2.30pm Mon–Fri and 12–6pm Sat–Sun. Children allowed in the restaurant and garden only.

🛢 **FELLOWS BITTER 3.9% ABV**
🛢 **POSTHASTE**

OPEN *All day, every day.*

The Forest Tavern
Mansfield Road, Nottingham NG1 3FT
☎ *(0115) 947 5650* Max Amos

Castle Rock Hemlock, Woodforde's Wherry, Greene King Abbot and Marston's Pedigree always available, plus a guest, from a micro-brewery if possible, perhaps Whim Hartington Bitter or Exmoor Gold.

A traditional building on the outside, inside a continental café. Piped music. Night club at the back of premises. Food served unti! 10.30pm. No children.

OPEN *4–11pm Mon–Tues; 12–11pm Wed–Sat; 12–10.30pm Sun.*

The Golden Fleece
105 Mansfield Road, Nottingham NG1 3FN
☎ *(0115) 947 2843* Steven Creatorex

Marston's Pedigree, Cains Mild and Shipstone's brews always available plus guests, perhaps from Young's or a micro-brewery.

A nineteenth–century pub with an L-shaped bar and wooden floor. Occasional folk music. Food served 11am–8pm daily. Children allowed if eating.

OPEN *All day, every day.*

The Limelight Bar
Nottingham Playhouse, Wellington Circus, Nottingham NG1 5AF
☎ *(0115) 941 8467* Martin Smith

Bateman XB, Marston's Pedigree, Castle Rock Hemlock, Robinson's Best and Adnams Bitter among those beers always available, plus an ever-changing range of guest beers.

F reshly cooked bar and restaurant food is available from 12–8pm Mon–Sat and 12–2.30pm Sunday. Bookings available on request. Parking and garden. Children welcome in the restaurant and outside. Adjacent to Nottingham Playhouse and Nottingham Albert Hall.

OPEN *11am–11pm Mon–Sat; 12–10.30pm Sun.*

Lincolnshire Poacher
161–3 Mansfield Road, Nottingham NG1 3FR
☎ *(0115) 941 1584* Paul Montgomery

Bateman XB, XXXB and Victory plus Marston's Pedigree at all times. Also up to five guest beers, mostly from small independent brewers such as Kelham Island, Springhead, Shardlow, Highwood etc.

A traditional alehouse. No juke box, no games machines, lots of conversation. Bar food available at lunchtimes and evenings. Parking and garden. Children allowed at the management's discretion. Just north of the city centre on the left-hand side. On the A612 Newark to Southwell road.

OPEN *11am–3pm and 5–11pm Mon–Thurs; 11am–11pm Fri–Sat; 12–10.30pm Sun.*

The Vat & Fiddle

Queensbridge Road, Nottingham NG2 1NB
☎ *(0115) 985 0611* Jerry Divine

The full range of Castle Rock ales brewed and served on the premises. Plus guest ales such as Archers Golden, Whim Hartington IPA, Everards Tiger or Belvoir Star Bitter also available. Micro-breweries favoured.

An old-fashioned alehouse, no machines, TV or music. Small beer garden under construction. Situated on the edge of Nottingham, near the railway station. Food served 12–3pm daily, plus Thurs–Sat 6–8pm. Children allowed if eating.

OPEN *All day, every day.*

Ye Olde Trip to Jerusalem

Brewhouse Yard, Castle Road, Nottingham, NG1 6AD
☎ *(0115) 947 3171* Patrick Dare (Manager)

A Hardys & Hansons tied house with Kimberley Mild, Classic and Best always available, plus Marston's Pedigree. Other seasonal Kimberley ales available as guests.

A three-bar pub built inside raw sandstone caves in the Castle Rock. Two courtyards. No music or juke box. Food served at lunchtime until 3pm during the week, and until 5pm at weekends. No children.

OPEN *All day, every day.*

OLLERTON

The Olde Red Lion

Eakring Road, Nr Ollerton, Wellow NG22 0EG
☎ *(01623) 861000* Vaughan Mitchell

A freehouse with Maypole Lion's Pride and Shepherd Neame Spitfire always available plus three guests, regularly including Charles Wells Bombardier.

A 400-year-old country village pub. No music or games. Food available at lunchtime and evenings in a separate dining area. Beer garden. Children allowed.

OPEN *11am–3.30pm and 6–11pm Mon–Fri; 11.30am–4pm and 6–11pm Sat; all day Sun. (Hours may vary during the winter.)*

RADCLIFFE ON TRENT

The Royal Oak

Main Road, Radcliffe on Trent NG12 2FD
☎ *(0115) 933 3798*

Up to 14 brews available including Marston's Pedigree, Timothy Taylor Landlord, Morland Old Speckled Hen and Fuller's London Pride. Also guests (200 per year) including Exmoor Gold and Black Sheep Bitter.

An Austrian-style pub with a cosy lounge. Bar food available at lunchtime. Car park. Children not allowed.

OPEN *11am–11pm Mon–Sat; 12–3.30pm and 7–10.30pm Sun.*

RETFORD

Market Hotel

West Carr Road, Ordsall, Nr Retford DN22 7SN
☎ *(01777) 703278* Graham Brunt

Exmoor Gold, Greene King Abbot Ale, Marston's Pedigree and Bitter, Timothy Taylor Landlord, Thwaites Bitter and Marston's Head Brewer's Choice usually available, plus three guest ales from local brewers.

Family-run traditionally decorated pub. Bar food available at lunchtime and evenings. Car park, conservatory restaurant, large banqueting suite. Children allowed. Located two minutes through the subway from the railway station.

OPEN *11am–3pm Mon–Fri; all day Sat; 12–4pm and 7–10.30pm Sun.*

UPTON

Cross Keys

Main Street, Upton, Nr Newark NG23 5SY
☎ *(01636) 813269* Mr and Mrs Kirrage

Bateman XXXB, Springhead Bitter and Marston's Pedigree always available plus two guest beers (150 per year) which may include Butts Bitter, Wild's Bitter, Enville, Whim, Oakham and Batham brews.

A seventeenth-century listed freehouse and restaurant. Open fires, beams, brasses etc. The former dovecote has been converted into a restaurant, the tap room has carved pews from Newark parish church. Bar food available at lunchtime and evenings. Restaurant open Friday and Saturday evenings and Sunday lunch. Car park, garden, children's area.

OPEN *11.30am–2.30pm and 5.30–11pm Mon–Sat; 12–2.30pm and 7–10.30pm Sun.*

WORKSOP

Manor Lodge Hotel

*Manor Lodge, off Mansfield Road, Worksop
S80 3DL*
☎ *(01909) 474177* Mr AE Ranshaw

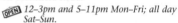 Mansfield, Adnams and Charles Wells brews plus six guest beers (60 per year) from Hardington, Brains, Ridleys, Woodforde's and Burton Bridge breweries etc.

T otally independent unusual five-storey Elizabethan manor pub/restaurant. Open fires. Bar and restaurant food available at lunchtime and evenings. Car park, garden and children's room. Accommodation. Follow the brown tourist signs down the lane off Mansfield Road.

OPEN *12–3pm and 5–11pm Mon–Fri; all day Sat–Sun.*

YOU TELL US

★ *The Golden Fleece,* Main Road, Upper Broughton
★ *Mallard,* Station Approach, Carlton Road, Worksop
★ *The Old Malt Shovel,* 25 Northgate, Nether Langwith
★ *O'Rourkes Bar,* 10 Raleigh Street, Nottingham
★ *The Plough,* 180 Nottingham Road, Mansfield
★ *The Red Lodge,* Fosse Way, Screveton
★ *Tom Hoskins,* Queen's Bridge Road, Nottingham
★ *The Willow Tree Inn,* Front Street, Barnby, Newark

Places Featured:

Bampton
Bledington
Bloxham
Bodicote
Chadlington
Chalgrove
Charlbury
Clifton
Crowell
Faringdon
Fifield

Great Tew
Henley-on-Thames
Long Wittenham
North Leigh
Oxford
Ramsden
South Moreton
Wantage
West Hanney
Witney
Woodcote

THE BREWERIES

THE HOOK NORTON BREWERY CO. LTD

The Brewery, Hook Norton, Banbury OX15 5NY
☎ *(01608) 737210*

 MILD 3.0% ABV
Easy-drinking mild.
BEST BITTER 3.4% ABV
Good well-hopped session bitter.
GENERATION 4.0% ABV
Malty, with good balancing hoppiness.
OLD HOOKY 4.6% ABV
Complex. Rounded and highly drinkable.
HAYMAKER 5.0% ABV
Smooth and full-bodied.
Plus seasonal beers.

MORLAND PLC

The Brewery, Ock Street, Abingdon OX14 5BZ
☎ *(01235) 553377*

 INDEPENDENT IPA 3.4% ABV
Refreshing, hoppy pale ale.
RUDDLES BEST BITTER 3.7% ABV
Malty, with good hoppy bitterness.
ORIGINAL BITTER 4.0% ABV
Dry and bitter with some balancing sweetness.
TANNERS JACK 4.4% ABV
Soft with malty sweetness and crisp finish.
RUDDLES COUNTY 4.9% ABV
Full-flavoured with hoppy bitterness.
OLD SPECKLED HEN 5.2% ABV
Full-bodied and flavour-packed.

OLD LUXTERS

*Vineyard, Winery and Brewhouse, Hambledon,
Henley-on-Thames RG9 6JW*
☎ *(01491) 638330*

 BITTER 4.0% ABV
Refreshing, well-hopped session bitter.
SPECIAL 4.5% ABV
Golden and smooth.
DARK ROAST 5.0% ABV
Plus occasional brews.

W H BRAKSPEAR & SONS PLC

*The Brewery, New Street, Henley-on-Thames
RG9 2BU*
☎ *(01491) 570200*

 MILD 3.0% ABV
Sweet and full-flavoured.
BITTER 3.4% ABV
Session bitter with hops throughout.
OLD 4.3% ABV
Sweet and rounded.
SPECIAL 4.3% ABV
Malty fruit with excellent hop balance.
Plus seasonal brews.

THE WYCHWOOD BREWERY CO. LTD

Eagle Maltings, The Crofts, Witney OX8 7AZ
☎ *(01993) 702574*

 SHIRES XXX 3.7% ABV
Fruit and malt flavour throughout.
SPECIAL 4.2% ABV
Balanced malt and hop flavour with some fruitiness.
HOBGOBLIN 4.5% ABV
Rich roast malt flavour with some fruit and hops.
Plus seasonal and occasional brews.

THE PUBS

BAMPTON

The Romany Inn

Bridge Street, Bampton OX18 2HA
☎ *(01993) 850237* Mrs Booth

Archers Village, Hook Norton Best and Mild, Donnington SBA always available plus two guest beers (100+ per year) which might include brews from Fuller's, Timothy Taylor, Adnams, Bateman, Black Sheep, Brakspear, Cotleigh, Greene King, Hop Back, Marston's, Morland, Ringwood, Robinson's, Titanic and Young's.

A seventeenth-century Grade II listed pub with Saxon arches in the cellar. Bar and restaurant food is available at lunchtime and evenings. Car park, garden, picnic tables and children's play area. Accommodation. Bampton is situated on the A4095 Witney to Faringdon road. The pub is in the centre of the village.

OPEN *11am–11pm.*

BLEDINGTON

The Kings Head Inn and Restaurant

The Green, Bledington OX7 6XQ
☎ *(01608) 658365* Michael Royce

A freehouse with Hook Norton Best and Wadworth 6X always available, plus two guests such as Uley Old Spot or Adnams Broadside.

D ating from 1535, this two-bar pub is situated on the village green. Inglenook fireplace, garden room, restaurant and en suite accommodation. Food available at lunchtime and evenings every day. Children allowed in the garden room only. Located four miles from Stow-on-the-Wold.

OPEN *11am–2.30pm and 6–11pm Mon–Sat; 12–2.30pm and 7–10.30pm Sun.*

BLOXHAM

The Red Lion Inn

High Street, Bloxham, Banbury OX15 4LX
☎ *(01295) 720352* Mr and Mrs Cooper

A freehouse with Wadworth 6X and Adnams Best always available, plus two guests such as Morland Old Speckled Hen or something from breweries such as Hampshire, Wychwood or Fuller's. Session bitters are generally popular.

A two-bar village pub with large garden and car park. Food served at lunchtime and evenings. No children.

OPEN *11.30am–2.30pm and 7–11pm Mon–Fri; 12–3pm and 7–11pm Sat–Sun (10.30 Sun).*

BODICOTE

The Plough Inn

Goose Street, Bodicote, Banbury OX15 4BZ
☎ *(01295) 262327* JW Blencowe

Home of the Bodicote Brewery, which was established in 1982 with the range of three brews always available, plus seasonal specials.

A small village pub with separate lounge/diner and saloon. Early Tudor building, 'Cruck' cottage design. Food served at lunchtime and evenings. Children allowed if eating.

BODICOTE BITTER 3.9% ABV
BODICOTE NO.9 4.3% ABV
3 GOSLINGS 4.1% ABV
A summer ale, light in colour.
PORTER 4.5% ABV
A black porter.
XXX 6.0% ABV
A winter ale.

OPEN *11am–3pm and 6–11pm.*

CHADLINGTON

The Tite Inn

Mill End, Chadlington OX7 3NY
☎ *(01608) 676475* Michael Willis

Archers Village always available plus three guest beers (50 per year) which may include Titanic White Star, Wychwood Dr Thirstys and Nix Wincott That. The emphasis is on smaller breweries.

A sixteenth-century Cotswold stone pub with superb country views. Bar and restaurant food is available at lunchtime and evenings. Car park, garden and garden room. Children allowed. Chadlington is just over two miles south of Chipping Norton off the A361.

OPEN *12–3pm and 6.30–11pm (winter 7–11pm); closed Mon (except bank holidays).*

CHALGROVE

The Red Lion

High Street, Chalgrove, Oxford OX44 7SS
☎ *(01865) 890625* Jonathan Hewitt

A freehouse with Fuller's London Pride and a Brakspear brew always available. Plus guests such as Timothy Taylor Landlord or Fuller's seasonal ales.

A one-bar village pub with separate dining area serving home-made food every lunchtime and evenings except Sundays. Beer garden. Children allowed.

OPEN *12–3pm and 5.30–11pm Mon–Thurs; 12–3pm and 6–11pm Fri–Sat; 12–3pm and 7–10.30pm Sun.*

The Rose & Crown
Market Street, Charlbury, Chipping Norton OX7 3PL
☎ *(01608) 810103* Mr T Page

Archers Best and Fuller's London Pride always available plus three guest beers (100 per year) from breweries such as Lichfield, Coach House, Smiles, Butcombe, Marston's, Timothy Taylor, Robinson's, Badger and Hook Norton etc.

A popular, one-room Victorian pub with a courtyard. No food. Parking, garden and children's room. Located in the town centre.

12–3pm and 5.30–11pm Sun–Thurs; all day Fri–Sat.

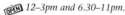

The Duke of Cumberland's Head
Clifton OX15 0PE
☎ *(01869) 338534*

Four beers always available including Hook Norton Best, Adnams Bitter and Wadworth 6X. Guests may include Hampshire King Alfred.

B uilt in the late 1600s, this thatched Oxfordshire village pub serves bar and restaurant food. Car park, attractive gardens, accommodation. Children allowed.

12–3pm and 6.30–11pm.

The Shepherd's Crook
The Green, Crowell, Nr Chinnor OX9 4RR
☎ *(01844) 351431* Mr Scowen

Hook Norton Best, Bateman XB, Batham Best, Timothy Taylor Landlord and Donnington Best usually available.

A quiet, one-bar country pub, no music or games. Beer garden. Food served 12–2.30pm and 7–9.30pm. Fish is a speciality. Bookings taken. Children allowed. The landlord claims that the toilets are the cleanest in the country!

11.30am–3pm and 5–11pm Mon–Fri; all day Sat–Sun.

The Bell
Market Place, Faringdon SN7 7HP
☎ *(01367) 240534* Howard and Sue Roberts

Wadworth 6X and IPA always available plus a variety of guest ales from breweries such as Butcombe, Ruddles, Badger and Adnams.

A thirteenth-century coaching inn with cobbled courtyard recently fully refurbished. Well-known for its floral displays in summer at the back of the hotel. A la carte restaurant and bar food is available at lunchtime and evenings. Eight en suite bedrooms, car park, children welcome.

10.30am–11pm Mon–Sat; 12–3pm and 7–10.30pm Sun.

Merrymouth Inn
Stow Road, Fifield OX7 6HR
☎ *(01993) 831652* Mr Andrew Flaherty

A freehouse with Pope's Traditional and Hardy Country (Thomas Hardy) always available, plus guests.

A n old-style, one-bar pub and restaurant with garden. Large non-smoking areas. Accommodation. Food available 12–2pm and 6.30–9pm. Children allowed.

11.30am–2.30pm and 6–11pm Mon–Sat; 12–2.30pm and 7–10.30pm Sun.

The Falkland Arms
Great Tew OX7 4DB
☎ *(01608) 683653* Tim and Ann Newman

Eight beers available at any one time from a range of about 350 per year. Badger Tanglefoot, Hook Norton Best and Wadworth 6X all favoured. Smaller brewers and some regionals preferred. Also country wines and draught cider.

A traditional seventeenth-century Oxfordshire village inn with a vast inglenook fireplace and smooth flagstones. High-backed settles, oak panelling and beams and sparkling brasses. Bar food every lunchtime and food served in a small dining room from 7–8pm Mon–Sat, booking essential. Parking and garden. Live folk music on Sundays. Accommodation. Filled clay pipes and snuff for sale. Off the B4022, five miles east of Chipping Norton.

11.30am–2.30pm and 6–11pm Mon–Sat; 12–3pm and 7–10.30pm Sun. Open all day Sat–Sun and bank holidays from Easter–October.

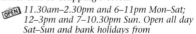

Bird in Hand
61 Greys Road, Henley-on-Thames RG9 1SB
☎ *(01491) 575775* Graham Steward

A freehouse with Brakspear Mild and Bitter and Fuller's London Pride always available, plus guests on two hand pumps. Examples include Timothy Taylor Landlord, Coniston Bluebird or Mordue Workie Ticket.

An old-fashioned one-bar pub. No music or games, not even a till! Large garden. Food served at lunchtime only. No children.

OPEN 11.30am–2.30pm and 7–11pm Mon–Fri; all day Sat–Sun.

Machine Man Inn
Long Wittenham, Abingdon OX14 4QP
☎ *(01865) 407835* Chris Lundsay

A freehouse with West Berkshire Good Old Boy, York Yorkshire Terrier and Rebellion Smuggler always available, plus various guests from breweries such as Crouch Vale.

A three-bar village pub with dining area and interconnected bars. Patio. Accommodation. Food served at lunchtime and evenings. Children allowed.

OPEN 12–3pm and 6–11pm (closed Sat lunchtime).

The Woodman Inn
New Yatt Road, North Leigh, Nr Witney OX8 6TT
☎ *(01993) 881790* Colin Dickenson

Wadworth 6X, Hook Norton Best and Wychwood Shires always available plus two guest beers (150 per year) from breweries such as Adnams, Shepherd Neame, Timothy Taylor, Cotleigh and Charles Wells. The Oxfordshire beer festival takes place here twice a year.

A local village pub on the edge of town, overlooking the Windrush valley. Bar food served at lunchtime and evenings. Car park and garden. Children allowed. Accommodation. Located off the A4095 Witney to Woodstock road.

OPEN 12–2.30pm and 6–11pm Mon–Fri; 12–3pm and 6–11pm Sat; 12–10.30pm Sun.

Folly Bridge Inn
38 Abingdon Road, Oxford OX1 4PD
☎ *(01865) 790106* Eddy Schofield

A Wadworth house with 6X, IPA, Summer Sault (seasonal) and Farmers Glory always available, plus Badger Tanglefoot. Also up to four guests perhaps including Sharp's Doom Bar or Shepherd Neame Spitfire.

A traditional two-bar English pub on the edge of Oxford. Disabled access, patio. Food served at lunchtime and evenings in an environment as smoke-free as possible (there are big smoke extractors). Children allowed.

OPEN All day, every day.

Turf Tavern
4 Bath Place, Oxford OX1 3SU
☎ *(01865) 243235* Trevor Walter

Morland Old Speckled Hen and Archers Golden among the brews always available plus a good selection of guests (442 served during 1998 from more than 200 different breweries).

One of the oldest pubs in Oxford, this is a small, country-style pub in the city centre. Two bars plus an inside and outside alehouse. Three patios. Food available 12–8pm. Children allowed.

OPEN All day, every day.

The Royal Oak
High Street, Ramsden OX7 3AW
☎ *(01993) 868213* John Oldham

Hook Norton Best and Archers Golden always available plus a guest (40 per year) such as Brakspear Special, Banks's Bitter, Caledonian 80/- and Titanic Premium.

A sixteenth-century pub, a former coaching inn, situated in a small village. Bar and restaurant food available. Car park and garden. Ramsden is halfway between Witney and Charlbury off the B4022.

OPEN 11.30am–2.30pm and 6.30–11pm Mon–Sat; 12–3pm and 7–10.30pm Sun.

SOUTH MORETON

The Crown Inn
High Street, South Moreton, Nr Didcot
OX11 9AG
☎ *(01235) 812262* Mr and Mrs Cook

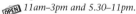 Wadworth IPA and 6X, Badger Tanglefoot and Adnams Best always available plus a guest beer (26 per year) from breweries all over the British Isles.

A n attractive village pub. Bar and restaurant food available. Car park and garden. Children allowed. The village is signposted from both Didcot and Wallingford.

OPEN *11am–3pm and 5.30–11pm.*

WANTAGE

The Royal Oak Inn
Newbury Street, Wantage OX12 8DF
☎ *(01234) 763129* Paul Hexter

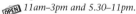 Wadworth 6X, Badger Best and Tanglefoot plus up to eight guest beers (200 per year) from breweries such as Archers, Arkell's, Brakspear, Butts, Foxley, Gibbs Mew, Hampshire, Hook Norton, Hop Back, Titanic, Wadworth and Wychwood.

F air deals and no frills at this freehouse. Navy paraphernalia decorates the bar. Bar food only available Friday and Saturday lunchtime. Accommodation.

OPEN *5.30–11pm Mon–Thurs; 12–2.30pm Fri–Sat; 5.30–11pm Fri; 7–11pm Sat; 12–3pm and 7–10.30pm Sun.*

WEST HANNEY

The Lamb Inn
West Hanney OX12 0LA
☎ *(01235) 868917* Peter Hall

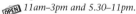 A freehouse with Young's Special, Butcombe Bitter and Shepherd Neame Spitfire always available, plus two guests changed four times a week from smaller and micro-breweries generally. The landlord tries to stock special beers and not repeat them.

A traditional freehouse. One bar, split into two, children's play area, garden. No juke box, but live music once a week. Annual beer festival on August bank holiday. Food served at lunchtime and evenings. Children allowed in the back room and garden.

OPEN *11.30am–2.30pm and 6–11pm.*

WITNEY

House of Windsor
31 West End, Witney OX8 6NQ
☎ *(01993) 704277* Maureen Mcintyre

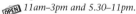 Wadworth 6X and Hook Norton Best always available plus two guest beers (50 per year) which may include Timothy Taylor Landlord, Fuller's London Pride, Archers Golden, Shepherd Neame Spitfire and Bishop's Finger.

N o machines, no pool or darts in this friendly pub. Coal fire in winter. Bar and restaurant food is available Wed–Sat evenings and Sunday lunchtime. Large beer garden. Children allowed. Off the A40 and straight across two mini-roundabouts.

OPEN *12–3.30pm Tues–Sun; 6–11pm every evening.*

WOODCOTE

The Highwayman
Exlade Street, Woodcote, Nr Reading RG8 0UE
☎ *(01491) 682020*

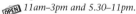 Fuller's London Pride, Wadworth 6X and Gibbs Mew Bishop's Tipple among those brews always available plus a couple of guests (30 per year) to include Adnams Broadside, Timothy Taylor Landlord, Hook Norton Old Hooky, Shepherd Neame Spitfire and Rebellion ales.

R ambling seventeenth-century country inn with two-roomed bar, beams and open fire. Bar and restaurant food available at lunchtime and evenings. Car park, garden, accommodation. Children allowed in restaurant. Signposted from the A4074 Reading to Wallingford Road.

OPEN *11am–3pm and 6–11pm Mon–Sat; 12–3pm and 7–10.30pm Sun.*

YOU TELL US

★ *The Abingdon Arms,* 21 Cornmarket, Thame
★ *Eyston Arms,* High Street, East Hendred
★ *Flower Pot Hotel,* Ferry Lane, Aston, Henley-on-Thames
★ *The George & Dragon,* Shutford, Banbury
★ *Hatchet,* High Street, Childrey
★ *The Lamb Inn,* Sheep Street, Burford
★ *Nut Tree Inn,* Murcott, Kidlington
★ *The Old Anchor Inn,* St Helen Wharf, Abingdon
★ *The Peyton Arms,* Stoke Lyne, Bicester
★ *The Red Lion,* Peppard Common, Rotherfield Peppard
★ *The Red Lion,* The Street, Brightwell-cum-Sotwell, Wallingford
★ *The Swan Hotel,* 9 Upper High Street, Thame
★ *Wharf House,* 14 Butterwyke Place, Oxford
★ *The White Lion,* Fritwell Road, Fewcott, Bicester

Places Featured:

Aston on Clun	Ironbridge
Bishops Castle	Little Stretton
Bouldon	Oakengates
Bridgnorth	Oldwoods
Candy	Pontesbury
Cardington	Shifnal
Coalbrookdale	Shrewsbury
Corfton	Wellington
Edgeley	Wistanstow

THE BREWERIES

HANBY ALES LTD
*New Brewery, Aston Park, Soulton Road, Wem
SY4 5SD*
☎ *(01939) 232432*

 BLACK MAGIC MILD 3.3% ABV
DRAWWELL BITTER 3.9% ABV
ALL SEASONS BITTER 4.2% ABV
SHROPSHIRE STOUT 4.4% ABV
WEM SPECIAL 4.4% ABV
CASCADE 4.5% ABV
SCORPIO PORTER 4.5% ABV
OLD WEMIAN ALE 4.9% ABV
TAVERNERS ALE 5.3% ABV
NUTCRACKER BITTER 6.0% ABV
CHERRY BOMB 6.0% ABV
JOY BRINGER 6.0% ABV
Plus seasonal ales and occasional brews.

SALOPIAN BREWERY
67 Mytton Oak Road, Shrewsbury SY3 8UQ
☎ *(01743) 248414*

SHROPSHIRE GOLD 3.8% ABV
Pale, with refreshing fruit and hop
flavours.
MINSTERLEY ALE 4.5% ABV
Smooth and malty with crisp hoppiness.
CHOIR PORTER 4.5% ABV
Mellow porter.
GINGERSNAP 4.5% ABV
Dark, wheat beer with ginger.
PUZZLE 4.8% ABV
Cloudy, white wheat beer.
JIGSAW 4.8% ABV
Black wheat beer.
GOLDEN THREAD 5.0% ABV
Golden, refreshing and moreish.
IRONBRIDGE STOUT 5.0% ABV
Dark with powerful flavours.
Plus occasional brews.

THE WOOD BREWERY LTD
Wistantow, Craven Arms SY7 8DG
☎ *(01588) 672523*

 SAM POWELL BEST 3.4% ABV
WOOD'S WALLOP 3.4% ABV
Dark, easy-drinking session bitter.
SAM POWELL ORIGINAL 3.7% ABV
Rounded with hop and grain flavours.
PARISH BITTER 4.0% ABV
Light-coloured, refreshing and hoppy.
SPECIAL BITTER 4.2% ABV
Well-rounded and fruity with good hoppiness.
SHROPSHIRE LAD 4.5% ABV
Complex and full of flavours.
SAM POWELL OLD SAM 4.6% ABV
Copper-coloured, rounded and hoppy.
WONDERFUL 4.8% ABV
Powerful flavours. Excellent winter warmer.
Plus seasonal and occasional beers.

WORFIELD BREWING CO. LTD
3 Main Street, Worfield, Bridgenorth WV15 5LF
☎ *(01476) 716320*

 JLK PALE ALE 3.8% ABV
Very pale, light and dry.
HOPSTONE BITTER 4.0% ABV
Slightly dark, full-bodied with good bitterness.
NAILER'S OBJ 4.2% ABV
Light and bitter. Hint of wheat malt and good
hoppiness.
SHROPSHIRE PRIDE 4.5% ABV
Full-bodied and malty with good balancing
hoppiness.
BURCOTE PREMIUM PALE 4.9% ABV
Pale and initially sweet with powerful bitter
finish.
REYNOLD'S REDNECK STRONG MILD 5.5% ABV
Full-bodied, dark-red and lightly hopped.

ASTON ON CLUN

The Kangaroo Inn
Clun Road, Aston on Clun SY7 8EW
☎ *(01588) 660263* Michelle Harding

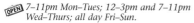 A freehouse with Charles Wells Bombardier and Roo Brew (a house beer produced by the Six Bells Brewery) always available, plus up to three guests from local or micro-breweries whenever possible. Recent examples have included brews from Burton Bridge, Holden's and Moorhouse's.

A prettily situated olde-worlde pub with scenic views. Friendly atmosphere, cosy fire, beer garden and barbecue. Food available in separate dining area at lunchtime and evenings. Children allowed. Situated on the B4368 towards Clun.

 7–11pm Mon–Tues; 12–3pm and 7–11pm Wed–Thurs; all day Fri–Sun.

BISHOPS CASTLE

The Six Bells
Church Street, Bishops Castle SY9 5AA
☎ *(01588) 638930* Neville Richards

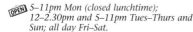 A freehouse and brewpub, home of The Six Bells Brewery. Three home brews are permanent fixtures plus seasonal ales such as Spring Forward and Old Recumbent when available. An annual beer festival takes place on the second weekend in July.

A traditional two-bar pub with no music or games. Patio. Food available at lunchtime and Fri–Sat evenings. Brewery tours available. Children allowed.

BIG NEV'S 3.8% ABV
Light-coloured session bitter with hop flavours.
MARATHON ALE 4.0% ABV
A darkish, malty brew.
CLOUD NINE 4.2% ABV
Hoppy with citrus flavours in the finish.
Seasonals:
BREW 101 4.8% ABV
SPRING FORWARD 4.6% ABV
OLD RECUMBANT 5.2% ABV
CASTLE STOUT 4.2% ABV
FESTIVAL PALE ALE 5.2% ABV
7 BELLS 5.5% ABV

5–11pm Mon (closed lunchtime); 12–2.30pm and 5–11pm Tues–Thurs and Sun; all day Fri–Sat.

The Three Tuns Inn
Salop Street, Bishops Castle SY9 5BW
☎ *(01588) 638797* Jan Cross

 A freehouse and brewpub with the range of three own brews always available plus seasonals and celebration ales three or four times a year. There is an annual beer festival.

An old-fashioned, town-centre brewpub; both the pub and the beer recipe date from 1642. Three bars, dining area, garden/yard. Brewery tours and brewery museum. Food available at lunchtime and evenings. Children allowed.

SEXTON 3.7% ABV
XXX 4.3% ABV
A best bitter.
STEAMER 4.5% ABV
Brewed for the August bank holiday only.
OFFA'S ALE 4.9% ABV
A strong bitter.
SCROOGE 6.5% ABV
A Christmas winter warmer.

12–3pm and 5–11pm Mon–Thurs; all day Fri–Sun.

BOULDON

The Tally Ho Inn
Bouldon, Nr Craven Arms SY7 9DP
☎ *(01584) 841362* Mr M Sheward

A freehouse with Church End Brewery ales usually available, plus one guest such as Thwaites Daniels Hammer or Morland Old Speckled Hen.

A traditional one-bar village pub with garden. Bar snacks available at lunchtime. Children allowed.

11am–3pm and 6–11pm Mon–Fri; all day Sat–Sun.

BRIDGNORTH

The Bear Inn
Northgate, Bridgnorth WV16 4ET
☎ *(01746) 763250* Mrs Gennard

A freehouse with Batham Best and Mild always available plus four guests from a wide-ranging list, such as Holden's Special, Salopian Golden Thread or Shepherd Neame The Bishop's Finger.

A two-bar town pub with garden. Food available at lunchtime only. No children.

1pm–3pm and 5pm–12am Mon–Sat; 12–3pm and 7–10.30pm Sun.

CANDY

The Old Mill Inn
Candy, Oswestry SY10 9AZ
☎ *(01691) 657058* Mr and Mrs Atkinson

Morland Old Speckled Hen always available plus two guests, perhaps an Adnams or Wood brew.

A traditional one-bar country pub with restaurant, garden and children's area. Disabled access. B&B. Food available at lunchtime and evenings. Children allowed.

11am–3pm and 6–11pm Mon and Wed–Sat (closed Tues); 12–3pm and 7–10.30pm Sun.

CARDINGTON

The Royal Oak
Cardington, Church Stretton SY6 7JZ
☎ *(01694) 771266*
David and Christine Baugh

Wood Shropshire Lad, Hobsons Best and Marston's Pedigree always available.

The oldest pub in Shropshire, this is a very old-fashioned country freehouse, situated in a picturesque hiking/cycling area. One bar, dining area and patio. Food available Tues–Sun lunchtime and Tues–Sat evenings. Children allowed.

Closed Mon; 12–3pm and 7–11pm Tues–Sun.

COALBROOKDALE

The Coalbrookdale Inn
12 Wellington Road, Coalbrookdale, Telford TF8 7DX
☎ *(01952) 433953* Mike Fielding

Fuller's London Pride always available plus up to five guest ales from micro-breweries, both local and across the country.

A traditional village pub with one bar, non-smoking area, air filtration systems and patio. Food served 12–2pm and 6–8pm daily. Children allowed in designated areas.

12–3pm and 6–11pm Mon–Sat; 12–3pm and 7–10.30pm Sun.

CORFTON

The Sun Inn
Corfton, Diddlebury, Craven Arms SY7 9DF
☎ *(01584) 861239* Norman Pierce

A minimum of two guest ales always available, with smaller and micro-breweries favoured. There are plans to start brewing.

A traditional, friendly village freehouse. Two bars, non-smoking dining area, garden. Winner of 'Open to All' award for disabled access. Food available at lunchtime and evenings. Children allowed.

11am–2.30pm and 6–11pm (10.30pm Sun).

EDGELEY

Olde Vic
1 Chatham Street, Edgeley

Timothy Taylor Landlord always available plus five guest beers (700 per year), all from micro-breweries and independents – no big brewers. Names include Wyre Piddle, Bullmastiff, Wye Valley, Goose Eye and Cotleigh.

S mall and cosy pub with beer garden for barbecues. Quiz nights. A CAMRA pub of the year. Bar food served at lunchtime and evenings. Car park. Children welcome. Situated near Stockport railway station.

12–3pm and 5.30–11pm Mon–Thurs; all day Fri–Sun.

IRONBRIDGE

Ironbridge Brasserie & Wine Bar
29 High Street, Ironbridge, Telford TF8 7AD
☎ *(01952) 432716* Mr Hull

A freehouse with ales from the local Hobsons brewery always available plus two constantly changing guests. Brains SA is a regular feature, but there are too many others to mention.

A village pub/wine bar/restaurant. One bar, dining area and patio. Food available Fri–Sun lunchtime and Tues–Sun evenings. Children allowed.

6.30–11pm Mon–Thurs (closed lunchtimes); 12–2pm and 6.30–11pm Fri–Sun.

LITTLE STRETTON

The Ragleth Inn
Ludlow Road, Little Stretton, Church Stretton SY6 6RB
☎ *(01694) 722711* D Chilcott

A freehouse with Hobsons Best always available plus two alternating guests that might include Charles Wells Bombardier, Morland Old Speckled Hen, Shepherd Neame Spitfire, Mole's Best, Hobsons Town Crier or a Tomintoul ale.

A traditional two-bar country pub with dining area and garden. Limited disabled access. Food available at lunchtime and evenings. Children allowed.

12–2.30pm and 6–11pm; all day Sat–Sun.

OAKENGATES

The Crown Inn
Market Street, Oakengates, Telford TF2 6EA
☎ *(01952) 610888* John Ellis

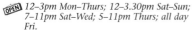 A freehouse with Hobsons Best always available plus up to eight guests changing two or three times a week. So far, over 1,000 ales have been served in four years. Hundreds of breweries featured. Hook Norton, Hanby Ales, Burton Bridge, Wye Valley, Slaters and Lichfield are just a few of the regulars. Only Shropshire beers are sold during the Shropshire Beer Week. Other beer festivals held twice a year on the first weekends in May and October.

A town-centre pub with three drinking areas, a small yard with picnic tables. Rolls available at lunchtime only. Children allowed in designated areas. Located near the bus station.

OPEN *12–3pm Mon–Thurs; 12–3.30pm Sat–Sun; 7–11pm Sat–Wed; 5–11pm Thurs; all day Fri.*

OLDWOODS

The Romping Cat
Oldwoods, Shrewsbury SY4 3AS
☎ *(01939) 290273* Mr Simcox

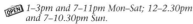 A freehouse with Fuller's London Pride among the brews always available, plus four guests from breweries such as Adnams, Bateman or Greene King and local breweries such as Salopian.

A traditional rural pub with one bar, no machines or music. Beer garden. No food. No children.

OPEN *1–3pm and 7–11pm Mon–Sat; 12–2.30pm and 7–10.30pm Sun.*

PONTESBURY

The Horseshoes Inn
Minsterley Road, Pontesbury, Shrewsbury SY5 0QJ
☎ *(01743) 790278* Mrs Scott

 A freehouse with up to four guest ales. Regulars include Fuller's London Pride, but all breweries are featured.

A rural pub with one bar. Food available at lunchtime and evenings. Children allowed if eating. Accommodation.

OPEN *12–3pm and 7–11pm (10.30pm Sun).*

SHIFNAL

The White Hart
High Street, Shifnal TF11 8BH
☎ *(01952) 461161* Andy Koczy

A freehouse with Enville Ale, Chainmaker Mild, Simpkiss Bitter and Ind Coope Burton Ale permanently available, plus two guests from micro-breweries whenever possible. Recent examples include Exmoor Gold and Moorhouse's Pendle Witches Brew.

A coaching inn in a traditional timbered building, two bars, beer garden. Food available at lunchtime only. Children allowed.

OPEN *12–3pm and 6–11pm Mon–Thurs; all day Fri–Sun.*

SHREWSBURY

The Dolphin Inn
48 St Michael's Street, Shrewsbury SY1 2EZ
☎ *(01743) 350419* Nigel Morton

A freehouse with Hoskins and Oldfield ales always available, plus four guests from smaller and micro-breweries – no nationals. Phoenix Brewery in Manchester is regularly supported. There are plans to start brewing.

A pub dedicated to real ales. No lager or beers from national breweries. Traditional decor, wide-ranging, friendly clientele. Coffee available. No food. No children.

OPEN *5–11pm only.*

The Peacock Inn
42 Wenlock Road, Shrewsbury SY2 6JS
☎ *(01743) 355215* C Roberts

Marston's ales are a speciality here, with Pedigree and Owd Roger always available, plus seasonal brews and other guests such as Banks Mild on one hand pump.

A pub/restaurant with one bar, beer garden, disabled access. Food available at lunchtime and evenings in separate dining area. Children allowed.

OPEN *11.30am–3pm and 6–11pm (10.30pm Sun).*

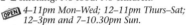

WELLINGTON

The Cock Hotel

148 Holyhead Road, Wellington, Telford
TF1 2DL
☎ *(01952) 244954* Peter Arden

🍺 A freehouse with Chester's Dark Mild among the beers always available plus four guests which might include Hobsons Town Crier, Enville White and occasionally Heaven's Gate, a house brew produced by the Salopian Brewery.

A traditional pub with two bars, one non-smoking. No food. No children.

🗓 *4–11pm Mon–Wed; 12–11pm Thurs–Sat; 12–3pm and 7–10.30pm Sun.*

WISTANSTOW

The Plough Inn

Wistanstow, Craven Arms SY7 8DG
☎ *(01588) 673251* Kay Edwards

🍺 A freehouse with Wood Shropshire Lad and Parish Bitter always available, plus one guest.

A traditional two-bar country pub with restaurant and patio. Food available at lunchtime and evenings. Children allowed.

🗓 *12–3pm and 7–11pm (10.30pm Sun).*

YOU TELL US

★ *All Nations Inn,* Coalport Road, Madeley, Telford (brewpub)
★ *The Castle Vaults Inn,* Castle Gates, Shrewsbury
★ *The Crown Inn,* Munslow, Craven Arms
★ *The Fox & Hounds,* High Street, Stottesdon
★ *The Horseshoe Inn,* Bridges
★ *The King's Arms Hotel,* Church Street, Cleobury Mortimer
★ *The Last Inn,* Wellington Road, Church Aston, Newport
★ *The Mutton & Mermaid,* Shrewsbury
★ *The Old Vaults,* High Street, Ironbridge
★ *The Railway Inn,* Yorton
★ *The Railwayman's Arms,* Hollybush Road, Bridgnorth
★ *The Red Lion,* Bridgnorth Road, Shatterford
★ *The Royal Oak,* Ellerdine Heath, Telford
★ *The Three Fishes,* 4 Fish Street, Shrewsbury
★ *The White Horse Inn,* The Square, Clun, Craven Arms

Places Featured:

Allerford Crossing	Langley Marsh
Ashcott	Leigh Common
Barrington	Luxborough
Bath	Martock
Bleadon	Nether Stowey
Bridgwater	North Curry
Burcott	Pitminster
Burnham on Sea	Pitney
Chard	Rode
Culmhead	Shurton
Frome	Taunton
Hardington Moor	Trudoxhill
Huish Episcopi	Williton
Kelston	Wincanton
Langford Budville	Yeovil

THE BREWERIES

ABBEY ALES LTD
The Abbey Brewery, Lansdown Road, Bath BA1 5EE
☎ *(01225) 444437*

 BELLRINGER 4.2% ABV

ASH VINE LTD
Unit F, Vallis Trading Estate, Robins Lane, Frome
☎ *(01373) 300041*

BITTER 3.5% ABV
Hops and bitterness throughout.
CHALLENGER 4.1% ABV
Malty, with a well-hopped, bitter finish.
BLACK BESS PORTER 4.2% ABV
Darker, with fruit flavours and a hoppy finish.
DECADENCE 4.5% ABV
Malty with some fruitiness.
HOP & GLORY 5.0% ABV
Powerful hoppy flavour with some sweet fruitiness.
Plus monthly brews.

BATH ALES LTD
Henstridge BA8 0HE
BATH SPA 3.7% ABV
Pale and quenching.
GEM 4.1% ABV
Well-rounded flavours with balancing hops.
BARNSTORMER 4.5% ABV
Roast malt flavour with some fruitiness.
Plus seasonal brews.

BERROW BREWERY
Coast Road, Berrow, Burnham-on-Sea TA8 2QU
☎ *(01278) 751345*

 BEST BITTER 3.9% ABV
Smooth and well-balanced.
PORTER 4.5% ABV
Mellow and fruity.
TOPSY TURVY 6.0% ABV
Golden, fruity and refreshing.

BUTCOMBE BREWERY LTD
Rusling House, Butcombe, Bristol BS40 7XQ
☎ *(01275) 472240*

BITTER 4.0% ABV
Smooth, rounded and well-hopped.
WILMOT'S PREMIUM ALE 4.8% ABV
Mellow, well-balanced. Hoppy, with fruit flavours.

COTLEIGH BREWERY
Ford Road, Wiveliscombe, Taunton TA4 2RE
HARRIER SPA 3.6% ABV
Pale, with hoppiness throughout.
TAWNY 3.8% ABV
Flavoursome and well-hopped.
BARN OWL 4.5% ABV
Smooth, refreshing with hoppy finish.
OLD BUZZARD 4.8% ABV
Dark, complex winter brew.
Plus occasional and seasonal brews.

COTTAGE BREWING CO.

The Old Cheese Dairy, Lovington, Castle Cary BA7 7PS
☎ *(01963) 240551*

 SOUTHERN BITTER 3.7% ABV
WHEELTAPPERS ALE 4.0% ABV
CHAMPFLOWER 4.2% ABV
SOMERSET AND DORSET ALE 4.4% ABV
GOLDEN ARROW 4.5% ABV
OUR KEN 4.5% ABV
GREAT WESTERN REAL ALE 5.4% ABV
NORMAN'S CONQUEST 7.0% ABV
Plus monthly special brews.

EXMOOR ALES LTD

The Brewery, Golden Hill, Wiveliscombe, Taunton TA4 2NY
☎ *(01984) 623798*

 ALE 3.8% ABV
Smooth and full-flavoured, with malt throughout.
FOX 4.2% ABV
Easy-drinking and flavour-packed.
GOLD 4.5% ABV
Initially sweet, with a hoppy finish.
HART 4.8% ABV
Malty, with balancing hoppiness.
STAG 5.2% ABV
Well-balanced with lingering finish.
BEAST 6.6% ABV
Dark, with powerful roast malt flavour.
Plus occasional brews.

HENSTRIDGE BREWERY LTD

Bow Bridge, Henstridge Trading Estate, Henstridge BA8 0TH
☎ *(01963) 363150*

 VICKERYS 4.1% ABV
Hoppy and bitter with underlying malt and fruit.

JUWARDS BREWERY

c/o Fox Brothers & Co. Ltd, Wellington TA21 0AW
☎ *(01823) 667909*

 BITTER 3.8% ABV
PREMIUM 4.8% ABV
Plus occasional brews.

MOOR BEER COMPANY

Whitley Farm, Whitley Lane, Ashcott, Bridgwater TA7 9QW
☎ *(01458) 210050*

 WITHY CUTTER 3.8% ABV
AVALON SPRING 4.0% ABV
AVALON AUTUMN 4.0% ABV
MERLINS MAGIC 4.3% ABV
PEAT PORTER 4.5% ABV
SUMMERLAND GOLD 5.0% ABV
OLD FREDDY WALKER 7.3% ABV
Plus occasional brews.

OAKHILL BREWERY

The Old Maltings, Oakhill, Bath BA3 5BX
☎ *(01749) 840134*

 BITTER 3.5% ABV
Light and hoppy.
BEST BITTER 4.0% ABV
Malty and refreshing.
BLACK MAGIC STOUT 4.0% ABV
Rich malty flavour with some hoppiness.
MENDIP GOLD 4.5% ABV
Golden, smooth and rounded.
YEOMAN 5.0% ABV
Balanced fruit and hop flavours.

RCH BREWERY

West Hewish, Nr Weston-super-Mare BS24 6RR
☎ *(01934) 834447*

 HEWISH IPA 3.6% ABV
Delicate flavours throughout.
PG STEAM 3.9% ABV
Bursting with flavours. Full-bodied for gravity.
PITCHFORK 4.3% ABV
Golden, refreshing and dangerously drinkable.
OLD SLUG PORTER 4.5% ABV
Very dark, traditional porter. Complex flavours.
EAST STREET CREAM 5.0% ABV
Refreshing, clean flavour, fruity and deceptive.
FIREBOX 6.0% ABV
Powerful bitter with a multitude of flavours.
Plus occasional beers.

THE PUBS

ALLERFORD CROSSING

The Victory Inn

Allerford Crossing, Norton Fitzwarren, Nr Taunton TA4 1AL
☎ *(01823) 461282* NR Pike

Church End What the Fox's Hat, Cottage Golden Arrow and many many more. Twelve beers always available, 150 per year.

Recently refurbished to enhance the olde-worlde charm and character. Food is available at lunchtime and evenings. Car park, gardens, patio, family room, skittle alley, children's play area and pet's corner with donkeys, sheep, guinea pigs etc. A well room is available for hire. Take the Norton Fitzwarren road, turn off after Taunton Cider to Allerford.

OPEN *11am–3pm and 6–11pm.*

...ington – Nr Illminster
(Barrington (out)) "The Royal Oak"
p 219

Leigh Common   Wincanton
                      p221
        Hunters Lodge Inn,

            Wincanton
The Bear Inn.   p 224

Doddiscombsleigh   Exeter
        The Nobody Inn   p 73

Lapford   Nr Crediton
The Old Malt Scoop Inn.

ASHCOTT

Ring o'Bells

High Street, Ashcott, Bridgwater TA7 9PZ
☎ *(01458) 210232* John Foreman

A freehouse with three hand pumps serving a range of constantly changing real ales. The local Moor Beer Company in Ashcott is regularly supported, plus smaller independents and micros, too many to mention.

A medium-sized village pub with three bars, non-smoking dining area and beer garden. Food available at lunchtime and evenings. Children allowed.

(OPEN) *12–2.30pm and 7–11pm (10.30pm Sun).*

BARRINGTON

The Royal Oak

Barrington, Nr Illminster TA19 0JB
☎ *(01460) 53455* Mr Jarvis

At least five guest beers always available (300 per year) from all corners of the United Kingdom.

A Grade II listed building, sixteenth-century cyder house. Bar and restaurant food served at lunchtime and evenings. Car park, garden and children's room. Follow the National Trust signs for Barrington Court.

(OPEN) *12–3pm and 5.30–11pm Mon–Thurs; 12–11pm Fri–Sun (10.30pm Sun).*

BATH

Hatchett's

6–7 Queen Street, Bath BA1 1HE
☎ *(01225) 425045* Mr and Mrs Cruxton

Up to five beers always available including a house bitter. The three or four guest beers may include Smiles Exhibition, Shepherd Neame Spitfire, Badger Hard Tackle and Exmoor Gold.

A nineteenth-century pub in Bath city centre with bars upstairs and down. The house bitter is available at £1.50. All beers at reasonable prices. Bar food available at lunchtime. Down a side street in the city centre.

(OPEN) *11am–11pm Mon–Sat; 12–10.30pm Sun.*

The Hobgoblin

47 St James' Parade, Bath BA8 1UZ
☎ *(01225) 460785* Fidelna Tracy (manager)

A freehouse specialising in Wychwood ales, so Hobgoblin always available plus two guests.

A lively town pub with a student clientele. Two bars, tables outside. Food available Mon–Wed 12–2.30pm; Thurs–Fri 12–5pm and Sat 12–4pm. Children allowed.

(OPEN) *All day, every day.*

The Old Farmhouse

1 Lansdown Road, Bath BA1 5EE
☎ *(01225) 316162* John Bradshaw

Wadworth 6X and IPA, Badger Tanglefoot and beers from Butcombe and Abbey Ales always available, plus occasional guests.

A town pub and restaurant. Two bars, live jazz four nights a week. Patio. Food available. Well-behaved children allowed.

(OPEN) *All day, every day.*

The Old Green Tree

12 Green Street, Bath BA1 2JZ
☎ *(01225) 448259*
Nick Luke and Sarah le Fèvre

Only stocks draught beer from micro-breweries within a 60-mile radius. Five beers always available including Wickwar Brand Oak Bitter. Others rotated slowly including brews from Uley, Cottage, RCH, Abbey, Bath Ales and Oakhill.

Small oak-lined city-centre pub. No music or machines. Bar food at lunchtime. On a small street in city centre between Milsom Street and the post office.

(OPEN) *11am–11pm Mon–Sat; 7–10.30pm Sun.*

The Pig & Fiddle

2 Saracen Street, Bath BA1 5BR
☎ *(01225) 460868* Gregory Duckworth

Ash Vine Bitter, Challenger and Hop and Glory among six beers always available. Approximately 100 guest beers per year including Crouch Vale Golden Duck, Fuller's London Pride, Exmoor Stag and Butcombe Bitter.

Very busy town-centre pub but with very relaxed atmosphere. Large outside area including garden. Bar food available at lunchtime. Children not allowed. Opposite the Hilton Hotel.

(OPEN) *11.30am–11pm summer; 11.30am–3pm and 5–11pm winter.*

BLEADON

The Queen's Arms

Celtic Way, Bleadon, Nr Weston-super-Mare BS24 0NF
☎ *(01934) 812080* Mr and Mrs Roads

Smiles brews always available straight from the barrel plus guests including Wadworth 6X, Badger Tanglefoot, Crown Buckley Reverend James Original, Bateman XXXB, Greene King Abbot, Fuller's London Pride, Shepherd Neame Spitfire and Adnams Broadside.

Typical village pub. Bar food available at lunchtime and evenings. Car park. Children allowed. The only pub in Bleadon.

(OPEN) *11am–2.30pm and 5.30–11pm.*

BRIDGWATER

The Fountain Inn

1 West Quay, Bridgwater TA6 3HL
☎ *(01278) 424115*
Gordon Kinnear and Gen Ridgley

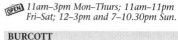 Wadworth 6X and IPA, Badger Tanglefoot and Butcombe Bitter always available plus two guests such as Rockingham Forest Gold or seasonal Wadworth ales like Summer Sault.

A traditional one-bar town-centre pub. Background music. Rolls and bar snacks available at lunchtimes only. Several beer festivals held every year, one main festival and then two or three smaller ones throughout the year with eight beers on at a time. No children.

OPEN *11am–3pm Mon–Thurs; 11am–11pm Fri–Sat; 12–3pm and 7–10.30pm Sun.*

BURCOTT

The Burcott Inn

Wookey Road, Burcott, Wells BA5 1NJ
☎ *(01749) 673874* Ian Stead

A freehouse with Cottage Brewery's Broadgauge always available, plus two guests changing regularly. These may be Timothy Taylor Landlord or Teignworthy Springtide or brews from Cotleigh or Hop Back.

A two-bar country pub with restaurant and garden. Food available at lunchtime and evenings. Children allowed in the garden or inside if eating.

OPEN *11.30am–2.30pm Mon–Fri; 11.30am–3pm Sat–Sun; 6–11pm daily (10.30pm Sun).*

BURNHAM ON SEA

The Royal Clarence Hotel

31 The Esplanade, Burnham on Sea TA8 1BQ
☎ *(01278) 783138*

RCH Pitchfork, PG Steam, East Street Cream and Butcombe Bitter always available plus many other guests, changed throughout the year.

An old coaching hotel under new ownership. Hosts two beer festivals per year and many cabaret attractions. Bar food available all day. Conference facilities. New sports bar with giant TV. Parking, accommodation. Children allowed. Take M5 junction 22, then make for the sea front. The hotel is by the pier.

OPEN *11am–11pm Mon–Sat; 12–10.30pm Sun. Sports bar has a late licence (1am).*

CHARD

The Bell & Crown Inn

Combe Street, Chard TA20 1JP
☎ *(01460) 62470* Marilyn Randall

Otter Bitter and Shepherd Neame Canterbury Jack are permanent fixtures, plus three guests such as Shepherd Neame Spitfire, Morland Tanners Jack or seasonal and celebration ales brewed for special occasions.

A quiet, old-fashioned pub with gas lights. No music. Beer garden. Food available Tues–Sun lunchtime and Fri–Sat evenings. Children allowed.

OPEN *11.30am–3pm and 7–11pm (10.30pm Sun).*

CULMHEAD

Holman Clavel Inn

Culmhead, Taunton TA3 7EA
☎ *(01823) 421432* Tara Laurance

A freehouse with Butcombe Bitter always available plus three weekly changing guests such as Butcombe Gold, Otter Ale, Church End Vicar's Ruin and What the Fox's Hat, Concertina Bengal Tiger or a Juwards brew.

A fourteenth–century rural pub with garden. Food available at lunchtime and evenings. Children allowed.

OPEN *12–3pm and 5–11pm (10.30pm Sun).*

FROME

The Horse & Groom

East Woodlands, Frome BA11 5LY
☎ *(01373) 462802* Ann-Marie Gould

Greene King IPA, Wadworth 6X and a Butcombe brew always available, plus one guest, changing weekly, which might be Bateman XB or a Brakspear brew.

A two-bar country freehouse with log fires, flag floors, restaurant, conservatory and beer garden. Restaurant and bar food available at lunchtime and evenings. Children allowed in the restaurant only.

OPEN *11.30am–2.30pm and 6.30–11pm (10.30pm Sun).*

The Royal Oak Inn
Moor Lane, Hardington Moor, Yeovil BA22 9NW
☎ *(01935) 862354* 'Hag' Harris

 Ales from Butcombe, Brakspear and Branscombe always available plus two guests such as Hook Norton Old Hooky or a Slaters (Eccleshall) brew. Annual themed beer festival held in May each year.

A rural farmhouse freehouse. Two bars, dining area, beer garden, motorcycle-friendly. Food available at lunchtime and evenings. No children.

 12–2.30pm and 7–11pm daily (10.30pm Sun).

The Rose & Crown
Huish Episcopi, Langport TA10 9QT
☎ *(01458) 250494* Steve Pittard

A freehouse with a Teignworthy ale always available plus three guests such as Branscombe Vale Summa That, Hop Back Summer Lightning or others from local breweries.

A country pub with central servery and lots of smaller adjoining rooms. Beer garden. Food available at lunchtime and evenings. Children allowed.

11.30am–2.30pm and 5.30–11.30pm Mon–Thurs; all day Fri–Sun.

The Old Crown
Bath Road, Kelston, Nr Bath
☎ *(01225) 423371*

Butcombe Bitter, Smiles Best, and Wadworth 6X always available plus Wadworth Old Timer in winter only.

Traditional old-English pub and restaurant with open fire, original flagstones, candle-light and good atmosphere. Bar food at lunchtime (not Sun), restaurant Thurs–Sat evenings only. Car park and garden. On A43 Bitton to Bath road, three miles outside Bath.

11.30am–2.30pm and 5–11pm Mon–Fri; 11.30am–3pm and 5–11pm Sat; 12–3pm and 7–10.30pm Sun.

Martlett Inn
Langford Budville, Wellington TA21 0QZ
☎ *(01823) 400262* Mr Owen

A freehouse with Cotleigh Tawny and Barn Owl and Exmoor Ale always available, plus one guest.

A traditional one-bar country pub with dining area and beer garden. Food available at lunchtime and evenings. Children allowed in designated areas.

12–2.30pm and 7–11pm Mon–Sat; 12–3pm and 7–10.30pm Sun.

The Three Horseshoes
Langley Marsh, Wiveliscombe, Nr Taunton TA4 2UL
☎ *(01984) 623763* John Hopkins

Palmers IPA and Ringwood Best always available plus up to three guest beers including Wadworth 6X, Young's Bitter, Dartmoor Best and brews from Butcombe, Shepherd Neame, Harveys and Morland.

An old, unspoilt, no-nonsense traditional pub. No juke box or games machines. Bar and restaurant food is available at lunchtime and evenings. Car park, garden and children's room. Children allowed in the restaurant. Follow the B3227 to Wiveliscombe, then follow signs to Langley Marsh.

12–3pm and 7–11pm (10.30pm Sun).

Hunters Lodge Inn
Leigh Common, Wincanton BA9 8LD
☎ *(01747) 840439* Mr Bent

A freehouse but with Oakhill Brewery ales usually available plus a range of guests from micro-breweries.

A country pub with bars, dining area and beer garden. Food available at lunchtime and evenings. Children allowed.

All day, every day.

LUXBOROUGH

Royal Oak of Luxborough

Exmoor National Park, Luxborough, Nr Dunster TA23 0SH
☎ *(01984) 640319* Mr K Draper

Cotleigh Tawny, Exmoor Gold and Flowers IPA always available plus up to four guest beers (150 per year) such as Shepherd Neame Spitfire, Exmoor Beast, Cottage Golden Arrow and Cotleigh Harrier SPA, plus brews from Ash Vine, Moor and Bateman.

An unspoilt rural pub with loads of beams, flagstones etc. Farmhouse tables. Bar and restaurant food available at lunchtime and evenings. Car park and garden. Children allowed in the restaurant. En suite accommodation. Off the A396, four miles south of Dunster.

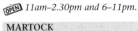 *11am–2.30pm and 6–11pm.*

MARTOCK

The Nag's Head

East Street, Martock TA12 6NF
☎ *(01935) 823432* Christopher Bell

A freehouse with Otter Bitter among the brews always available, plus two weekly changing guests such as Timothy Taylor Landlord, RCH East Street Cream, Badger Tanglefoot or other seasonal and celebration ales.

A local village pub with two bars (lounge and public), non-smoking dining area, beer garden, children's play area, accommodation, disabled access at rear. Home-made food available at lunchtime and evenings. Children allowed in the garden play area only. Can be difficult to find, but worth it! Phone for directions.

12–3pm Fri–Sun; 6–11pm daily.

NETHER STOWEY

The Rose & Crown

St Mary Street, Nether Stowey TA5 1LJ
☎ *(01278) 732265* Malcolm and Jill Bennett

A freehouse always offering beers from Cotleigh, Moor and Oakhill plus one other guest pump serving brews from Cottage, Archers, Slaters (Eccleshall) or Ash Vine.

A traditional fifteenth-century coaching inn. One bar, restaurant and beer garden. Food available at lunchtime and evenings. Children allowed.

All day, every day.

NORTH CURRY

The Bird in Hand

1 Queen Street, North Curry, Taunton TA3 6LT
☎ *(01823) 490248* Michael Gage

A freehouse with Badger Tanglefoot and Otter Bitter always available, plus four weekly changing guest pumps perhaps featuring Cotleigh Tawny, RCH Pitchfork, Fuller's London Pride or Exmoor Gold.

A traditional one-bar country pub with log fires and beer garden. Food available at lunchtime and evenings. Children allowed at lunchtime only.

12–3pm Tues–Sun (closed Mon lunch); 7–11pm daily.

PITMINSTER

The Queen's Arms

Pitminster, Nr Taunton TA3 7AZ
☎ *(01823) 421529*
Chris and Fay Handscombe

Cotleigh Tawny always available plus up to five guests including Everards Tiger and brews from Ballard's, Teignworthy, Cottage Brewery, etc.

A traditional stone-built pub with a dining room in an attached fourteenth-century restaurant. No background music or games machines. Bar and restaurant food available at lunchtime and evenings. Fish and shellfish specialities. Car park and garden. Children allowed in the bar until 8pm. Follow the signs for Corfe from Taunton and turn right in Corfe.

11am–3pm and 5–11pm.

PITNEY

Halfway House

Pitney, Nr Langport TA10 9AB
☎ *(01458) 252513*

Beers from Teignworthy, Oakhill, Cotleigh, Butcombe and Bridgwater always available plus guests (100 per year) such as Ringwood Old Thumper, Timothy Taylor Landlord, Hop Back Summer Lightning and Wheat Beer.

A real ale pub with flagstone floors and log fires. No music or games machines. Bar food is available at lunchtime and evenings. Car park and garden. Well-behaved children allowed. CAMRA Somerset pub of the year. On the main road between Somerton and Langport (B3151).

11.30am–2.30pm and 5.30–11pm.

RODE

The Bell Inn
13 Frome Road, Rode BA3 6PW
☎ *(01373) 830356* Jeff Simmons

Two guest pumps offering real ales such as Eldridge Pope Royal Oak (Thomas Hardy).

A food-oriented country pub specialising in seafood. Two bars, dining area and beer garden. Food available at lunchtime and evenings. Children allowed.

OPEN *12–3pm and 7–11pm (10.30pm Sun).*

SHURTON

The Shurton Inn
Shurton, Bridgwater TA5 1QE
☎ *(01278) 732695* Dennis Gooden

A freehouse with two Exmoor ales always available, plus one changing guest.

A country pub with one big bar, dining area and beer garden. Food available at lunchtime and evenings. Children allowed.

OPEN *11am–2.30pm and 6–11pm (10.30pm Sun).*

TAUNTON

The Eagle Tavern
South Street, Taunton TA1 3AF
☎ *(01823) 275713* Chris Handscombe

Greene King Abbot and a Robinson's brew always available, plus one guest from an independent brewery such as Juwards or Dartmoor.

A country-style pub in the town, with wooden floors and open fire. Beer garden. Food available at lunchtime and evenings. Children allowed until 8pm.

OPEN *11am–3pm (5pm in summer) and 6–11pm (10.30pm Sun.)*

Perkin Warbeck
22 East Street, Taunton TA1 3LP
☎ *(01823) 335830* Mike Davies

A Wetherspoon's pub with Marston's Pedigree among the beers always available, plus two guests such as Exmoor Gold and Stag or Butcombe ales, but beers from any brewery may be stocked if available.

A one-bar town-centre pub. Non-smoking areas, patio. Food avaiable all day, every day. No children.

OPEN *All day, every day.*

TRUDOXHILL

The White Hart
Trudoxhill, Nr Frome BA11 2DT
☎ *(01373) 836324* Mark Chalkley

This freehouse was once a brewpub, the home of the Ash Vine Brewery, but Ash Vine's expansion forced it to move to bigger premises and become a separate, independent brewery. The close links between the pub and brewery are maintained though, and a good range of Ash Vine ales are always available. One or two guests every week might include Wadworth 6X, Fuller's London Pride, Morland Old Speckled Hen or a Butcombe brew. Occasional themed evenings with beers to suit.

A sixteenth-century county pub. One bar, restaurant, garden and children's play area. Food available 11.30am–9pm daily. Children allowed.

OPEN *All day, every day.*

WILLITON

The Egremont Hotel
1 Fore Street, Williton, Taunton TA4 4PX
☎ *(01984) 632500* A Yon

A freehouse with RCH Pitchfork, Butcombe Gold and an Oakhill brew always available, plus guests such as Hop Back Summer Lightning served straight from the barrel.

A town-centre hotel with two bars, one mainly serving ciders. Restaurant, beer garden, accommodation. Food available in the restaurant at lunchtime and evenings, and bar snacks all day. Children allowed.

OPEN *All day, every day.*

The Forester's Arms Hotel
Long Street, Williton, Taunton TA20 3PX
☎ *(01984) 632508* Mr Gobal

A freehouse with Cotleigh Tawny and Harrier SPA always available, plus three guests from breweries such as Berrow, Brains or Ash Vine.

A two-bar village pub with dining area, beer garden, accommodation. Food served at lunchtime and evenings. Children allowed, if eating.

OPEN *All day, every day.*

WINCANTON

The Bear Inn
12 Market Place, Wincanton BA9 9LP
☎ *(01963) 32581 Ian Wainwright*

A freehouse with Greene King Abbot always available plus two guests. Regulars include Ringwood Best and Fortyniner, Slaters (Eccleshall) Original and many more, too many to mention.

An old coaching inn with food available at lunchtime and evenings in a separate dining area. Accommodation. Children allowed.

> *All day, every day.*

YEOVIL

The Armoury
1 The Park, Yeovil BA20 1DY
☎ *(01935) 471047 Rebecca Keeble*

Wadworth 6X and IPA and a Butcombe brew always available plus two guest ales such as Adnams Broadside.

A traditional real ale house with one environmentally controlled bar. Patio, plans for a skittle alley. Food available at lunchtime and evenings. No children.

> *11am–3pm and 5–11pm Mon–Thurs; all day Fri–Sun.*

YOU TELL US

★ *The Bear & Swan,* South Parade, Chew Magna
★ *The Bear Inn,* North Street, Wiveliscombe, Taunton
★ *The Black Swan Hotel,* North Street, Langport
★ *The Cooper's Arms Hotel,* Market Street, Highbridge
★ *The Cottage Inn,* Champford Lane, Wellington
★ *The Crown,* Keynsham
★ *The Crown Inn,* 34 South Street, Crewkerne (brewpub)
★ *The Fox & Badger Inn,* Railway Lane, Wellow, Bath
★ *The King's Head Inn,* Main Street, Higham
★ *The Queens Arms Inn,* Corton Denham
★ *The Ring of Bells,* Hinton Blewitt
★ *The Ring of Bells,* Pit Hill Lane, Moorlinch, Bridgewater
★ *The Star,* Pill
★ *The White Horse Inn,* South Cheriton, Templecombe
★ *The Wood Street Inn,* Taunton
★ *The Woolpack Inn,* Shepherd's Way, St Georges

Places Featured:

Bignall End
Burton upon Trent
Eccleshall
Fazeley
Harriseahead
Ipstones
Leek

Lichfield
Marston
Shraley Brook
Stafford
Stoke-on-Trent
Stone

THE BREWERIES

THE ECCLESHALL BREWERY

The St George Hotel, Castle Street, Eccleshall ST21 6DF
☎ *(01785) 850300*

 SLATERS BITTER 3.6% ABV
Balanced easy-quaffer.
TOP NOTCH 3.8% ABV
Summer brew.
SLATERS ORIGINAL 4.0% ABV
Complex and smooth.
TOP TOTTY 4.0% ABV
Well-balanced with good hoppiness.
SLATERS PREMIUM 4.4% ABV
Full-bodied and deceptively smooth.
SLATERS SUPREME 4.7% ABV
Creamy, full-bodied and hoppy.

MARSTON, THOMPSON & EVERARD PLC

The Brewery, Shobnall Road, Burton upon Trent DE14 2BW
☎ *(01283) 531131*

BITTER 3.8% ABV
Well-balanced, easy-drinking brew.
PEDIGREE 4.5% ABV
Smooth and rounded.
OWD RODGER 7.6% ABV
Dark and powerful, with some sweetness.
Plus seasonal brews.

SHRALEY BROOK BREWERY

Knowle Bank Road, Shraley Brook, Audley, Stoke-on-Trent ST7 8DS
☎ *(01782) 723792*

CHARLES FIRST BREW 4.2% ABV
A very light and hoppy bitter.
EXECUTIONER 4.9% ABV
Hoppy, medium-strength.
GOLDEN SOVEREIGN 5.2% ABV
Hoppy, but full-bodied and darker.

TITANIC BREWERY

Harvey Works, Lingard Street, Burslem, Stoke-on-Trent ST6 1ED
☎ *(01782) 823447*

BEST BITTER 3.5% ABV
Quenching and hoppy.
LIFEBOAT 4.0% ABV
Fruit and bittersweet flavour, with a dry finish.
PREMIUM BITTER 4.1% ABV
Golden, with hoppiness throughout.
STOUT 4.5% ABV
Rich roast malty flavour and some hoppiness.
WHITE STAR 4.8% ABV
Pale, quenching and decepively drinkable.
CAPTAIN SMITH'S STRONG ALE 5.2% ABV
Smooth, rounded roast flavour with good hoppiness.
WRECKAGE 7.2% ABV
Classic winter brew.
Plus monthly brews.

THE PUBS

BIGNALL END

The Plough

Ravens Lane, Bignall End
☎ *(01782) 720469* Mr Gillespie

Broughton Merlin's Ale, Butterknowle Bitter, Fuller's London Pride, Morland Old Speckled Hen and Young's brews always available plus various guest beers supplied through the Caledonian Brewery.

A traditional Victorian working men's pub. Cold food available at lunchtime. Car park, garden, children's room. No children in bar. Easy to find.

OPEN *11am–11.30pm Mon–Wed; 11am–11pm Thurs–Fri; 11–midnight Sat; 12.30–11pm Sun.*

BURTON UPON TRENT

The Alfred

Derby Street, Burton upon Trent DE14 2LD
☎ *(01283) 562178* Steve Greenflade

A Burton Bridge Brewery tenancy with Bridge Bitter, Summer Ale, Festival Ale, Burton Porter, Mild and XL Bitter available. Plus one guest, which changes constantly (more than 250 beers served in less than three years). Breweries supported include Leatherbritches and Iceni.

A two-bar town pub with dining area and beer garden. Food served every lunchtime and Mon–Sat evenings. Children allowed.

OPEN *11am–3pm and 6–11pm Mon–Thurs; all day Fri–Sat; 12–3pm and 7–10.30pm Sun.*

Burton Bridge Inn

Bridge Street, Burton upon Trent DE14 1SY
☎ *(01283) 536596* Kevin McDonald

Home of the Burton Bridge Brewery with Bridge Bitter, Porter and Festival Ale always available. Seasonal ales always a feature, for example Summer Ale or Gold Medal Ale. Other guests rotated on two pumps including beers from Timothy Taylor and York breweries.

A one-bar town brewpub. Dining area, patio, brewery tours. Food served lunchtimes. Children allowed.

SUMMER ALE 3.8% ABV
A light golden bitter, brewed during BST.
XL BITTER 4.0% ABV
BRIDGE BITTER 4.2% ABV
Normal brown bitter.
PORTER 4.5% ABV
A dark beer.
SPRING ALE 4.7% ABV
Seasonal.
STAFFORDSHIRE KNOT BROWN ALE 4.8% ABV
Brewed each autumn.
TOP DOG STOUT 5.0% ABV
A winter ale.
HEARTY ALE 5.0% ABV
A Christmas brew.
BATTLE BREW 5.0% ABV
Brewed each July.
FESTIVAL ALE 5.5% ABV
Slightly sweet with a bitter finish.
Plus one new beer each month, always called Gold Medal Ale and at 4.5% ABV, but brewed to varying recipes.

OPEN *11.30am–2.30pm and 5.30–11pm.*

The Roebuck

Station Street, Burton upon Trent DE14 1BT
☎ *(01283) 568660* Ray Ashley

Marston's Pedigree, Morland Old Speckled Hen, Greene King Abbot, Ind Coope Burton Ale and a house brew called Roebuck Bitter always available, plus two guests (approx 700 served over eight years).

F ringe-of-town pub with one open-plan room, small patio, accommodation. Food served 12 noon–11pm. No children.

OPEN *11am–11pm Mon–Fri; 11am–3pm and 6–11pm Sat; 12–3pm and 7–10.30pm Sun.*

Thomas Sykes Inn

Anglesey Road, Burton upon Trent DE14 3PF
☎ *(01283) 510246* Colin Hall

A freehouse with Marston's Pedigree and Owd Rodger usually available plus three guests such as Greene King Abbot or Morland Old Speckled Hen.

A town pub built in an old stable with a cobbled floor. One bar, snug and beer garden. No food. Children allowed.

 11.30am–2.30pm and 5–11pm Mon–Thurs; all day Fri; 11.30am–2.30pm and 7–11pm Sat; 12–2.30pm and 7–10.30pm Sun.

ECCLESHALL

The George Hotel

Castle Street, Eccleshall ST21 6DF
☎ *(01785) 850300* Gerard and Moyra Slater

The Eccleshall Brewery is located on the premises, so the Slaters Ales range of up to six beers are brewed and available here plus a variety of guests.

Opened in March 1995 by Gerard and Moyra Slater. The beer is brewed by their son, Andrew. The brewery is a ten-barrel plant. The George is a sixteenth-century coaching inn with olde-worlde beams, log fires, real ales, malt whisky. Bar and restaurant food available. Car park. Accommodation.

All day, every day.

FAZELEY

The Plough & Harrow

Atherstone Street, Fazeley B78 3RF
☎ *(01827) 289596* Paul Kilby

Two brews always available plus two guests such as Morland Old Speckled Hen, Wadworth 6X, Thwaites Daniels Hammer or Fuller's London Pride.

A one-bar village pub. Beer garden. En suite accommodation. New restaurant with food served at lunchtime and evenings. Children allowed.

11.30am–3pm and 5.30–11pm Mon–Thurs; all day Fri–Sun.

HARRISEAHEAD

The Royal Oak

42 High Street, Harriseahead, Stoke-on-Trent ST7 4JT
☎ *(01782) 513362* Barry Reece

A freehouse with Fuller's London Pride and Charles Wells Bombardier often available plus a couple of others from independent and micro-breweries whenever possible. Beers from the Isle of Man are especially favoured.

A traditional village pub with one bar and a lounge. Car park. No food. No children.

7–11pm Mon–Fri; 12–3pm and 7–11pm Sat–Sun.

IPSTONES

The Linden Tree

47 Froghall Road, Ipstones, Stoke-on-Trent ST10 2NA
☎ *(01538) 266370* Graham Roberts

A freehouse with guests such as Whim Hartington IPA and Arbor Light or a Wadworth ale.

A country pub with separate 50-seater non-smoking restaurant. Beer garden. Food served at lunchtime and evenings. Children allowed.

12–3pm and 6–11pm (10.30pm Sun).

LEEK

The Swan Hotel

2 St Edward Street, Leek ST13 5DS
☎ *(01538) 382081* Mrs Julie Ellerton

Young's Special always available plus three or four rotating guests. Wadworth 6X, Wychwood Hobgoblin and Robinson's Frederics are regular features, plus seasonal specials.

A four-bar town-style pub and hotel in moorlands, with an additional bar called JD's attached, which is a young person's modern themed sports bar. Food served at lunchtime and evenings. Children allowed. Function room. Bridal suite. Past winner of CAMRA's pub of the year and pub of the month.

11am–3pm and 7–11.30pm.

The Wilkes Head

16 St Edward Street, Leek ST13 5DA
☎ *(01538) 383616* Mr Kerr-Ledell
(temporary)

The Whim Ales flagship pub, with Magic Mushroom Mild, Hartington IPA and Snow White, plus Broughton Old Jock and other seasonal or occasional specials such as Whim Arbor Light, Hartington Bitter and Black Christmas.

A n award-winning town pub, famous for its ales. Small and cosy with large beer garden. Rolls and sandwiches available. Children and dogs welcome. Accommodation.

OPEN *All day, every day.*

LICHFIELD

The Queen's Head

Queen Street, Lichfield WS13 6QD
☎ *(01543) 410932* Roy Harvey

Adnams Best, Timothy Taylor Landlord and Marston's Pedigree always available, plus three guests, which might include Fuller's London Pride, Exmoor Gold or Greene King Abbot.

A traditional, small, back-street pub. No music, small TV, one games machine. Bar food available at lunchtime (12–2.30pm), but the pub is really famous for its selection of cheeses, of which 20 different ones are available all day. Children allowed.

OPEN *All day Mon–Sat; 12–3pm and 7–10.30pm Sun.*

MARSTON

The Fox Inn

Marston, Nr Church Eaton ST20 0AS
☎ *(01785) 84072*

Eight beers available including Coach House (Joule) Old Priory, Mansfield Old Baily and Charles Wells Eagle. Plus Lloyds and Wood brews and loads of guests from Wychwood, Timothy Taylor etc.

A n unadulterated alehouse in the middle of nowhere. Bar and restaurant food available at lunchtime and evenings. Car parking and children's room. Field for tents and caravans. Accommodation.

OPEN *12–3 pm and 6–11pm.*

SHRALEY BROOK

The Rising Sun

Knowle Bank Road, Shraley Brook, Stoke-on-Trent ST7 8DS
☎ *(01782) 720600* Jill Holland

Home of the Shraley Brook Brewing Company with the range of three home brews avaiable plus guest beers such as Cottage Golden Arrow, RCH Pitchfork and Archers' Golden.

A traditional country pub with three serving rooms, real fires, function room, restaurant, beer garden and a one-acre paddock with Shetland ponies. Plans for brewery tours. Homemade food served at lunchtime and evenings, including real chips! Children allowed.

OPEN *5.30–11pm Mon–Thurs; all day Fri–Sun.*

STAFFORD

The Stafford Arms

43 Railway Street, Stafford
☎ *(01785) 253313* Mike Watkins

Six Titanic beers available plus four guests (400 per year) including brews from Orkney, Caledonian, Sutton and many other small independent breweries.

A traditional pub with bar food available at lunchtime and evenings. CAMRA pub of the year 1994. Car park, garden, bar billiards, skittle alley and brewery trips. Children allowed. Just by the railway station.

OPEN *12–11pm Mon–Sat.*

Tap & Spile

Peel Terrace, Stafford ST16 3HE
☎ *(01785) 223563* Mr S Tudeswall

A selection of eight cask ales always available, each changing three times a week so 24 different ales on offer each week. These might well include Timothy Taylor Landlord and Black Sheep Bitter.

A village pub. Non-smoking dining area, beer garden. Food served at lunchtime only. Children allowed.

OPEN *All day, every day.*

Hogshead

2–6 Percy Street, Hanley, Stoke-on-Trent ST1 1NF
☎ *(01782) 209585* Brett Ritzkowski

 A Whitbread house with an extensive range of cask ales always available. Chester Mild, Morland Old Speckled Hen and Wadworth 6X on permanently, plus a range of six guests such as Titanic Best or Premium. Each month one beer is featured as Beer of the Month on special offer (buy three get one free).

A town pub in a city-centre location. One bar, disabled access and lift. Non-smoking area. Food available all day. Children allowed before 6pm.

OPEN *All day, every day.*

The Tontine Alehouse

20 Tontine Street, Hanley, Stoke-on-Trent ST1 1AQ
☎ *(01782) 263890* Becky Smith

Marston's Pedigree always available, plus four weekly changing guest ales from independent breweries all over the country – too many to mention!

A one-bar, city-centre pub with beer garden. Food served at lunchtime only. Children allowed, if eating.

OPEN *All day Mon–Sat; closed Sun.*

The Pheasant Inn

Old Road, Stone ST15 8HS
☎ *(01785) 814603* Mrs Glover

Two guest ales among the brews always available. Regular examples include Greene King Abbot, Timothy Taylor Landlord and Morland Old Speckled Hen. Seventeen beers served every ten weeks.

A Victorian two-bar pub on the outskirts of town. Recently redecorated dining room and a child-safe beer garden with lockable access though the pub. Food available at lunchtime, bookings only for evenings. Children allowed, if accompanied and if eating.

OPEN *All day, every day.*

The Star Inn

Stafford Road, Stone ST15 8QW
☎ *(01785) 813096* Nathan Jander

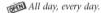 Banks's Bitter and Original and Marston's Pedigree always available plus two guests such as Cameron Strongarm.

An edge-of-town pub situated by the canal with access to the towpath. Two bars, garden and patio. Food available all day. Children allowed.

OPEN *All day, every day.*

★ *The Butcher's Arms*, Reapsmoor
★ *The Cat Inn*, Bridgnorth Road, Enville
★ *The Crossways*, Nelson Place, Newcastle-under-Lyme
★ *Den Engel*, Birch House, St Edward Street, Leek
★ *The Dog & Partridge*, Swinscoe
★ *The Greyhound Inn*, Burston, Stafford, Stone
★ *The Plough & Harrow*, High Street, Kinver
★ *The Plough Inn*, Etruria Road, Etruria, Stoke-on-Trent
★ *The Red Lion*, Great Chatwell
★ *The Star*, Market Place, Penkridge
★ *The White Swan*, Coventry Road, Kingsbury, Tamworth

Places Featured:

Bungay	Ipswich
Bury St Edmunds	Kersey
Carlton Colville	Laxfield
Edwardstone	Lowestoft
Framsden	Pin Mill
Freckenham	Southwold
Gislingham	Walton
Hasketon	

THE BREWERIES

ADNAMS & CO. PLC

Sole Bay Brewery, Southwold IP18 6JW
☎ *(01502) 727200*

BITTER 3.7% ABV
Clean and well-hopped, with fruity flavours.
EXTRA 4.3% ABV
Citrus flavours throughout, with good hoppiness.
BROADSIDE 4.7% ABV
Powerful malty brew with balancing hoppiness.
Plus seasonal brews.

BRETTVALE BREWING CO.

132 High Street, Bildeston IP7 7ED
☎ *(01449) 741434*

BEST BITTER 3.8% ABV
BLONDIE 4.0% ABV
FIRST GOLD 4.3% ABV
Very bitter.
BILLY 4.8% ABV
DARK VADER 5.4% ABV
Complex, roast character.

COX & HOLBROOK

Hillcroft House, High Road, Great Finborough, Stowmarket IP14 3QA
☎ *(01449) 770682*

BOUY'S BITTER 3.2% ABV
SHELLEY DARK 3.6% ABV
SESSION BITTER 4.0% ABV
Plus occasional brews.

GREEN JACK BREWING CO. LTD

Oulton Broad Brewery, Harbour Road Industrial Estate, Lowestoft NR32 3LZ
☎ *(01502) 587905*

BITTER 3.5% ABV
CANARY 3.8% ABV
GRASSHOPPER 4.2% ABV
ORANGE WHEAT BEER 4.2% ABV
GOLDEN SICKLE 4.8% ABV
GONE FISHING 5.0% ABV
LURCHER STRONG ALE 5.4% ABV
Plus seasonal and occasional brews.

GREENE KING PLC

Westgate Brewery, Bury St Edmunds IP33 1QT
☎ *(01284) 763222*

XX DARK MILD 3.0% ABV
Sweeter, dark mild.
IPA 3.6% ABV
Hoppy session bitter.
TRIUMPH
ABBOT ALE 5.0% ABV
Rounded and flavoursome.

MAULDONS

7 Addison Road, Chilton Industrial Estate, Sudbury CO10 6YW
☎ *(01787) 311055*

MOLETRAP 3.8% ABV
Rounded easy-quaffer.
PORTER 3.8% ABV
Smooth porter.
EATONSWILL OLD 4.0% ABV
Dark, old ale.
MACMILLAN (2 BOB) 4.0% ABV
Malty throughout.
SQUIRES 4.2% ABV
Well-balanced malt and hops.
BLACK SATIN 4.5% ABV
Dark, rounded with good hoppy bitterness.
SUFFOLK PRIDE 4.8% ABV
Powerful hoppiness throughout.
BLACK ADDER 5.3% ABV
Stout.
WHITE ADDER 5.3% ABV
Easy-drinking and well-hopped.
SUFFOLK COMFORT 6.6% ABV
Superb barley wine.
Plus seasonal brews.

NETHERGATE BREWERY CO. LTD
11–13 High Street, Clare CO10 8NY
☎ *(01787) 277244*

 IPA 3.6% ABV
Clean hop flavour.
UMBEL ALE 3.8% ABV
Distinctive hoppy and coriander flavours.
BEST BITTER 4.0% ABV
Malty and bitter.
AUGUSTINIAN ALE 4.8% ABV
OLD GROWLER 5.0% ABV
Soft, chocolate malt flavours.
UMBEL MAGNA 5.0% ABV
Porter with coriander.
Plus seasonal brews.

ST PETER'S BREWERY CO. LTD
St Peter's Hall, St Peter South Elmham, Bungay NR35 1NQ
☎ *(01986) 782322*

 BEST BITTER 3.7% ABV
Light, easy-quaffer.
EXTRA 4.4% ABV
Hoppy, porter-style beer.
FRUIT BEER (ELDERBERRY) 4.7% ABV
Wheat beer with added elderberry.
FRUIT BEER (GRAPEFRUIT) 4.7% ABV
Refreshing citrus fruit flavour.
GOLDEN ALE 4.7% ABV
Golden, lager-style beer.
MILD 4.7% ABV
Sweeter, chocolate malt flavour, delicate hoppiness.
SPICED ALE 4.7% ABV
Spicy lemon and ginger flavour.
WHEAT BEER 4.7% ABV
Refreshing, clear and distinctive.
HONEY PORTER 5.1% ABV
Original-style porter with honey.
OLD STYLE PORTER 5.1% ABV
Original porter. Blend of old ale and younger bitter.
STRONG ALE 5.1% ABV
Smooth, soft and well-rounded.
SUMMER ALE 6.5% ABV
Superb balance and easy to drink.

TOLLEMACHE & COBBOLD BREWERY
Cliff Road, Ipswich IP3 0AZ
☎ *(01473) 231723*

 MILD 3.2% ABV
BITTER 3.5% ABV
ORIGINAL 3.8% ABV
IPA 4.2% ABV
Plus seasonal and occasional brews.

The Chequers Inn
23 Bridge Street, Bungay NR35 1HD
☎ *(01986) 893579* Michael and Kim Plunkett

A freehouse with Adnams Best, Fuller's London Pride, Timothy Taylor Landlord and Woodforde's Wherry always available plus a good selection of guests changing frequently. More than 900 different beers served in less than three years.

A seventeenth-century, two-bar town pub with log fire, two beer gardens and patio. Food available Mon–Sat lunchtime only. Children allowed.

All day, every day.

The Green Dragon
29 Broad Street, Bungay NR35 1EE
☎ *(01986) 892681* William and Rob Pickard

Adnams Best plus the four beers from the Green Dragon range brewed and served on the premises.

The pub was bought in 1991 from Brent Walker by William and Rob Pickard. The three-barrel brewery was built and the pub refurbished. Due to increased demand, a second brewery was then built and the capacity expanded to eight barrels. The Green Dragon is a popular pub with a friendly atmosphere. Bar food is available at lunchtime and evenings. Car park, garden, children's room.

MILD 3.4% ABV
CHAUCER ALE 3.7% ABV
BRIDGE STREET BITTER 4.5% ABV
DRAGON 5.5% ABV

11am–3pm and 5–11pm Mon–Thurs; 11am–11pm Fri–Sat; 12–3pm and 7–10.30pm Sun.

The Queen's Head
39 Churchgate Street, Bury St Edmunds IP33 1RG
☎ *(01284) 761554* Alistair Torkington

A freehouse with Adnams Broadside, Nethergate IPA and Ind Coope Burton Ale always available, plus guests rotating on one hand pump including, perhaps, Elgood's Black Dog Mild or Timothy Taylor Landlord.

A town-centre pub with a young clientele, particularly in the evenings. One big bar, restaurant, beer garden, conservatory and games room. Food available 12–9pm. Children allowed in the conservatory, garden, games room and restaurant only.

All day, every day.

CARLTON COLVILLE

The Bell Inn

82 The Street, Carlton Colville, Lowestoft NR33 8JR
☎ (01502) 582873 Karen Chipperfield

Green Jack Bitter and Grasshopper always available plus seasonal Green Jack specials such as Gone Fishing and Ripper. Two guests, straight from the barrel, might come from breweries such as Wolf, Woodforde's, Elgood's and Chalk Hill.

A village pub and restaurant with original flagstone floor and open fires. One long bar, disabled access, beer garden. Food available at lunchtime and evenings. Children allowed.

OPEN *11am–3pm and 5–11pm Mon–Thurs; all day Fri–Sun.*

EDWARDSTONE

The White Horse Inn

Mill Green, Edwardstone, Sudbury CO10 5PX
☎ (01787) 211211 Mrs Baker

A freehouse with Greene King IPA plus a frequently changing mild always available (perhaps Elgood's Black Dog). Also two guests from local breweries such as Tolly Cobbold or further afield such as Cottage.

A two-bar village pub with log fires in winter. Beer garden. Caravan and camping club on site for five caravans. Food available at lunchtime and evenings. Children allowed.

OPEN *12–2pm Tues–Sun (closed Mon lunchtime) and 6.30–11pm Mon–Sat (10.30pm Sun).*

FRAMSDEN

The Doberman

The Street, Framsden, Nr Stowmarket
☎ (01473) 890461 Sue Frankland

Adnams Best and Broadside always available and guests such as Felinfoel Double Dragon, Charles Wells Bombardier, Morland Old Speckled Hen, Smiles and Everards brews.

A 400-year-old, traditional thatched and beamed Suffolk village pub. Bar food available. Car park, garden, accommodation. Children not allowed. Easy to find.

OPEN *11.30am–2.30pm and 7–11pm Mon–Sat; 12–3pm and 7–10.30pm Sun.*

FRECKENHAM

The Golden Boar

The Street, Freckenham, Bury St Edmunds IP28 8HZ
☎ (01638) 723000 Alan Strachan

A freehouse with four pumps serving a range of real ales. Adnams Best, Woodforde's Wherry and Nethergate brews are regulars, plus specials and seasonals such as Charles Wells Summer Solstice.

The only pub in Freckenham, this is a restored old-style country village pub with old brickwork and fireplaces, separate dining area and garden. Food available at lunchtime and evenings. Children allowed. There are plans for accommodation.

OPEN *All day Mon–Sat; 12–4pm and 7–10.30pm Sun.*

GISLINGHAM

Six Bells

High Street, Gislingham, Eye IP23 8JD
☎ (01379) 783349 Mr Buttle

A freehouse with Buttles Bitter (a house ale from Old Chimneys) always available plus two guests changing monthly and not repeating, if possible. Shepherd Neame Spitfire and Brakspear ales are recent examples.

A traditional one-bar village pub with non-smoking dining area and disabled facilities. Food available Tues–Sun lunchtimes and evenings. Children allowed. Function room. Situated near Thornham Walks.

OPEN *12–3pm and 6.30–11pm (10.30pm Sun).*

HASKETON

The Turk's Head Inn

Low Road, Hasketon, Woodbridge IP13 6JG
☎ (01394) 382584 Tom Thomas

Tolly Cobbold Original, Shooter, Mild and IPA plus Young's Special among the brews always available, plus a range of guests changing fortnightly.

A two-bar country village pub with huge log fires and low beams. Food available at lunchtime and evenings. Decorated with brewery memorabilia and antiques. Beer garden and patio. Camping and caravaning in three acres of meadow. No children.

OPEN *12–3pm Tues–Sun (closed Mon lunchtime) and 6–11pm Mon–Sat (10.30pm Sun).*

IPSWICH

The Cricketers
51 Crown Street, Ipswich IP1 3JA
☎ *(01473) 225910* Michael Paddington

A Wetherspoon's pub. Shepherd Neame Spitfire and Woodforde's Wherry among the brews always available plus three guests such as Hop Back Summer Lightning and a range of bottled beers.

A town-centre pub. Large non-smoking area and two beer gardens. Food available all day. Children allowed at weekends only up to 6pm.

[OPEN] *All day, every day.*

The Fat Cat
288 Spring Road, Ipswich IP4 5NL
☎ *(01473) 726524* John Keetley

A freehouse with up to 18 real ales served straight from the barrel and rotating all the time. Woodforde's Wherry and Adnams brews are regular features.

A spit and sawdust pub with wooden floor, no music or machines. One bar, beer garden. Rolls available at lunchtime. Well-behaved children allowed. On the outskirts of town.

[OPEN] *All day, every day.*

The Plough
2 Dog's Head Street, Ipswich IP4 1AD
☎ *(01473) 288005* Stuart Greaney

Marston's Bitter and Pedigree always available plus nine guest beers (100s per year) from breweries such as Black Sheep, Adnams, Titanic, Nethergate, Exmoor, Cotleigh, Morland, Shepherd Neame, Daleside, Burton Bridge, Bateman, Cains, Caledonian, Coachouse, Gales and Jennings.

A traditional ale house with wooden floors. Bar food available at lunchtime. Children allowed. Next to the old cattle market bus station.

[OPEN] *11am–3pm and 5–11.30pm Mon–Thur;*
11am–11pm Fri–Sat; 7–10.30pm Sun.

The Tap & Spile
76 St Helens Street, Ipswich
☎ *(01473) 211270*

Eight beers always available (160 per year) from a wide range of ales offered by independent brewers from all parts of the United Kingdom.

A traditional alehouse. Bar food is served at lunchtime (except Sunday). Car park, garden and children's room. Close to Suffolk College and County Hall.

[OPEN] *11am–3pm and 5–11pm Mon–Wed;*
11am–11pm Thur–Sat; 12–3pm and
7–10.30pm Sun.

KERSEY

The Bell
Kersey
☎ *(01473) 823229* Paul Denton

Three or four beers always available plus brews from a guest list including Shepherd Neame Spitfire, Fuller's London Pride, Adnams Bitter and Greene King Abbot.

Built in 1380, a timber-framed Tudor-style property with log fires and cobbles. Bar and restaurant food available at lunchtime and evenings. Car park, garden, private dining room. Children allowed. Signposted from Hadleigh.

[OPEN] *11am–3pm and 6.30–11pm Mon–Sat;*
12–3pm and 7–10.30pm Sun.

LAXFIELD

The King's Head Inn
Gorams Mill Lane, Laxfield, Woodbridge
IP13 8DW
☎ *(01986) 798395* Michelle Flowley

A freehouse with all beers served straight from the barrel. Adnams Best and Broadside always available plus a selection of guest ales such as Adnams Mild, Extra or seasonals such as Regatta, Greene King IPA and Triumph, and Marston's Pedigree. Celebration ales also sold as available.

Known locally as The Low House, a well-preserved 600-year-old country village pub built in an old tap room. Food served 12–2pm and 7–9pm daily. Beer garden. Music nights on Tuesdays. Carriage rides to nearby Tannington Hall. Separate family room and card room. B&B. Children allowed.

[OPEN] *11am–3pm and 6–11pm Mon, Wed–Sat;*
all day Tuesday; 12–3pm and 7–10.30pm
Sun.

LOWESTOFT

The Crown Hotel
High Street, Lowestoft NR32 1HR
☎ *(01502) 500987* Mandy Henderson

A Scott's Brewery house with Blues and Bloater and Hopleaf always available, plus seasonal specials such as Golden Best.

A town pub with wooden floors and winter fires. Food available at lunchtime only. Patio. Children allowed if eating.

[OPEN] *All day, every day.*

The Triangle Tavern

29 St Peter's Street, Lowestoft NR32 1QA
☎ *(01502) 582711* Kerri Smith

 Green Jack Bitter, Best and Golden Sickle always available plus other Green Jack brews and a selection of constantly changing guests – ten available at any one time.

Owned by the Green Jack Brewing Company and based in the High Street next to the recently developed Triangle Market Place, a two-bar pub, fully refurbished in December 1998. Rolls available at lunchtime. Parking nearby.

OPEN *11am–11pm.*

The Butt & Oyster

Pin Mill, Chelmondiston, Ipswich IP9 1JW
☎ *(01473) 780764* Dick Mainwaring

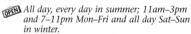 Tolly Cobbold Mild, Bitter, Original, IPA and Shooter always available plus other specials. One guest ale served straight from the cask, generally from a local brewery.

A sixteenth-century inn with one bar, smoking room and riverside seating area. Food available at lunchtime and evenings. Children allowed.

OPEN *All day, every day in summer; 11am–3pm and 7–11pm Mon–Fri and all day Sat–Sun in winter.*

SOUTHWOLD

The Lord Nelson

East Street, Southwold IP18 6EJ
☎ *(01502) 722079* Mr Illstone

An Adnams house with Best and Broadside always available, plus seasonal ales such as Regatta in summer or celebration ales such as Millennium.

A traditional town pub by the seaside. Beer garden, disabled access. Food available at lunchtime and evenings. Children allowed.

OPEN *All day, every day.*

WALTON

The Tap & Spile

303 High Street, Walton
☎ *(01394) 282130* Mr Wheeler

Eight beers always available, changed regularly but possibly including Nethergate and Greene King brews plus Woodforde's Wherry.

Old-fashioned, friendly Suffolk town pub. Bar food available at lunchtime. Car park, garden, children's play area. Children over 14 allowed in bar.

OPEN *11am–3pm and 5–11pm Mon–Thurs; 11am–11pm Fri–Sat; 11am–3pm and 7–10.30pm Sun.*

YOU TELL US

★ *The Angel Hotel,* Market Place, Lavenham, Sudbury
★ *The Blue Boar Inn,* 28 Oulton Street, Oulton, Lowestoft
★ *Cornwallis Arms,* Brome
★ *Fleetwood's,* 25 Abbeygate Street, Bury St Edmunds
★ *The Hare & Hounds,* Heath Road, East Bergholt
★ *The Kings Head Hotel,* 132 High Street, Bildeston, Ipswich
★ *The Lion,* The Street, Theburton
★ *The Moon & Mushroom,* High Road, Swilland, Ipswich
★ *The Oak Tavern,* Lowestoft
★ *The Queen's Head,* Capel St Mary Road, Great Wenham
★ *Rose & Crown,* Whiting Street, Bury St Edmunds
★ *Tap & Spile,* 303 High Street, Felixstowe
★ *The Victoria,* Earl Soham
★ *The Viking Hotel,* Corton Road, Lowestoft
★ *The Welcome,* 182 London Road, Lowestoft
★ *The White Hart,* Broad Street, Boxford
★ *The White Horse,* Hopton Road, Thelnetham

Places Featured:

Bletchingley
Churt
Claygate
Coldharbour
Dorking
Englefield Green
Farnham
Godalming
Knaphill
Milford

Puttenham
Redhill
Shackleford
West Byfleet
West Clandon
Windlesham
Woking
Woodstreet Village
Wrecclesham

THE BREWERIES

ALCHEMY BREWING CO.
Lyon Road, Hersham KT12 3PU
☎ *(01932) 703860*

 HALCYON DAYS 3.8% ABV
AURUM ALE 4.6% ABV

HOGS BACK BREWERY
Manor Farm, The Street, Tongham GU10 1DE
☎ *(01252) 783000*

HAIR OF THE HOG 3.5% ABV
TRADITIONAL ENGLISH ALE 4.2% ABV
Smooth, well-balanced flavours.
HOP GARDEN GOLD 4.6% ABV
Refreshing with good fruity hoppiness.
RIP SNORTER 5.0% ABV
Balanced and well-rounded.
Plus seasonal and occasional brews.

THE PILGRIM BREWERY
11c West Street, Reigate RH2 9BL
☎ *(01737) 222651*

 SURREY BITTER 3.7% ABV
Hoppy, with a good mixture of flavours.
PORTER 4.0% ABV
Dark with roast malt flavour.
PROGRESS 4.0% ABV
Red and malty.
CRUSADER 4.9% ABV
Gold, with hops and malt throughout.
SPRING BOCK 5.2% ABV
Wheat beer.
Plus seasonal brews.

WELTONS NORTH DOWNS BREWERY
Unit 24, Vincent Works, Vincent Lane, Dorking RH4 3HQ
☎ *(01306) 888655*

DORKING PRIDE AND JOY 2.8% ABV
BEST 3.8% ABV (new name: **PREDATOR**)
OLD COCKY 4.3% ABV
Plus special brews – as many as 40 per year.

THE PUBS

BLETCHINGLEY

William IV
Little Common Lane, Bletchingley, Redhill RH1 4QF
☎ *(01883) 743278* Brian Strange

 Greene King IPA, Wadworth 6X and a Harveys brew always available plus three monthly changing guests such as Young's Special, Marston's Pedigree or Shepherd Neame Spitfire.

A Victorian country pub on the edge of the village. Two small bars, dining room and beer garden. Food available at lunchtime and evenings. Children allowed.

🍺 *11.30am–3pm and 6–11pm Mon–Sat; all day Sun.*

CHURT

The Crossways Inn
Churt, Nr Farnham GU10 2JE
☎ *(01428) 714323* Paul Ewens

A freehouse with Cheriton Best, Ringwood Fortyniner and Shepherd Neame The Bishop's Finger always available, plus at least four guests such as Shepherd Neame Spitfire or Hampshire Lionheart. At least ten different beers are served every week, with more from micro-breweries than not. Also real cider from the barrel.

A country village local, winner of Summer Pub of the Year 1999. Two bars, beer garden. Food available at lunchtime only. Well-behaved children allowed. On the main road.

🍺 *11am–3.30pm and 5–11pm Mon–Thurs; all day Fri–Sat; 12–4pm and 7–10.30pm Sun.*

CLAYGATE

The Griffin
58 Common Road, Claygate, Esher KT10 0HW
☎ *(01372) 463799* Tom Harrington

A freehouse with Fuller's London Pride and Badger Dorset Best always available plus two constantly changing guests such as Bateman XB or a Pilgrim ale. Winter warmers on during the colder months. Micro-breweries and smaller independents favoured.

A traditional two-bar village pub with log fires, beer garden and disabled access. Food available Mon–Sat lunchtimes. Children allowed.

🍺 *All day, every day.*

COLDHARBOUR

The Plough Inn
Coldharbour Lane, Coldharbour, Nr Dorking RH5 6HD
☎ *(01306) 711793* Mr and Mrs Abrehart

Nine beers always available from Ringwood, Hogs Back, Badger, Adnams and Shepherd Neame. Two beers brewed on the premises under the name of the Leith Hill Brewery. Seasonal brews, guests, topical and special beers. Also a farm cider on hand pump.

A traditional family-run seventeenth-century pub. Allegedly the highest freehouse in south-east England. Bar and restaurant food served at lunchtime and evenings. Car parking. Children allowed. Accommodation. Just over three miles south-west of Dorking.

🛢 **CROOKED FURROW 4.2% ABV**
Hoppy, light bitter.
TALLYWHACKER 5.6% ABV
Very dark ale. Strong, roasted barley flavour.

🍺 *11.30am–3pm and 6.30–11pm Mon–Fri; 11am–11pm Sat–Sun.*

DORKING

The King's Arms
45 West Street, Dorking RH4 1BU
☎ *(01306) 883361* Mr Yeatman

Fuller's London Pride, Wadworth 6X, Marston's Pedigree, Eldridge Pope Royal Oak (Thomas Hardy) and one Burton brew always available. Two guests changing every week from micro-breweries and independents – the smaller and more unusual, the better!

A country-style pub in a town location, this is the oldest building in Dorking. More than 500 years old with oak beams, inglenook fireplace, restaurant and courtyard garden. Food available lunchtimes and evenings. Children allowed.

🍺 *11am–11pm (10.30pm Sun).*

The Beehive
34 Middle Hill, Englefield Green, Nr Egham TW20 0JQ
☎ *(01784) 431621* Mr and Mrs McGranaghan

Fuller's London Pride, Hop Back Summer Lightning and Gales HSB and Best always available plus four guest beers, changing weekly, from breweries such as Adnams, Bateman, Everards, Hoskins & Oldfield, Kemptown, Nethergate, Oldbury, Orkney, Thwaites and Young's. Beer festivals at May and August bank holidays.

A country pub now surrounded by expensive houses. Real home-made food available at lunchtime and evenings. Open log fire in winter. Car park and garden. Just off the A30 between Ferrari's and Royal Holloway College.

11am–11pm Mon–Sat; 12–10.30pm Sun.

The Ball & Wicket
104 Upper Hale Road, Farnham GU9 0PB
☎ *(01252) 735278* Gary Wallace

Home of the Hale and Hearty Brewery, with Upper Ale and Wicket Bitter always available plus Wadworth 6X and B&T Dragonslayer. Seasonals and celebration ales such as the homebrewed Spring Ale.

A country freehouse and brewpub on the village green. No food. Children allowed.

UPPER ALE 3.8% ABV
WICKET BITTER 4.3% ABV
SPRING ALE 5.3% ABV
Seasonal.

4–11pm Mon–Fri; 12–11pm Sat; 12–3pm and 7–10.30pm Sun.

The Duke of Cambridge
East Street, Farnham GU9 7TH
☎ *(01252) 717667* Matthew Birch

No permanent beers but Fuller's London Pride is a regular feature while the other six pumps serve a range that changes all the time. The aim is to specialise in ales from micro-breweries such as The Brewery on Sea, Beckett's, Hogs Back and Branscombe Vale. Scottish breweries also often featured. More than 500 beers served in two years. Also a selection of unusual malt whiskies.

A town freehouse dating from the 1830s. Food served every lunchtime and Mon–Sat evenings in a separate dining area. Beer garden. Entertainment. B&B. Children allowed if eating.

11am–3pm and 5.15–11pm Mon–Fri; all day Sat–Sun.

The Shepherd & Flock
Moor Park Lane, Farnham GU9 9JB
☎ *(01252) 716675* Steven Hill

A freehouse with Hampshire 1066, Hogs Back TEA, Fuller's London Pride and Gales HSB always available plus three guests, perhaps including Hop Back Summer Lightning, Badger Tanglefoot or Beckett's brews.

Situated on the outskirts of town, on Europe's biggest inhabited roundabout! A well-known local meeting place, close to the North Downs. Old building with one bar and 50-seater dining room. Food available lunchtimes and evenings. Beer garden. Children allowed in the dining room only.

11am–3pm and 5.30–11pm Mon–Thurs; all day Fri–Sun.

The Anchor Inn
110 Ockford Road, Godalming GU7 1RG
☎ *(01483) 417085* Mr and Mrs Jenkins

Badger Tanglefoot, Hogs Back and Brakspear brews among those always available plus guests (60 per year) from Gales, Hop Back, Ringwood, Titanic, Fuller's, Pilgrim and Wychwood.

A real ale pub with bar billiards and a good mixed clientele. Simple bar food available at lunchtime. Parking and beer garden. On the edge of town on the main road.

12–3pm and 5.30–11pm.

The Old Wharf
5 Wharf Street, Godalming GU7 1NN
☎ *(01483) 419543* Anna Shairp

Wadworth 6X among the beers always available plus four guests straight from the barrel, such as Fuller's London Pride or Hogs Back TEA.

A Hogshead town pub. Food available 12–9pm Sun–Thurs; 12–7pm Fri–Sat. No children.

All day, every day.

The Hooden Takes a Knap

134 High Street, Knaphill GU21 2QH
☎ *(01483) 473374* Sean Bain

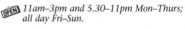 Greene King Abbot always available plus one guest such as Marston's Pedigree or Hook Norton Best.

A bistro-style country pub, previously known as The Garibaldi. One small bar, beer garden and BBQ. Mexican food available lunchtimes and evenings in a separate dining area. Live blues on Tuesdays. Children allowed. On the crossroads of Knaphill High Street.

OPEN *11am–3pm and 5.30–11pm Mon–Thurs; all day Fri–Sun.*

The Red Lion

Old Portsmouth Road, Milford, Godalming GU8 5HJ
☎ *(01483) 424342* Lou-Ann Marshall

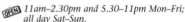 A Gales house with Butser Bitter, GB and HSB always available plus guests such as Badger Tanglefoot, Everards Tiger, Hampshire Glory and Marston's Pedigree changing fortnightly. Tries not to repeat the beers.

A village pub with skittle alley. Two bars, non-smoking and smoking dining areas, beer garden and children's play area, good disabled access. Food available every lunchtime and Mon–Sat evenings. Children allowed.

OPEN *11am–2.30pm and 5.30–11pm Mon–Fri; all day Sat–Sun.*

The Good Intent

62 The Street, Puttenham, Guildford GU3 1AR
☎ *(01483) 810387* William Carpenter

Badger Best always available, plus a selection of guests such as Hogs Back TEA, Hop Back Thunder Storm and Hampshire Pendragon.

A one-bar country pub with food available at lunchtime and evenings. Beer garden. No children.

OPEN *11am–3pm and 6–11pm Mon–Fri; all day Sat–Sun.*

The Hatch

44 Hatchlands Road, Redhill RH1 6AT
☎ *(01737) 764593* Michael McAvee

A Shepherd Neame house with Bishop's Finger, Spitfire and Master Brew always available, plus up to three seasonal or celebration ales such as Goldings or 1698.

A town pub with horseshoe-shaped bar, log-effect fires and oak beams. Beer garden, front patio, pool room. Food availabe 12–2pm and 7–9pm. Children allowed in the garden and pool room only. Situated on the A25.

OPEN *12–3pm Mon–Sun; 5.30–11pm Mon–Sat; 7–10.30pm Sun.*

The Cyder House

Pepperharrow Lane, Shackleford, Godalming GU8 6AN
☎ *(01483) 810360* Philip Nisbett

Badger Dorset Best and Tanglefoot always available plus three guests such as Hogs Back TEA.

A light and airy Victorian country pub dating from 1880. One big bar, log fires, beer garden. Situated in a pretty village location. Friendly atmosphere. Food available at lunchtime and evenings. Children allowed.

OPEN *11am–3pm and 5.30–11pm Mon–Fri; all day Sat–Sun.*

The Plough Inn

104 High Road, West Byfleet KT14 7QT
☎ *(01932) 353257* Carol Wells

A freehouse with eight pumps serving brews such as Fuller's London Pride and beers from Hogs Back, Hop Back and other independents.

A traditional two-bar village pub with beams and two log fires. Beer garden, car park. Food available Mon–Fri 12–2pm but there are plans for a conservatory which will become an evening restaurant when completed. No children.

OPEN *11am–3pm and 5–11pm (10.30pm Sun).*

The Onslow Arms
The Street, West Clandon, Guildford GU4 7TE
☎ *(01483) 222447* Alan Peck

 A freehouse with Fuller's London Pride and brews from Young's, Brakspear and Hogs Back always available plus one rotating guest such as Ringwood Old Thumper, Morland Old Speckled Hen or Greene King Abbot. Also celebration ales as available.

A well-known sixteenth-century coaching inn with four bars and food available at lunchtime and evenings in a restaurant and a carvery bistro. Large car park, disabled access. Garden and patio with arbours. Cocktail lounge. Function rooms. Helipad. Children allowed.

⃞ *All day, every day.*

The Windmill
London Road, Windlesham GU20 6PJ
☎ *(01276) 472281*
Richard and Sandra Hailstone

There may be 13 real ales available at any one time. Hop Back Summer Lightning, Adnams Broadside, Badger (Gibbs Mew) Bishop's Tipple always available plus guests (up to 700 per year) including brews from Ringwood, Hampshire, Archers, Hogs Back, Pilgrim and Rebellion. Always willing to support micro-breweries and will try any new brews. Three beer festivals held each year, with 100 brews at each festival.

S mall, friendly pub with two bars and a dining area. No pool tables. Food available. Car park. Large beer garden. Children allowed under parental control. Situated on the main A30.

⃞ *11am–11pm.*

Wetherspoons
51 Chertsey Road, Woking GU21 5AJ
☎ *(01483) 722818* Robin Duberley

A Hogs Back beer always available plus up to six guests. Examples may include Marston's Pedigree, Morland Old Speckled Hen and Shepherd Neame Spitfire.

A one-bar town pub with no music or TV. Front drinking terrace, disabled access and toilets. Food available all day (11am–10pm) with a non-smoking seating area available. No children.

⃞ *All day, every day.*

The Royal Oak
89 Oak Hill, Woodstreet Village, Guildford GU3 3DA
☎ *(01483) 235137* Tony Oliver

A freehouse with Hogs Back TEA always available plus four constantly changing guests. Hop Back Summer Lightning and Cottage Wheeltappers are just two examples from a huge range (850 in less than four years).

A good old-fashioned country pub. One bar, beer garden. Food available Mon–Sat lunchtime. Over 14s only allowed.

⃞ *11am–3pm and 5–11pm Mon–Fri; 11am–3.30pm and 5–11pm Sat; 12–3.30pm and 7–10.30pm Sun.*

The Bat & Ball
Boundstone, Wrecclesham, Farnham GU10 4RA
☎ *(01252) 794564* Andy Bujok

A freehouse with Young's Special, Fuller's London Pride and a Brakspear ale always available, plus four guests including brews such as Archers Golden, Harveys Best, Hop Back Summer Lightning and many, many more.

A traditional country pub with open fires, two bars, restaurant, children's room and play area, beer garden, disabled access. Food available at lunchtime and evenings. Children allowed.

⃞ *12–11pm (10.30pm Sun).*

The Sandrock

*Sandrock Hill Road, Wrecclesham, Farnham
GU10 4NS*
☎ *(01252) 715865* Mr and Mrs Bayliff

Eight beers available. Batham, Enville and Brakspear brews always on offer plus guests (100 per year) from Holden's, Hampshire, Ballard's, Hogs Back and Cheriton etc.

A small, no-frills pub. CAMRA pub of the year. Bar food available at lunchtime (except Sunday). Car park and garden. Children allowed. Along the bypass, left at roundabout onto the A325, left into School Hill, over the crossroads into Sandrock Hill Road.

OPEN *All day, every day.*

YOU TELL US

★ *Aitch's Bar-Café*, Angel Court, High Street, Godalming
★ *The Blue Boy*, Station Road, Farnham
★ *The Brewery at the Hog & Stump*, 88 London Road, Kingston-upon-Thames
★ *The Crown*, 38 High Street, Egham
★ *The Dover Arms*, 31 Guildford Road, Ash
★ *The Feathers*, The Broadway, Laleham
★ *Foxley Hatch*, 8 Russell Hill Road, Purley
★ *H G Wells' Planets*, Crown Square, Woking
★ *The Hedgehog & Hogshead*, 2 High Street, Sutton
★ *The Moon on the Hill*, 5–9 Hill Road, Sutton
★ *The Surrey Oaks*, Parkgate Road, Newdigate, Dorking
★ *Tap & Spile*, 40 Station Road, Egham
★ *Tap & Spile*, 13 Stoke Fields, Guildford
★ *The Thurlow Arms*, Off Baynards Lane, Baynards
★ *The Triple Crown*, 15 Kew Foot Road, Richmond
★ *The Two Brewers*, 19 Wood Street, Kingston-upon-Thames
★ *The Whispering Moon*, 25 Ross Parade, Woodcote Road, Wallington

Places Featured:

Amberley	Horsham
Arundel	Hove
Ashurst	Icklesham
Balcombe	Lewes
Battle	Litlington
Beckley	Maplehurst
Bexhill-on-Sea	Midhurst
Brighton	Old Heathfield
Burpham	Oving
Butbourne	Pett
Compton	Robertsbridge
Crawley	Rudgwick
Eastbourne	Rye
East Grinstead	St Leonards on Sea
East Hoathly	Seaford
Elsted Marsh	Shoreham
Exceat Bridge	Sidlescoombe
Fernhurst	Stoughton
Fishbourne	Tarring
Frant	Telham
Gungarden	Thakeham
Hailsham	Ticehurst
Halfway Bridge	West Ashling
Hastings	West Chiltington
Haywards Heath	Worthing
Herstmonceux	Yapton

THE BREWERIES

ARUNDEL BREWERY

Ford Airfield Estate, Arundel, West Sussex BN18 0BE
☎ *(01903) 733111*

 1999 3.5% ABV
BEST 4.0% ABV
Well-balanced and malty with some fruitiness.
ARUNDEL GOLD 4.2% ABV
Gold-coloured with good hoppiness.
ARUNDEL SPECIAL BITTER (ASB) 4.5% ABV
Malty with some sweetness.
STRONGHOLD 5.0% ABV
Rounded and full-flavoured.
OLD KNUCKLER 5.5% ABV
All the flavours are here. Winter brew.
Plus seasonal and occasional brews.

THE BREWERY ON SEA

24 Winston Business Centre, Chartwell Road, Lancing, West Sussex BN15 8TU
☎ *(01903) 851482*

 LANCING SPECIAL DARK 3.5% ABV
Dark and hoppy mild.
SPINNAKER BITTER 3.5% ABV
Light and well-hopped.
SPINNAKER CLASSIC 4.0% ABV
Mellow and malty.
RAIN DANCE 4.4% ABV
Light-coloured, refreshing wheat beer.
SPINNAKER BUZZ 4.5% ABV
Golden, with hoppiness and honeyed sweetness.
BLACK ROCK 5.5% ABV
Powerful, roast malt flavour.
SPECIAL CREW 5.5% ABV
Pale and deceptively drinkable for gravity.
RIPTIDE 6.5% ABV
Rounded and full-flavoured.
TIDAL WAVE 7.0% ABV
Dark and well-balanced.
Plus seasonal and occasional brews.

THE CUCKMERE HAVEN BREWERY

Exceat Bridge, Cuckmere Haven, Seaford, West Sussex BN25 4AB
☎ *(01323) 892247*

 BEST BITTER 4.1% ABV
SAXON KING STOUT 4.2% ABV
GENTLEMEN'S GOLD 4.5% ABV
GUV'NER 4.7% ABV

DARK STAR BREWING CO.

55–56 Surrey Street, Brighton BN1 3PB
☎ *(01273) 701758*

 ALE TRAIL ROAST MILD 3.5% ABV
PALE ALE 3.7% ABV
OLD ALE 4.2% ABV
PENGUIN STOUT 4.2% ABV
GOLDEN GATE BITTER 4.3% ABV
OLD FAMILIAR 5.0% ABV
SUMMER HAZE 5.0% ABV
DARK STAR 5.0% ABV
CLIFF HANGER PORTER 5.5% ABV
MELTDOWN 6.0% ABV
PAVILION BEAST 6.0% ABV

HARVEY & SONS (LEWES) LTD

The Bridge Wharf Brewery, 6 Cliffe High Street, Lewes, East Sussex BN7 2AH
☎ *(01273) 480209*

 XX MILD 3.0% ABV
Dark in colour, soft and sweet.
SUSSEX PALE ALE 3.5% ABV
Balanced and well-hopped.
SUSSEX BEST BITTER 4.0% ABV
Hoppiness throughout.
XXXX OLD ALE 4.3% ABV
Full-bodied, nutty seasonal brew.
ARMADA ALE 4.5% ABV
Golden and hoppy, with dryness in the aftertaste.
Plus seasonal brews.

KING & BARNES LTD

18 Bishopric, Horsham, West Sussex RH12 1QP
☎ *(01403) 270470*

 MILD 3.5% ABV
Dark with delicate hoppiness and some sweetness.
SUSSEX 3.5% ABV
Refreshing hoppiness throughout.
BROADWOOD 4.2% ABV
Malty sweetness with hoppy finish.
FESTIVE 5.0% ABV
Flavoursome and full-bodied.
Plus seasonal and occasional brews.

ROTHER VALLEY BREWING CO.

Station Road, Northiam TN31 6QT
☎ *(01797) 252922*

 **LIGHTERMAN 3.2% ABV**
LEVEL BEST 4.0% ABV
BLUES 5.0% ABV
Plus occasional brews.

WHITE BREWING CO.

The 1066 Country Brewery, Pebsham Farm Ind. Est., Pebsham Lane, Bexhill
☎ *(01424) 731066*

THE PUBS

AMBERLEY

The Sportsman's Arms

Crossgates, Amberley, Arundel, West Sussex BN18 9NR
☎ *(01798) 831787 Chris Shanaham*

 A freehouse with Young's Bitter and Special, Fuller's London Pride and a house ale called Miserable Old Bugger (brewed especially by the Brewery on Sea in Lancing). Occasional guests, particularly porters in winter.

An edge-of-village pub with wonderful views across the valley. Three bars, patio area, hexagonal revolving pool table, dining area in conservatory. Home to the Miserable Old Buggers Club. Food served at lunchtime and evenings. Well-behaved children and dogs welcome.

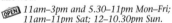 *11am–2.30pm and 6–11pm Mon–Fri; 11am–3pm and 6–11pm Sat; 12–3pm and 7–10.30pm Sun.*

ARUNDEL

The King's Arms

36 Tarrant Street, Arundel, West Sussex BN18 9DN
☎ *(01903) 882312 Charlie Malcolmson*

A freehouse always serving Fuller's London Pride and Young's Special plus two guests such as Hop Back Summer Lightning, Rye and Coriander or Crop Circle, or brews from Harveys or Cottage. Small producers always well-represented.

A small, country-style pub dating from 1625, situated out of the town centre. Two bars, patio, table seating at the front. Sandwiches available Mon–Thurs lunchtimes, bar menu Fri–Sun lunchtimes. Children allowed.

11am–3pm and 5.30–11pm Mon–Fri; 11am–11pm Sat; 12–10.30pm Sun.

ASHURST

The Fountain Inn

Ashurst, Nr Steyning, West Sussex BN44 3AP
☎ *(01403) 710219*
Mark and Christopher White

 Harveys Best and Fuller's London Pride plus a constantly changing range of guests, which may include Harveys Gold or Gales HSB.

An unspoilt sixteenth-century inn with low beams, a flagstone floor and large inglenook fireplace. Picturesque cottage garden and large duck pond. No machines or music. Bar and restaurant food served at lunchtime and evenings (light snacks only Sunday pm and Monday pm). Large car park and garden. Children under 14 not allowed inside the pub. Located on the B2135 north of Steyning.

11.30am–2.30pm and 6–11pm Mon–Sat; 12–3pm and 7–10.30pm Sun.

BALCOMBE

The Cowdray Arms

London Road, Balcombe, Haywards Heath, West Sussex RH17 6QD
☎ *(01444) 811280* Gerry McElhatton

 Harveys Best Bitter, Greene King Abbot, IPA and Mild always available plus two guests such as Greene King Triumph or Arundel, Bateman, Elgood's or Harveys brews.

A one-bar Victorian pub with high ceilings. Non-smoking dining area, traditional pub games. Garden and car park. Food served at lunchtime and evenings. Children allowed.

11am–3pm and 5.30–11pm Mon–Sat; 12–3pm and 7–10.30pm Sun.

BATTLE

The Squirrel Inn

North Trade Road, Battle, East Sussex TN33 9LJ
☎ *(01424) 772717* Mr and Mrs Coundley

 Harveys ales always available plus several guests (200 per year) including Rother Valley Level Best and brews from Gales and Mansfield etc. New and seasonal beers ordered as and when available.

An eighteenth-century old drover's pub in beautiful countryside surrounded by fields. Family-run freehouse. Unspoilt public bar with log fires. New restaurant (suitable for functions and weddings). Two large beer gardens, ample parking, purpose-built children's room. Families welcome. Located just outside Battle on the A271.

11am–3pm and 5–11pm Mon–Fri; 11am–11pm Sat; 12–10.30pm Sun.

BECKLEY

The Rose & Crown

Northiam Road, Beckley, Nr Rye, East Sussex TN31 6SE
☎ *(01797) 252161* Alice Holland

 Harveys Best, Adnams Broadside, Hook Norton Best and Fuller's ESB always available plus three guests, from smaller breweries if possible. Recent examples include Adnams Regatta, Cotleigh Kiwi and Wyre Piddle Piddle in the Wind but there are too many to list – over 400 in three years.

An old coaching inn on a site which has been occupied by a pub since the twelfth century. Dining area, large garden, petanque and grumpy landlord! Food available at lunchtime and evenings. Well-behaved children allowed.

11.30am–3pm and 5–11pm Mon–Thurs; all day Fri–Sun.

BEXHILL-ON-SEA

The Rose & Crown

Turkey Road, Bexhill-on-Sea, East Sussex TN39 5HH
☎ *(01424) 214625*
Michelle Lynn and Chris Powell

 Greene King Abbot and Martha Greene Bitter always available plus two changing guests, perhaps from Harveys.

One bar, dining area, large-screen TV, darts, disabled toilets and beer garden. Food served all day. Under 14s allowed until 9pm.

All day, every day.

BRIGHTON

The Cobbler's Thumb

10 New England Road, Brighton, East Sussex BN1 4GG
☎ *(01273) 605636* Stuart McDougal

 A freehouse serving Harveys Best and Badger Tanglefoot plus seasonal guests from both breweries.

A traditional locals' pub with wooden floors in the public bar and a lounge with real fire. Four pints for the price of three on a selected brew. Food available weekday lunchtimes and a Sunday roast. Children allowed in the garden or inside until 7pm.

11am–11pm Mon–Sat; 12–10.30pm Sun.

The Evening Star

55–6 Surrey Street, Brighton, East Sussex
BN1 3PB
☎ *(01273) 328931*
Peter Skinner and Rob Jones

The home of the Dark Star Brewing Company. Nine real ales always available including the Skinner's and Dark Star ranges plus a rotating guest list that runs into thousands.

A brewpub established in 1994 using a unique space-saving full-mash mini-brewing system. Production began in December 1994. In July 1995, Peter Skinner teamed up with brewer Rob Jones, who founded the Pitfield Brewery in 1981 and, more recently, the Brewery on Sea in Sussex. Together, they founded the Dark Star Brewing Company. The Evening Star is a specialist real ale house with wooden floors and church pews. Bar food is available at lunchtime. Children not allowed. Just 150 yards from railway station.

OPEN *12–11pm (10.30pm Sun).*

The Lion & Lobster

24 Sillwood Street, Brighton, East Sussex
BN1 2PS
☎ *(01273) 776961* Jack Harding

Five guest beers (200 per year) which might include Badger Tanglefoot, Morland Old Speckled Hen, Timothy Taylor Landlord, Harveys Best, Spinnaker Buzz and Hyde's Anvil Bitter.

A n Irish family-run pub with a great atmosphere. All ages welcome. Bar and restaurant food available at lunchtime and evenings. Parking and children's room. Located 200 yards from the seafront, in between the Bedford Hotel and Norfolk Hotel.

OPEN *11am–11pm Mon–Sat; 12–3pm and 7–10.30pm Sun.*

The Miller's Arms

1 Windmill Street, Brighton, East Sussex
BN2 2GN
☎ *(01273) 380580* Sue Ruff and Clara Dove

Shepherd Neame Master Brew always available plus up to three guest ales at any one time, Greene King Triumph is a regular, Cottage Brewery's Merchant Navy also put in a recent appearance, along with many others.

S ituated upon a hill with impressive views of Brighton below. A one-bar freehouse, with no games except darts. Well-maintained patio garden. Members of the CAMRA Ale Trail. Food available at lunchtime and evenings in a separate dining area. Well-behaved children allowed, but no dogs. Formerly called the Sir Loyne of Beef.

OPEN *All day, every day.*

The Sussex Yeoman

7 Guildford Road, Brighton, East Sussex
BN1 3LU
☎ *(01273) 327985* Rosie Dunton

Greene King IPA and Abbot plus a Harveys ale always available. Also occasional seasonal guests.

A trendy pub decorated in orange and blue with a young clientele (25–40) and a relaxed atmosphere. Games nights feature board games, or a pop quiz on Wednesday evenings. Bar snacks and fuller menu available until 9.30pm. No children.

OPEN *12pm–close.*

Tap & Spile

67 Upper Gloucester Road, Brighton, East Sussex
BN1 3LQ
☎ *(01273) 329540*

Up to four brews. Shepherd Neame Spitfire, Badger Tanglefoot or beers from Bateman and other smaller breweries are among the regular guests. Seasonals and specials as available.

A quaint 1930s-style alehouse, with church pews, wooden floor and a pool room with quarry tiles. A locals' pub, nice and friendly. No food. No children.

OPEN *12–3pm and 5–11pm Mon–Thurs; all day Fri–Sun.*

BURPHAM

The George & Dragon

Burpham, Nr Arundel, West Sussex BN18 9RR
☎ *(01903) 883131* James Rose

 Arundel Best and Harveys Best always available plus five guest beers (100 per year) from breweries such as Woodforde's, Hop Back, Cotleigh, Harviestoun, Ash Vine etc.

L ocated in a small village two miles from Arundel off the main track, with some of the best views of the Arun valley. Excellent walking all around. Bar and restaurant food available (restaurant evenings and Sunday lunch only). Car park. Children over 12 allowed.

OPEN *11am–2.30pm and 6–11pm Mon–Sat; 12–3pm and 7–10.30pm Sun.*

BUTBOURNE

The Rising Sun

The Street, Butbourne, Pulborough, West Sussex RH20 2HE
☎ **(01798) 812191** Regan Howard

A freehouse serving Fuller's London Pride, Greene King Abbot and King and Barnes Sussex Ale plus a minimum of two guests such as Harveys Sussex and Hogs Back TEA, or something from breweries such as Cottage.

A 400-year-old pub with Victorian frontage in walking country. Two bars, wooden floors, dining area, mixed clientele with very friendly landlord! Food served at lunchtime and evenings. Children allowed.

OPEN *11am–3pm and 6–11pm (10.30pm Sun).*

COMPTON

The Coach & Horses

Compton, Nr Chichester, West Sussex PO18 9HA
☎ *(01705) 631228* David Butler

Fuller's ESB always available plus five guest beers (100s per year) from breweries including Cheriton, Adnams, Cottage, Hop Back, Timothy Taylor and Hook Norton.

S ituated on the Sussex Downs, a coaching inn built in 1500 with exposed beams and a Victorian extension. Bar and restaurant food is available at lunchtime and evenings. Car parking, garden and skittle alley. Children allowed. Good walking. Take the signed road to Uppark House (B2146).

OPEN *11am–2.30pm and 6–11pm Mon–Sat; 12–3pm and 7–10.30pm Sun.*

CRAWLEY

The Swan Inn

Horsham Road, Crawley, West Sussex RH11 7AY
☎ *(01293) 527447* Jo Harmer

Fuller's London Pride, Greene King Abbot and Wadworth 6X among the brews always on offer, plus two guests, often from Gales (for instance HSB or GB).

A n old local with friendly clientele. Live bands. Pool table. Beer garden. No food. Children allowed in the garden, or inside until 6pm.

OPEN *11am–11.30pm Mon–Sat; 12–10.30pm Sun.*

EASTBOURNE

The Lamb Inn

36 High Street, Old Town, Eastbourne, East Sussex BN21 1HH
☎ *(01323) 720545* Mrs Hume

Tied to Harveys Brewery, so Harveys Bitter always available.

A n old-style, three-bar pub with seating at the side. Food available at lunchtime and evenings. Children allowed.

OPEN *10.30am–3pm and 5.30–close Mon–Thurs; all day Fri–Sat; 12–4pm and 7–10.30pm Sun.*

The Windsor Tavern

165 Langney Road, Eastbourne, East Sussex BN22 8AH
☎ *(01323) 726206* Shirley Verhulpen

Wadworth 6X and Greene King Abbot always available. Also Hoegaarden Belgian lager.

A quiet country-style pub in the middle of town. Large garden, no juke box or pool table. Food available at lunchtime and evenings. Children allowed in the garden or up to 8pm inside.

OPEN *All day Mon–Sat; 12–3pm and 7–10.30pm Sun.*

EAST GRINSTEAD

The Ship Inn

*Ship Street, East Grinstead, West Sussex
RH19 4RG*
☎ *(01342) 312089* Mr R Connor

A freehouse always serving Harveys Best, Fuller's London Pride, Young's Special and Bitter plus one guest, changing monthly.

A n olde-worlde sixteenth-century locals' pub decorated with Guinness memorabilia. Large bar, restaurant and function room. Huge beer garden. Darts, pool, football and golf teams. B&B. Home-made food available Mon–Sat 12–2.30pm. Well-behaved children allowed. Situated off the High Street.

10am–11pm Mon–Sat; 12–10.30pm Sun.

EAST HOATHLY

The King's Head

*1 High Street, East Hoathly, Lewes, East Sussex
BN8 6DR*
☎ *(01825) 840238* Mrs Wallace

A freehouse with Harveys Best always available plus three guests such as Hop Back Summer Lightning, Fuller's London Pride and Morland Old Speckled Hen.

F ormerly a coach house with a big barn restaurant, function room and beer garden. Food available at lunchtime and evenings. Children and dogs welcome.

11am–4pm daily; 6–11pm Mon–Sat, 7–10.30pm Sun.

ELSTED MARSH

Elsted Inn

Elsted Marsh, West Sussex GU29 0JT
☎ *(01730) 813662*

All Ballard's brews usually available plus Fuller's London Pride and a guest beer (52 per year) usually from Arundel, Cheriton or Brewery on Sea.

F ormerly owned by Ballard's, a friendly, old-fashioned Victorian railway pub. Restored inside, with wooden shutters, wood floor, open fires. Very cosy in winter, very cool in summer. No canned music or juke box. Good bar and restaurant food available at lunchtime and evenings. Car park, garden, boules pitch. Children allowed in garden. Accommodation. Off the A272 between Midhurst and Petersfield, marked Elsted and Harting.

11am–3pm and 5.30–11pm Mon–Fri (6–11pm Sat); 12–3pm and 7–10.30pm Sun.

EXCEAT BRIDGE

The Golden Galleon

Exceat Bridge, Cuckmere Haven, Seaford, East Sussex BN25 4AB
☎ *(01323) 892247* Stefano Diella

Home of the Cuckmere Haven Brewery, with Cuckmere Haven Best etc always available plus a range of guests (300 per year) including Greene King IPA, Shepherd Neame Bishop's Finger and Crouch Vale, Black Sheep, Ballard's, Adnams and Timothy Taylor brews.

T hey have been brewing here since 1994 in small five-barrel tanks. The pub is a prominent, fourteenth-century, black and white timbered building in the Cuckmere valley with beams and open fires in winter. Bar and restaurant food available at lunchtime and evenings. Car park, garden, conservatory, non-smoking room. Accommodation. Children allowed, but not near the bar. Open all day at weekends in summer. Off the A259 on the River Cuckmere. Two miles from Seaford railway station.

11am–3pm and 5.30–11pm Mon–Sat; 11am–11pm Sun.

FERNHURST

The King's Arms

Midhurst Road, Fernhurst, West Sussex GU27 3HA
☎ *(01428) 652005*
Annabel and Michael Hurst

King's Arms Ale (brewed especially by the Brewery on Sea) and Otter Bright always available plus three guests (300 in three years) perhaps including Hogs Back TEA, Timothy Taylor Landlord, Ringwood Fortyniner and RCH Pitchfork.

A seventeenth-century freehouse with oak beams and fireplaces. An L-shaped bar with servery to dining area, plus hay barn for live bands, weddings etc. Surrounded by farmland, customers may come by horse or helicopter. Food available at lunchtime and evenings. Children allowed until 7pm, over 14s thereafter.

11.30am–3pm and 5.30–11pm Mon–Sat; 12–3pm only Sun.

FISHBOURNE

The Bull's Head

99 Fishbourne Road, Fishbourne, Nr Chichester, West Sussex PO19 3JP
☎ *(01243) 785707* Roger Jackson

Gales beers always available plus five guests (150 per year) from traditional family brewers from Adnams to Young's and small independents such as Ash Vine. Repeat favourites include the Kelham Island range, Brewery on Sea brews, Conciliation Ale and Hop Back Summer Lightning.

A converted seventeenth-century farmhouse with a country atmosphere, just one mile from the city centre. Bar and restaurant food available at lunchtime and evenings except Sunday. Car park, garden and children's room. On the A259.

📖 *11am–3pm and 5.30–11pm Mon–Fri; 11am–11pm Sat; 12–10.30pm Sun.*

FRANT

Abergavenny Arms

Frant Road, Frant, East Sussex
☎ *(01892) 750233* Les Brackley

Eleven beers available including Rother Valley Level Best and Harveys brews plus 400 guests per year including Exe Valley Devon Glory and many, many micro-brews.

B uilt in the 1430s, a large, two-bar country pub. The lounge bar was used as a courtroom in the eighteenth century, with cells in the cellar. Bar and restaurant food available at lunchtime and evenings. Car park, garden. Children allowed. Easy to find.

📖 *11am–3pm and 6–11pm Mon–Sat; 12–3pm and 7–10.30pm Sun.*

GUNGARDEN

The Ypres Castle Inn

Gungarden, Rye, East Sussex TN31 7HH
☎ *(01797) 223248* Richard Pearce

A freehouse with Harveys Bitter and Mild always available plus up to four guests such as Charles Wells Bombardier, Badger Tanglefoot, Young's Bitter and Coach House Coachman's Best. Local brewers favoured whenever possible.

A n old-fashioned weatherboarded pub dating from the seventeenth century. No juke box, games or machines. Non-smoking area, safe garden. Food available at lunchtime and evenings plus Sunday carvery (book for food at weekends). Well-behaved children allowed until 9.30pm, if accompanied. Ring for directions – can be hard to find.

📖 *All day, every day.*

HAILSHAM

The Bricklayers Arms

1 Ersham Road, Hailsham, East Sussex BN27 3LA
☎ *(01323) 841587* Ray Gosling

Fuller's ESB, Shepherd Neame Bishop's Finger and Greene King Abbot always available straight from the barrel, plus occasional seasonal guests.

T wo bars, pool and billiards. Hot snacks available until 8pm. Beer garden. Children allowed in the garden only.

📖 *11am–3pm and 5–11pm (10.30pm Sun).*

HALFWAY BRIDGE

Halfway Bridge Inn

Halfway Bridge, Nr Petworth, West Sussex GU28 9BP
☎ *(01798) 861281* Simon and James Hawkins

Cheriton Pots Ale and Gales HSB always available plus two guests (100 per year) changed each week often from Brewery on Sea, Hampshire or Arundel breweries. Also local cider.

B uilt in 1710 on the A272 halfway between Midhurst and Petworth, an authentic staging post on the Dover to Winchester road. Four rooms around a central serving area, inglenook fireplace. Bar and restaurant food at lunchtime and evenings. Car park, garden, non-smoking area, traditional games. Children over 10 allowed.

📖 *11–3pm and 6–11pm Mon–Sat; 12–3pm and 7–11pm Sun.*

HASTINGS

The Carlisle

Pelham Street, Hastings, East Sussex TN34 1PE
☎ *(00424) 420193* Mike Ford

A freehouse serving three brews from the Forge Brewery plus seasonal guests.

A bikers' pub but with a mixed clientele. Rock music, bar games. Large function room. Outside seating on concrete mushrooms. Food available at lunchtime and evenings. Children allowed until 7pm.

📖 *All day, every day.*

SUSSEX   247

First In Last Out

15 High Street, Hastings, East Sussex TN34 3EY
☎ *(01424) 425079 Mr Biggs*

Two beers brewed on the premises and always available. Two guest ales such as Hop Back Rye and Coriander, but always changing. Smaller breweries favoured and normally their stronger brews.

Definitely a real ale house, known locally as FILO, with lots of character and charisma. No pool, music or machines. Food available 12–3pm Tues–Sat in a separate restaurant. Beer garden. Children allowed during the daytime only.

CROFTERS BEST BITTER 4.0% ABV
CARDINAL SUSSEX PORTER 4.4% ABV

All day, every day.

The Star

1 The Broadway, Haywards Heath, West Sussex RH16 3AQ
☎ *(01444) 413267 Philip Jordon*

Up to 13 beers. Marston's Pedigree, Fuller's London Pride, Brakspear Bitter, Greene King Abbot and Morland Old Speckled Hen always available plus several guests (78 per year) including Timothy Taylor Landlord, Archers Old Cobleigh, Hook Norton Old Hooky, Exmoor Gold and Hop Back Summer Lightning.

A large real ale house in the town centre. Bar food served at lunchtime and evenings. Car park and garden. Accommodation. Follow the one-way system.

11am–11pm Mon–Sat; normal hours Sun.

The Brewer's Arms

Gardner Street, Herstmonceux, East Sussex BN27 4LB
☎ *(01323) 832226 Barry Dimmack*

Greene King IPA and Triumph and a Harveys ale always available plus two or three guests. Examples include Archers Golden and Swale Kentish Pride, but the selection is changing all the time.

An Elizabethan pub dating from 1580. Low beams, wood panelling, many clocks. Food available at lunchtime (not Tuesday) and evenings in a separate dining area. Garden. Children allowed in the garden only.

12–2.30pm and 6–11pm Mon–Sat; 12–3pm and 7–10.30pm Sun.

The Foresters Arms

43 St Leonards Road, Horsham, West Sussex RH13 6EH
☎ *(01403) 254458 Jo Mainstone*

Three real ales including brews from Shepherd Neame always available.

A small pub with a large garden for outdoor games which is also child- and dog-friendly. Barbecues, quiz nights, happy hours etc. Food only on special occasions (such as BBQs), children in garden only.

12–3.30pm and 6–11pm Mon–Fri; all day at weekends.

The Malt Shovel

Springfield Road, Horsham, West Sussex RH12 2PG
☎ *(01403) 254543 Steve Williams*

Gales GB among the beers always available, plus up to six guests including Timothy Taylor Landlord, or something from Cottage or Weltons. A beer festival is held in February or March.

A traditional pub with floorboards, real fires, one bar, patio and car park. Food served until 7pm (9.30pm on Mondays). Children over 14 allowed.

All day, every day.

Hedgehog & Hogshead

100 Goldstone Villas, Hove, East Sussex BN3 3RU
☎ *(01273) 733660 Danny Barclay*

A freehouse and brewpub with two beers produced on the premises and always available.

One large bar with TV for sport etc. Outside seating. Food available 12–3pm daily, including Sunday roasts. Curry night on Thursdays, live music Fri–Sat evenings. Children allowed in designated licensed area.

BB 4.2% ABV
ORIGINAL 5.2% ABV

All day, every day.

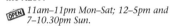

ICKLESHAM

The Queen's Head

Parsonage Lane, Icklesham, Winchelsea, East Sussex TN36 4BL
☎ *(01424) 814552* Ian Mitchell

A freehouse with Greene King IPA and either Old Forge or Brother's Best from the Forge Brewery always available, plus two fortnightly changing guests such as Greene King Abbot, Ringwood Old Thumper and Hop Back Summer Lightning.

A Jacobean pub dating from 1632. Farm implements on ceiling, boules pitch, function room, beer garden overlooking Rye. Food available at lunchtime and evenings. Under 12s allowed until 8.30pm. Situated off the A259.

OPEN *11am–11pm Mon–Sat; 12–5pm and 7–10.30pm Sun.*

LEWES

The Black Horse Inn

55 Western Road, Lewes, East Sussex BN7 1RS
☎ *(01273) 473653* Vic Newman

Greene King IPA and Triumph, Archers Golden and a Harveys ale always available, plus two guests from a range of independent brewers.

B uilt in 1800 as a hotel, this is a quiet, two-bar pub situated on the main road through Lewes. Bar billiards, darts, cribbage, beer garden. Bar snacks available at lunchtime. No children.

OPEN *11am–2.30pm and 5.30–11pm Mon–Sat; 12–2.30pm and 7–10.30pm Sun.*

The Brewer's Arms

91 High Street, Lewes, East Sussex BN7 1XN
☎ *(01273) 475524* Kevin Griffin

A freehouse with Harveys Best always available plus up to four real ales constantly rotating. Harveys seasonals regularly featured, as well as brews such as Fuller's London Pride, Rother Valley Spirit Level or something from Arundel, Brewery on Sea, Northdown, Bateman, Cuckmere, Rector Ales, Larkins, Hampshire and Cottage. Also real ciders.

T here has been a pub on this site since 1540. Well-equipped, with two bars, children's room, extractor fans (for smokers), pool and large-screen TV. Bar food available until 7pm, snacks until 11pm. Children welcome, and dogs if on a lead.

OPEN *All day, every day.*

The Elephant & Castle

White Hill, Lewes, East Sussex BN2 2DJ
☎ *(01273) 473797* Dave Whiting

A freehouse with Harveys Best, Morland Old Speckled Hen and Charles Wells Bombardier always available.

A n old Sussex pub with one bar and a function room. Meeting place for the Bonfire Society. A themed menu is available at lunchtimes only. Children allowed.

OPEN *All day, every day.*

The Gardener's Arms

45 Cliffe High Street, Lewes, East Sussex BN7 2AN
☎ *(01273) 474808* Peter Skinner

Brews from the Dark Star Brewing Company always available plus several guests (100s per year) from small independents.

S ister-pub of the Evening Star, Brighton. No juke box or games machines. Wooden floor, wooden tables and chairs. Bar food available at lunchtime. Parking. Opposite the Harveys Brewery.

OPEN *11am–3pm Mon–Wed; all day Thurs–Sat; usual Sun hours.*

LITLINGTON

The Plough & Harrow

Litlington, Nr Alfriston, East Sussex BN26 5RE
☎ *(01323) 870631* Roger Taylor

Badger Best and Tanglefoot always available plus four guests from a large list including Wadworth 6X, Charles Wells Bombardier and Eagle IPA, Fuller's London Pride and brews from Harveys and Buchanan.

A fifteenth-century freehouse with oak beams, two bars and a busy restaurant. Bar and restaurant food available. Car park and garden. Children allowed in the restaurant. Three miles south of the A27, two miles from the nearest village (Alfriston).

OPEN *11am–2.30pm and 6.30–11pm.*

MAPLEHURST

The White Horse Inn

Park Lane, Maplehurst, Horsham, West Sussex
RH13 6LL
☎ *(01403) 891208* Simon Johnson

A freehouse with Weltons Dorking Pride and Harveys Best always available, plus four guests, changed weekly, such as Hogs Back TEA, King and Barnes Best, Butcombe Gold, Harveys Armada or Brewery on Sea Spinnaker. Smaller independents and micro-breweries favoured.

A traditional three-bar pub with no juke box, machines or piped music. Non-smoking area, conservatory, garden with good views. Food served at lunchtime and evenings. Children allowed. Situated less than two miles north of the A272 and south of the A281.

12–2.30pm and 6–11pm Mon–Sat;
12–3pm and 7–10.30pm Sun.

MIDHURST

The Crown Inn

Edinburgh Square, Midhurst, West Sussex
GU29 9NL
☎ *(01730) 813462* Paul Stevens

Fuller's London Pride and Cheriton Pots available at £1.59 plus up to eight guests (150 per year). Favoured breweries include Cheriton, Hampshire, Ballards, Hogs Back, Tripple F, Oakham, Rooster's, Ringwood, Hop Back, Woodforde's, etc.

A sixteenth-century traditional freehouse hosting occasional beer festivals. Bar and restaurant food served at lunchtime and evenings. Parking, garden, function/games room. Children allowed in the restaurant. Accommodation. Behind and below the church in the old part of the town.

11am–11pm Mon–Sat; 12–10.30pm Sun.

OLD HEATHFIELD

The Star

Church Street, Old Heathfield, East Sussex
TN21 9AH
☎ *(01435) 863570* Mr and Mrs Chappell

Harveys brews and Fuller's London Pride always available plus a guest (50 per year) such as Harviestoun Ptarmigan, Hop Back Summer Lightning, Black Sheep Best; also Daleside Old Legover, Gravesend Shrimpers, NYBC Flying Herbert, Daleside Monkey Wrench and Burton Bridge Hearty Ale etc.

A freehouse built in 1348, licensed in 1388. Original beams and open fires. Famous gardens and views. Bar and restaurant food served at lunchtime and evenings. Car park and garden. Children allowed. At a dead end of a road to the rear of Old Heathfield church.

11.30am–3pm and 5.30–11pm.

OVING

The Gribble Inn & Brewery

Oving, Nr Chichester, West Sussex PO20 6BP
☎ *(01243) 786893* Brian and Cyn Elderfield

Gribble Ales all available. Wobbler only from September to March.

The Gribble Inn's brewery is now in its twelfth year and still going strong. Rob Cooper, the head brewer, is constantly developing new beers, using only the best quality hops and malts with no additives or extra sugars, the latest in his range of fine ales and beers being known as Fursty Ferret, a nut-brown beer. This picturesque sixteenth-century inn is a traditional country pub, serving good, wholesome home-cooked food at both lunchtime and evenings, seven days a week. Car park, large garden, no-smoking area, children's room, skittle alley.

EWE BREW 3.8% ABV
GRIBBLE ALE 4.1% ABV
FURSTY FERRET 4.2% ABV
OVING BITTER 4.5% ABV
REG'S TIPPLE 5.0% ABV
BLACK ADDER II 5.8% ABV
PIG'S EAR OLD ALE 6.0% ABV
WOBBLER 7.2% ABV

11am–3pm and 5.30–11pm Mon–Sat;
12–3pm and 7–10.30pm Sun.

PETT

The Two Sawyers

Pett Road, Pett, Nr Hastings, East Sussex
TN35 4HB
☎ *(01424) 812255* Peter Newmark-Payne

A freehouse with Petts Progress and Forge Bitter from the nearby Old Forge Brewery always available. Two weekly changing guests such as Hop Back Summer Lightning, Greene King Abbot and Gales GB and HSB.

An olde-worlde pub with two bars, restaurant, beer garden, boules pitch and B&B. Food available at lunchtime and evenings. Children allowed in the dining area only.

11.30am–3pm and 6–11pm Mon–Thurs; all day Fri–Sun.

ROBERTSBRIDGE

The Seven Stars Inn

High Street, Robertsbridge, East Sussex TN32 5AJ
☎ *(01580) 880333* Ruth McGregor

Harveys Sussex Bitter, Greene King Abbot and IPA and Marston's Pedigree always available, plus up to five guests such as Arundel 1999 and Rother Valley Level Best.

An early-medieval pub, dating from the eleventh century. One bar, pool, video games, car park, beer garden. Food available at lunchtime and evenings. Children and dogs welcome.

All day, every day.

RUDGWICK

The Thurlow Arms

Baynards, Rudgwick, Horsham, West Sussex
RH12 3AD
☎ *(01403) 822459* Martin Gibbs

A freehouse. Badger Tanglefoot and Best plus Ringwood Best always available, also one monthly changing guest such as Hogs Back TEA.

Built in the old lodging house on the old railway line from Guildford to Shoreham with lots of railway memorabilia. Three bars, games room, small restaurant. Food served at lunchtime and evenings. Children allowed in separate play area. Tucked away in the middle of nowhere between Rudgwick and Cranleigh.

11am–3pm and 6–11.30pm Mon–Sat; all day Sun.

RYE

The Inkerman Arms

Harbour Road, Rye Harbour, Rye, East Sussex
TN31 7TQ
☎ *(01797) 222464* Mrs May

A freehouse serving a selection of real ales from one of two local brewers (Old Forge or Rother Valley) plus one varying Greene King ale always available.

A traditional harbourside pub with one bar, lounge and dining area. Boules pitch, garden. Full menu available every day, with fish and chips a speciality. Well-behaved children welcome.

12–3pm and 7–11pm Mon–Thurs; all day Fri–Sat; 12–3pm and 7–10.30pm Sun.

ST LEONARDS ON SEA

The Dripping Spring

34 Tower Road, St Leonards on Sea, East Sussex
RN37 6JE
☎ *(01424) 434055* Mr and Mrs Gillitt

Arkell's 3B and Fuller's London Pride plus at least one local beer from the Pett Brewing Company (Old Forge). Other guests (100 per year) from as far afield as possible, preferably 4% ABV and over.

A small two-bar public house with attractive courtyard to the rear. Bar food available at lunchtime. Car parking. Situated in a side street off the A21.

11am–3pm and 5–11pm Mon–Thurs; all day Fri–Sun.

SEAFORD

The Wellington

Steyne Road, Seaford, East Sussex BN25 1HT
☎ *(01323) 890032* Mr Hutchins

Fuller's London Pride, Greene King IPA, Abbot and Martha Greene plus a Harveys ale always available. Also one guest from an independent or micro-brewery, changing daily.

A community pub with two bars and a function roon. Parking nearby. Food available at lunchtime only. Children allowed.

All day, every day.

SHOREHAM

The Lazy Toad

*88 High Street, Shoreham-by-Sea, West Sussex
BN43 5DB*
☎ *(01273) 441622* Mr Cederberg

Greene King Abbot, Badger Tanglefoot, Shepherd Neame Spitfire and Gales Festival Mild among the beers always available plus up to three guests.

A small, friendly freehouse with one big bar. Food served only at lunchtime. Children over 14 allowed.

OPEN *All day, every day.*

SIDLESCOOMBE

The Queen's Head

*The Green, Sidlescoombe, Battle, East Sussex
TN33 0QA*
☎ *(01424) 870228* John Cook

Young's Bitter always available plus one guest from an independent brewery. Rother Valley and Pett (Old Forge) brews are popular choices.

A country pub with beams and brasses, on the village green. Beer garden, car park. Bread and cheese available at lunchtime only. Children allowed.

OPEN *10am–2.30pm and 6–11pm.*

STOUGHTON

The Hare & Hounds

Stoughton, West Sussex
☎ *(01705) 631433*

Adnams Broadside, Ringwood Best and Gales HSB always available plus four guest beers (from an endless list) such as Hop Back Summer Lightning, Timothy Taylor Landlord, Fuller's ESB, Brakspear etc.

More than 300 years old, a flint-built pub nestling on the Sussex Downs. Bar food available at lunchtime and evenings. Car park and garden. Children allowed. Signposted at Walberton off the B2146.

OPEN *11am–3pm and 6–11pm Mon–Sat; 12–4pm and 7–10.30pm Sun.*

TARRING

The Vine Inn

*High Street, Tarring, Worthing, West Sussex
BN14 7NN*
☎ *(01903) 202891* David Asman

Badger Dorset Best, Champion Ale and Tanglefoot, Ringwood True Glory, Hop Back Summer Lightning and a Harveys ale always available plus two constantly changing guests such as Harveys Old and and Gribble Oving Bitter and Black Adder II.

An old-fashioned pub in a listed building dating from 1645. Live entertainment on Mondays, enormous garden and courtyard, car park. Bar snacks available at lunchtime, plus Sunday roasts. Children allowed in the garden only.

OPEN *11am–3pm and 6–11pm Mon–Sat; all day Sun.*

TELHAM

The Black Horse Inn

*Hastings Road, Telham, Battle, East Sussex
TN33 0SH*
☎ *(01424) 773109* Mr Dunford

A range of Shepherd Neame ales always available.

A one-bar pub with restaurant, beer garden and boules pitch. Music festival held on Spring Bank Holiday every year. Food available at lunchtime and evenings. Children allowed in the restaurant only.

OPEN *11am–3pm and 5.30–11pm (10.30pm Sun).*

THAKEHAM

The White Lion Inn

*The Street, Thakeham Village, West Sussex
RH20 3EP*
☎ *(01798) 813141* William Newton

A freehouse with Harveys Best and Old Flame and Arundel Best always available.

A two-bar, 500-year-old alehouse with garden. Pub grub available at lunchtime and evenings. Well-behaved children allowed.

OPEN *11am–4pm and 5.30–11pm Mon–Sat; 12–3.30pm and 6.30–10.30pm Sun.*

TICEHURST

The Bull Inn

Dunster Mill Lane, Three Legged Cross, Nr Ticehurst, East Sussex TN5 7HH
☎ *(01580) 200586* Mrs Josie Wilson-Moir

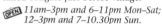 Up to seven brews always available including Rother Valley Level Best, Morland Old Speckled Hen, King and Barnes Sussex and Harveys ales plus hundreds of guests per year including brews from Adnams, Iceni etc.

Whealden Hall House was built between 1385 and 1425 in good walking country and has been a pub for 100 years. There are two bars with an adjoining restaurant. Food available at lunchtime and evenings (not Sunday and Monday evenings). Car park, garden, children's play area. Coming into Ticehurst from the north on the B2099, turn left beside corner house called Tollgate just before village.

🍺 *11am–3pm and 6–11pm Mon–Sat; 12–3pm and 7–10.30pm Sun.*

WEST ASHLING

The Richmond Arms

Mill Road, West Ashling, West Sussex PO18 8EA
☎ *(01243) 575730* Alan Gurney

 Harveys Sussex and Greene King Abbot and IPA always available, plus up to seven guests such as Hop Back Summer Lightning, Hanby Cascade and Fuller's Summer Ale. Seasonal ales always popular.

A comfortable and cosy Victorian pub. Two bars, open fires, skittle alley, pool, darts etc. Terrace garden at the front. Bar food available at lunchtime and evenings. Well-behaved children allowed. Situated half a mile from Funtington.

🍺 *11am–2.30pm and 5.30–11pm Mon–Fri; all day Sat–Sun.*

WEST CHILTINGTON

The Five Bells

Smock Alley, West Chiltington, West Sussex RH20 2QX
☎ *(01798) 812143*

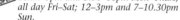 Five beers always available from an ever-changing range. Favoured brewers include Ballards, Adnams, Bateman, Black Sheep, Brakspear, Bunces, Cheriton, Exmoor, Fuller's, Gales, Greene King, Guernsey, Harveys, Hogs Back, Hook Norton, Jennings, King & Barnes, Mansfield, Palmers, St Austell, Shepherd Neame, Smiles, Samuel Smith, Timothy Taylor and Young's.

An attractive Edwardian-style version of a Sussex farmhouse. Bar and restaurant food available at lunchtime and evenings. Car park, conservatory and beer garden. Well-behaved children allowed. Ask for directions.

🍺 *11am–3pm and 6–11pm.*

WORTHING

The Richard Cobden

2 Cobden Road, Worthing, West Sussex BN11 4BD
☎ *(01903) 236856* Mike Wilson

 Greene King IPA and Wadworth 6X always available plus two guests such as Greene King Abbot.

A typical 1950s street-corner boozer with one bar and a patio. Food served at lunchtimes (not Sunday).

🍺 *11am–3pm and 5.30–11pm Mon–Thurs; all day Fri–Sat; 12–3pm and 7–10.30pm Sun.*

YAPTON

The Lamb Inn

Bilsham Road, Yapton, Arundel, West Sussex BN18 0JN
☎ *(01243) 551232* John Etherington

Harveys Sussex Ale and Greene King Abbot always available, plus one guest changing fortnightly.

An edge-of-village pub on the road side. Brick floors, large open fire, dining area, car park, garden with children's play area, and petanque/boules. Food served every lunchtime and evening. Children allowed. Located on a minor road between the A259 and Yapton village.

🍺 *11am–3pm and 5.30–11pm Mon–Thurs; 11am–3pm and 5–11pm Fri; 12–3.30pm and 6–11pm Sat; 12–4.30pm and 6.30–10.30pm Sun. Open all day at weekends during the summer.*

The Maypole Inn

Maypole Lane, Yapton, Arundel, West Sussex
BN18 0DP
☎ *(01243) 551417* Keith McManus

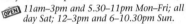 A freehouse with Ringwood Best always available plus up to six guests. Hop Back Summer Lightning, Cheriton Pots Ale or something from Skinner's may be featured. Smaller breweries well-represented.

A country pub with public and lounge bars, log fires, skittle alley, small garden. Bar snacks available at lunchtime and Sunday roasts. Children allowed in the public bar only until 8.30pm.

11am–3pm and 5.30–11pm Mon–Fri; all day Sat; 12–3pm and 6–10.30pm Sun.

YOU TELL US

★ *The Alma Arms,* Framfield Road, Uckfield
★ *The Cock Robin,* Station Hill, Wadhurst
★ *The Cricketer's Arms,* Berwick
★ *The Duke of Cumberland,* Henley
★ *The Earl of March,* Lavant Road, Lavant
★ *Farm Tavern,* 13 Farm Road, Hove
★ *The Fletcher Arms,* Station Road, East Preston, Littlehampton
★ *The Foresters Arms,* Graffham
★ *The Green Man,* The Green, Horsted Keynes, Haywards Heath

★ *The Griffin,* High Street, Fletching
★ *The Hand-in-Hand,* 33 Upper St James Street, Brighton
★ *Hatter's,* 2–10 Queensway, Bognor Regis
★ *The Horse & Groom,* Singleton
★ *The Laughing Fish,* Station Road, Isfield
★ *The Linden Tree,* 47 High Street, Lindfield, Haywards Heath
★ *The Old Barn Free House,* 42 Felpham Road, Bognor Regis
★ *The Old Oak Inn,* Cane Heath, Arlington
★ *The Ostrich Hotel,* Station Road, Robertsbridge
★ *The Prince Albert,* 48 Trafalgar Street, Brighton
★ *The Prince of Wales,* Station Road, Heathfield
★ *The Peacock Inn,* Shortbridges, Piltdown
★ *The Ram Inn,* Firle Street, Firle, Lewes
★ *The Red Lion Inn,* Old Shoreham Road, Shoreham-by-Sea
★ *The Stanley Arms,* 47 Wolseley Road, Portslade
★ *The Swan Hotel,* 27–9 High Street, Arundel
★ *The Sussex Brewery,* Hermitage
★ *Vinols Cross,* 8 Top Road, Sharpthorne
★ *The White Lion,* 74 Claremont Road, Seaford
★ *The Wyndham Arms,* Rogate

Places Featured:

Byker
Felling
Gosforth
Jesmond
Low Fell
Newcastle upon Tyne
North Hylton

North Shields
South Shields
Sunderland
Wardley
Washington
Westmoor
Whitley Bay

THE BREWERIES

BIG LAMP BREWERS

Big Lamp Brewery, Grange Road, Newburn,
Newcastle upon Tyne NE15 8NL
☎ *(0191) 267 1689*

BITTER 3.9% ABV
MULLIGAN'S STOUT 4.4% ABV
PRINCE BISHOP ALE 4.8% ABV
PREMIUM 5.2% ABV
Plus seasonal brews.

FEDERATION BREWERY

Lancaster Road, Dunston NE11 9JR
☎ *(01827) 251002*

BUCHANAN BEST BITTER 3.6% ABV
DANGE YA MAGGOT 4.0% ABV
BUCHANAN ORIGINAL 4.4% ABV
SALMON LEAP 4.7% ABV
TUMMY TICKLER 4.7% ABV

MORDUE BREWERY

Unit 21a, West Chirton North Industrial Estate,
Shiremoor NE29 8SF
☎ *(0191) 296 1879*

FIVE BRIDGE BITTER 3.8% ABV
GEORDIE PRIDE 4.2% ABV
WORKIE TICKET 4.5% ABV
BLACK MIDDEN STOUT 4.6% ABV
RADGIE GADGIE 4.8% ABV
Plus seasonal ales.

THE PUBS

BYKER

The Cumberland Arms

Byker Buildings, Byker, Newcastle upon Tyne
NE6 1LD
☎ *(0191) 265 6151*

Five beers always available from a constantly changing range (250 per year) but including Marston's Pedigree and Fuller's London Pride.

An unchanged pub established in 1832 overlooking the Ouseburn Valley. Well known for its live music (traditional and rock). No food available. Parking, garden under development. Children allowed in the function room. Over Byker Bridge, then first right, second right, above farm.

OPEN *12–11pm (10.30pm Sun).*

The Free Trade Inn

St Lawrence Road, Byker, Newcastle upon Tyne
NE6 1AP
☎ *(0191) 265 5764* Richard Grey (Manager)

Mordue Workie Ticket and Geordie Pride, Marston's Pedigree and a Mordue seasonal ale such as Summer Tyne always available plus one guest, usually another Mordue beer such as Five Bridges, Radgie Gadgie or seasonals.

A traditional town pub with a lovely view of the River Tyne. Two beer gardens, one bar. No food. Children allowed during the daytime and early evening only.

OPEN *11am–11pm (10.30pm Sun).*

The Tap & Spile

*33 Shields Road, Byker, Newcastle upon Tyne
NE6 1DJ*
☎ *(0191) 276 1440* Peter Bland

Twelve beers always available from a constantly changing range (450 per year) with Bateman Valiant, Charles Wells Eagle and Black Sheep Bitter among them.

B eamed theme pub with open fires and friendly atmosphere. Bar food available at lunchtime and evenings. Car park. Children allowed. Easy to find.

OPEN *12–11pm (10.30pm Sun).*

The Old Fox

13 Carlisle Street, Felling, Gateshead NE10 0HQ
☎ *(0191) 420 0357* Valerie White

A freehouse with Bateman XB and a Banks ale always available plus three guests from breweries such as Durham, Northumberland or Mordue. Beers also stocked at customers' request – previous examples have included Marston's Pedigree or Black Sheep Bitter.

A real ale pub in town location, with coal fire, one bar and garden. Bar snacks available at lunchtime. Children allowed if eating.

OPEN *12–11pm (10.30pm Sun).*

The Wheatsheaf

26 Carlisle Street, Felling, Gateshead NE10 0HQ
☎ *(0191) 420 0659* Jim Storey

A range of Big Lamp beers such as Bitter, Price Bishop, Premium Ale, Sandgates or Keelman Bitter always available.

A n old-fashioned community pub with one bar. Sandwiches and pies available. Children allowed until 7pm.

OPEN *12–11pm (10.30pm Sun).*

Gosforth Hotel

High Street, Gosforth
☎ *(0191) 285 6617* John Burtle

Marston's Pedigree is one of eight beers always available. Guests including Bateman XB, Coach House Coachman's Best and Adnams and Burton Bridge brews.

T raditional Victorian alehouse. Bar food available at lunchtime. Car park, accommodation. Children allowed.

OPEN *11am–11pm Mon–Sat; 12–2.30pm and 7–10.30pm Sun.*

Legendary Yorkshire Heroes

Archibold Terrace, Jesmond
☎ *(0191) 281 3010* Colin Colquhoun

Nine beers always available from a rotating list including Black Sheep Bitter and brews from Jennings, Big Lamp and Thwaites.

A lively refurbished modern pub within an office complex. Bar food available on weekday lunchtimes. Four pool tables, big screen sports, live bands Thursday to Saturday. Children allowed at lunchtimes only.

OPEN *11am–11pm Mon–Sat; 12–10.30pm Sun.*

The Ale Taster

*706 Durham Road, Low Fell, Gateshead
NE9 6JA*
☎ *(0191) 487 0770* Lawrence Gill

Mordue Workie Ticket and Radgie Gadgie always available plus up to six guests such as Timothy Taylor Landlord, Badger Tanglefoot or an Ash Vine brew. Two beer festivals held every year in May and September, serving 30 extra beers.

A n old coaching inn with beams and wooden floors, in the town centre. One bar, snug area, large courtyard with children's play area. Food available until 6pm. Children allowed.

OPEN *11am–11pm Mon–Sat; 12–10.30pm Sun.*

The Bodega
125 Westgate Road, Newcastle upon Tyne NE1 4AG
☎ *(0191) 221 1552* Colin Howse

Mordue Workie Ticket, Geordie Pride and Durham Magus among the brews permanently available, plus one guest from breweries such as Border, Shepherd Neame, Black Sheep and Ridleys. Beers changed weekly.

A traditional real ale pub on the outskirts of the town centre. One bar, food available 11am–2.30pm Mon–Sat and 12–2.30pm Sun. No children.

OPEN *11am–11pm Mon–Sat; 12–10.30pm Sun.*

The Head of Steam
2 Neville Street, Newcastle Upon Tyne NE1 5EN
☎ *(0191) 232 4379* Julian Ive

A freehouse with Black Sheep Bitter always available plus up to six guests from a wide range of breweries including, among others, Black Sheep, Young's and Shepherd Neame.

A two-bar, city-centre pub with food available at lunchtime. No children.

OPEN *12–11pm (10.30pm Sun).*

The Tap & Spile
1 Nun Street, Newcastle upon Tyne
☎ *(0191) 232 0026*

Twelve beers always available from a constantly changing range (200 per year) with names such as Durham Canny Lad and Magus, Mordue Workie Ticket and Bateman Yellow Belly.

More than 100 years old, with a ground-floor and basement bar. Bar food available at lunchtime. Children allowed for meals. Live bands in the cellar. Two minutes from the railway station and Greys Monument.

OPEN *11am–11pm Mon–Sat; 12–10.30pm Sun.*

The Tut & Shive
52 Clayton Street West, Newcastle upon Tyne NE1 4EX
☎ *(0191) 261 6998*

A Castle Eden ale always available plus three guests such as Marston's Pedigree or seasonal ales from Marston's.

A friendly town-centre pub with a mixed clientele of young students and business people. Two bars. Hot sandwiches available at lunchtime only. No children. Situated near the railway station.

OPEN *11am–11pm (12–11pm in summer) Mon–Sat; 12–10.30pm Sun.*

The Three Horseshoes
Washington Road, North Hylton, Sunderland SR5 3HZ
☎ *(0191) 536 4183* Frank Jamieson

Three guest ales such as Morland Old Speckled Hen and Charles Wells Bombardier. Annual beer festival held at the end of July.

A traditional country pub with two bars (public and lounge), separate dining area, open fire, pool, darts etc. Food available lunchtimes and evenings. Children allowed. Follow signs for Air Museum, by Nissan entrance.

OPEN *12–3pm and 6.30–11pm (10.30pm Sun).*

Chain Locker
New Quay, North Shields NE29 6LQ
☎ *(0191) 258 0147* Peter McAlister

A freehouse with Mordue Workie Ticket and Radgie Gadgie always available plus four daily changing guests including, perhaps, Mordue Five Bridges and Timothy Taylor Landlord.

A riverside pub by a ferry landing on a fresh fish quay. One bar, styled in a nautical theme, plus separate dining area and beer garden. Food available at lunchtime only. Children allowed.

OPEN *11am–11pm (10.30pm Sun).*

The Garricks Head
Saville Street, North Shields NE30 1NT
☎ *(0191) 296 2064* Ken Ladell

A freehouse with four pumps all serving a range of weekly changing real ales. Morland Old Speckled Hen, Charles Wells Bombardier, Young's Special and Hartleys XB are examples.

A traditional two-bar town pub with function room and restaurant. Food available at lunchtime and evenings. Children allowed in the restaurant only.

OPEN *11am–11pm Mon–Sat; 12–10.30pm Sun.*

The Porthole

11 New Quay, North Shields NE29 6LQ
☎ *(0191) 257 6645* Mike Morgan

Five beers always available from a large list (156+ per year) including Fuller's London Pride and Adnams Broadside.

A n old-fashioned friendly pub with a maritime theme, on the banks of the Tyne. Bar food served at lunchtime and evenings. Car park. Children allowed. Near the North Shields ferry landing.

(OPEN) *11am–11pm Mon–Sat; 12–10.30pm Sun.*

Shiremoor House Farm

Middle Engine Lane, North Shields NE29 8DZ
☎ *(0191) 257 6302* Bill Kerridge

A freehouse with Mordue Workie Ticket always available plus up to five guests such as Moorhouse's Pendle Witches Brew, Jennings Cumberland, Timothy Taylor Landlord, Swale India Summer Pale Ale or Durham Brewery's Celtic. Beers changed two or three times a week.

A converted farmhouse with two bars, stone floors and separate restaurant. CAMRA award winner for best pub conversion. Food available 12–10pm daily. Children allowed.

(OPEN) *11am–11pm (10.30pm Sun).*

The Tap & Spile

184 Tynemouth Road, North Shields NE30 1EG
☎ *(0191) 257 2523*

Black Sheep Special always available plus eight guest beers from a large list.

A real ale bar with a friendly atmosphere. Bar food served at lunchtime. Parking. Opposite the magistrates court in North Shields.

(OPEN) *11.30am–11pm Mon–Sat; 12–3pm Sun.*

SOUTH SHIELDS

Dolly Peel

137 Commercial Road, South Shields NE33 1SQ
☎ *(0191) 427 1441* Ken Taylor

A freehouse with Timothy Taylor Landlord, Black Sheep Bitter and Durham Scotch always available, plus two guest pumps serving local real ales such as Mordue Regular, Workie Ticket or Radgie Gadgie and occasional celebration ales.

A traditional suburban pub with two bars and outside seating. Sandwiches only. No bottled beers. No children.

(OPEN) *11am–11pm Mon–Sat; 12–3pm and 6.30–10.30pm Sun.*

SUNDERLAND

The Tap & Barrel

Nelson Street, Sunderland SR2 8EF
☎ *(0191) 514 2810* Michael Riley

Everards Tiger and Timothy Taylor Landlord among the brews always available, plus four or five guests from a large selection including Banbury Old Vic and Thwaites Bloomin' Ale. Beers changed weekly.

A n old-fashioned pub with two bars and a separate dining area. Food available 4–8pm Mon–Fri and 12–4pm Sat–Sun. Children allowed, if eating.

(OPEN) *4–11pm Mon–Fri; all day Sat–Sun.*

The Tap & Spile

Salem Street, Hendon, Sunderland
☎ *(0191) 232 0026* Janice Faulder

Nine beers always available from a list of 400+ including North Yorkshire Best, Bateman XB, Charles Wells Bombardier and Marston's Pedigree.

T raditional three-bar alehouse with bare boards and exposed brickwork. Bar food available at lunchtime. Function room. Children allowed in eating area.

(OPEN) *11am–11pm Mon–Sat; 12–3pm and 7–10.30pm Sun.*

WARDLEY

The Green

White Mare Pool, Wardley, Gateshead NE10 8YB
☎ *(0191) 495 0171* Deborah Mackay

A freehouse with six guest ales always available. Timothy Taylor Landlord, Jennings Cumberland, Big Lamp Bitter, Black Sheep Special and Oakham American Blonde are some of the regular features.

A traditional village pub with one bar and one lounge. Patio and restaurant. Disabled facilities. Food available all day, every day. Children allowed in the lounge if eating.

(OPEN) *11.30am–11pm Mon–Sat; 12–10.30pm Sun.*

WASHINGTON

The Sandpiper

Easby Road, Washington NE38 7NN
☎ *(0191) 416 0038* Lynda Margaret Bewick

Up to six guests such as Marston's Pedigree, Black Sheep Bitter, Fuller's London Pride, something from Daleside or Phoenix Wobbly Bob.

A locals' village community pub with two bars, games area and patio. Charity events held. Food available at lunchtime only. Children allowed until 7pm, if supervised.

(OPEN) *11am–11pm (10.30pm Sun).*

WESTMOOR

George Stephenson Inn

Great Lime Road, Westmoor, Newcastle upon Tyne NE12 0NJ
☎ *(0191) 268 1073* Richard Costello

Two guests from local independent and micro-breweries such as Mordue, Northumberland and Big Lamp always available.

A community beer drinker's pub with lounge, bar and garden. Adult clientele, no games, live music during week. Food available Mon–Fri lunchtimes. No children.

(OPEN) *12–3pm and 5–11pm Mon–Thurs; all day Fri–Sat; 12–4pm and 7–10.30pm Sun.*

WHITLEY BAY

The Briar Dene

71 The Links, Whitley Bay NE26 1UE
☎ *(0191) 252 0926* Mrs Gibson

Mordue Workie Ticket and Summertime, Black Sheep Riggwelter and a Yates ale always available, plus five or six guests such as Mordue Radgie Gadgie among others. Six beer festivals held each year with 50–60 brews at each.

A seaside pub with one bar, family room, lounge and children's play area. Food available 11am–2.30pm and 5–10pm. Children allowed in the family room and play room only.

(OPEN) *11am–11pm Mon–Sat; 12–10.30pm Sun.*

The Fat Ox

278 Whitley Road, Whitley Bay NE26 2TG
☎ *(0191) 251 3852* Mr Carling

Four Rivers Moondance, Black Sheep Bitter and Fox Hat (a house brew produced by the Four Rivers brewery) always available plus three regularly changing guests, perhaps from Rudgate, Ruddles or Morland. Beers not repeated if possible.

A traditional one-bar town-centre pub. Food available at lunchtime only. Children allowed until 3pm. Disabled facilities.

(OPEN) *11.30am–11pm Mon–Fri; 11am–11pm Sat; 12–10.30pm Sun.*

YOU TELL US

★ *The Archer,* Archbold Terrace, Jesmond
★ *Benton Ale House,* Front Street, Benton, Newcastle upon Tyne
★ *Holborn Ross & Crown,* East Holbourne, South Shields
★ *The Keelman,* Grange Road, Newburn
★ *Magnesia Bank,* 1 Camden Street, North Shields
★ *The Melvich Hotel,* Melvich, Sunderland
★ *The Old Cross,* Barmoor Lane, Old Ryton Village, Ryton
★ *The Potter's Wheel,* Sun Street, Sunniside
★ *The Riverside,* 3 Commercial Road, South Shields
★ *Shipwrights Arms Hotel,* Rotherfield Road, North Hylton, Sunderland
★ *The Station Hotel,* Hills Street, Gateshead

THE BREWERIES

COX'S YARD

Bridgefoot, Stratford upon Avon CV37 6YY
☎ *(01789) 404600*

 JESTER ALE 3.8% ABV

Plus seasonal ales.

FRANKTON BAGBY BREWERY

The Stables, Green Lane, Church Lawford, Rugby CV23 9EF

 SQUIRES BREW 4.1% ABV

WARWICKSHIRE BEER CO. LTD

Queen Street, Cubbington, Leamington Spa CV32 7NA
☎ *(01926) 450747*

BEST 3.9% ABV
FFIAGRA 4.2% ABV
ST PATRICK'S ALE 4.4% ABV
CASTLE ALE 4.6% ABV
GOLDEN WONDER 4.9% ABV
RAGGED STAFF 5.5% ABV
Plus seasonal and occasional brews.

THE PUBS

ALCESTER

The Three Tuns

34 High Street, Alcester B49 5AB
☎ *(01789) 766550* D Parker

Home of the Bull's Head Brewery, with three ales produced and served on the premises. In addition, up to six guests are available. Everards Tiger, Hobsons Best, Wood Shropshire Lad, Fuller's London Pride, Lichfield Resurrection, North Yorkshire Dizzy Dick, Mildmay Old Horse Whip, Brains SA and Brandy Cask Brandysnapper are all popular brews.

A sixteenth-century public house with open-plan bar, converted back from a wine bar. Beer festivals are held every three months. Occasional live music. Sandwiches only.

BULLHEAD LIGHT 4.5% ABV
GLOBE ALE
GENESIS
11am–11pm Mon–Sat; 12–10.30pm Sun.

ARDENS GRAFTON

The Golden Cross

Wixford Road, Ardens Grafton, Bidford-on-Avon B50 4LG
☎ *(01789) 772420*
Pat and Roger Vardy-Smith

A freehouse serving Timothy Taylor Landlord, Hobsons and Jouster ales plus three twice-weekly changing guests.

An old-style country village pub overlooking the Cotswolds and Malverns. Beams, flagstone floors, 50-seater restaurant. Various displays and small exhibitions. The Ardens MG Club holds its meetings in the pub. Food available at lunchtime and evenings. Children allowed.

11am–2.30pm and 6–11pm (10.30pm Sun.)

EATHORPE

Eathorpe Park Hotel
The Fosse, Eathorpe, Leamington Spa
CV33 9DQ
☎ *(01926) 632632* Mrs Grinnell

A Church End ale always available plus two guests from breweries such as Hook Norton and Fat God's.

A hotel and restaurant with one bar and accommodation. Disabled access. Bar and restaurant food available at lunchtime and evenings. Children allowed.

All day, every day.

GREAT WOLFORD

The Fox & Hounds
Great Wolford CV36 5NQ
☎ *(01608) 674220* Mrs Seddon

Hook Norton Best and Shepherd Neame Spitfire always available plus hundreds of guests per year (up to five at any one time) including Wychwood Best, Morland Old Speckled Hen and brews from Eldridge Pope, Smiles and Thwaites.

A n atmospheric sixteenth-century pub with stone-flagged floors, Tudor fireplace and dining room. Bar food served at lunchtime and evenings. Car park, terrace, accommodation. Children allowed in the dining room.

12–3pm and 7–11pm (10.30pm Sun).

LONG LAWFORD

The Sheaf & Sickle
Coventry Road, Long Lawford, Rugby CV23 9DT
☎ *(01788) 544622* Steve Townes

Ansells Bitter and Mild always available plus two guests from breweries such as Eldridge Pope, Church End, Ash Vine and Judges. Aims not to repeat the beers.

A n old village coaching inn with saloon, lounge and restaurant. Beer garden. Food available at lunchtime and evenings. Children allowed.

12–2.30pm and 6–11pm Mon–Fri; all day Sat–Sun.

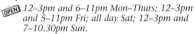
RUGBY

The Victoria Inn
1 Lower Hillmorton Road, Rugby CV21 3ST
☎ *(01788) 544374* Mrs White

A freehouse with Cottage Champflower among the brews always available plus two guests such as Hartley XB (Robinson's), Greene King IPA, Hook Norton and Shepherd Neame brews.

A locals' pub just outside the town centre. Two bars, original mirrors in both rooms. Disabled access. Food available at lunchtime only. No children.

12–3pm and 6–11pm Mon–Thurs; 12–3pm and 5–11pm Fri; all day Sat; 12–3pm and 7–10.30pm Sun.

SHIPSTON-ON-STOUR

The Coach & Horses
16 New Street, Shipston-on-Stour CV36 4EM
☎ *(01608) 661335* Bob Payne

Hook Norton Best always available plus three guests from a long list including Hook Norton Haymaker, Wye Valley Brew 69, Dorothy Goodbody's Summertime Ale, Ash Vine Toxic Waste, Bateman XXXB and XB.

A 250-year-old village pub in the Cotswolds serving bar and restaurant food at lunchtime and evenings. Car park, garden, accommodation. On the A3400 Birmingham to Oxford road, on the Oxford side of town.

11am–11pm (10.30pm Sun).

YOU TELL US

★ *The Alexandra Arms,* James Street, Rugby
★ *The Boars Head,* Church Street, Hampton Lucy
★ *The Castle,* Edgehill
★ *The Crown,* High Street, Stockton
★ *The Little Lark,* 108 Alcester Road, Studley
★ *Lord Nelson Inn,* Priory Road, Alcester
★ *The Navigation,* Old Warwick Road, Lapworth
★ *The Old Fourpenny Shop,* 27 Crompton Street, Warwick
★ *The Old Smithy,* 1 Green Lane, Church Lawford
★ *Raglan Arms,* 50 Dunchurch Road, Rugby
★ *The Rose & Crown,* Ratley
★ *The Three Horseshoes,* 22 Sheep Street, Rugby
★ *The White Swan,* All Saints Square, Bedworth
★ *The White Swan,* 100 High Street, Henley-in-Arden
★ *Wyandotte Inn,* Park Road, Kenilworth

THE BREWERIES

BATHAMS LTD

*The Delph Brewery, Delph Road, Brierley Hill
DY5 2TN*
☎ *(01384) 77229*

MILD ALE 3.5% ABV
BEST BITTER 4.3% ABV
Inconsistent now, but a classic when right.
Plus seasonal beers.

THE BEOWULF BREWING CO.

*Waterloo Buildings, 14 Waterloo Road, Yardley,
Birmingham B25 8JR*
☎ *(0121) 706 4116*

NOBLE BITTER 4.0% ABV
Dry, with powerful bitterness.
WIGLAF 4.3% ABV
Golden and malty with strong hoppy flavours.
SWORDSMAN 4.5% ABV
Pale, refreshing and fruity.
HEROES BITTER 4.7% ABV
Golden and hoppy with some sweetness.
MERCIAN SHINE 5.0% ABV
Pale and hoppy with dry finish.
Plus seasonal brews.

CANUK BREWING CO.

12 St James Avenue, Rowley Regis B65 8AH
☎ *(0121) 559 5863*

SPRING STREET 3.8% ABV
Very pale, hoppy and refreshing.
ST JAMES 4.2% ABV
Full-bodied and hoppy.
MICK'S TICK 5.0% ABV
Powerful chocolate malt flavour.

ENVILLE ALES

*Enville Brewery, Cox Green, Enville, Stourbridge
DY7 5LG*
☎ *(01384) 873728*

CHAINMAKER MILD 3.6% ABV
Dark, with some sweetness and smooth malty finish.
BEST BITTER 3.8% ABV
Bitter, well-balanced with good hoppiness.
SIMPKISS BITTER 3.8% ABV
Gold-coloured, quenching and well-hopped.
NAILMAKER MILD 4.0% ABV
Dark and sweeter with dry finish.
CZECHMATE SAAZ 4.2% ABV
Dry and fruity in the Czechoslovakian style.
WHITE 4.2% ABV
A clear, refreshing wheat beer.
ALE 4.5% ABV
Pale yellow, honeyed sweetness and hoppy finish.
PORTER 4.5% ABV
Dark, complex roast malt and fruit, and dry finish.
GINGER BEER 4.6% ABV
Excellent summer brew, delicate ginger flavour.
PHOENIX IPA 4.8% ABV
Superb IPA using new Phoenix hop variety.
GOTHIC ALE 5.2% ABV
Black and rich, with honey flavours.
Plus occasional brews.

HIGHGATE & WALSALL BREWING CO. LTD
Sandymount Road, Walsall WS1 3AP
☎ *(01922) 644453*

 DARK MILD 3.2% ABV
FOX'S NOB 3.6% ABV
BITTER 3.7% ABV
SADDLERS BEST BITTER 4.0% ABV
BREACALIS 4.3% ABV
BLACK PIG 4.4% ABV
Plus seasonal brews.

HOLDEN'S BREWERY
PO Box 20, George Street, Woodsetton, Dudley DY1 4LN
☎ *(01902) 880051*

 MILD 3.6% ABV
Malty and well-balanced.
BITTER 3.9% ABV
Gold-coloured, quenching session beer.
XB 4.1% ABV
Refreshing and hoppy with some sweetness.
SPECIAL 5.1% ABV
Golden, balanced and far too easy to drink.

THE WOLVERHAMPTON & DUDLEY BREWERIES PLC
PO Box 26, Park Brewery, Bath Road, Wolverhampton WV1 4NY
☎ *(01902) 711811*

HANSON'S MILD 3.3% ABV
Maltiness throughout.
BANKS'S MILD 3.5% ABV
Quenching, hoppy mild.
BANKS'S BITTER 3.8% ABV
Hoppy, with a good combination of flavours.

THE PUBS

ALLESLEY

Rainbow Inn and Brewery
73 Birmingham Road, Allesley Village, Coventry CV5 9GT
☎ *(01203) 402888*

Piddlebrook, Belcher's Wood, Firecracker and Sley Alle brewed and served on the premises plus at least two guest beers.

B rewing started in October 1994 providing ale only for the pub and a few beer festivals. Production at the two-barrel plant takes place twice a week. An unpretentious pub in a village location. Grade II listed building dating from around 1650. Bar and restaurant food served at lunchtime and evenings. Parking, garden. Children allowed. Just off the main A45 at Allesley.

PIDDLEBROOK 3.8% ABV
BELCHER'S WOOD 4.2% ABV
SLEY ALLE 4.8% ABV
FIRECRACKER 4.8% ABV
11am–11pm.

AMBLECOTE

The Maverick
Brettell Lane, Amblecote, Stourbridge DY8 4BA
☎ *(01384) 824099* Mark Boxley

A freehouse with Banks's Bitter and Mild always available plus one guest pump perhaps serving Enville Ale or a Kimberley brew.

A town pub with an American Western theme. One bar, beer garden. Bar snacks and burgers available all day. Children allowed.

All day, every day.

BIRMINGHAM

The Anchor
308 Bradford Street, Birmingham B5 6ET
☎ *(0121) 622 4516* Dean Passell

A freehouse with a good selection of real ales. Four or five available during the week and up to eight at weekends. Favourites include RCH Pitchfork, Exmoor Gold and ales from Daleside, Church End and Wye Valley. Two beer festivals held each year.

S ituated outside the city centre, a well-preserved three-bar pub. Food available at lunchtime and evenings. No children.

11am–11pm (10.30pm Sun).

The Old Fox
54 Hurst Street, Birmingham B5 4TD
☎ *(0121) 622 5080* Pat Murray

Marston's Pedigree and Morland Old Speckled Hen always available plus two guests, changed twice-weekly, such as Wychwood The Dog's Bollocks, Trash and Tackle or Burton Bridge brews.

A n eighteenth-century town freehouse with stained-glass windows, situated in a modern area near the Hippodrome. Food available 12–8pm daily in a separate dining area. Outside seating. No children.

11.30am–11pm (10.30pm Sun).

BORDESLEY GREEN

The Tipsy Gent
157 Cherrywood Road, Bordesley Green, Birmingham B9 4XE
☎ *(0121) 772 1858* Paul and Jackie Rackam

A freehouse with Fuller's London Pride among its permanent features, plus one guest, such as Exmoor Gold, changed weekly. Smaller and independent brewers favoured.

A traditional one-bar town pub with stone floors and open fires. Food available Mon–Fri lunchtimes only. Beer garden. No children.

11am–11pm (10.30pm Sun).

The Bull & Bladder

10 Delph Road, Brierley Hill DY5 2TN
☎ *(01384) 78293* Mr Wood

 Bathams Mild, Best and XXX always available.

A lso known as The Vine, this is the brewery tap for Bathams, which is situated behind. A multi-roomed pub with open fires. Bar food available at lunchtime. Car park, garden, children's room.

 12–11pm Mon–Sat; 12–4pm and 7–10.30pm Sun.

The Nursery Tavern

38–9 Lord Street, Chapelfields, Coventry CV5 8DA
☎ *(01203) 674530* Harry Minton

Four guest ales usually featured from breweries such as Church End, Fat God's, Wolf, RCH and Hampshire.

A small, 150-year-old, village-style pub in a town location. Beams, wooden floors. Bar snacks available Mon–Fri; breakfasts Sat–Sun and Sunday lunches. Children allowed in the back room and garden.

11am–11pm Mon–Sat; 12–10.30pm Sun.

The Old Windmill

22 Spon Street, Coventry CV1 3BA
☎ *(01203) 252183* Lynn Ingram

Marston's Pedigree, Morland Old Speckled Hen and a Banks's ale always available, plus two guests such as Badger Tanglefoot or beers from breweries such as Church End, Orkney, Buchanan and other micros.

A Grade II listed Tudor building situtated in the town centre. The oldest pub in Coventry with beams, stone floor, old range in one bar and inglenook fireplaces. Food available at lunchtime in non-smoking restaurant. Children allowed in the restaurant only.

11am–11pm Mon–Sat; 12–3pm and 7–10.30pm Sun.

The Waterfall

132 Waterfall Lane, Cradley Heath B64 6RG
☎ *(0121) 561 3499* Marie Smith

Nine beers always available including brews from Bathams. Also Enville Ale, Holden's Special, Hook Norton Old Hooky and Marston's Pedigree. Plus guests such as Oak Double Dagger, Titanic White Star, RCH Fiery Liz and Gibbs Mew Bishop's Tipple plus something from Burton Bridge and Wood.

A traditional Black Country pub. Bar food available at lunchtime and evenings. Car park, garden with waterfall, children's room. Also function room for party and quiz nights, etc. Up the hill from the old Hill Station.

12–3pm and 5–11pm Mon–Thurs; all day Fri–Sun.

Little Barrell

68 High Street, Dudley DY1 1PY
☎ *(01384) 235535* Mrs Day

Wadworth 6X always available plus three guests such as Morland Old Speckled Hen, Holden's XB, Shepherd Neame Bishop's Finger, Wychwood Hobgoblin or King & Barnes brews. Seasonal and celebration beers as available.

A small, traditional town pub with wooden floors. One bar, dining area. Food available at lunchtime only. Children allowed if eating.

11am–11pm (10.30pm Sun).

The Waggon & Horses

21 Stourbridge Road, Halesowen B63 3TU
☎ *(0121) 602 2082* Peter Rawson

Bathams Bitter, Enville Simpkiss and Enville Ale, Everards and Waggoners brews always available plus up to ten guests (800 per year) from far and wide.

A West Midlands Victorian boozer. Bar food available at lunchtime. Car parking. Children allowed.

12–11pm (10.30pm Sun).

HIGHGATE

The Lamp Tavern

*157 Barford Street, Highgate, Birmingham
B5 6AH*
☎ *(0121) 622 2599* Eddie Fitzpatrick

A freehouse with Stanway Stanney Bitter, Everards Tiger, Marston's Pedigree and Church End Grave Digger always available, plus one guest pump serving beers such as Shepherd Neame Bishop's Finger or Church End What the Fox's Hat.

A small, friendly village pub situated near the town. Bar snacks available at lunchtime. No children.

All day Mon–Sat; 12–3pm and 8–10.30pm Sun.

HOCKLEY

The Church Inn

*22 Great Hampton Street, Hockley, Birmingham
B18 6AQ*
☎ *(0121) 515 1851* Mr Wilkes

Ansells Mild, Morland Old Speckled Hen and a Bathams ale always available, plus one guest.

A Victorian town pub with one servery and two adjoining rooms. Food available at lunchtime and evenings. Children allowed.

11.45am–11pm Mon–Fri; 11.45am–3pm and 6–11pm Sat; closed Sun.

LOWER GORNAL

The Fountain Real Ale Bar

8 Temple Street, Lower Gornal
☎ *(01384) 834888* Alan Brookes

Badger Tanglefoot, Burton Bridge Stairway to Heaven, Everards Tiger, Shepherd Neame Bishop's Finger and Adnams Broadside always available plus four guest beers such as Kelham Island Pale Rider, Hop Back Summer Lightning, Berrow Topsy Turvy, Moorhouse Pendle Witches Brew, Fuller's ESB, RCH Pitchfork, etc. Beer festivals four times a year.

A real ale bar with a warm and pleasant atmosphere. Bar food served at lunchtime and evenings. Parking, garden and function room. Children allowed.

7–11pm Mon–Fri; 12–3pm and 7–11pm Sat; 12–3pm and 7–10.30pm Sun.

OLDBURY

The Waggon & Horses

Church Street, Oldbury B69 3AD
☎ *(0121) 552 5467* Ian Stuart

Enville Ale, Marston's Pedigree, Everards Old Original and Tiger plus something from Holden's always available. Also a traditional mild. Many guests (200 per year) including Bateman Yellow Belly, Timothy Taylor Landlord, Berrow Topsy Turvy, Red Cross OBJ, Greene King Abbot Ale, Brains Reverend James Original and many more.

A Victorian, Grade II listed building with tiled walls, copper ceiling and original brewery windows. Bar food available at lunchtime and evenings. Car parking. Children allowed when eating. Function room with capacity for 40 people. At the corner of Market Street and Church Street in Oldbury town centre, next to the library.

12–3pm and 5–11pm Mon–Thur; 11am–11pm Fri; 11am–3pm and 6–11pm Sat; 12–3pm and 8–10.30pm Sun.

PENSNETT

The Holy Bush Inn

Bell Street, Pensnett, Brierley Hill DY5 4HJ
☎ *(01384) 78711* Ian Trafford

Batham Mild and Bitter always available.

A small two-bar pub with beer garden. No food. Children allowed.

All day, every day.

SEDGLEY

The Beacon Hotel

129 Bilston Street, Sedgley, Dudley DY3 1JE
☎ *(01902) 883380*

Sarah Hughes Pale Amber, Suprise and Dark Ruby always available, plus Snowflake from Nov to Feb. Various guest beers served on a daily basis.

The Sarah Hughes Brewery, which operates on the premises, reopened in 1987 after a 30-year closure, and now supplies around 500 pubs with guests beers. Visitors welcome for brewery tours, but booking is essential.

M&V MILD 3.3% ABV
UPNORTON 3.6% ABV
PALE AMBER 4.0% ABV
SEDGLEY SURPRISE 5.0% ABV
DARK RUBY MILD 6.0% ABV
SNOWFLAKE 8.0% ABV

12–2.30pm and 5.30–10.45pm Mon–Thur; 12–2.30pm and 5.30–11pm Fri; 11.30–3pm and 6–11pm Sat; 12–3pm and 7–10.30pm Sun.

The Four Crosses Inn

1 Green Lane, Shelfield, Walsall WS4 1RN
☎ *(01922) 682518* Mr Holt

A freehouse with Marston's Pedigree and Banks's Bitter and Mild always available, plus two weekly changing guests from smaller and micro-breweries such as Burton Bridge and Ash Vine.

A traditional two-bar pub on the outskirts of town. Games in the bar, beer garden. No food. No children.

OPEN *All day Mon–Sat; 12–3pm and 7–10.30pm Sun.*

The Griffin Inn

Church Road, Shustoke B46 2LP
☎ *(01675) 481567*

At least six Church End brews plus Marston's Pedigree always available. Also 200 guest beers per year.

A large country freehouse with oak beams and open fires set in large grounds. The Church End brewery is next to the pub. Bar food is available at lunchtime (except Sunday). Car park, garden. Children allowed in the conservatory and grounds. Take the B4114 from Coleshill.

GRAVEDIGGERS 3.8% ABV
WHAT THE FOX'S HAT 4.2% ABV
WHEAT A BIX 4.2% ABV
M-REG GTI 4.4% ABV
PEWS PORTER 4.5% ABV
OLD PAL 5.5% ABV

OPEN *12–3pm and 7–11pm Mon–Sat; 12–2.30pm and 7–10.30pm Sun.*

The Bear Tavern

500 Bearwood Road, Smethwick B66 4BX
☎ *(0121) 429 1184* Brendan Gilbride

Marston's Pedigree and Morland Old Speckled Hen always available plus five weekly changing guests. Regulars include Hardys and Hansons Kimberley Best and Greene King Abbot.

A locals' pub built after the Second World War, although there has been a pub on the site for 300 years. A mix of the traditional and modern. Four bars, fireplace, beer garden, disabled access. Food available all day. Children allowed.

OPEN *All day, every day.*

The Harvester

Tanhouse Farm Road, Solihull B92 9EY
☎ *(0121) 742 0770* Mrs Harwood

A freehouse with Charles Wells Bombardier always available plus two guests such as Morland Old Speckled Hen. Beers served are always between 3.7% and 5% ABV.

A modern community pub with two bars, pool room, dining area in lounge, garden. Food available at lunchtime and evenings. Children allowed.

OPEN *12–2.30pm and 6–11pm Mon–Thurs; 12–3pm and 6–11pm Fri–Sat; 12–3pm and 7–10.30pm Sun.*

The Robin Hood Inn

196 Collis Street, Amblecote, Stourbridge DY8 4EQ
☎ *(01384) 821120*

Bathams Bitter, Enville Ale, Everards Beacon, Tiger and Old Original always available plus three guests (120 per year) such as Timothy Taylor Landlord, Badger Tanglefoot, Shepherd Neame Bishop's Finger, Fuller's ESB, Exmoor Gold and Hook Norton Old Hooky.

A family-run, cosy Black Country freehouse. Good beer garden. Non-smoking dining room. Bar and restaurant food available. Parking. Children allowed in the pub when eating. Accommodation.

OPEN *12–3pm and 6–11pm Mon–Sat; 12–10.30pm Sun.*

The Port 'n' Ale

178 Horseley Heath, Great Bridge, Tipton DY4 7DS
☎ *(0121) 557 7249* Kevin Taylor

A freehouse with Greene King Abbot Ale, Banks's Original, Exmoor Gold and Timothy Taylor Landlord always available, plus two guest pumps regularly serving RCH beers such as Pitchfork or something like Burton Bridge Summer Ale, Badger Tanglefoot or Cotleigh Barn Ale. Some 64 different ales were served during the period March to July 1999.

A Victorian pub situated out of town. Bar, lounge and beer garden. No food. Children allowed in the garden only. Just down the road from Dudley Port railway station.

OPEN *12–3pm and 5–11pm Mon–Fri; 12–11pm Sat; 12–4.30pm and 7–10.30pm Sun.*

The Old Crown

56 Sandwell Road, West Bromwich B70 8TG
☎ *(0121) 525 4600* Mr Patel

A freehouse with three hand pumps serving beers such as Fuller's London Pride, Young's Special and something from Church End, Somerset, Cottage and Enville Ales.

An open-plan town pub. Food available at lunchtime and evenings in a non-smoking area. Children allowed in the non-smoking area only.

11am–4pm and 5–11pm (6–11pm Sat).

The Vine

152 Roebuck Street, West Bromwich B70 6RD
☎ *(0121) 553 2866* Mr Patel

A freehouse with two real ales always available. Breweries featured include Wood, Lichfield and Wye Valley, among others.

A traditional two-bar pub with beams and gardens. Children's play area. Food available at lunchtime and evenings – barbecues and currys are specialities. Children allowed. Situtated out of town.

11.30am–2.30pm and 5–11pm Mon–Thurs; all day Fri–Sun.

The Brewer's Droop

44 Wolverhampton Street, Willenhall WV13 2PS
☎ *(01902) 607827* Ruth Faulkner

A freehouse with Bathams Bitter and Charles Wells Eagle IPA always available, plus a range of guests changing twice-weekly, such as Holden's Special and Badger Tanglefoot.

A traditional town-centre pub decorated with bric-a-brac, particularly relating to motorbikes. Two bars, pool table. Food available at lunchtime and evenings. Children allowed until 9pm.

12–3.30pm and 6–11pm Mon–Thurs; all day Fri–Sat; 12–4pm and 7–10.30pm Sun.

The Falcon Inn

Gomer Street West, Willenhall WV13 2NR
☎ *(01902) 633378* Mick Taylor

A freehouse with Hyde's Bitter and Mild, Banks's Mild, Greene King Abbot and Timothy Taylor Landlord, plus a Porter or a Stout always available. Also a wide range of guests, for example, Red Cross OBJ, Freeminer Celestial Steam Gale, Bunces Danish Dynamite, RCH Pitchfork, Fuller's ESB, Archers Golden, Ringwood 4X, Freeminer Deep Shaft Stout and Slaughter Porter or beers from Wye Valley, Hop Back or Burton Bridge. Beers changed at least every three days, but the record is 1hr 50mins!

A 1930s back-street boozer with stone floors, beams and vines. Bar and lounge, non-smoking area, beer garden. Children allowed until 8.30pm.

12–11pm (10.30pm Sun).

Tap & Spile

35 Princess Street, Wolverhampton WV1 1HD
☎ *(01902) 713319* Jason Caskerino (Manager)

Mansfield Highgate Dark Mild and Tap & Spile Premium always available, plus up to six guest ales of which Charles Wells Bombardier, Wychwood Hobgoblin, Badger Tanglefoot and Fuller's London Pride are regular features.

A locals' town pub with wooden floors, open fire, one main bar and snug rooms. Food available 12–4pm. Beer garden. Children allowed until 7pm.

All day Mon–Sat; 12–3pm and 7–10.30pm Sun.

YOU TELL US

★ *Biggin Hall Hotel*, Binley Road, Copsewood, Coventry
★ *The Black Eagle*, 16 Factory Road, Hockley, Birmingham
★ *The Black Horse*, 52 Delph Road, Brierley Hill
★ *The Brown Lion*, 33 Wednesbury Road, Pleck, Walsall
★ *The Bull's Head*, Barston Lane, Barston, Solihull
★ *The Chindit Inn*, 113 Merridale Road, Wolverhampton
★ *The Clarendon Hotel*, 38 Chapel Ash, Wolverhampton
★ *The Dry Dock*, 21 Windmill End, Netherton
★ *The Exchange Vaults*, Cheapside, Wolverhampton
★ *The Figure of Eight*, 236–9 Broad Street, Birmingham
★ *The Great Western*, Sun Street, Wolverhampton
★ *Hogshead*, Bordeaux House, Foster Street, Stourbridge
★ *King Edward VII*, 88 Stourbridge Road, Hawne, Halesowen
★ *The Moon Under Water*, Lichfield Street, Wolverhampton

★ *The Newhampton Inn*, Riches Street, Wolverhampton
★ *The Old Blue Ball*, 19 Hall End Road, Wednesbury
★ *The Park Inn*, George Street, Woodsetton, Dudley
★ *The Pavilions*, 229 Alcester Road South, Kings Heath, Birmingham
★ *The Princess*, 115 Bridgnorth Road, Wollaston
★ *The Queen's Tavern*, 23 Essex Street, Birmingham
★ *The Red Hen*, 78 St Anne's Road, Cradley Heath
★ *The Rising Sun*, 116 Horseley Road, Tipton
★ *The Spread Eagle*, Birmingham New Road, Bilston
★ *The Starving Rascal*, Brettell Lane, Amblecote, Stourbridge
★ *The Swan Inn*, 10 Brewell Lane, Amblecote
★ *The Swan Inn*, Wolverhampton Road, Pelsall, Walsall
★ *Tap & Spile*, 33 High Street, Brierley Hill
★ *Tap & Spile*, John Street, Walsall
★ *The Trumpet*, 58 High Street, Bilston
★ *Unicorn*, 145 Bridgnorth Road, Wollaston, Stourbridge
★ *The Vine Inn*, Bell Street, Wednesbury

Places Featured:

Bradford-on-Avon
Charlton
Chippenham
Corsham
Devizes
East Knoyle
Ebbesbourn Wake
Enford
Figheldean
Ford
Hamptworth
Hullavington

Lacock
Little Cheverell
Lower Chicksgrove
Malmesbury
Pewsey
Quemerford
Rowde
Salisbury
Shrewton
Stapleford
Swindon
Wroughton

THE BREWERIES

ARCHERS ALES LTD

Penzance Drive, Swindon SN5 7JL
☎ *(01793) 879929*

 VILLAGE BITTER 3.5% ABV
Malty, with hop and fruit notes.
BEST BITTER 4.0% ABV
Bitter with some sweetness.
BLACK JACK PORTER 4.6% ABV
Dark, roasted malt, winter brew.
GOLDEN BITTER 4.7% ABV
Superb balance, a classic beer.
Plus seasonal brews.

ARKELLS BREWERY LTD

Kingsdown Brewery, Swindon SN2 6RU
☎ *(01793) 823026*

 2B 3.2% ABV
Light and quenching with good bitter
hoppiness.
3B 4.0% ABV
Amber, balanced and hoppy.
KINGSDOWN ALE 5.0% ABV
Smooth, rounded and flavour-packed.
Plus seasonal brews.

THE HOP BACK BREWERY PLC

*Unit 22–4, Batten Road, Downton Business
Centre, Downton, Salisbury SP5 3HU*
☎ *(01725) 510986*

 GFB 3.5% ABV
Smooth and full-flavoured for gravity.
BEST BITTER 4.0% ABV
Well-balanced, easy-drinking.
ENTIRE STOUT 4.5% ABV
Powerful roast malt flavour.
SUMMER LIGHTNING 5.0% ABV
Superb, pale and quenching with good hoppiness.
THUNDERSTORM 5.0% ABV
Mellow wheat beer.
Plus seasonal and occasional brews.

MOLE'S BREWERY

5 Merlin Way, Bowerhill, Melksham SN12 6TJ
☎ *(01225) 708842*

 TAP 3.5% ABV
Malty with clean, balancing bitterness.
BEST BITTER 4.0% ABV
Golden with quenching, hoppy finish.
LANDLORD'S CHOICE 4.5% ABV
Darker, with hops, fruit and malty finish.
BREW 97 5.0% ABV
Malty with fruity sweetness and good hoppiness.
Plus seasonal brews.

STONEHENGE ALES (BUNCES BREWERY)

*The Old Mill, Mill Road, Netheravon, Salisbury
SP4 9QB*
☎ *(01980) 670631*

 BENCHMARK 3.5% ABV
Malt flavours with good balancing hoppy
bitterness.
PIGSWILL 4.0% ABV
Mellow and hoppy.
BEST BITTER 4.1% ABV
Refreshing malt and fruitiness with bitter finish.
HEEL STONE 4.3% ABV
Quenching fruity flavour.
DANISH DYNAMITE 5.0% ABV
Golden and far too easy to drink!
OLD SMOKEY 5.0% ABV
Rich and smoky.
Plus seasonal brews.

TISBURY BREWERY LTD

Church Street, Tisbury SP3 6NH
☎ *(01747) 870986*

STONEHENGE BITTER 3.8% ABV
Full-flavoured session bitter.
ARCHIBALD BECKETT 4.3% ABV
Superb balance
NADDERJACK 4.3% ABV
Gold-coloured, with bittersweet flavour.
OLD WARDOUR 4.8% ABV
Dark with rich roast malt and fruit flavour.
Plus seasonal brews.

USHERS OF TROWBRIGE PLC

Director's House, 68 Fore Street, Trowbridge BA14 8HQ
☎ *(01225) 774289*

BEST BITTER 3.8% ABV
Bright and smooth with hops and barley flavour.
FOUNDERS ALE 4.5% ABV
Hoppy, fruit flavour.

WADWORTH & CO. LTD

Northgate Brewery, Devizes SN10 1JW
☎ *(01380) 723361*

HENRY'S ORIGINAL IPA 3.8% ABV
Well-balanced and smooth, with malt throughout.
SUMMERSAULT 4.0% ABV
Quenching, lager-style beer.
6X 4.3% ABV
Rich, with malt flavours.
FARMERS GLORY 4.5% ABV
Deep-coloured and smooth.

THE PUBS

BRADFORD-ON-AVON

The Beehive

Trowbridge Road, Bradford-on-Avon BA15 1UA
☎ *(01225) 863620* Mrs C Crocker

A freehouse with Butcombe ales always available plus five guests such as Fuller's London Pride, Burton Bridge Draught Excluder, Dobbins' Drop, Blackpool Bitter and Stairway to Heaven (aka Celestial Gateway).

A pub situated next to the home of Sir John Betjeman, on the side of the canal. One bar, no music, open fires. Beer garden features a boules pitch and an antique pump dating from 1880. Also open for coffee. Food available every lunchtime and Mon–Sat evening. Children allowed.

12–2.30pm and 7–11pm (10.30pm Sun).

CHARLTON

The Horse & Groom

The Street, Charlton, Malmesbury SN16 9DL
☎ *(01666) 823904* Nicola King

Archers Village and Wadworth 6X always available, plus three guests such as Uley Old Spot, Smiles Best, Abbey Bell Ringer or Ridleys Spectacular.

A traditional country village pub with beams, fires and wooden floors. Two bars, beer garden, accommodation. Food served at lunchtime and evenings in a separate dining area. Well-behaved children allowed.

12–3pm and 7–11pm Mon–Fri; all day Sat–Sun.

CHIPPENHAM

The Peterborough Arms

Dauntsey Lock, Chippenham SN15 4HD
☎ *(01249) 890409* Nicky Brown

Wadworth 6X and Archers Best always available plus up to six guests such as Smiles Best, Hook Norton Best, Cottage Wheeltappers or something from Mole's. Ales changed weekly in the summer, twice-monthly in the winter.

A two-bar country freehouse with beams, fires, non-smoking dining area and large beer garden. Food available lunchtimes and evenings. Children and dogs welcome.

11am–2.30pm and 6–11pm Mon–Fri; all day Sat–Sun and bank holidays.

CORSHAM

The Two Pigs

38 Pickwick, Corsham SN13 0HY
☎ *(01249) 712515* Dickie and Ann Doyle

Stonehenge Pigswill always available plus three guests (200 per year) including Church End brews, Hop Back Summer Lightning, Greene King Abbot and Wood Shropshire Lad. Guest ales rotating constantly, two in ABV range 4.1–4.6% and one at 5%+ ABV.

A traditional wood-panelled pub with stone floors. No food. Parking nearby. Covered courtyard, No children. Live blues music on Monday. On the A4 between Chippenham and Bath.

7–11pm Mon–Sat; 12–2.30pm and 7–10.30pm Sun.

The British Lion

9 Estcourt Street, Devizes SN10 1LQ
☎ *(01380) 720665* Michael Dearing

A rotating session bitter always available at £1.50 a pint, such as Wychwood Shires, Tisbury Best Bitter, Ash Vine Bitter, Oakhill Bitter plus two guests (about 100 a year) from Ash Vine, Abbey Ales, Bath Ales, Butts, Cottage, Goff's, Hop Back, Mole's, Moor, Oakhill, RCH, Stonehenge (Bunces), Wychwood, Wye Valley, York. Also winter specials and a real cider.

A straightforward locals' community pub for all ages. Car park and garden. On the main Swindon (A361) road, opposite The Green.

11am–11pm Mon–Sat; all day Sun.

The Fox & Hounds

The Green, East Knoyle, Salisbury SP3 6BN
☎ *(01747) 830573* Andrew Knight

A freehouse with Smiles Golden Brew, Ringwood Fortyniner and Wadworth 6X always available, plus a minimum of three guests from breweries such as Church End or Hampshire. Ales from smaller breweries stocked whenever possible.

A country village pub with beams, slate floors, conservatory and garden. Food available at lunchtime and evenings. Children allowed in the conservatory and garden.

11am–2.30pm and 6–11pm (10.30pm Sun).

The Horseshoe Inn

Ebbesbourne Wake SP5 5JF
☎ *(01722) 780474*

Wadworth 6X, Ringwood Best and Adnams Broadside always available straight from the barrel, plus a guest (12 per year) perhaps from Bateman, Poole, Felinfoel, Fuller's, Tisbury or Hop Back breweries.

A remote, old-fashioned unspoilt pub hung with old tools of a bygone age. Bar and restaurant food available lunchtime and evenings (except Monday). Car park, garden, accommodation. Children are allowed if eating. From Salisbury (A354), turn right to Bishopston, Broadchalke then on to Ebbesbourne Wake.

11.30am–3pm and 6.30–11pm.

The Swan

Longstreet, Enford, Nr Pewsey SN9 6DD
☎ *(01980) 670338* Bob Bone

A good choice of real ales available, changing regularly but usually including brews from Smiles, Fuller's, Ringwood and Shepherd Neame.

Old thatched and beamed pub with open fires. Bar food available at lunchtime and evenings. Car park, garden, restaurant. Easy to find.

12–3pm and 7–11pm Mon–Sat; 12–4pm and 7–10.30pm Sun.

The Wheatsheaf

High Street, Figheldean, Nr Salisbury SP4 8JJ
☎ *(01980) 670357*

Hop Back brews always available plus a couple of guests (20 per year) including ales from Titanic, Eldridge Pope, Young's, Exmoor, Hook Norton and Wychwood.

A single-bar pub with open fire and alcoves. Family room, garden. Bar food available lunchtime and evening (not Monday). Off the A345, north of Amesbury.

12–3pm and 7–11pm (closed Monday lunchtime).

The White Hart

Ford, Nr Chippenham SN14 8RP
☎ *(01249) 782213* Peter and Kate Miller

Up to 12 beers at any one time. Smiles Best, Marston's Pedigree, Wadworth 6X and Fuller's London Pride always available. Four guests may include Hook Norton Best, Marston's Owd Rodger, Shepherd Neame Spitfire, Black Sheep Best, Morland Old Speckled Hen and Uley brews.

Old coaching inn off the A420 on the edge of a river. One main bar, restaurant and buttery. Bar food available at lunchtime. Restaurant open at lunchtime and evenings. Car parks, river terrace, accommodation. Children allowed in the buttery.

11am–2.30pm and 5–11pm Mon–Sat; usual hours Sun.

HAMPTWORTH

The Cuckoo Inn

*Hamptworth Road, Hamptworth, Nr Salisbury
SP5 2DU*
☎ *(01794) 390302* Ray Proudley

 Wadworth 6X, Badger Tanglefoot, Cheriton Pots Ale, Hop Back Summer Lightning and GFB always available plus three guest beers from a long list including brews from Bunces, Adnams, Ringwood, Hampshire, Shepherd Neame and Cottage breweries.

A 300-year-old thatched pub in the New Forest. Bar food available at lunchtime and evenings. Car park, garden, play area, petanque area, children's room. Just off the A36 near Hamptworth golf course.

OPEN *11.30am–2.30pm and 6–11pm Mon–Fri;
11.30am–11pm Sat; 12–3pm and
7–10.30pm Sun.*

HULLAVINGTON

The Queen's Head

*23 The Street, Hullavington, Chippenham
SN14 6DP*
☎ *(01666) 837221* Yvette Hicks

 A freehouse with Archers Village and Golden always available, plus one guest changing every fortnight. Wadworth 6X is a favourite, as are beers from the Berkeley Brewing Group.

A n old country-style pub with two open coal fires, beams and pine furniture. No food at present, but a restaurant is planned. Accommodation. Children allowed.

OPEN *12–2pm and 7–11pm Mon–Fri; 12–3pm
and 7–11pm Sat; 12–3pm and 7–10.30pm
Sun.*

LACOCK

The Bell Inn

Bowden Hill, Lacock, Chippenham SN15 2PJ
☎ *(01249) 730308*
Sandra and David Goddard

 Wadworth 6X and Smiles Best always available, plus three monthly changing guests from breweries such as Wickwar, Bateman, Adnams and Tisbury.

A traditional rural freehouse built in converted cottages. One bar, dining area, beer garden, accommodation. Food available lunchtimes and evenings. Children allowed.

OPEN *11am–2.30pm and 6–11pm in summer;
11am–2.30pm and 7–11pm in winter.*

The Rising Sun

*32 Bowden Hill, Lacock, Nr Chippenham
SN15 2PP*
☎ *(01249) 730363* Mr and Mrs Maxwell

 Five beers always available including Mole's Tap, Best, Landlord's Choice, Brew 97 and Black Rat. Guests include Crouch Vale Willie Warmer and Wadworth 6X.

A Cotswold stone pub with flagstone floors and open fires. Bar food available at lunchtime and evenings. Car park, garden. Children allowed. Turn into village, then go up Bowden Hill.

OPEN *11am–3pm and 6–11pm Mon–Sat;
12–3pm and 7–10.30pm Sun.*

LITTLE CHEVERELL

The Owl

Low Road, Little Cheverell, Devizes SN10 4JS
☎ *(01380) 812263* Sally Buckle

 A freehouse with Wadworth 6X always available plus three constantly changing guests from independent breweries such as Hop Back, Oak Hill, Ash Vine, Ringwood or Uley.

A country pub with beams and a woodburning stove. One bar, separate dining area. Large streamside beer garden. Food available at lunchtime and evenings. Children allowed.

OPEN *12–2.30pm and 7–11pm Tues–Sat;
12–3pm and 7–10.30pm Sun; closed Mon.*

LOWER CHICKSGROVE

The Compasses Inn

Lower Chicksgrove, Tisbury, Salisbury SP3 6NB
☎ *(01722) 714318* Caren Bold

 A freehouse with Wadworth 6X and Tisbury Stonehenge always available, plus one guest ale.

A beamed pub with open fires and wooden floors situated in a country hamlet. Small dining area, beer garden, accommodation. Food available Tues–Sun lunchtime and Tues–Sat evenings. Well-behaved children allowed.

OPEN *11am–3pm and 6–11pm Tues–Sat;
12–3pm and 6–10.30pm Sun; closed Mon
except bank holidays, but then closed Tues.*

The Smoking Dog

62 High Street, Malmesbury SN16 9AT
☎ *(01666) 825823* Matt Ward

 Wadworth 6X, Archers Best and a house brew called Harry's (brewed by Archers) always available, plus at least three guests. These might be Gibbs Mew Bishop's Finger, Fuller's London Pride or a Young's ale, or seasonal and more obscure ales from smaller breweries. A porter is always available in winter.

A traditional small-town pub with log fires, beams and wooden floor. No music or machines. Food available in an à la carte restaurant, plus bar snacks all day. Beer garden. Children allowed.

🍺 *11.30am–11pm Mon–Sat; 12–10.30pm Sun.*

The Cooper's Arms

37–9 Ball Road, Pewsey SN9 5BL
☎ *(01672) 562495* Mr Dainton

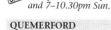 A freehouse with Wadworth 6X and Oakhill Mendip Gold always available, plus two guests from local breweries such as Hop Back, Tisbury, Stonehenge, Ringwood, Cottage or Butts whenever possible.

A thatched country pub in a picturesque area. Bar snacks available. Beer garden. Function room. Live music. Children allowed.

🍺 *12–2pm and 7–11pm Mon–Sat; 12–4pm and 7–10.30pm Sun.*

The Talbot Inn

Quemerford, Calne SN11 0AR
☎ *(01249) 812198* Paul Picken

Wadworth 6X always available plus up to four guests such as Morland Old Speckled Hen, Shepherd Neame Spitfire, Fuller's London Pride, Elgood's Greyhound or Exmoor Heart.

A village pub with a reputation for good food and real ales. One bar, wooden floors, beams, children's play area, large beer garden and car park. Conservatory doubles as dining area. Food available at lunchtime and evenings. Children allowed in the conservatory and garden only.

🍺 *11am–11pm Mon–Sat; 12–10.30pm Sun.*

The George & Dragon

High Street, Rowde, Devizes SN10 2PN
☎ *(01380) 723053* Tim Withers

A freehouse with three hand pumps serving a selection of real ales from local West Country breweries whenever possible, or other smaller and micro-breweries. Breweries regularly featured include Abbey Ales, Tisbury, Ash Vine and Hop Back.

A seventeenth-century village pub with beams, wooden floor and open fires. One bar, dining area and beer garden. Food available Tues–Sat lunchtime and evenings. Children allowed.

🍺 *12–3pm and 7–11pm (10.30pm Sun).*

The Blackbird Inn

30 Churchfields Road, Salisbury SP2 7NW
☎ *(01722) 802828* Mr Leonard

Up to four real ales available. Breweries regularly featured include Hop Back, Stonehenge, Tisbury, Ringwood, Hampshire, Cottage and Isle of Skye. An annual beer festival is held on the last three days of August, with a selection of 12 real ales.

A one-bar pub situated at the back of the railway station. No music or machines. Light snacks at lunchtime, rolls only in the evenings. Children allowed in the back yard only.

🍺 *12–3pm and 5–11pm Mon–Thurs; all day Fri–Sat; 12–6pm Sun (closed Sun pm).*

The Deacon Arms

118 Fisherton Street, Salisbury SP2 7QT
☎ *(01722) 504723* Frank Keay

A freehouse with Hop Back GFB always available plus two guests including, perhaps, Cheriton Best, RCH Pitchfork or Hop Back Summer Lightning.

A community pub with two bars, wooden floors, open fires in winter and air conditioning in summer. Accomodation. No food. Children allowed.

🍺 *5–11pm Mon–Fri; 12–11pm Sat; 12–10.30pm Sun.*

The Star Inn

69 Brown Street, Salisbury SP1 2AS
☎ *(01722) 327137* Mrs Bugler

A freehouse with Wadworth 6X, Fuller's London Pride and Oakhill Triple Crown always available, plus two guests such as Hop Back GFB or Bunces Sign of Spring.

A traditional one-bar town pub on the ring road. Rolls available. Children allowed.

🍺 *11am–11pm (10.30pm Sun).*

Tom Brown's

225 Wilton Road, Salisbury SP2 7JY
☎ *(01722) 335918*

A Goldfinch Brewery tied house with a range of Goldfinch beers rotated on three pumps and always available: Tom Brown's Best, Flashman's Clout, Midnight Blinder and Midnight Sun.

A basic one-bar town pub for real ale drinkers. No food. No children.

OPEN *6–11pm Mon–Fri; 12–3pm and 6–11pm Sat; 12–3pm and 6–10.30pm Sun.*

The Village Freehouse

33 Wilton Road, Salisbury SP2 7EF
☎ *(01722) 329707*

Oakhill Mendip Gold plus Abbey Somerset and Bellringer always available. Also three guests, constantly changing.

A small street-corner pub with a friendly atmosphere. Bar snacks available at lunchtime and evenings. Children allowed. Two minutes from Salisbury railway station.

OPEN *4–11pm Mon; 12–11pm Tues–Sat; 12–5pm and 7–10.30pm Sun.*

The Wig & Quill

1 New Street, Salisbury SP1 2PH
☎ *(01722) 335665* Ken Stanforth

A Wadworth tied house with 6X and IPA, Badger Tanglefoot and a Wadworth seasonal ale always available. Other guests rotated on one hand pump, from independents such as Butcombe, Exmoor, Felinfoel or Charles Wells.

A city-centre pub, a mix of the traditional and the modern. One bar with three separate adjoining areas, open fires and beer garden. Food served at lunchtime only 12–2.30pm. Children allowed.

OPEN *11am–11pm Mon–Sat; 12–3pm and 7–10.30pm Sun.*

The George Inn

London Road, Shrewton, Salisbury SP3 4DH
☎ *(01980) 620341* Tony Cliff

A freehouse with Ushers Best and Wadworth 6X always available plus a choice of two guests. Ringwood Fortyniner and Gales HSB are regular features.

A remote country pub with traditional beams, open fires, one main bar, covered patio area and a 50–60 seater restuarant. Food available at lunchtime and evenings. Children allowed.

OPEN *11.30am–3pm and 6–11pm Mon–Fri; all day Sat–Sun in summer, regular hours in winter.*

The Pelican Inn

Warminster Road, Stapleford, Salisbury SP3 4LT
☎ *(01722) 790241* Mr Pitcher

Ringwood Best, Otter Ale and Greene King Abbot always available, plus one guest. Perhaps Fuller's London Pride or something from a small local or other independent brewer.

A country freehouse with inglenooks, open fireplaces, two linked bars, one large and one small, dining area and beer garden. Food available at lunchtime and evenings. Children allowed in the dining area only.

OPEN *11am–2.30pm and 6–11pm (10.30pm Sun).*

The Famous Ale House

146 Redclife Street, Swindon SN2 2BY
☎ *(01793) 522503* Mr Omara

Archers Village and Golden always available plus a choice of two guest ales such as Morland Old Speckled Hen or Golden Promise. New beers on once a week.

An olde-worlde locals' community pub. One bar, restaurant and garden. Food served 12–2.30pm and 6.30–9pm daily. Children allowed in the garden only.

OPEN *11am–11pm (10.30pm Sun).*

The Glue Pot Inn

5 Emlyn Square, Swindon SN1 5BP
☎ *(01793) 523935* Mr Reid

Archers Village, Golden and Best always available, plus one guest such as Fuller's ESB or London Pride, or ales from local or Scottish breweries.

A town pub in the centre of Swindon, located by the railway museum. One small bar, patio. Bar snacks available at lunchtime only. No children.

OPEN *All day, every day.*

The Savoy

38 Regent Street, Swindon SN1 1JL
☎ *(01793) 533970* Val Docherty

A Wetherspoon's pub. Archers Golden, Best and Village always available plus three guest ales. Previous favourites have included Ringwood Old Thumper and Hop Back Summer Lightning but the aim is not to repeat the beers if possible. Beer festivals held every March and October, with 50 real ales at each.

A one-bar town-centre pub. No music or games. Food available all day in non-smoking dining area. Children allowed.

OPEN *10.30am–11pm Mon–Sat; 12–10.30pm Sun.*

WROUGHTON

The Carter's Rest
High Street, Wroughton SN4 9JU
☎ *(01793) 812288* Mrs Woods

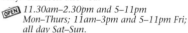 Archers Village, Best and Golden always available, plus four guests changing weekly from breweries such as Tom Hoskins, Smiles and Ash Vine.

A country village pub with two bars and a patio area. Food available at lunchtime only. Children allowed.

11.30am–2.30pm and 5–11pm Mon–Thurs; 11am–3pm and 5–11pm Fri; all day Sat–Sun.

★ *Angel,* 3 Church Street, Westbury
★ *Black Horse,* Wroughton
★ *Bruce Arms,* Easton Royal
★ *Carriers Arms,* Highworth Road, Stockton, South Marston
★ *Check Inn,* Woodland View, Wroughton
★ *Cross Keys,* 65 Bradenstoke, Bradenstoke
★ *Cross Keys,* Lyes Green, Corsley, Warminster
★ *Devizes Inn,* 55 Devizes Road, Salisbury
★ *Dove Inn,* Corton
★ *Dumb Post,* Dumb Post Hill, Bremhill, Calne
★ *George's Railway,* 5 Union Road, Chippenham
★ *Goddard Arms,* Wood Street, Clyffe Pypard
★ *Golden Fleece,* Folly Lane, Shaw, Melksham
★ *Jolly Huntsman,* High Street, Kington St Michael
★ *Kicking Donkey,* Brokerswood
★ *Nettlebridge Inn,* Nettlebridge
★ *New Inn,* Winterbourne Monkton
★ *Old Nick,* 61 Station Road, Wootton Bassett
★ *Old Spotted Cow,* Marston Meysey
★ *Prince Leopold,* Upton Lovell, Warminster
★ *Prince of Wales,* 94 High Street, Dilton Marsh, Westbury
★ *Quarryman's Arms,* Box Hill, Box
★ *Red Lion,* 6 The City, Melksham
★ *Talbot Inn,* Berwick St John
★ *Wheatsheaf,* 32 Newport Street, Swindon
★ *Wheatsheaf,* Ermin Street, Swindon
★ *White Hart,* Lane End, Corsley, Warminster
★ *Wyndham Arms,* 27 Estcourt Road, Salisbury

Places Featured:

Barnsley	Liversedge
Batley	Lund
Beck Hole	Malton
Bradford	Mexborough
Brearton	Middlesbrough
Bridlington	North Duffield
Brompton	Northallerton
Burley	Old Mixenden
Cawood	Ossett
Catcliffe	Pontefract
Cropton	Pool-in-Wharfedale
Dewsbury	Pudsey
Doncaster	Ripon
Guisborough	Scarborough
Halifax	Selby
Harrogate	Sheffield
Hebden Bridge	Sowerby Bridge
Helperby	Staveley
Holmfirth	Stokesley
Horbury	Sutton upon Derwent
Huddersfield	Thorne
Hull	Tockwith
Ingleton	Wakefield
Keighley	Wentworth
Knaresborough	Whitby
Knottingley	Wombwell
Leeds	Wortley
Linthwaite	York

THE BREWERIES

ABBEYDALE BREWERY

Unit 8, Aizlewood Road, Sheffield, South Yorkshire S8 0XX
☎ *(0114) 281 2712*

MATINS 3.6% ABV
Pale and flavoursome for gravity.
BEST BITTER 4.0% ABV
Smooth and malty with good hoppiness.
MOONSHINE 4.3% ABV
Fruity easy quaffer.
ARCHANGEL 4.7% ABV
Pale and quenching.
DARK ANGEL 4.7% ABV
Dark and rounded.
ABSOLUTION 5.3% ABV
Golden, smooth and refreshing.
BLACK MASS 6.6% ABV
Stout, with good hoppiness.

BARGE & BARREL BREWING CO.

Park Road, Elland, West Yorkshire HX5 9HP
☎ *(01422) 373623*

BARGEE 3.8% ABV
BEST BITTER 4.0% ABV
NETTLETHRASHER 4.4% ABV
BLACK STUMP 5.0% ABV
LEVELLER 5.7% ABV

BARNSLEY BREWERY CO. LTD

Wath Road, Elsecar, Barnsley, South Yorkshire S74 8HJ
☎ *(01226) 741010*

BITTER 3.8% ABV
OAKWELL 4.0% ABV
IPA 4.2% ABV
Plus seasonal and occasional brews.

BLACK DOG BREWERY

St Hilda's Business Centre, The Ropery, Whitby,
North Yorkshire YO22 4EU
☎ *(01947) 821467*

 WHITBY ABBEY ALE 3.8% ABV
Light and hoppy.
FIRST OUT 4.0% ABV
Hoppy and bitter.
RHATAS/BLACK DOG SPECIAL 4.6% ABV
Dark, rich and smooth.
Plus seasonal brews

THE BLACK SHEEP BREWERY

Wellgarth, Masham, Ripon, North Yorkshire
HG4 4EN
☎ *(01765) 689227*

 BEST BITTER 3.8% ABV
Golden, well-hopped and refreshing.
SPECIAL 4.4% ABV
Good body, hoppy and bitter.
RIGGWELTER 5.9% ABV
Mouthfilling flavours.

BRISCOE'S BREWERY

16 Ash Grove, Otley, West Yorkshire LS21 3EL
☎ *(01943) 466515*

 ROMBALD'S REVIVER 3.8% ABV
PUDDLED AND BARMY ALE 5.8% ABV

BROWN COW BREWERY

Brown Cow Road, Barlow, Selby, North Yorkshire
YO8 8EH
☎ *(01757) 618974*

 BEST BITTER 3.8% ABV
WOLFHOUND 4.3% ABV
Plus occasional brews.

CAPTAIN COOK BREWERY LTD

White Swan, Stokesley, North Yorkshire TS9 5BL
☎ *(01642) 710263*

 SUNSET 4.0% ABV
MAORI MISTRESS 4.2% ABV
SLIPWAY 4.2% ABV
BLACK JET 4.5% ABV

DALESIDE BREWERY

Camwal Road, Starbeck, Harrogate, North
Yorkshire HG1 4PT
☎ *(01423) 880022*

NIGHT JAR 3.7% ABV
OLD LUBRICATION 4.1% ABV
OLD LEGOVER 4.1% ABV
GREEN GRASS OLD ROGUE ALE 4.5% ABV
CRACKSHOT 4.5% ABV
MONKEY WRENCH 5.3% ABV
MOROCCO ALE 5.5% ABV
RIPON'S JEWEL 5.8% ABV

DRUMMONDS BREWERY

443 London Road, Sheffield, South Yorkshire
S2 4HJ
☎ *(0114) 255 4024*

 BULLDOG 4.0% ABV
DREGS 4.6% ABV

FERNANDES BREWERY

Kirkgate, Wakefield, West Yorkshire
☎ *(01924) 291709*

FRANKLINS BREWERY

Bilton Lane, Bilton, Harrogate, North Yorkshire
HG1 4DH
☎ *(01423) 322345*

GLENTWORTH BREWERY

Glentworth House, Crossfield Lane, Skellow,
Doncaster, South Yorkshire DN6 8PL
☎ *(01302) 725555*

LIGHTYEAR 3.9% ABV
LITTLE GEM 3.9% ABV
NORTHERN LIGHTS 3.9% ABV
OLDE SKELLOW 3.9% ABV
ROSE OF YORKSHIRE 3.9% ABV
STARLIGHT 3.9% ABV
BRASSED OFF 4.1% ABV
MALT TEASER 4.2% ABV
BUTTERCROSS 4.3% ABV
DANUM 4.3% ABV
PLATINUM BLONDE 4.3% ABV
YORKSHIRE GOLD 4.3% ABV
DIZZY BLONDE 4.5% ABV
GLAD TIDINGS 4.5% ABV
HARVEST GOLD 4.5% ABV
HOPCORN 4.5% ABV
LIGHTMAKER 4.5% ABV
OLD FLAME 4.5% ABV
POT O GOLD 4.5% ABV
FULL MONTY 5.0% ABV
HENPECKED 5.0% ABV
WELL'ARDE 5.0% ABV
Plus seasonal brews.

GOOSE EYE BREWERY

Ingrow Bridge, South Street, Keighley, West
Yorkshire BD21 5AX
☎ *(01535) 605807*

BITTER 3.8% ABV
Golden and malty with some fruitiness.
BRONTE BITTER 4.0% ABV
Malty and well-balanced.
NO IDEA 4.0% ABV
SUMMER JACKS 4.2% ABV
WHARFEDALE BITTER 4.5% ABV
GOLDEN GOOSE 4.5% ABV
POMMIE'S REVENGE 5.2% ABV
Straw-coloured, soft and smooth.
Plus occasional brews.

H B CLARK & CO. (SUCCESSORS) LTD

Westgate Brewery, Wakefield, West Yorkshire WF2 9SW
☎ *(01924) 372306*

 TRADITIONAL BITTER 3.8% ABV
Amber-coloured, with some fruitiness.
CITY GENT 4.2% ABV
Pale golden, fruity and quenching.
FESTIVAL ALE 4.2% ABV
Pale with refreshing fruit flavours.
BLACK CAP BITTER 4.4% ABV
Powerful maltiness with hoppy aroma.
BURGLAR BILL 4.4% ABV
Full-bodied and well-hopped throughout.
OLDEN HORNET 5.0% ABV
Golden and hoppy.
Plus seasonal brews.

HAMBLETON ALES

The Brewery, Holme on Swale, Thirsk, North Yorkshire YO7 4JE
☎ *(01845) 567460*

 BITTER 3.6% ABV
STALLION 4.2% ABV
GOLD FIELDS 4.2% ABV
STUD 4.3% ABV
NIGHTMARE 5.0% ABV
Plus 4% monthly special.

HUDDERSFIELD BREWERY

Ivy Street East, Huddersfield, West Yorkshire
☎ *(01484) 300028*

THE HULL BREWERY

144–8 English Street, Hull, East Yorkshire HU3 2BT
☎ *(01482) 586364*

 MILD 3.6% ABV
BITTER 3.8% ABV
ELWOODS BEST BITTER 3.8% ABV
Plus seasonal and occasional brews.

KELHAM ISLAND BREWERY

23 Alma Street, Sheffield, South Yorkshire S3 8SA
☎ *(0114) 249 4804*

BITTER 3.8% ABV
GOLDEN EAGLE 4.2% ABV
GATECRASHER 4.4% ABV
PALE RIDER 5.2% ABV
Plus seasonal and occasional brews.

THE KITCHEN BREWERY LTD

Unit J, Shaw Park, Silver Street, Aspley, Huddersfield, West Yorkshire HD5 9AF
☎ *(01484) 300028*

 TUBBY TANGERINE 4.0% ABV
Blonde colour and refreshing with a hint of tangerine.
TORMENTED TURNIP 4.5% ABV
Pale and hoppy with some fruity sweetness.
ROCKING RHUBARB 5.0% ABV
Malty, with a hint of rhubarb.
Up to 12 different beers available plus seasonal brews. Beer range changes regularly.

MARSTON MOOR BREWERY

Crown House, Kirk Hammerton, York, North Yorkshire YO26 8DD
☎ *(01423) 330341*

 CROMWELL BITTER 3.6% ABV
BREWERS PRIDE 4.2% ABV
MERRIE MAKER 4.5% ABV
BREWER'S DROOP 5.0% ABV
TROOPER 5.0% ABV

NORTH YORKSHIRE BREWERY

Pinchinthorpe, Gisborough, North Yorkshire TS14 8HG
☎ *(01287) 630200*

ROOSTER'S BREWERY

Unit 20, Claro Court Business Centre, Claro Road, Harrogate, North Yorkshire HG1 4BA
☎ *(01423) 561861*

 JAK'S 3.9% ABV
Golden and soft with fruity sweetness.
SPECIAL 3.9% ABV
Pale, with citrus-fruit freshness.
YANKEE 4.3% ABV
Pale, soft and fruity.
CREAM 4.7% ABV
Smooth and soft, with fruit flavours.
ROOSTER'S 4.7% ABV
Golden brown, sweet and fruity.
Plus occasional and seasonal brews. Additional brews produced under the Outlaw Brewing Co. label.

RUDGATE BREWERY

2 Centre Park, Marston Business Park, Rudgate, Tockwith, York, North Yorkshire YO26 8QF
☎ *(01423) 358382*

 VIKING 3.8% ABV
BATTLEAXE 4.2% ABV
MILD 4.4% ABV
Plus seasonal brews.

SAMUEL SMITH OLD BREWERY

High Street, Tadcaster, North Yorkshire LS24 9SB
☎ *(01937) 832225*

 OLD BREWERY BITTER 4.0% ABV
Rounded and flavoursome.

TIMOTHY TAYLOR & CO. LTD

*Knowle Spring Brewery, Keighley, West Yorkshire
BD21 1AW*
☎ *(01535) 603139*

DARK MILD 3.5% ABV
Mellow and malty with balancing hoppiness.
GOLDEN BEST 3.5% ABV
Balanced, crisp and hoppy.
PORTER 3.8% ABV
Sweeter winter brew.
BEST BITTER 4.0% ABV
Refreshing, hoppy and bitter.
LANDLORD 4.3% ABV
Distinctive combination of malt, hops and fruit.
RAM TAM 4.3% ABV
Landlord with added caramel.

TIGERTOPS BREWERY

Oakes Street, Wakefield, West Yorkshire
☎ *(01229) 716238*

TOMLINSONS BREWERY

Skinner Lane, Pontefract, West Yorkshire
☎ *(01977) 780866*

WAWNE BREWERY

*14 Greens Lane, Wawne, East Yorkshire
HU7 5XT*
☎ *(01482) 835400*

MONKS MILD 3.2% ABV
ST. PETER'S BITTER 3.8% ABV
WAGHEN BITTER 4.1% ABV
Plus occasional brews.

WEST YORKSHIRE BREWERY

*Victoria Buildings, Burnley Road, Luddendenfoot,
Halifax, West Yorkshire HX2 6AA*
☎ *(01422) 885930*

YORKSHIRE MAN 4.1% ABV
Pale and malty with dry hoppy finish.

WORTH BREWERY

Worth Way, Keighley, West Yorkshire BD21 5LP
☎ *(01535) 611914*

YORK BREWERY

Toft Green, Micklegate, York YO1 1JT
☎ *(01904) 621162*

STONEWALL 3.7% ABV
Malty with hoppy finish.
BRIDESHEAD 4.0% ABV
Well-balanced with some fruitiness.
YORKSHIRE TERRIER 4.2% ABV
Gold-coloured with good hoppy bitterness.
CENTURION'S GHOST ALE 5.0% ABV
Millennium brew.
Plus seasonal and occasional brews.

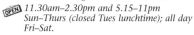

THE PUBS

BARNSLEY

Miller's Inn

*Dearne Hall Road, Barnsley, South Yorkshire
S75 1LX*
☎ *(01226) 382888* Mr and Mrs Alan Dyson

A freehouse with Timothy Taylor Landlord and Barnsley Oakwell always available, plus one guest from breweries such as Kitchen, Shepherd Neame or Fuller's.

A riverside two-bar village pub with separate dining area and garden. Food available Wed–Sun lunchtime and Sun–Mon, Wed–Thurs evenings. Children allowed.

OPEN *11.30am–2.30pm and 5.15–11pm
Sun–Thurs (closed Tues lunchtime); all day
Fri–Sat.*

BATLEY

The Oaklands

*Bradford Road, Batley, West Yorkshire
WF17 5PS*
☎ *(01924) 444181*

Up to six beers available. Always something from local breweries plus at least three guests from Wild's, Timothy Taylor or Tomlinson's.

A busy circuit pub. Bar food available at lunchtime and evenings. Car park, garden. Children allowed up to 7pm.

OPEN *12–3pm and 5–11pm; all day Fri–Sat.*

BECK HOLE

Birch Hall Inn

*Beck Hole, Goathland, North Yorkshire
YO22 5LE*
☎ *(01947) 896245*

A wide choice of beers always available, including Black Sheep Bitter and local brews from Cropton, Black Dog and Daleside Brewery. Many more guests through the year from further afield.

T iny, traditional unspoilt pub with two bars dating from 1600s. CAMRA pub of the year. No juke box or games machines. Bar food available at lunchtime and evenings. Garden. Children allowed. Between Pickering and Whitby.

OPEN *11am–11pm in summer; usual hours in
winter.*

The Beehive Inn

583 Halifax Road, Bradford, West Yorkshire BD6 2DU
☎ *(01274) 678550* Kevin Guster

Two guest ales always available, regulars include Yorkshire ales like Timothy Taylor Landlord and Black Sheep Bitter, but also beers from any brewery in the country. Seasonal ales for Christmas and Bonfire Night when possible.

A one-bar locals' pub on the outskirts of Bradford. Bar snacks available all day. Children allowed.

11am–11pm (10.30pm Sun).

The Castle Hotel

20 Grattan Road, Bradford, West Yorkshire BD1 2LU
☎ *(01274) 393166* James Duncan

Mansfield Riding and Riding Mild always available plus seven guest beers (200 per year) from brewers such as Goose Eye, Ridleys, Brains, Moorhouse's, Marston's, Eldridge Pope, Jennings, Wadworth, Shepherd Neame and many more.

A pub built like a castle in 1898. Bar food is served at lunchtime from Monday to Thursday and until 7.30pm on Friday and Saturday. Parking at weekends and evenings. Children not allowed. Located in the city centre.

11.30am–11pm Mon–Sat; closed Sun.

The Corn Dolly

110 Bolton Road, Bradford, West Yorkshire BD1 4DE
☎ *(01274) 720219* Mr Duncan

Up to 12 beers available. Moorhouse's Bitter, Black Sheep and Black Bull always available, plus four guests (500 per year) from brewers including Fuller's, Charles Wells, Wadworth and Goose Eye.

C AMRA Bradford Pub of the Year 1993 and 1994. Bar food is available at lunchtime. Car park and garden. Situated off Forster Square.

11.30am–11pm.

The Fighting Cock

21–3 Preston Street, Bradford, West Yorkshire BD7 1JE
☎ *(01274) 726907* Kevin Quill

At least ten beers on sale. Brews from Timothy Taylor and Black Sheep always available plus many guests (200 per year) from Greene King, Fuller's, Archers, Jennings and Ringwood etc.

A friendly back-to-basics original ale house. Bar food available at lunchtime. Go left on Thornton Road from the cinema in the city centre, then left again at the lights.

11am–11pm Mon–Sat; 11am–3pm and 7–10.30pm Sun.

Haigy's Bar

31 Lumb Lane, Bradford, West Yorkshire BD8 7QU
☎ *(01274) 731644* Mrs Haig

A freehouse serving Greene King Abbot, Timothy Taylor Landlord and a Black Sheep ale plus two weekly changing guests from breweries such as Fuller's.

A n edge-of-town pub with traditional decor, painted in Bradford City colours, but with a modern feel. Games, pool, disco at weekends. Disabled access, beer garden. Food available at lunchtime and evenings. Children allowed in the afternoons only.

5pm–1am Mon–Thurs; 12pm–1am Fri–Sat; closed Sun except Festival for Yorkshire Day.

The Idle Cock

Bolton Road, Bradford, West Yorkshire BD2 4HT
☎ *(01274) 639491* Jim Wright

Samuel Smith OBB, Black Sheep Special, Timothy Taylor Landlord and Vaux Samson always available plus several guests (130 per year) including Tomintoul Stag, Hop Back Summer Lightning, Fuller's London Pride, Daleside Old Legover, Joseph Holts etc.

A York stone pub with two separate bars, part wood, part flagstone floors, wooden bench seating. A proper no-frills alehouse. Bar food is available. Parking and garden. Follow the 'Idle' signs along Bolton Road for approximately two miles from the city centre.

11.30am–11pm Mon–Sat; 12–3pm and 7–10.30pm Sun.

The Shearbridge

111 Great Horton Road, Bradford, West Yorkshire BD7 1PS
☎ *(01274) 732136* Rob Heir

 Marston's Pedigree among the beers always available plus up to four guests, such as Harviestoun Schiehallion or a Black Sheep ale.

A students' pub with beams, wooden floors and beer garden. Food available at lunchtime and evenings. No children.

OPEN *12–11pm (10.30pm Sun).*

BREARTON

The Malt Shovel

Brearton, Nr Knaresborough, North Yorkshire HG3 3BX
☎ *(01423) 862929* Mr Mitchell

 Five beers always available including 100 guests per year. Favourites include Durham Canny Lad, Jennings Sneck Lifter, Old Mill Bitter, Black Sheep Bitter and Daleside brews.

A sixteenth-century beamed village inn, with open fires in winter. Bar food available at lunchtime and evenings. Car park, garden. Children allowed. Off the B6165.

OPEN *12–3pm and 6.45–11pm Mon–Sat; 12–3pm and 7–10.30pm Sun.*

BRIDLINGTON

The Old Ship Inn

90 St John's Street, Bridlington, East Yorkshire YO16 7JS
☎ *(01262) 670466*

Up to seven beers always available.

A two-bar country pub with dining area and beer garden. Food available. Children allowed.

OPEN *11am–11pm (10.30pm Sun).*

BROMPTON

The Crown Inn

Station Road, Brompton, Northallerton, North Yorkshire DL6 2RE
☎ *(0160) 977 2547* Mrs Addington

Two guest ales such as Marston's Pedigree in addition to the two regular brews.

A traditional country inn with one bar, coal fires and a small garden. There are plans to serve food in the near future. Children allowed.

OPEN *12–3pm and 7–11pm Mon–Thurs; all day Fri–Sun.*

BURLEY

The Fox & Newt

9 Burley Street, Burley, Leeds, West Yorkshire LS3 1LD
☎ *(01132) 432612* Roy Cadman

A wide range of guest ales always available. Regulars include Young's Special, Greene King Abbot, Timothy Taylor Landlord, Wadworth 6X, Marston's Pedigree, Fuller's London Pride and Caledonian 80/-. The beers are changed weekly.

An old-style pub with a wooden floor. Food available at lunchtime only in a separate dining area. Children allowed for lunches only.

OPEN *All day, every day.*

CAWOOD

The Ferry Inn

2 King Street, Cawood, Selby, North Yorkshire YO8 3TL
☎ *(01757) 268515* Fred Thorpe

A freehouse serving Mansfield Riding and Timothy Taylor Landlord plus two guests, perhaps Black Sheep Special or a Cropton Brewery ale.

A sixteenth-century village inn with stone floor, beams, log fires and beer garden. Bar food available at lunchtime and evenings. Separate dining area planned. Children allowed. Near the river.

OPEN *12–3pm Wed–Fri; 6.30–11pm Mon–Fri; all day Sat–Sun.*

CATCLIFFE

The Waverley

Nursery Bungalow, Brinsworth Road, Catcliffe, Rotherham, South Yorkshire S60 5RW
☎ *(01709) 360906* Ron Woodthorpe

A freehouse with four hand pumps serving a range of guest brews. Regular breweries supported include Glentworth, Slaters (Eccleshall), Drummonds, Banks's and Timothy Taylor.

A large suburban pub with separate lounge and children's room, garden and play area. Disabled access and toilets. Food available at lunchtime and evenings. Children allowed in children's room only.

OPEN *12–4pm and 6–11.30pm Mon–Fri; all day Sat; 12–4pm and 7–10.30pm Sun.*

CROPTON

The New Inn

*Cropton, Nr Pickering, North Yorkshire
YO18 8HH*
☎ *(01751) 417310* Sandra Lee

Home of the Cropton Brewery, so a selection of Cropton beers always available.

C ropton Brewery was established in 1984 in the basement of the New Inn in this tiny moorland village. It owes its existence to the deep-seated local fear that, one day, the harsh moors winter weather would prevent the beer waggon from getting through. The brewery's reputation has since spread and, as demand exceeded capacity, a new purpose-built brewery was constructed in an adjacent quarry. Bar and restaurant food is served at lunchtime and evenings. Car park, garden, children's room, accommodation.

KING BILLY BITTER 3.6% ABV
TWO PINTS BEST BITTER 4.0% ABV
HONEY GOLD 4.2% ABV
SCORESBY STOUT 4.2% ABV
UNCLE SAM'S BITTER 4.4% ABV
BACKWARDS BITTER 4.7% ABV
MONKMAN'S SLAUGHTER BITTER 6.0% ABV

11am–3pm and 6.30–11pm; all day Sat.

DEWSBURY

West Riding Licensed Refreshment Rooms

Station Buildings, Wellington Road, Dewsbury, West Yorkshire WF13 1HF
☎ *(01924) 459193* Paul Kloss

A freehouse with Black Sheep Bitter and Timothy Taylor Landlord always available, plus up to five guests from breweries such as Ossett, Durham, Abbeydale and Kelham Island. Close links with local breweries: Rooster's made a 150th Anniversary Ale especially for the pub.

S ituated in the railway station and doubling as a waiting room, this is a real ale pub with one central bar, wooden floors and beer garden. Live music on Thursdays. Music festival venue. Food available every lunchtime, plus Tuesday nights (Pie Nights) and Wednesday nights (Curry Nights). Children allowed in designated areas.

11am–11pm (10.30pm Sun).

DONCASTER

The Hallcross

*33–4 Hallgate, Doncaster, South Yorkshire
DN1 3NL*
☎ *(01302) 328213*

Home of the Stocks Brewery, so Stocks brews produced and served on the premises.

T he brewery was established in 1981 behind the pub. It is owned and run by Cooplands, a Doncaster bakers, on the site of the first shop, which was opened in 1931 to sell home-made sweets. The pub is of traditional Victorian style with a beer garden. Bar food is served at lunchtime and evenings. Parking, children allowed.

 BEST BITTER 3.9% ABV
Light hoppy ale brewed for the northern taste.
SELECT 4.7% ABV
Premium ale of smooth and slightly malty character.
ST LEDGER PORTER 5.1% ABV
Award-winning, almost black, full-flavoured ale with deep fruit and roast malt flavours. A hoppy finish.
GOLDEN WHEAT 4.7% ABV
OLD HORIZONTAL 5.4% ABV
Strong ale with a distinctive nutty flavour, good body and excellent head retention, flavoured with a delicate blend of Fuggles and Goldings hops.

11am–11pm.

The Salutation

*14 South Parade, Doncaster, South Yorkshire
DN1 2DR*
☎ *(01302) 368464* Lisa Potts

Marston's Pedigree always available plus up to seven guests from a range that might include Bateman XB and Dark Mild, Black Sheep ales, Scottish brews from Maclay and Caledonian and seasonal and celebration ales as available.

A 300-year-old, two-bar pub with a haunted cellar. Food available 11am–10.30pm daily. Function room, beer garden. Just outside the town centre. Children allowed in the garden at weekends only.

11am–11pm Mon–Sat; 12–10.30pm Sun.

GUISBOROUGH

The Tap & Spile

11 Westgate, Guisborough, North Yorkshire
TS14 6BG
☎ *(01287) 632983* Angela Booth

Tap & Spile Premium (brewed by Mansfield), always available plus six guests (200 per year) which may include Hambleton ales and those from Hull Brewery, Cotleigh, Big Lamp and Durham.

P lenty of olde-worlde charm, a beamed ceiling, non-smoking room, snug and beer garden. Bar food available at lunchtime. Parking. Children allowed. Situated on the main street in Guisborough.

11.30am–11pm Mon–Sat; 12–3pm and 7–10.30pm Sun.

HALIFAX

Tap & Spile

1 Clare Road, Halifax, West Yorkshire HX1 2HX
☎ *(01422) 353661* Chris Dalton

Black Sheep Bitter, Big Lamp Bitter, Fuller's London Pride always available, plus up to four guests, not repeated if possible, from breweries such as Broughton Ales, Fuller's, Hop Back and Hambleton.

A traditional town pub in a listed building, with one bar and a dining area. Plans for a beer garden. Food available at lunchtime only. No children.

All day, every day.

The Three Pigeons Ale House

1 Sunfold, South Parade, Halifax, West Yorkshire
HX1 2LX
☎ *(01422) 347001* Jeff Amos

A freehouse with Timothy Taylor Landlord and Best and Black Sheep Bitter and Special always on offer, plus three guests such as specials from Timothy Taylor (such as Golden Best), Church End Gravedigger and Shepherd Neame Dark Mild.

A unique, unspoilt 1930s Art Deco pub just outside the city-centre. Real fires, one bar and three parlour rooms. Patio at front. Food available at lunchtime and evenings. Children allowed in designated area.

12–11pm (10.30 Sun).

HARROGATE

The Alderman Fortune

51 Parliament Street, Harrogate, North Yorkshire
HG1 2RE
☎ *(01423) 502759* Kevin Powsland

A good selection of up to seven guest ales, regularly featuring Timothy Taylor Landlord, Shepherd Neame Spitfire, Ward's Waggle Dance and Black Sheep Best and Special, but also many other seasonal and celebration ales.

A traditional two-bar town pub (formerly The Pump Rooms) with wooden floors, low ceilings and poetry on the walls. Food available every lunchtime and Mon–Thurs evenings. No children.

11am–11pm (10.30pm Sun).

The Tap & Spile

Tower Street, Harrogate, North Yorkshire
HG1 1HS
☎ *(01423) 526785* Roger Palmer

No permanent beers, but a constantly changing range of guest ales. Rooster's and Daleside are regular breweries featured, but two new beers are served every week.

A two-bar pub situated just off the town centre. Stone walls, half-carpet in public bar and lounge, one non-smoking, fireplace. Patio at front. Food available at lunchtime only. Children allowed in non-smoking room only.

All day, every day.

HEBDEN BRIDGE

The Fox & Goose

9 Heptonstall Road, Hebden Bridge, West Yorkshire HX7 6AZ
☎ *(01422) 842649* Robin Starbuck

Goose Eye Bitter always available plus three guest beers (400 per year) including Exmoor Gold, Old Mill Bitter, Fuller's London Pride and Orkney Dark Island.

A small, friendly three-roomed pub with a wide variety of customers. Foreign bottled beers also stocked. Bar food is available at lunchtime and evenings. Garden. Children allowed. Off the A646.

11.30am–3pm and 7–11pm.

The Golden Lion Inn
Main Street, Helperby, York, North Yorkshire
YO61 2NT
☎ *(01423) 360870* Irene and Graham Forest

A freehouse with Timothy Taylor Bitter always available plus four guests from breweries such as Cumberland, Jennings, Wadworth, Oakhill, Bateman, Shepherd Neame, Titanic, Caledonian and Fuller's.

A traditional village country inn with stone floor and fires. One bar, food available Fri–Sun evenings only. Children allowed

OPEN *6–11pm only Mon–Fri; 12–11pm Sat;*
12–10.30pm Sun.

The Farmer's Arms
2–4 Liphill Bank Road, Holmfirth, West
Yorkshire HD7 1LG
☎ *(01484) 683713* Mr Drummond

Six beers always available including Black Sheep Bitter. Guests might include Black Sheep Special and John Eastwood's Best Bitter.

An eighteenth-century pub. Bar food available. Parking nearby. Garden and function room. Small parties catered for. Accommodation. Children allowed. Off the A635.

OPEN *6–11pm Mon–Fri; 12–11pm Sat;*
12–10.30pm Sun.

The King's Arms
27 New Street, Horbury, Wakefield, West
Yorkshire WF4 6NB
☎ *(01924) 264329* Mike Davidson

A Marston's house with Pedigree, Bitter and others available, plus one guest pump regularly featuring a Banks's ale.

A one-bar village pub with wooden floors in bar area. Pool and games area. Conservatory, dining area, garden. Food currently available 5–7 pm. Children allowed.

OPEN *3–11pm Mon–Thurs; 12–11pm Fri–Sat;*
12–4pm and 7–10.30pm Sun.

The Old Court Brewhouse
Queen Street, Huddersfield, West Yorkshire
HD1 2SL
☎ *(01484) 454035*

Four Old Court Brewery beers produced and served on the premises.

A brewpub with the brewery part raised up from the lower floor and visible from the public bar. This listed building was formerly the county court. Bar and restaurant food available at lunchtime and evenings (Mon–Sat). Metered parking, garden.

COPPERS 3.4% ABV
M'LUD 3.5% ABV
1825 4.5% ABV
MAXIMUM SENTENCE 5.5% ABV

OPEN *Ring for details.*

Rat & Ratchet
40 Chapel Hill, Huddersfield, West Yorkshire
HD1 3EB
☎ *(01484) 516734*

Fourteen ales at all times. Three home brews plus Adnams Best, Bateman Mild, Mansfield Old Baily, Marston's Pedigree, Timothy Taylor Landlord and several more.

The brewery opened at the Rat and Ratchet in December 1994. A popular pub with beer festivals and special events held regularly.

THE GREAT GNAWTHERN 4.0% ABV
THE GREAT ESCAPE 4.2% ABV
CRATCHET'S CHRISTMAS CRACKER 4.3% ABV

OPEN *12–11pm.*

Springbank Tavern
29 Spring Bank, Hull, East Yorkshire HU3 1AS
☎ *(01482) 581879* Mr and Mrs JF Egan

Mansfield Bitter, Riding Bitter and Riding Mild always available plus up to three guests per week including Black Dog Mild and Timothy Taylor Landlord, with the emphasis on small breweries.

A one-room alehouse with traditional games (darts and dominoes). Students and locals provide mixed clientele. Background music, but no juke box. Bar food available 12–2pm daily. Street parking, disabled facilities. Children allowed in the bar for meals. Just off the city centre.

OPEN *11am–11pm Mon–Sat; 12–3pm and*
7–10.30pm Sun.

Ye Olde Black Boy
150 High Street, Hull, East Yorkshire HU1 1PS
☎ *(01482) 326516* Barry Fenn

Nine guest beers served (300 per year), from Hambleton, Rooster's, Cropton, North Yorkshire and Bateman breweries.

The first Tap & Spile charter house. The original building dates back to 1331. Traditional wood-panelled walls and floors. Upstairs bar open for food at lunchtimes and on Friday and Saturday evenings. Bar food available at lunchtime and evenings. Parking. Children allowed in the upstairs bar when having food. Situated on the Old High Street, next to the River Hull.

OPEN *12–3pm and 7–11pm Mon–Thurs; all day Fri–Sun.*

INGLETON

The Wheatsheaf Inn
22 High Street, Ingleton, North Yorkshire LA6 3AD
☎ *(01524) 241275* Mr Thompson

A freehouse with Black Sheep Bitter and Special, Riggwelter and Moorhouse's Pendle Witches Brew among the beers always available.

An olde-worlde one-bar country pub with dining area and beer garden. Disabled access. Accommodation. Food available at lunchtime and evenings. Children allowed.

OPEN *12–11pm (10.30pm Sun).*

KEIGHLEY

The Old White Bear
6 Keighley Road, Crosshills, Keighley, West Yorkshire BD20 7RN
☎ *(01535) 632115*

Two brews produced and served on the premises plus guests beers.

The owner ran the Goose Eye Brewery from 1978 to 1991 but wanted to produce a fuller beer using natural water and ingredients, so he started production in the old stables here in 1993. The pub was built in 1735 and retains its original beams. Bar and restaurant food available at lunchtime and evenings. Car park, small garden. Children allowed if kept under control.

BITTER 3.9% ABV
BARNSLEY BITTER 3.9% ABV

OPEN *11.30am–3pm and 5–11pm Mon–Thurs (not Mon lunch); 11.30am–11pm Fri–Sat; 12–4pm and 7–10.30pm Sun.*

KNARESBOROUGH

Blind Jacks
19 Market Place, Knaresborough, North Yorkshire HG5 8AL
☎ *(01423) 869148* David Llewellyn

A traditional alehouse with five beers always available including Timothy Taylor Landlord, Village Brewer's White Boar and Bull Premium, Black Sheep Bitter and Daleside Green Grass, plus three rotating guest beers from independent breweries including Hambleton Bitter, Daleside Legover, Crompton Two Pints and Goose Eye ales.

A seventeenth-century listed building, beamed with wooden floors and lots of mirrors. Children and dogs allowed in. Parking nearby.

OPEN *5.30–11pm Mon; 4–11pm Tue–Thur; 12–11pm Fri–Sat; 12–10.30pm Sun.*

KNOTTINGLEY

The Steam Packet Inn
Racca Green, Knottingley, West Yorkshire WF11 8AT
☎ *(01977) 677266*
Helen Mellor and Mark Spriggs

A freehouse with Kent Garden Game Keeper plus two guests, changing every weekend, from Beartown Brewery, Wye Valley and Tomlinson's, among others.

A small-town pub with lounge bar, public bar, function room and beer garden. Currently under refurbishment. No food. Children allowed but not at the bar.

OPEN *All day, every day.*

LEEDS

The City of Mabgate
45 Mabgate, Leeds, West Yorkshire LS9 7DR
☎ *(01132) 457789* Mr K Broughton

Black Sheep Bitter and Timothy Taylor Landlord among the brews always available plus up to four guests such as Fuller's London Pride or other beers from smaller breweries such as Rooster's and Durham. Beers change frequently, usually every day, the record is Eldridge Pope Royal Oak, which changed after two hours!

A town-centre pub, winner of CAMRA's Pub of the Year 1998. Two bars, non-smoking area and garden. Food available 12–2pm Mon–Fri. Children allowed until 7pm.

OPEN *12–11pm Mon–Sat; 12–4pm and 7.30–10.30pm Sun.*

The Duck & Drake

43 Kirkgate, Leeds, West Yorkshire LS2 7DR
☎ *(0113) 246 5806* Mr and Mrs Morley

Timothy Taylor Landlord always available plus six guests (300 per year) from breweries including Jennings, Clark's, Exmoor, Rooster's and Pioneer. Also real cider.

A traditional alehouse with wooden floors, coal fires, bare boards and live bands. Bar food served at lunchtime. Get to Leeds market and ask for directions.

OPEN *All day, every day.*

The Eagle Tavern

North Street, Sheepscar, Leeds, West Yorkshire LS2 1AF
☎ *(0113) 245 7146* Mr Vaughan

A Samuel Smith tied house. Old Brewery Bitter always available, plus other seasonal ales. CAMRA Yorkshire Pub of the Year 1995.

An 1826 Georgian building close to the city centre. Bar food available at lunchtime and evenings. Occasional live music. Parking. Ten minutes walk out of the city centre. B&B accommodation.

OPEN *11.30am–2.30pm and 5.30–11pm Mon–Fri; 11.30am–2.30pm and 6–11pm Sat; 12–3pm and 7–10.30pm Sun.*

The Old Vic

17 Whitecote Hill, Leeds, West Yorkshire LS13 3LB
☎ *(0113) 256 1207* Craig Seddon

A freehouse with Timothy Taylor Landlord and Black Sheep Bitter among the brews always available, plus four guests from breweries such as Coach House and Hambleton.

Three rooms plus a function room decorated with old Bramley photographs. Patio. Disabled access and toilets. Situated on the outskirts of town. No food. Well-behaved children allowed.

OPEN *4–11pm Mon–Thurs; 2–11pm Fri; 11am–11pm Sat; 12–3pm and 7–10.30pm Sun.*

Sair Inn

Lane Top, Linthwaite, Huddersfield, West Yorkshire HD7 5SG
☎ *(01484) 842370*

A dozen Linfit beers are brewed and served on the premises.

Home of the award-winning Linfit Brewery, which began production in 1982 for the Sair Inn and free trade, and increased its capacity in 1994. The pub is a traditional nineteenth-century inn with four rooms, stone floors and open fires. Parking in road, children's room.

DARK MILD 3.0% ABV
BITTER 3.7% ABV
SWIFT 4.2% ABV
GOLD MEDAL 4.2% ABV
SPECIAL 4.3% ABV
AUTUMN GOLD 4.7% ABV
ENGLISH GUINEAS STOUT 5.3% ABV
OLD ELI 5.3% ABV
LEADBOILER 6.6% ABV
ENOCH'S HAMMER 8.6% ABV

OPEN *7.30–11pm Mon–Fri; 12–3pm and 7.30–11pm Sat–Sun and public holidays.*

The Black Bull

37 Halifax Road, Liversedge, West Yorkshire WF15 6JR
☎ *(01924) 403779* Mr Toulson

A freehouse with Timothy Taylor Landlord and Black Sheep Special always available, plus four guests such as Samuel Smith Old Brewery Bitter, Glentworth Light Year or a Clark's brew. Also seasonals, specials and celebration ales as available.

Two bars, beamed ceilings. Disabled access at rear. No food. Children allowed in the afternoons only. Situated out of town.

OPEN *12–4pm and 7–11pm Mon–Thurs; all day Fri; 11am–4pm and 7–11pm Sat; 12–4pm and 7–10.30pm Sun.*

LUND

The Wellington Inn
19 The Gren, Lund, Driffield, East Yorkshire
YO25 9TE
☎ *(01377) 217294* Russell Jeffrey

 A freehouse with Timothy Taylor Landlord, Black Sheep Best and Bateman Dark Mild always available, plus two or three guests from local micro-breweries such as Black Dog Whitby Abbey, or something from Old Mill or Isle of Skye.

A two-bar country village pub with three log fires, flag floors and patio. Bar food available at lunchtime and a separate restaurant is open in the evenings. Children allowed

 7–11pm only Mon; 12–3pm and 7–11pm Tues–Sat (10.30pm Sun).

MALTON

Suddaby's Crown Hotel
Wheelgate, Malton, North Yorkshire YO17 7HP
☎ *(01653) 697580*
R Suddaby, C Jewell and A Brayshaw

 Malton Pale Ale, Double Chance, Pickwick's Porter, Crown Bitter, St Andrew's Top Marks Bitter and Owd Bob available plus guests.

The Malton Brewery Company was formed in 1984 by Bob Suddaby, Geoff Woollons and Colin Sykes in the converted stables behind Suddaby's Crown Hotel. The first pint was pulled in February 1985. The pub is traditional in character, located in the town centre and popular with locals and visitors alike. No juke box but pub games and TV showing the latest starting prices for the day's horse racing meetings. Bar food available at lunchtime (except Sunday and Tuesday). Parking, children's room. Accommodation.

PALE ALE 3.3% ABV
Hoppy and refreshing.
DOUBLE CHANCE BITTER 3.8% ABV
Fruity with good hoppy bitterness.
PICKWICK'S PORTER 4.2% ABV
Dark, smooth and malty.
CROWN BITTER 4.5% ABV
Smooth, with balanced flavours.
ST ANDREW'S TOP MARKS BITTER 5.2% ABV
Malty and bitter.
OWD BOB 6.0% ABV
A winter special.

 11am–11pm Mon–Sat; 12–4pm and 7–10.30pm Sun.

MEXBOROUGH

The Falcon
12 Main Street, Mexborough, South Yorkshire
S64 9DW
☎ *(01709) 513084* Mr Seedring

 Old Mill Bitter always available plus several seasonal, celebration or guest ales.

A traditional brewery tap room situated out of the town centre. No food. No children.

 All day Mon–Sat; 12–3pm and 7–10.30pm Sun.

MIDDLESBROUGH

The Isaac Wilson
61 Wilson Street, Middlesbrough, North Yorkshire TS1 1SB
☎ *(01642) 247708* Norma Hardisty

 Up to six guests, with Timothy Taylor Landlord a regular feature.

A town pub with food available 11am–10pm daily. No music or TV. Non-smoking area, disabled access. No children.

 All day, every day.

The Malt Shovel
92 Corporation Road, Middlesbrough, North Yorkshire TS1 2RR
☎ *(01642) 213213* Martin Gilbert

 Black Sheep Best Bitter and Special Strong Bitter always available plus many guest beers including a good selection from the smaller independents.

Live music and quiz nights. Food available at lunchtime. Parking, disabled toilets and children's area. Children not allowed in the bar.

 11am–11pm Mon–Sat; 12–10.30pm Sun.

NORTH DUFFIELD

The King's Arms
Main Street, North Duffield, Selby, North Yorkshire YO8 5RG
☎ *(01757) 288492* Martin Lamb

 A freehouse with Black Sheep Bitter always available plus up to three guests such as Timothy Taylor Landlord or a Hambleton, Jubilee or Lifeboat ale. Celebration ales as available.

A village pub with one bar, beamed ceilings and inglenook fireplace. Bar food available, plus restaurant menu in non-smoking restaurant during evenings only. Children allowed. Beer garden.

 4–11pm Mon–Fri; all day Sat–Sun.

The Tanner Hop

*2 Friarage Street, Northallerton, North Yorkshire
DL6 1DP*
☎ *(0160) 977 8482* Brian Simpson

Four guest ales always available. Two beer festivals held each year, each offering 12 different brews.

A very busy, lively town freehouse built in a converted furniture warehouse. All wooden floors, old wooden chairs and empty beer barrels. Jenga games available. Live music. Bar snacks available. Function room with catering for parties. Children allowed.

OPEN *7–11pm Mon–Wed; 7–12pm Thurs; 7pm–1am Fri; 2pm–1am Sat; 12–10.30pm Sun.*

The Hebble Brook

*2 Mill Lane, Old Mixenden, Halifax, West
Yorkshire HX2 8UH*
☎ *(01422) 242059* Teresa Ratcliffe

Black Sheep Special always available plus Old Mill Nellie Dean most of the time. Also up to five guests such as Thwaites Bloomin' Ale and Daniels Hammer or Banbury Old Vic.

A country community pub with lounge and games room. Stone floors in the games room, open fires, wooden ceilings in lounge, garden. Food currently available at lunchtime. No children.

OPEN *12–3pm and 5.30–11pm Mon–Thurs; all day Fri–Sun.*

The Brewer's Pride

*Low Mill Road, Healey Road, Ossett, West
Yorkshire WF5 8ND*
☎ *(01924) 273865* Sally Walker

A brewpub, home of the Ossett Brewing Company. Excelsior and Special Bitter always available as well as Timothy Taylor Landlord. Also up to four guests from breweries such as Durham, Morland, Coach House and Cottage.

A traditional real ale house in an old stone building in the old Healy Mills area. No music, etc. Open fires, beer garden. The Ossett Brewing Co. is on site with brewery tours available. Food available 12–2pm Mon–Sat; and Wednesday evenings. Children allowed up to 8pm.

OPEN *12–3pm and 5.30–11pm Mon–Thurs; all day Fri–Sun and bank holidays*

The Counting House

*Swales Yard, Pontefract, West Yorkshire
WF8 1DG*
☎ *(01977) 600388* Louise Horner

No permanent beers, just a changing range of up to eight ales from breweries such as Black Sheep, Jennings, Old Mill and Four Rivers.

A town pub on two levels in a medieval building. Food available at lunchtime only. Children allowed.

OPEN *11am–3pm and 7–11pm (10.30pm Sun).*

The Tap & Spile

*28 Horsefair, Pontefract, West Yorkshire
WF8 1NX*
☎ *(01977) 700679* Mr Coles

Tomlinson's Sessions and something from Cotleigh Brewery always available plus up to nine guest beers from everywhere.

Two beer festivals per year, usually in April and November. Situated opposite Pontefract bus station.

OPEN *12–11pm Mon–Sat; 12–3pm and 7–10.30pm Sun.*

The Hunter's Inn

*Harrogate Road, Pool-in-Wharfedale, Nr Otley,
North Yorkshire LS21 2PS*
☎ *(0113) 284 1090* Geoff Nunn

Seven guest beers always available (300+ per year), including brews from Abbeydale, Black Sheep, Cropton, Daleside, Durham, Enville, Everards, Fuller's, Goose Eye, Hook Norton, Sarah Hughes, Jennings, Kelham Island, Moorhouse's, Oakham, Greene King, Old Mill, Tomlinson's, Rooster's, Outlaw, Ossett, Rudgate, Slaters (Eccleshall), Hambleton, Black Dog, Marston Moor and many others from all over the country.

Pub with real ale, real fire and real characters, from bikers to business people. Warm, friendly welcome. Bar food available 12–2.30pm every day except Tuesdays. Car park, garden patio with tables and chairs, pool table, juke box, stone fireplace. Children are allowed but not encouraged too much (no play area). One mile from Pool-in-Wharfedale, on the Harrogate road. Seven miles from Harrogate.

OPEN *All day, every day.*

The Commercial Hotel

48 Chapetown, Pudsey, West Yorkshire LS28 8BS
☎ *(0113) 2577153 Michelle Farr*

 A freehouse serving a range of real ales.

A lively town pub with Friday evening
disco, Saturday evening '60s and '70s
music and live entertainment once a month.
Free dripping and black pudding on the bar
on Sundays. Patio. No children.

OPEN *All day, every day.*

One Eyed Rat

*51 Allhallowgate, Ripon, North Yorkshire
HG4 1LQ*
☎ *(01765) 607704*

 Timothy Taylor Landlord and Black
Sheep Bitter always available, plus four
guests, constantly changing, which may be
from Rooster's, Durham, Hambledon, Fuller's
or any other independent brewery. No beers
from national breweries served. A real
freehouse.

U nspoilt, terraced pub, very popular.
Superb beer garden. No food, no music,
no TV, but fine ales and good conversation.
Children allowed in beer garden only.

OPEN *6–11pm Mon–Wed; 12–2pm and 6–11pm
Thur–Fri; 12–3pm and 6–11pm Sat;
12–3pm Sun.*

The Highlander

*15–16 The Esplanade, Scarborough, North
Yorkshire YO11 2AF*
☎ *(01723) 373426 Mrs Dawson*

 Young's IPA among the brews always
available, plus up to five guests such as
Barnsley Bitter, Black Dog Whitby Abbey Ale,
Wyre Piddle Piddle in the Wind, Wychwood
Dog's Bollocks and Fisherman's Whopper.
Also a good selection of whiskies.

O n the South Cliff Esplanade, a traditional
pub with real fires. Food available at
lunchtime only in a separate dining area.
Children allowed until 6pm. Patio.
Accommodation.

OPEN *11am–11pm (10.30pm Sun).*

The Hole in the Wall

*26 Vernon Road, Scarborough, North Yorkshire
YO11 2NH*
☎ *(01723) 373746 Ann Pearson*

 A freehouse with Shepherd Neame
Master Brew, Fuller's ESB and one
Durham brewery beer always available, plus a
constantly changing range of guests such as
Timothy Taylor Landlord and ales from
across the country – Orkneys to Cornwall –
served as available. Some 2,000 beers served
over 16 years.

A traditional wooden-floored real ale pub
in a town location. No music, no games.
Food available at lunchtime only. No
children. Dogs welcome.

OPEN *11.30am–2.30pm and 7–11pm Mon–Fri;
11.30am–3pm and 7–11pm Sat; 12–3pm
and 7–10.30pm Sun.*

The Scalby Mills Hotel

*Scalby Mills Road, Scarborough, North Yorkshire
YO12 6RP*
☎ *(01723) 500449 Julia Bennett*

Daleside Monkey Wrench and Old
Lubrication always available, plus a
selection of guests including, perhaps,
Daleside Nightjar, Barnsley Bitter, Fools Gold
or Crackshot.

A seaside freehouse built in an old mill
with the Cleveland Way behind it. Two
bars, original stonework and beams. Outside
seating. Food available at lunchtime only.
Children allowed until 6pm. Dogs allowed in
the smaller of the two bars. Situated near the
Sealife Centre.

OPEN *All day, every day.*

The Tap & Spile

*94 Falsgrave Road, Scarborough, North Yorkshire
YO12 5AZ*
☎ *(01723) 363837*
IM Kilpatrick and V Office

Big Lamp Bitter always available plus
guest ales including Bateman, Jennings
and Old Mill brews and Tap & Spile
Premium. Also two guest ciders.

A lovely old coaching inn with low beams,
old Yorkshire stone floor and non-
smoking room. Bar food available
11.30am–3pm Mon–Fri, 11.30am–4.30pm
Sat, 12.30–3pm Sun. Car park, garden,
children's room. Turn left out of the railway
station, going towards the roundabout.

OPEN *11am–11pm.*

SELBY

The Albion Vaults
1 The Crescent, New Street, Selby, North Yorkshire YO8 4PT
☎ *(01757) 213817* Patrick Mellors

An Old Mill Brewery tied house serving only Old Mill ales. Old Traditional and Bullion always available, plus either Old Curiosity, Spring Eternal or Nellie Dean.

An old dark-wood pub with brick fireplaces, taproom and lounge. Beer garden, disabled access. Food available at lunchtime and evenings. Organises brewery tours of The Old Mill Brewery, which is four miles away, during October–April. Children allowed up to 7pm.

OPEN *12–11pm (10.30pm Sun).*

The Royal Oak
70 Ousegate, Selby, North Yorkshire YO8 4NJ
☎ *(01757) 291163* Simon Compton

Three guest pumps with ales such as Timothy Taylor Landlord, Eccleshall Top Totty or Swale Indian Summer Pale Ale.

A real ale pub comprising a balance of the traditional and the modern: live music in a Grade II listed building with wooden floors and original beams. Beer garden. No food. Children allowed on Sunday afternoons only.

OPEN *12pm–close.*

SHEFFIELD

The Broadfield
Abbeydale Road, Sheffield, South Yorkshire S7 1FR
☎ *(0114) 255 0200* Angela Jackson

Three or four guest ales such as Morland Old Speckled Hen, Wadworth 6X, seasonal and celebration ales available.

A two-bar pub with snooker and pool room and beer garden. Just out of the town centre. Food available 12–7pm daily, plus Sunday breakfast at 11am. Children allowed.

OPEN *11am–11pm Mon–Sat; 11am (for breakfast)–10.30pm Sun.*

Cask & Cutler
1 Henry Street, Infirmary Road, Sheffield, South Yorkshire S3 7EQ
☎ *(0114) 249 2295* Neil Clarke

Six regularly changing guest beers (400 new ones last year), including a pale, hoppy bitter, a mild and a stout or porter. Main breweries used are Durham, Glentworth, Hart, Ossett, Whim, Abbeydale, Church End and Cottage. No nationals. Also serve Weston's Old Rosie cider. There are plans to open a micro-brewery at the rear of the pub.

A largely unspoilt, two-roomed street-corner local. Bar food available Tues–Fri lunchtimes. On-street parking. Real fire in cold weather. Beer garden. Situated 100 yards from Shalesmoor supertram stop. Adjacent to the junction of the A61 and B6079, one mile north of the city centre.

OPEN *5.30–11pm Mon; 12–2pm and 5.30–11pm Tues–Thur; 12–11pm Fri–Sat; 12–3pm and 7–10.30pm Sun.*

The Fat Cat
23 Alma Street, Sheffield, South Yorkshire S3 8SA
☎ *(0114) 249 4801*

Kelham Island brews plus six guest beers, constantly alternating. In total, the pub has now served more than 3,100 guest ales.

This olde-worlde pub is a Kelham Island Brewery tied house, with no music, no machines, real fires and ten real ales. It is situated in a back street near the city centre. Food served at lunchtime. Parking, garden, children's room.

OPEN *12–3pm and 5.30–11pm Mon–Sat; 12–3pm and 7–10.30pm Sun.*

The Frog & Parrot
Division Street, Sheffield, South Yorkshire S1 4GF
☎ *(0114) 272 1280* Mr Perkins

A brewpub with a selection of own brews always available. Guests served between June and September, one at a time, such as Marston's Pedigree or a Castle Eden ale.

A one-bar town pub, a young person's venue, particularly at weekends. Bar food available at lunchtime from 12–2pm and 12" pizzas served in the evenings until 11pm. No children.

MR DOO'S 3.4% ABV
RECKLESS 4.6% ABV
ARMAGEDDON 6.2% ABV
CONQUEROR 6.9% ABV
ROGER AND OUT 12.6% ABV
Served in third-of-a-pint measures.

OPEN *11am–11pm (10.30pm Sun).*

Morrissey's East House

19 Spital Hill, Sheffield, South Yorkshire S4 7LG
☎ *(0114) 272 6916* Rita Fielding

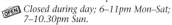 A freehouse with Timothy Taylor Landlord and Abbeydale Moonshine among the beers always available, plus one guest such as Morland Old Speckled Hen or Timothy Taylor Dark Mild or Golden Best.

A student pub, situated conveniently close to the local curry houses! No food. Children allowed until 8pm.

OPEN *Closed during day; 6–11pm Mon–Sat; 7–10.30pm Sun.*

The Old Grindstone

3 Crookes, Sheffield, South Yorkshire S10 1UA
☎ *(0114) 266 0322* Margaret Shaw

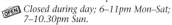 Up to six guest ales such as Glentworth Full Monty and Little Gem. The repeating of beers is generally avoided.

A one-bar local community pub. Food available at lunchtime and evenings. No children.

OPEN *All day, every day.*

The Tap & Spile

48 Waingate, Sheffield, South Yorkshire S3 8LB
☎ *(0114) 272 6270* K Fletcher

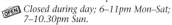 Tap & Spile Bitter and Premium always available plus six guest beers (200 per year) from independent brewers only.

A traditional alehouse with two rooms. Traditional pub games (no pool), background music only. Folk music Wednesdays, quiz night Thursdays. Bar food available at lunchtime. Situated 100 yards from Sheffield canal basin, five minutes from the railway station.

OPEN *11.30am–3pm and 5.30–11pm Mon–Fri; 11.30am–3pm and 7–11pm Sat; 7–10.30pm Sun.*

SOWERBY BRIDGE

The Moorcock Inn

Norland, Sowerby Bridge, West Yorkshire HX6 3RP
☎ *(01422) 832103* Mr Kitson

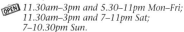 A freehouse with Samuel Smith Old Brewery Bitter always available plus two guest ales including, perhaps, Coach House Innkeeper's Special Reserve or Phoenix Old Oak Bitter.

A one-bar country pub with wooden beams, restaurant and outside area. Food available at lunchtime and evenings. Children allowed. Disabled access.

OPEN *12–3pm and 5.30–11pm (10.30pm Sun).*

The Moorings

Canal Basin, Sowerby Bridge, West Yorkshire HX6 2AG
☎ *(01422) 833940* Tony Mulgraw

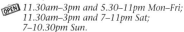 Black Sheep Special among the brews always available plus three guests, often from Ossett (such as Silver King, Silver Link, Quick Silver or Silver Fox) but also from Moorhouse's and Kitchen.

A small family-run pub with good quality beers, food and service. Beams, stone walls, wooden floors. Function room. Seating on canal side. Food available at lunchtime and evenings. Children allowed.

OPEN *12–11pm (10.30pm Sun).*

The Navigation Inn

47 Holmes Road, Sowerby Bridge, West Yorkshire HX6 3LF
☎ *(01422) 831636* Andy Dawson

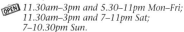 Two Tom Eastwood beers always available plus one guest such as Moorhouse's Navigation (a house brew produced especially for The Navigation Inn).

An old country village pub near a boatyard. Two bars, two gardens. Holiday cottage next door available for rent. Food available Wed–Sun lunchtime and evenings. Children allowed.

OPEN *12–3pm and 4.30–11pm Mon–Thurs; all day Fri–Sun.*

STAVELEY

The Royal Oak

Main Street, Staveley, Nr Knaresborough, North Yorkshire HG5 9LD
☎ *(01423) 340267*

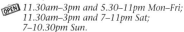 Four beers always available plus two guests (25 per year) from small independent breweries.

A typical country pub, cosy, friendly, with open fires and two bars. Bar and restaurant food available at lunchtime and evenings (not Sunday and Monday evenings). Car park, garden, children's play area.

OPEN *12–3pm and 6–11pm Mon–Sat; 12–5pm and 7–10.30pm Sun.*

The White Swan

1 West End, Stokesley, Middlesbrough, North Yorkshire TS9 5BL
☎ *(01642) 710263*
June Harrison and Brian Skipp

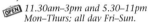 A brewpub with the full range of Captain Cook Brewery beers brewed on site and always available in the pub. Also occasional guests such as Daleside Crackshot and Castle Eden Ale.

A market town pub with one bar, open fire, no music or games. Brewery on premises, tours available. Winner of the National Ploughman's Award 1997. Ploughman's (selection of 20 cheeses), pâtés and cold pies only. No children.

OPEN *11.30am–3pm and 5.30–11pm Mon–Thurs; all day Fri–Sun.*

St Vincent Arms

Main Street, Sutton upon Derwent, East Yorkshire
☎ *(01904) 608349* Philip Hopwood

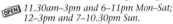 Fuller's Chiswick, London Pride and ESB and Timothy Taylor Landlord always available plus guests including Adnams Extra, Old Mill Bitter, Charles Wells Bombardier, Mansfield Old Baily and seasonal and special ales.

About 200 years old, with white-washed walls. Two bars, four rooms, open fires. Bar and restaurant food available at lunchtime and evenings. Car park, beer garden, non-smoking room. Children allowed. On main road through village.

OPEN *11.30am–3pm and 6–11pm Mon–Sat; 12–3pm and 7–10.30pm Sun.*

Canal Tavern

South Parade, Thorne, Doncaster, South Yorkshire DN8 5DZ
☎ *(01405) 813688* Mr Murrigton

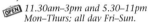 A freehouse with one guest ale changing weekly and not repeated if at all possible. Examples have included Thwaites Bloomin' Ale, Greene King Triumph and Marston's Pedigree.

A two-bar canalside country pub with dining area. Coal fires in winter, waterside beer garden. Food available at lunchtime and evenings. Children allowed, if eating.

OPEN *11am–3pm and 5.30–11pm Mon–Fri; all day Sat–Sun.*

The Spotted Ox

Westfield Road, Tockwith, York, North Yorkshire YO26 7PY
☎ *(01423) 358387* James Ray

 A freehouse with a selection of three cask ales always available, constantly changing.

A country pub with three bars decorated with the pump clips of past beers sold. Food available at lunchtime and evenings. Beer garden. Children allowed.

OPEN *All day in summer; in winter 11am–3pm and 5.30–11pm Mon–Thurs; all day Fri–Sun.*

The Talbot & Falcon

58 Northgate, Wakefield, West Yorkshire WF1 3AP
☎ *(01924) 201693* Glen Plunkett

 Marston's Pedigree and Timothy Taylor Landlord always available plus a range of guest ales such as Hop Back Summer Lightning, Badger Tanglefoot and something form Broughton and Tomintoul. Also specials from breweries such as Leatherbritches and Malcolm's of Grimsby when available. Beer Festivals held four to six times a year.

A traditional town-centre pub under refurbishment. Plans for dining area. Disabled access. Food available 12–7pm. Children allowed. Located by the bus station.

OPEN *11am–11pm (10.30pm Sun).*

The White Hart

77 Westgate End, Wakefield, West Yorkshire WF2 9RL
☎ *(01924) 375887*
Debbie Chetwood and David Hobson

 Six real ales always available from a wide range of independent breweries. Beers changed weekly.

A traditional alehouse with flagstone floors and real log fires in winter. All-year-round beer garden, which is covered and heated in winter. Quiz night on Tuesdays. Free supper served on Tuesdays, Wednesdays and Sundays. Well-behaved children allowed.

OPEN *12–11pm (10.30pm Sun).*

WENTWORTH

The George & Dragon

85 Main Street, Wentworth, Rotherham, South Yorkshire S62 7TN
☎ *(01226) 742440* Gary and John Sweeting

🍺 A freehouse always serving Timothy Taylor Landlord and a Stones ale, plus a good selection of guests, not repeated if possible, from breweries such as Ossett, Glentworth and Oakham.

A country village pub with two bars, two real fires and stone floors. Breakfast served 10am–12pm; lunch served 12–2.30pm and evening meals served 5.30–9pm in a separate dining area. Large beer garden with children's playground. Children allowed if eating.

OPEN *10am–11pm (10.30pm Sun).*

WHITBY

The Duke of York

Church Street, Whitby, North Yorkshire YO22 4DE
☎ *(01947) 600324* Laurie Bradley

🍺 Whitby's Black Dog Special often available plus two guests such as Timothy Taylor Landlord and Adnams Regatta.

A seafaring pub, a mix of the traditional and the modern, with oak beams and modern decor. Food available 12–9pm. Children allowed.

OPEN *All day, every day.*

Tap & Spile

New Quay Road, Whitby, North Yorkshire YO21 1DH
☎ *(01947) 603937* Mr Fleming

🍺 Mansfield Tap & Spile always available, plus four guests such as Daleside Country Style and Four Rivers Moondance. Around 450 beers served in the past five years. Celebration and seasonal ales where possible.

A three-roomed town pub with two bars, wooden floors and beams and one non-smoking room. Food available every day from 12pm. Children allowed in designated area. Entertainment most nights (generally Folk music and Irish bands, Blues on Wednesday). Located by the railway station.

OPEN *All day, every day.*

WOMBWELL

Royal Oak Hotel

13 Burch Street, Wombwell, South Yorkshire
☎ *(01254) 883541* Helen Jones

🍺 Five real ales available from a long list including Brewery on Sea Spinnaker Bitter and Bateman brews.

A 1920s-style town-centre pub. Bar food available at lunchtime and evenings. Car park, accommodation. Children allowed at restricted times.

OPEN *11am–11pm Mon–Sat; 12–10.30pm Sun.*

WORTLEY

Wortley Arms Hotel

Halifax Road, Wortley, South Yorkshire S30 4DB
☎ *(0114) 288 2245*

🍺 Home of the Wortley Brewery, with Wortley beers brewed and served on the premises plus a range of guests.

The brewery started up in December 1991 producing Earls Ale. It closed for six weeks in spring 1992 for refurbishment. The sixteenth-century coaching house inn has oak beams, wood panels and an open fire. Bar and restaurant food available at lunchtime and evenings. Car park, children's room, no-smoking room, accommodation.

BEST BITTER 3.6% ABV
EARLS ALE 4.2% ABV
COUNTESS ALE 5.8% ABV

OPEN *12–2.30pm and 5.30–11pm Mon–Fri; 12–11pm Sat; 12–3pm and 7–10.30pm Sun.*

YORK

The Blue Bell

53 Fossgate, York, North Yorkshire YO1 9TF
☎ *(0190) 465 4904* Mr T Worrall

🍺 Marston's Pedigree always available, plus up to five constantly changing guest ales.

The smallest pub in York with the oldest pub interior in York (last decorated in 1903). Two small rooms with bar in between and drinking corridor. Lookalike real fires! Sandwiches available until 4pm Mon–Sat. No children.

OPEN *12–11pm (10.30pm Sun).*

The Maltings

Tanners Moat, York, North Yorkshire YO1 16HU
☎ *(01904) 655387* Maxine Collinge

Black Sheep Bitter always available plus six guests changing daily (700 per year). Too many to mention but with an emphasis on small, independent brewers. Beer festivals twice a year. Also Belgian bottled and draught beers, fruit wines and four traditional ciders.

S mall city-centre freehouse. CAMRA Yorkshire Pub of the Year 1994–95 and Cask Ale Pub of Great Britain 1998. Pub grub served at lunchtime. Situated on Lendal Bridge. Further information available on website www.maltings.co.uk.

OPEN *11am–11pm Mon–Sat; 12–10.30pm Sun.*

Spread Eagle

98 Walmgate, York, North Yorkshire
☎ *(01904) 635868* Michael Dandy

Seven or eight beers always available. Guests including Mansfield Riding Bitter and Old Baily and Timothy Taylor Landlord.

P opular Victorian-style freehouse. Bar and restaurant food available at lunchtime and evenings. Garden. Children allowed.

OPEN *11am–11pm Mon–Sat; 12–10.30pm Sun.*

The Tap & Spile

Monkgate, York, North Yorkshire
☎ *(01904) 656158* Vicki Office

Eleven beers always available from a long list including Old Mill Bitter and brews from Marston Moor, Big Lamp and Ushers.

T raditional city-centre alehouse. Bar food available at lunchtime and evenings. Car park, garden. Children not allowed.

OPEN *11.30am–11.30pm Mon–Sat; 12–10.30pm Sun.*

YOU TELL US

★ *Barnes Wallace*, Station Road, Howden
★ *Beer Street*, Nowell's Yard, Dewsbury
★ *The Bell Hotel*, Market Place, Driffield
★ *The Black Horse Inn*, The Green, Altwick
★ *The Blacksmith's Arms*, Main Street, Flaxton
★ *Boon's*, Queen Street, Horbury
★ *The Brewer's Arms*, 10 Pontefract Road, Snaith
★ *The Concertina Band Club*, 9a Dolcliffe Road, Mexborough
★ *The Cross Keys*, 283 Halifax Road, Hightown
★ *The Cross Keys*, 649 Rochdale Road, Walsden, Todmorden
★ *The Crown*, Main Street, Dishforth
★ *The Duke of Wellington*, 104 Peel Street, Hull
★ *The Elm Tree*, 5 Elm Tree Square, Embsay
★ *Fanny's Ale & Cider House*, 63 Saltaire Road, Shipley
★ *The Fleece*, Ripponden Bank, Barkisland, Ripponden
★ *The Fleece Inn*, 67 Main Street, Haworth
★ *George & the Dragon*, Market Place, Kirkbymoorside
★ *George & the Dragon*, Main Street, Melmerby
★ *Hill Inn*, Chapel-le-Dale
★ *Indigo Alley*, 4 North Main Road, Scarborough
★ *The Jug Inn*, Main Street, Chapel Haddlesey
★ *The Keighley & Worth Railway Buffet Car*, The Station, Keighley
★ *Keystones*, 4 Monkgate, York
★ *The King's Head*, Gunnerside
★ *The King's Head*, Market Place, Malton
★ *The Kirklands Hotel*, 605 Leeds Road, Outwood
★ *Limes*, 38 Broom Lane, Rotherham
★ *The Lord Rosebery*, 85–7 Westborough, Scarborough
★ *The Lundhill Tavern*, Beechhouse Road, Hemingfield
★ *Mr Boon's*, Denby Dale, Huddersfield
★ *The Marton Arms*, Thornton-in-Lonsdale
★ *The Midhopestones Arms*, Mortimer Road, Midhopestones
★ *Milestone*, 12 Peaks Mount, Waterthorpe, Sheffield
★ *The Minerva Hotel*, Nelson Street, Hull
★ *The Mission*, Posterngate, Hull
★ *The Moorcock Inn*, Langdale End
★ *The New Barrack Tavern*, 601 Penistone Road, Sheffield
★ *The Old Bridge Inn*, Priest Lane, Ripponden
★ *The Old Hall Inn*, Threshfield
★ *The Packhorse Hotel*, Carr Lane, Laithwaite
★ *The Red Lion*, Clarence Street, Hull
★ *The Queen's Head*, Wednesday Market, Beverley
★ *The Star Inn*, Weaverthorpe
★ *The Station Hotel*, Knott Lane, Easingwold
★ *The Tap & Spile*, Flemingate, Beverley
★ *The Tap & Spile*, 26 Sackville Street, Bradford
★ *The Tap & Spile*, Spring Bank, Hull
★ *The Tap & Spile*, High Street, Northallerton
★ *The Tempest Arms*, Elslack
★ *The Waggon & Horses*, 48 Gillygate, York
★ *The Zetland Hotel*, 9 High Street, Marske

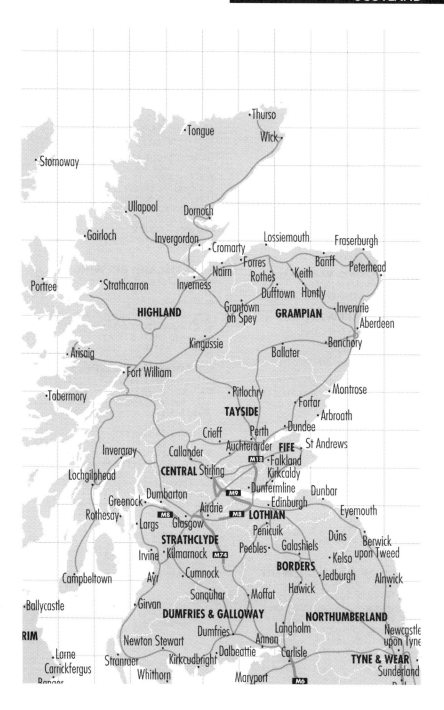

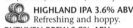

AVIEMORE BREWERY CO. LTD

Unit 12, Dalfaber Industrial Estate, Aviemore PH22 1PY
☎ *(01479) 812060 (Brewery tours)*

HIGHLAND IPA 3.6% ABV
Refreshing and hoppy.
RUTHVEN BREW 3.8% ABV
Copper-coloured and malty with delicate bitterness.
STRATHSPEY 4.2% ABV
Dark, hoppy and complex.
WOLFE'S BREW 4.6% ABV
Dark and well-balanced.
WEE MURDOCH 4.8% ABV
Powerful malt flavour with some hoppiness.
CAIRNGORM 5.0% ABV
Golden, refreshing and far too easy to drink.

BEER NECESSITIES

101–3 St. Leonards Street, Edinburgh EH8 9QY
☎ *(0131) 667 9160*

ST LEONARD'S ALE 4.0% ABV
CAPITAL ALE 4.2% ABV
ARTHUR'S ALE 4.2% ABV

BELHAVEN BREWERY CO.

Spott Road, Dunbar EH42 1RS
☎ *(01368) 862734*

60/- 2.9% ABV
Roast character with smooth malty palate.
70/- 3.5% ABV
Nutty with a light sweet finish.
SANDY HUNTER'S TRADITONAL ALE 3.6% ABV
Malty and nutty palate with hoppy nose and flavour.
IPA 4.0% ABV
80/- 4.2% ABV
Malty and nutty.
ST ANDREW'S ALE 4.9% ABV
Well-balanced and distinctive with dry after-palate.
Plus seasonal brews.

BLACK ISLE BREWERY

Taeblair, Munlochy IV8 8NZ
☎ *(01463) 811304*

RED KITE 4.2% ABV

BRIDGE OF ALLAN BREWERY

Queen's Lane, Bridge of Allan, Stirling SK9 4HD
☎ *(01786) 834555*

STIRLING DARK MILD 3.2% ABV
STIRLING BITTER 3.7% ABV
STIRLING BRIG 4.2% ABV
STIRLING IPA 4.2% ABV
Plus seasonal ales.

BROUGHTON ALES LTD

Broughton ML12 6HQ
☎ *(01899) 830345 (Brewery tours)*

IPA 3.8% ABV
Summer ale.
GREENMANTLE ALE 3.9% ABV
Maltiness, with bittersweet flavour, and hoppy finish.
SPECIAL BITTER 3.9% ABV
As above, but dry-hopped.
MERLIN'S ALE 4.2% ABV
Gold-coloured, with dry hop flavour combined with malt.
OATMEAL STOUT 4.2% ABV
Powerful, malty flavour and hoppy bitterness.
80/- 4.2% ABV
THE GHILLIE 4.5% ABV
Hoppy fruit flavours throughout.
BLACK DOUGLAS 5.2% ABV
Dark and malty.
OLD JOCK 6.7% ABV
Dark copper-coloured, with fruit and roast flavours.

BURNTISLAND BREWING CO.

Burntisland Brewery, High Street, Burntisland KY3 9AA
☎ *(01592) 873333*

BLESSING OF BURNTISLAND 3.8% ABV
ALEXANDER'S DOWNFALL 4.3% ABV
DOCKYARD RIVETS 5.1% ABV
Excellent, lager style.

CALEDONIAN BREWING CO.

42 Slateford Road, Edinburgh EH11 1PH
☎ *(0131) 3371286 (Brewery tours)*

70/- 3.5% ABV
Refreshing and malty with delicate hoppiness.
DEUCHARS IPA 3.8% ABV
Pale, well-hopped and refreshing. Ever-popular.
80/- 4.1% ABV
Golden, full-flavoured award winner.
ERA 4.1% ABV
Ruby-coloured, with roast malt flavour.
PORTER 4.1% ABV
Dark, with powerful chocolate malt flavour.
MURRAYS HEAVY 4.3% ABV
Malty sweetness with good hoppy balance.
DOUBLE AMBER 4.6% ABV
Rich, malty and full-bodied.
GOLDEN PROMISE 5.0% ABV
Light-coloured, hoppy organic beer.
EDINBURGH STRONG ALE 6.4% ABV
Powerful, but easy-drinking for gravity.
Plus seasonal beers.

HARVIESTOUN BREWERY LTD

Devon Road, Dollar FK14 7LX
☎ *(01259) 742141*

 BROOKER'S BITTER & TWISTED 3.8% ABV
Blond with refreshing citrus fruit flavours.

WAVERLEY 70/- 3.7% ABV
Refreshing and hoppy with lingering finish.

ORIGINAL 80/- 4.1% ABV
Malty, with balancing hops and fruit. Some sweetness.

PTARMIGAN 4.5% ABV
Pale, with Bavarian hops.

SCHIEHALLION 4.8% ABV
Superb, real cask lager.

Plus seasonal and occasional brews.

HEATHER ALE

Craigmill, Strathaven ML10 6PB
☎ *(01357) 529529*

 FRAOCH 4.1% ABV
Heather ale – available all year.

GROZET 5.0% ABV
Gooseberry wheat beer – available Aug–Nov.

PICTISH 5.3% ABV
Heather ale – available Dec–Mar.

EBULUM 6.5% ABV
Elderberry black – available Oct–Jan.

THE INVERALMOND BREWERY

Inveralmond Way, Inveralmond, Perth PH1 3UQ
☎ *(01738) 449448*

 INDEPENDENCE 3.8% ABV
Well-balanced malt and hops with some spiciness.

OSSIAN'S ALE 4.1% ABV
Golden and hoppy.

THRAPPLEDOUSER 4.3% ABV
Amber, quenching with good hoppiness.

LIA FAIL 4.7% ABV
Smooth, dark and full-flavoured.

THE ISLE OF SKYE BREWING CO. (LEANN AN EILEIN) LTD

Uig, IV51 9XY
☎ *(01470) 542477 (Brewery tours)*

 YOUNG PRETENDER 4.0% ABV
Gold-coloured and lightly hopped with dry finish.

RED CUILLIN 4.2% ABV
Slightly malty, with some fruit and hoppy finish.

HEBRIDEAN GOLD 4.3% ABV
Smooth with good hoppy bitterness.

BLACK CUILLIN 4.5% ABV
Stout-like, with hints of chocolate and honey.

BLAVEN 5.0% ABV
Golden, fruity and well-balanced.

MACLAY GROUP PLC

Thistle Brewery, Alloa FK10 1ED
☎ *(01259) 723387*

 60/- ALE 3.4% ABV
70/- ALE 3.6% ABV
Copper-coloured and hoppy.

BROADSWORD 3.8% ABV
Amber, full-bodied and fruity.

80/- ALE 4.0% ABV
Smooth and full-flavoured.

KANE'S AMBER 4.0% ABV
Hoppy and well-balanced.

WALLACE INDIA PALE ALE 4.5% ABV
Easy-quaffing IPA.

OAT MEAL STOUT 4.5% ABV
Smooth and fruity with a hint of chocolate malt.

Plus seasonal brews.

THE ORKNEY BREWERY

Quoyloo, Sandwick KW16 3LT
☎ *(01856) 841802 (B/tours)*

 NORTHERN LIGHT 3.8% ABV
Golden, refreshing and mellow.

RAVEN ALE 3.8% ABV
Superb malt, hop, citrus fruit flavours and nuttiness.

DRAGONHEAD STOUT 4.0% ABV
Black, powerful roast maltiness, with nutty flavours.

THE RED MACGREGOR 4.0% ABV
Mellow and malty with nut and hoppy finish.

DARK ISLAND 4.6% ABV
Smooth, flavour-packed and easy to drink.

SKULLSPLITTER 8.5% ABV
Beautifully smooth and hoppy with dry finish.

SULWATH BREWERS LTD

Gillfoot Brewery, Southerness, Kirkbean DG2 8AY
☎ *(01387) 255849 (Brewery tours)*

 KNOCKENDOCH 3.8% ABV
CRIFFEL 4.6% ABV

Plus occasional brews.

TOMINTOUL BREWERY

*Mill of Auchriachan, Tomintoul, Ballindalloch
AB37 9EQ*
☎ *(01807) 580333*

 LAIRD'S ALE 3.8% ABV
Dark, malty 70/- with hoppy balance.

STAG 4.1% ABV
Hoppy with balancing, soft maltiness.

NESSIE'S MONSTER MASH 4.4% ABV
Rounded, with malt flavours.

NO.3X 4.4% ABV
Dark, full-bodied and sweet throughout.

CULLODEN 4.6% ABV
Dark, with nutty flavour and some hoppiness.

WILD CAT 5.1% ABV
Complex malt and fruit, with powerful
hoppiness.

Plus monthly beers.

TRAQUAIR HOUSE BREWERY

Traquair Estate, Innerleithen EH44 6PW
☎ *(01896) 831370 (B/tours)*

 BEAR ALE 5.0% ABV
Full-bodied and fruity with good dryness
in the hoppy finish.

VALHALLA BREWERY

New House, Baltasound, Unst ZE2 9DX
☎ *(01957) 711348*

 AULD ROCK 4.5% ABV
Smooth, malty and full-bodied robust
hoppiness.

BORDERS

Places Featured:

Allanton	Greenlaw
Bonchester Bridge	Innerleithen
Denholm	Newcastleton
Eyemouth	St Mary's Loch
Galashiels	

THE PUBS

ALLANTON

The Allanton Inn

Allanton, Duns, Berwickshire TD11 3JZ
☎ *(01890) 818260* John Ward

A free house with four pumps offering a
range that changes weekly. Ales from
Northumberland, Border and Belhaven
breweries are all popular in a mix of nationals
and independents.

A country inn with pool, darts and a juke
box. Restaurant, en suite bed and
breakfast. Food at lunchtime and evenings.
Children allowed. Signposted.

OPEN *12–2.30pm Mon–Fri; 6–11pm Mon–Wed;
6pm–12am Thurs; 6–1am Fri; all day
Sat–Sun.*

BONCHESTER BRIDGE

Horse & Hound Hotel

Bonchester Bridge, Hawick TD9 8JN
☎ *(01450) 860645* Mr and Mrs Hope

Maclay, Charles Wells and Border brews
always available plus a guest beer
(20 per year) perhaps from Longstone,
Bateman, Jennings, Caledonian, Belhaven
or Holt breweries.

A former coaching inn dating from 1704
with comfortable accommodation and
non-smoking areas. Bar and restaurant food is
available at lunchtime and evenings. Car
park. Children's certificate. Hawick is seven
miles from Carter Bar on the
England–Scotland border.

OPEN *11.30am–3pm and 6–11pm.*

DENHOLM

Auld Cross Keys Inn

Main Street, Denholm, Roxburghshire TD9 8NU
☎ *(01450) 870305* Peter Ferguson

 A freehouse with eight pumps offering real ales supplied through the Broughton brewery, rotated and constantly changing.

P ublic bar, lounge bar, function room. Food lunchtimes and evenings. Children allowed.

5–11pm Mon; 11am–2.30pm and 5–11pm Tues–Wed; 11am–2.30pm and 5pm–12am Thurs; 11am–2pm and 5pm–1am Fri; all day Sat and Sun.

EYEMOUTH

The Ship Hotel

Harbour Road, Eyemouth, Berwickshire TD14 5HT
☎ *(01890) 750224* Mr RD Anderson

 Leased from Carlsberg Tetley, this pub has Caledonian 80/- and Border Farne Island Pale Ale always available. A guest, changed frequently in summer, is also offered. Caledonian Deuchars IPA is a popular choice.

A local fishermen's pub and family-run hotel near the harbour with lounge bar and separate dining area. Food at lunchtime and evenings. Children allowed.

All day, every day.

GALASHIELS

Ladhope Inn

33 High Buckholmside, Galashiels, Borders TD1 2HR
☎ *(01896) 752446* Mrs Johnston

 A freehouse with a varied range of constantly changing ales.

O n the main road; first pub on the A7. Toasted sandwiches only. Children allowed.

All day, every day.

GREENLAW

Cross Keys Inn

3 The Square, Greenlaw, Duns TD10 6UD
☎ *(01361) 10247* Mary O'Brian

Two real ales always available, regulars including Timothy Taylor Landlord and Caledonian Deuchars IPA.

A very old-fashioned freehouse with one bar and a restaurant area. Food at lunchtime and evenings. Children allowed.

Closed daily between 2.30 and 5pm.

INNERLEITHEN

Traquair Arms Hotel

Traquair Road, Innerleithen, Borders EH44 6PD
☎ *(01896) 830229* Mr Anderson

A freehouse with real ales on three pumps offering the local Traquair House Bear Ale on draught. Broughton Greenmantle Ale and Black Douglas also often available plus occasional others.

A country-style pub with one bar and separate dining area. Food served all day. Children allowed.

All day, every day.

NEWCASTLETON

The Grapes Hotel

16 Douglas Square, Newcastleton, Roxburghshire TD9 0QD
☎ *(01387) 375245* Jim McDonald

Up to eight pumps operating, with Caledonian Deuchars IPA among the beers always available. Guests are changed monthly.

A small hotel with restaurant. Food at lunchtimes and evenings. Children allowed until 8.30pm (residents later).

All day, every day.

ST MARY'S LOCH

Tibbie Shiels Inn

St Mary's Loch, Selkirk, Borders TD7 5LH
☎ *(01750) 42231* Mrs Brown

A freehouse offering two real ales, usually Broughton Greenmantle Ale and Caledonian 80/-.

A remote coaching inn with a non-smoking dining area. Food at lunchtime and evenings. Children allowed.

All day, every day.

Places Featured:

Alva
Bridge of Allan
Dollar
Dunblane

Pool of Muckhart
Sauchie
Stirling
Tillicoultry

THE PUBS

ALVA

Cross Keys Inn
*120 Stirling Street, Alva, Clackmannanshire
FK12 5EH*
☎ *(01259) 760409* Mrs Michie

Tied to Maclay with three of the brewery's ales always available. Up to three guests, changed weekly, may include Brains Buckley's Best or Maclay 80/- and Wallace IPA.

An old-fashioned pub with two bars. Food at lunchtime and evenings. Children allowed.

[OPEN] *All day, every day.*

BRIDGE OF ALLAN

The Queen's Hotel
*24 Henderson Street, Bridge of Allan, Stirling,
Stirlingshire FK9 4HD*
☎ *(01786) 833268* Mr Ross

A freehouse with beers Stirling Brig, Bitter, IPA and Dark Mild from the local Bridge of Allan Brewery permanently available, plus seasonal specials. Also Burton brews.

A two-bar pub with restaurant and occasional live entertainment. Food at lunchtime and evenings. Children allowed.

[OPEN] *All day, every day.*

DOLLAR

Castle Campbell Hotel
*11 Bridge Street, Dollar, Clackmannanshire
FK14 7DE*
☎ *(01259) 742519* Miss Cara Walters

A freehouse with real ale on two pumps. Usually Fuller's London Pride and Harviestoun 80/-.

A traditional, very busy pub with a separate dining area and lounge bar. Food at lunchtime and evenings. Children allowed.

[OPEN] *All day, every day.*

The King's Seat Inn
*19 Bridge Street, Dollar, Clackmannanshire
FK14 7DE*
☎ *(01259) 742515* Mr and Mrs McGuee

Seven beers always available from a constantly changing range (300 per year) including Fuller's London Pride, Timothy Taylor Landlord, Orkney Dark Island, Eldridge Pope Thomas Hardy and others from Adnams, Caledonian, Jennings, Harviestoun, Burton Bridge and Greene King breweries.

A village inn serving families (with a children's certificate). Bar and restaurant food available at lunchtime and evenings. Parking. Accommodation. Dollar is on the main A91 road between Stirling and St Andrews.

[OPEN] *11am–2.30pm and 5pm–12am Mon–Sat;
12.30–2.30pm and 6.30–11pm Sun.*

The Lorne Tavern
*17 Argyll Street, Dollar, Clackmannanshire
FK14 7AR*
☎ *(01259) 743423* Jim Nelson

A freehouse with Harviestoun and Abbeydale brews always available. Two pumps, changed every four days, offer guests which include regulars from Backdykes and Inveralmond breweries. Others featured include the Maclay range.

A traditional local with separate restaurant. Children allowed in the dining room.

[OPEN] *All day, every day.*

DUNBLANE

The Tappit Hen
Kirk Street, Dunblane, Perthshire FK15 0AL
☎ *(01786) 825226* Eric Billett

Up to four real ales changed weekly including something from Belhaven.

A one-bar community pub. No food. No children. Opposite the cathedral.

[OPEN] *All day, every day.*

The Muckhart Inn

Pool of Muckhart, Muckhart, Clackmannanshire
FK14 7JN
☎ *(01259) 781324* Derek Graham

A freehouse and micro-brewery serving Devon Original, Pride and Thick Black plus others.

A one-bar pub with beamed ceilings and log fires. Food at lunchtime and evenings. Children allowed.

OPEN *All day, every day.*

Mansfield Arms

7 Main Street, Sauchie, Nr Alloa,
Clackmannanshire FK10 3JR
☎ *(01259) 722020* John Gibson

Three beers brewed and served on the premises.

CAMRA Scottish Pub of the Year in 1993, started brewing in May 1994. The four-barrel brewhouse was built from spare parts and discarded equipment and now produces cask ales in the English tradition. Food is available in the bar until 9pm. Car park, garden. Children allowed. Just north of Alloa.

DEVON ORIGINAL 3.8% ABV
DEVON THICK BLACK 4.1% ABV
DEVON PRIDE 4.6% ABV

OPEN *11am–midnight.*

The Birds & Bees

Easter Cornton Road, Causewayhead, Stirling
FK9 5PB
☎ *(01786) 463384* Darren Mitchell

A freehouse with three real ales on the menu. Caledonian 80/- and Fuller's London Pride always available, plus one guest a week.

A traditional farmhouse-style pub in the middle of a housing estate. Food at lunchtime and evenings. Children allowed.

OPEN *10am–3pm and 5pm–12am Mon–Thurs; all day Fri–Sun.*

The Woolpack

1 Glassford Square, Tillicoultry,
Clackmannanshire FK13 6AH
☎ *(01259) 750332* Mr D McGhee

A freehouse with Harviestoun Ptarmigan 85/- and Orkney Dark Island always available. A guest beer, changed every two days, is also offered.

Built around 1700, a one-bar pub with restaurant and children's room. Food served all day. No children in the bar. Off the beaten track, no signposts. Head towards the Glen.

OPEN *All day, every day.*

Places Featured:

Bladnoch	Haugh of Urr
Canonbie	Kirkcudbright
Castle Douglas	Langholm
Dalbeattie	Lockerbie
Dumfries	Newton Stewart
Gatehouse of Fleet	Portpatrick
Glenluce	

THE PUBS

BLADNOCH

The Bladnoch Inn
Bladnoch, Wigtown, Nr Newton Stewart,
Wigtownshire DG8 9AB
☎ *(01988 402200)* Peter McLaughlin

Freehouse with up to nine beers available including Sulwath Criffel and Morland Old Speckled Hen. Others from breweries such as Belhaven are rotated twice-weekly.

A country inn and restaurant overlooking the river next to the old distillery. Food at lunchtime and evenings. Children allowed.

OPEN *All day, every day.*

CANONBIE

The Riverside
Canonbie DG14 0UX
☎ *(013873) 71295/71512* Mr and Mrs Phillips

Caledonian IPA and an organic lager always available plus occasional, alternating guest beers.

A civilised English-style country inn on the River Esk. Bar and restaurant food available at lunchtime and evenings. Car park and garden. Accommodation. Children allowed. Situated 14 miles north from the M6 junction 44.

OPEN *11am–2.30pm and 6.30–11pm.*

CASTLE DOUGLAS

The Royal Hotel
17 King Street, Castle Douglas,
Kirkcudbrightshire DG7 1AA
☎ *(01556) 502040* Mrs Bennett

A freehouse with Orkney Dark Island and Caledonian Deuchars IPA always available.

A small, family-run hotel with two bars and a separate restaurant. Children allowed.

OPEN *All day, every day.*

DALBEATTIE

The Pheasant Hotel
1 Maxwell Street, Dalbeattie DG5 4AH
☎ *(01556) 610345* Bill Windsor

A freehouse with Caledonian Deuchars IPA always available.

A high-street community pub, with TV and folk club. Second-floor dining area. Food at lunchtime and evenings. Children allowed.

OPEN *All day, every day.*

DUMFRIES

Douglas Arms
Friars Vennel, Dumfries DG1 2RQ
☎ *(01387) 256002* Mrs A Whitefield

Broughton Greenmantle Ale, Merlin's Ale, The Ghillie, Black Douglas and Old Jock always available plus one guest beer (150 per year) to include Whim Magic Mushroom Mild and Hartington Bitter.

An old-style pub with a real coal fire. No food available. Situated in the town centre.

OPEN *11am–11pm Sun–Thurs; 11am–midnight Fri–Sat.*

The New Bazaar
38 Whitesands, Dumfries DG1 2RS
☎ *(01387) 268776* Ian McConnell

Maclay Wallace IPA, Belhaven St Andrews and Broughton Greenmantle Ale always available plus a guest (150 per year) from a list including Timothy Taylor Landlord, Ringwood Old Thumper, Gales HSB, Greene King Abbot, Hop Back Summer Lightning, Orkney Dark Island, Bateman XXXB, Tomintoul Wild Cat, Moorhouse's Pendle Witches Brew and Coach House beers.

A traditional Victorian public house consisting of public bar, lounge and games room. The public bar has an old-fashioned gantry stocked with more than 200 malt and other whiskies. No food available. Car park, children's room. The pub is on the bank of the river.

OPEN *11am–midnight.*

Tam O'Shanter
117 Queensberry Street, Dumfries DG1 1BH
☎ *(01387) 254055* Doreen Johnston

Caledonian Deuchars IPA always available plus four guests, changed frequently, from a broad selection.

A traditional pub with upstairs restaurant. Food all day. Children allowed.

OPEN *All day, every day.*

GATEHOUSE OF FLEET

Masonic Arms
Ann Street, Gatehouse of Fleet, Nr Castle Douglas Kirkcudbrightshire DG7 2HU
☎ *(01557) 814335* Paul Irvin

A freehouse with up to seven ales available.

A traditional, English-style country inn with one bar, restaurant and conservatory. Food at lunchtime and evenings. Children allowed.

OPEN *Lunchtimes, and evenings from 5pm.*

GLENLUCE

Kelvin House Hotel
53 Main Street, Glenluce, Newton Stewart, Wigtownshire DG8 0PP
☎ *(01581) 300303* Christine Holmes

A freehouse offering three real ales, one changed once or twice a week. Orkney Red MacGregor and Burtonwood Top Hat always on the menu, with one guest from a good selection that may include Timothy Taylor Landlord and Orkney Dark Island.

An hotel off the A75, with residents' lounge, dining lounge, public bar and restaurant. Food at lunchtime and evenings, all day at weekends. Children allowed.

OPEN *11am–3pm and 5–11.30pm Mon–Fri; all day Sat–Sun.*

HAUGH OF URR

Laurie Arms Hotel
Haugh of Urr, Castle Douglas, Kirkcudbrightshire DG7 3YA
☎ *(01556) 660246* William Rundle

A freehouse offering four real ales including Timothy Taylor Landlord and Shipstone's Best, with guests from many different breweries changed weekly.

An old country pub with log fires and separate dining area. Food at lunchtime and evenings. Children allowed.

OPEN *11.45am–2.30pm and 5.30pm–midnight.*

KIRKCUDBRIGHT

Selkirk Arms Hotel
High Street, Kirkcudbright, Kirkcudbrightshire DG6 4JG
☎ *(01557) 330209* Mr and Mrs J Morris

A freehouse with Sulwath Criffel always available. A guest, changed weekly, might be Fuller's London Pride or other independent ale.

A Georgian hotel with public and lounge bars and a bistro. Food at lunchtime and evenings. Children allowed.

OPEN *All day, every day.*

LANGHOLM

The Crown Hotel
High Street, Langholm DG13 0GH
☎ *(01387) 380247* Mr Barry

Orkney brews always available in this freehouse plus a guest beer changed weekly.

An eighteenth-century coaching house with five bars and a dining area. Food served. Children allowed.

OPEN *All day, every day.*

LOCKERBIE

Somerton House Hotel
35 Carlisle Road, Lockerbie DG11 2DR
☎ *(01576) 202583* Alex Arthur

A freehouse always offering Caledonian Duchars IPA and Broughton Greenmantle. A guest is changed each week. Favourites include beers from Fuller's, Jennings and Caledonian breweries.

An hotel built in the 1880s with a separate dining area. Food served at lunchtime and evenings. Children allowed.

OPEN *All day, every day.*

NEWTON STEWART

The Creebridge House Hotel
Newton Stewart, Wigtownshire DG8 6NP
☎ *(01671) 402121* Mr Chris Walker

A freehouse with Timothy Taylor Landlord and Marston's Pedigree always available. Two or three guests are available each week. Favourites include Orkney Dark Island and Black Sheep Best Bitter.

A country-style pub with one bar and a dining room. En suite bedrooms, a brasserie and garden restaurant. Food at lunchtime and evenings. Children allowed.

OPEN *12–2.30pm Mon–Sun; 6–11pm Mon–Thurs; 6pm–12am Fri–Sat; 6.30–11pm Sun.*

The Glencairn Hotel

14 Arthur Street, Newton Stewart, Wigtownshire
DG8 6DE
☎ *(01671) 402355* Mr Moore

A freehouse with Maclay Broadsword always on offer.

An old-fashioned pub with a public bar, lounge bar and restaurant. Food at lunchtime and evenings. Children allowed.

OPEN *All day, every day.*

Harbour House Hotel

53 Main Street, Portpatrick, Stranraer,
Wigtownshire DG9 8JW
☎ *(01776) 810456* Ian Cerexhe

A freehouse with two real ale pumps. Black Sheep Best Bitter always available plus a guest beer during the summer.

Central hotel on the seafront with lounge bar overlooking the harbour. Outside seating and music most weekends. Separate dining area. Food at lunchtime and evenings. Children allowed.

OPEN *All day, every day.*

Places Featured:

Aberdour
Anstruther
Cupar
Kettlebridge

Kirkcaldy
Leslie
Leven

THE PUBS

ABERDOUR

Cedar Inn

20 Shore Road, Aberdour KY3 0TR
☎ *(01383) 860310* Janet Cadden

A freehouse offering six real ales, changed regularly (often daily).

A friendly locals pub with two bars and lounges. Food at lunchtime and evenings. Children allowed.

OPEN *All day, every day.*

ANSTRUTHER

Dreel Tavern

16 High Street, Anstruther KY10 3DL
☎ *(01333) 310727* Mr Scarsbrook

A freehouse with Orkney Dark Island a permanent fixture. Three guest beers, changed weekly, are also offered and these may include Timothy Taylor Landlord, Backdykes brews and Caledonian 80/-.

A sixteenth-century coaching inn with an extensive non-smoking dining area. Food at lunchtime and evenings. Children allowed.

OPEN *All day, every day.*

CUPAR

The Drookit Dug

43 Bonnygate, Cupar KY15 4BU
☎ *(01334) 55862* Christopher Burke

Three beers always available from a guest list (100 per year) that includes Eldridge Pope, Fuller's, Timothy Taylor and Young's breweries. All real ales £1 a pint.

A very traditional-looking town-centre pub with wood-lined walls. Bar food is available at lunchtime. Children's room. Situated on the corner at the second set of traffic lights.

OPEN *11am–12 or 1am.*

KETTLEBRIDGE

Kettlebridge Inn

9 Cupar Road, Kettlebridge
☎ *(01337) 830232* James Alkman

Five beers always available from a list that runs into hundreds.

A traditional village coaching inn in Fife golfing country on the A92 road to St Andrews. Open fires, lounge bar and restaurant. Bar and restaurant food available at lunchtime and evenings. Street parking, garden. Children allowed in restaurant only.

OPEN *12–2.30pm and 5–11pm Mon–Fri;*
12–midnight Sat; 12–11pm Sun.

Betty Nicol's
297 High Street, Kirkcaldy KY1 1JL
☎ *(01592) 642083* Mrs Nicol

A freehouse with Orkney Dark Island, Caledonian Deuchars IPA and Backdykes Malcolm range always available, plus a guest. Morland Old Speckled Hen, Timothy Taylor Landlord and Fuller's London Pride are regularly featured but many others also stocked as available.

Olde-worlde pub with separate room for children. Snacks and toasties only.

All day, every day.

Harbour Bar
469 High Street, Kirkcaldy KY1 2SN
☎ *(01592) 264270*

Home of the Fyfe Brewing Company offering the full range of Fyfe beers. Also guests from Belhaven Brewery and elsewhere.

The brewery is located in an old sailworks behind and above the pub. Auld Alliance, the first brew, was launched in May 1995 and there are now four more beers available, with further plans for expansion. The plant size is for two and a half barrels, with a ten-barrel per week restriction. The Harbour Bar is a traditional ale house. Snacks are available at lunchtime and evenings. Parking. Children not allowed.

ROPE OF SAND 3.7% ABV
Golden IPA-style brew.
AULD ALLIANCE 4.0% ABV
Ruby-coloured and heavily hopped.
LION SLAYER 4.2% ABV
Golden bitter.
FYFE FYRE 4.8% ABV
Straw-coloured and fruity.
CAULD TURKEY 6.0% ABV
Dark and dangerous.

11am–2.30pm and 5–midnight Mon–Thurs; 11am–midnight Fri–Sat; 12.30–midnight Sun.

Burns Tavern
187 High Street, Leslie, Glenrothes KY6 3DB
☎ *(01592) 741345* Margaret Wilkie

A freehouse, but with an agreement with Carlsberg-Tetley for a limited period, offering four real ales. Caledonian Duchars IPA and 80/- always available. One guest beer chosen each month by the customers is also always on offer.

An old Scottish pub with well-equipped en suite rooms. Only snacks available, with plans to expand the menu soon. Children allowed.

All day, every day.

Hawkshill Hotel
Hawkslaw Street, Leven KY8 4LS
☎ *(01333) 427033* Mrs Rossiter

A freehouse with Timothy Taylor Landlord always available, plus a guest beer changed weekly. Favourites include Orkney Dark Island, Exmoor Gold and Kelham Island Pale Rider.

A family inn with function room, separate dining area and beer garden. Food available lunchtimes and evenings. Children allowed.

11am–2.30pm and 6–12am Mon–Thurs; 11am–12am Fri–Sat; 12pm–12am Sun.

Places Featured:

Aberdeen
Elgin
Findhorn
Methlick

Portsoy
Ruthven
Stonehaven
Tomintoul

THE PUBS

ABERDEEN

The Blue Lamp
121–3 Gallowgate, Aberdeen AB25 1BU
☎ *(01224) 647472* Mr Brown

A freehouse with Caledonian 80/- and Duchars IPA always available. plus up to five guest beers. Regulars include Isle of Skye Young Pretender and many others from small Scottish breweries.

A pub combining the traditional and the contemporary, with live entertainment at weekends. Two bars, one with an early 1960s feel, the other spacious. Small function room available to hire. Sandwiches only. No children.

All day Mon–Sat; 12.30–3.30pm and 6.30–11pm Sun.

The Prince of Wales
7 St Nicholas Lane, Aberdeen AB10 1HF
☎ *(01224) 640597* Steven Christie

A freehouse with Tomintoul No. 3 and Caledonian 80/- always on the menu. Four guest beers, changed weekly, may include Isle of Skye Red Cuillin and Young Pretender, Timothy Taylor Landlord or Orkney Dark Island, but ales from other independents also available as and when.

A traditional old-style barn with one bar. No music. Food available at lunchtime. Children allowed.

All day, every day.

ELGIN

Sunninghill Hotel
Hay Street, Elgin, Morayshire IV30 1NH
☎ *(01343) 547799* Winnie Rose

A freehouse offering five real ales. Guests changed weekly, from Scottish breweries such as Isle of Skye, Orkney and Tomintoul.

A hotel lounge bar. Food at lunchtime and evenings. Children allowed.

All day, every day.

FINDHORN

Crown & Anchor Inn
Findhorn, Nr Forres, Morayshire IV36 3YF
☎ *(01309) 690243* Mrs Heather Burrell

A freehouse serving at least four real ales and up to seven in summer. Regulars include Timothy Taylor Landlord, Fuller's ESB and Bateman brews.

B uilt in 1739, a pub offering bed and breakfast accommodation, live entertainment and a lounge area. Food at lunchtime and evenings. Children allowed.

All day, every day.

Kimberley Inn
Findhorn, Nr Forres, Morayshire IV36 0YG
☎ *(01309) 690492* Mrs Hessel

A freehouse with real ale on two pumps in the winter and up to four in summer. Timothy Taylor Landlord and Orkney The Red MacGregor among those always on the menu. Guests may include Black Sheep Best Bitter or other ales from the Orkney brewery.

A one-bar village pub with non-smoking area and views across the bay. Food at lunchtime and evenings. Children allowed.

All day, every day.

METHLICK

The Gight House Hotel
Sunnybrae, Methlick, Ellon, Aberdeenshire AB41 7BP
☎ *(01651) 806389* Les Ros

Timothy Taylor Landlord and Broughton Merlin Ale are among the beers always on the menu. A guest beer, changed twice-weekly, might well be Isle of Skye Red Cuillin.

A freehouse with lounge, restaurant, two conservatories, children's play area and large garden with putting green. Food served at lunchtime and evenings during the week, all day at weekends. Situated about 20 miles from Aberdeen. Find Methlick and you will not be far away!

12–2.30pm and 5–12am Mon–Thurs; all day Fri–Sun.

The Shore Inn
The Old Barbour, Church Street, Portsoy,
Banffshire AB45 2QR
☎ *(01261) 842831* Mr Hill

 A freehouse with Isle of Skye Red
Cuillin among the brews always
available. A guest, changed weekly, is also
offered.

A traditional, 300-year-old pub,
overlooking a seventeenth-century
harbour. Separate restaurant. Food all day.
Children allowed.

All day, every day.

Borve Brew House
Ruthven, Huntley, Aberdeenshire AB54 4SR
☎ *(01466) 760343*

The full range of Borve Brews are
produced and available on the premises.

The Borve Brew House is a former school
house converted into a small brewery. It
relocated to Ruthven, a hamlet in the
foothills of the Grampian mountains, in
1988, having originated at Borve, on the Isle
of Lewis, in 1983. The beer is available
bottled or on draught. No food. Car park.
Children not allowed.

BORVE ALE 4.0% ABV
A session ale.
TALL SHIPS IPA 5.0% ABV
BORVE EXTRA STRONG 10% ABV
A connoisseur's beer.
Also various seasonal specials.

*11am–11pm Mon–Sat; 11am–2.30pm and
6.30–11pm Sun.*

The Marine Hotel
9–10 Shorehead, Stonehaven AB3 2JY
☎ *(01569) 762155* Mr and Mrs Duncan

 Timothy Taylor ales always available
plus four guests (200 per year) perhaps
from Orkney, Harviestoun and Tomintoul
breweries, plus a wide range of English ales.

The pub overlooks the harbour and has a
large bar with a juke box and pool table.
Bar and restaurant food served at lunchtime
and evenings. Local seafood. Parking. Follow
the signs to the harbour.

11am–12am.

The Glen Avon Hotel
1 The Square, Tomintoul, Ballindalloch,
Banffshire AB37 9ET
☎ *(01807) 580218* Robert Claase

A freehouse always offering Tomintoul
Wild Cat, Stag and Nessie's Monster
Mash. Guest beers changed weekly on two
pumps in summer.

A country pub with log fires and separate
dining area. Food at lunchtime and
evenings. Children allowed.

All day, every day.

Places Featured:

Aviemore	Lochranza
Avoch	Nairn
Dingwall	Sligachan
Inverness	Stromness
Kingussie	Ullapool

THE PUBS

AVIEMORE

Old Bridge Inn

Dalfaber Road, Aviemore, Inverness-shire PH22 1PX
☎ *(01479) 811137 Mr Reid*

Aviemore Ruthven Brew, Shipstone's Bitter and a house bitter always available in this freehouse. Plus a varied selection of guests.

S et in a rural location next to the River Spey. Separate dining area. Food at lunchtime and evenings. Children allowed.

OPEN *All day, every day.*

AVOCH

The Station Hotel

Bridge Street, Avoch, Moray, Ross-shire IV9 8GG
☎ *(01381) 620246 David Graham*

A freehouse with two guests, changed twice-weekly, which may include regulars such as Mansfield Old Baily or other occasional features.

A country village pub with two bars and a conservatory. Food at lunchtime and evenings. Children allowed.

OPEN *All day, every day.*

DINGWALL

The National Hotel

High Street, Dingwall, Ross-shire IV15 9HA
☎ *(01349) 862166 Bernard Justice*

Owned by the man behind the Iris Rose Brewery in Kingussie, so serving Roseburn Bitter, Gynack Glory, Black Five and others, plus a couple of guests such as Black Sheep Best Bitter.

A n elegant Georgian hotel with two bars and dining area. Food lunchtimes and evenings. Children allowed.

OPEN *All day, every day.*

INVERNESS

Clachnaharry Inn

17–19 High Street, Clachnaharry Road, Inverness PH38 4NG
☎ *(01463) 239806 David Irwin*

A freehouse offering four real ales, three from the cask. Regular favourites include Tomintoul Wild Cat and Nessie's Monster Mash, Adnams Broadside and Morland Old Speckled Hen.

A traditional old coaching inn next to the railway and canal. Lounge and public bar. The beer garden used to be a train platform. Food served all day. Children allowed in lounge only.

OPEN *All day, every day.*

The Heathmount Hotel

Kingsmills Road, Inverness IV2 3JU
☎ *(01463) 235877 Angus Murray*

A freehouse with Maclay 80/- and Isle of Skye Red Cuillin always on offer. Plus a couple of guests that might include Shepherd Neame Spitfire.

N ewly renovated pub, modern with an old touch. Smoking and non-smoking areas in the restaurant. Food at lunchtime and evenings. Children allowed. One minute from the town centre.

OPEN *All day, every day.*

The Royal Hotel

*High Street, Kingussie, Inverness-shire
PH21 1HX*
☎ *(01540) 661898* Bernard Justice

The pub forms part of the Iris Rose micro-brewery, producing 12 of its own ales. Up to nine beers available, including home brews and several guests.

A 52-bedroom hotel with a brewer's bar seating about 200 people and offering live entertainment. The restaurant serves food all day. Children allowed.

SUMMER ALE 3.5% ABV
CARL'S BEST BITTER 3.7% ABV
ROSEBURN BITTER 3.8% ABV
GINGER ALE 3.9% ABV
BADENOCH 80/ 4.0% ABV
LIQUORICE ALE 4.3% ABV
GYNACK GLORY 4.4% ABV
CRAIG BHEAG LAGER 4.4% ABV
STRATHSPEY HEAVY 4.6% ABV
BLACK 5 5.0% ABV
IPA 5.1% ABV
ZOE'S OLD GRUMPY 7.2% ABV

All day, every day.

Catacol Bay Hotel

*Catacol, Lochranza, Brodick, Isle of Arran
KA27 8HN*
☎ *(01770) 830231* Dave Ashcroft

A freehouse with Caledonian Deuchars IPA, Houston Killellan and Barochan always available plus up to three guest beers.

E asy-going, family-orientated pub, with lounge bar, dining room and pool room. Food all day till 10pm. Children allowed.

All day, every day.

The Invernairne Hotel

Thurlow Road, Nairn, Moray IV12 4EZ
☎ *(01667) 452039* Mrs Wilkie

Isle of Skye Red Cuillin always available plus one or two guests, changed fortnightly, which may include Belhaven brews or Fuller's London Pride.

A freehouse with a lounge bar and dining area. Regular live music. Food served evenings only. Children allowed.

5pm–12.30am all week.

The Sligachan Hotel

Sligachan, Isle of Skye IV47 8SW
☎ *(01478) 650204* Iain Campbell

A freehouse serving beers from the Isle of Skye brewery. Red Cuillin, Black Cuillin and Young Pretender always available. Two guests, changed frequently, may include Belhaven brews among other independents.

A 100-year-old building with a main public bar, lounge bar, pool tables. Live music. The only pub on the island with a late licence on Saturday. Food at lunchtime and evenings. Children allowed until 8pm.

All day, every day.

The Stromness Hotel

*Victoria Street, Stromness, Isle of Orkney
KW16 3AA*
☎ *(01856) 850298* Leona Macleod

A freehouse with Orkney The Red MacGregor and Dark Island always available.

T he largest hotel in Orkney, with 42 bedrooms. A separate restaurant serves food at lunchtime and evenings. Children allowed.

All day, every day.

The Ferryboat Inn

Shore Street, Ullapool, Ross-shire IV26 2UJ
☎ *(01854) 612366* Richard Smith

A freehouse offering six real ales. Regulars come from the Orkney brewery, others from further afield such as Wadworth 6X.

A n old-fashioned one-bar pub with coal fire and separate restaurant area. Food served at lunchtime and evenings. Children allowed.

All day, every day.

Places Featured:

East Linton
Edinburgh
Haddington
Linlithgow

Mid-Calder
North Berwick
South Queensferry

THE PUBS

EAST LINTON

The Drover's Inn

*5 Bridge Street, East Linton, East Lothian
EH40 3AG*
☎ *(01620) 860298* Michelle Findlay

A freehouse with Adnams Broadside and Caledonian 80/- always on the menu. Two guests, changed most days, include regular choices such as Inveralmond Lia Fail or Hardy Country Bitter.

An old-fashioned pub-restaurant with one bar. Smoking and non-smoking dining areas and bistro. Live entertainment and folk bands on Wednesdays. Children allowed.

11am–2.30pm and 5pm–midnight Mon–Sat; all day Sun.

EDINBURGH

The Bow Bar

80 West Bow, Edinburgh EH1 2HH
☎ *(0131) 226 7667* Bill Strachan

Caledonian ESA, Deuchars IPA and 80/- plus Timothy Taylor Landlord always available. Also Caledonian 70/-, Golden Promise etc, and ales from Harviestoun, Broughton, Belhaven, Border, Jennings, Everards, Maclay, Orkney, Tomintoul, Hook Norton, Bateman and Black Sheep breweries.

Take a step back in time to a genuine freehouse offering an unparalleled selection of real ales and malt whiskies. Bar food at lunchtime. Children not allowed.

11am–11.15pm.

Cambridge Bar

20 Young Street, Edinburgh EH2 4JB
☎ *(0131) 228 4266* Ian Laing

Caledonian 80/- and Deuchars IPA always on offer plus one guest, perhaps from the Harviestoun brewery.

Food at lunchtime only. Children allowed.

All day Mon–Sat; closed Sun.

Carter's Bar

185 Morrison Street, Edinburgh EH3 8DZ
☎ *(0131) 623 7023* Richard Treadgold

Owned by the Belhaven brewery, so Belhaven 70/-, St Andrew's Ale and Caledonian 80/- always available. Two guest beers change weekly; Marston's Pedigree and Caledonian Deuchars IPA are often featured.

Traditional wooden interior with feature gallery view into the bar. Rolls only. Children under 14 not allowed.

All day, every day.

The Cask & Barrel

115 Broughton Street, Edinburgh EH1 3RZ
☎ *(0131) 556 3132* Patrick Mitchell

Caledonian 80/- and Deuchars IPA are among the brews permanently available plus five guest beers from breweries such as Hop Back, Harviestoun, Mauldons, Hambleton, Cotleigh, Coach House, Shepherd Neame and Larkins.

A large horseshoe bar with a wide range of customers. Food available at lunchtime. From the east end of Queen Street, turn left off York Place.

11am–12am.

Cloisters Bar

26 Brougham Street, Edinburgh EH3 9JH
☎ *(0131) 221 9997* Benjamin Budge

A freehouse with Caledonian Deuchars IPA and Village White Boar always available. Guests changed once or twice a week. Dent Aviator, Timothy Taylor Landlord and Caledonian 80/- are regularly featured. Others include Shefford ales, Smiles Golden Brew, Spinnaker Buzz and Ringwood Fortyniner.

A central, old-fashioned, church-like pub, with one bar. No TV or music. Food lunchtimes only. Children allowed.

All day, every day.

The Cumberland Bar

1–3 Cumberland Street, Edinburgh EH3 6RT
☎ *(0131) 558 3134* Miss S Young

Caledonian Deuchars IPA and 80/- always on the menu. Guests, changed twice a week, may include Timothy Taylor Landlord, Kelham Island Pale Rider, Fuller's ESB or Greene King Abbot Ale.

A traditional one-bar alehouse. Food at lunchtime only. No children.

All day, every day.

The Guildford Arms

1 West Register Street, Edinburgh EH2 2AA
☎ *(0131) 556 4312* Paul Cronin

Caledonian 80/-, Deuchars IPA, Orkney Dark Island, Harviestoun Waverley 70/- and Schiehallion permanently available plus seven guest beers (260+ per year) including Traquair Bear Ale and Festival Ale, plus a massive selection from all over England.

A beautiful Jacobean pub. Restaurant food available at lunchtime. At the east end of Princes Street, behind Burger King.

OPEN *11am–11pm Mon–Wed; 11am–12am Thurs–Sat; 12.30–11pm Sun.*

Halfway House

24 Fleshmarket Close, High Street, Edinburgh EH1 1BX
☎ *(0131) 225 7101* David Richer

A freehouse offering five real ales. Regulars include Caledonian, York and Backdykes brews.

S mall city-centre pub serving an age group predominantly 25 to 50. Rolls only. No children. Close to Waverley Central train station.

OPEN *All day, every day.*

Homes Bar

102 Constitution Street, Leith, Edinburgh EH6 6AW
☎ *(0131) 553 7710* Patrick Fitzgerald

A freehouse with real ale on five pumps. Caledonian Deuchars IPA always available, plus regular guest beers, changed weekly, including Fuller's London Pride, Timothy Taylor Landlord and Hop Back Summer Lightning.

A n old-fashioned, drinking men's real ale pub. Lunches only. No children.

OPEN *All day, every day.*

Leslie's Bar

45 Ratcliffe Terrace, Edinburgh EH9 1SU
☎ *(0131) 667 5957* Gavin Blake

A freehouse with real ale on six pumps. Bass, Belhaven 80/-, Caledonian 80/- and Deuchars IPA, plus Timothy Taylor Landlord always available. One guest beer also offered, which is often a Maclay brew.

U nchanged in 100 years, with an old-fashioned gantry and open fire. One bar. Pies only. No children.

OPEN *All day, every day.*

Old Chain Pier

32 Trinity Crescent, Edinburgh EH5 3ED
☎ *(0131) 552 1233* Mr Nicol

Caledonian Deuchars IPA, Black Sheep Best Bitter and Timothy Taylor Landlord are more or less permanent fixtures here, plus one guest, changed every two days. Regulars include brews from Harviestoun and Moorhouse's.

A local with very mixed clientele, young and old. Non-smoking area. Food from 12–9.30pm. Children allowed.

OPEN *All day, every day.*

Royal Ettrick Hotel

13 Ettrick Road, Edinburgh EH10 5BJ
☎ *(0131) 228 6413* Mrs EM Stuart

Caledonian 80/- and Maclay Kanes Amber Ale always available, plus four guest beers from a large range that may include Timothy Taylor Landlord, Conciliation Ale, Titanic Best, Hook Norton Old Hooky, or Broughton, Greene King and Adnams ales.

P art of a mansion and conservatory built in 1875 in the leafy suburbs. Bar and restaurant food available at lunchtime and evenings. Morning and afternoon teas also served. Car park, garden, banqueting and conference facilities. Weddings catered for. Children allowed. Accommodation.

OPEN *11am–12am Mon–Sat; 12.30pm–midnight Sun.*

Southsider

3–5 West Richmond Street, Edinburgh EH8 9EF
☎ *(0131) 667 2003* Mr Hook

Four Maclay brews always available plus four guests including Old Bear Bitter, Border Rampart and Church End What the Fox's Hat. The emphasis is on smaller breweries and ales at 3.5–5%. Plus a strong ale in winter.

A lounge and public bar, popular with locals and students. Bar food available at lunchtime. Car park in the city centre. Children allowed at lunchtime only.

OPEN *11.30am–midnight.*

The Starbank Inn

64 Laverock Road, Edinburgh EH5 3BZ
☎ *(0131) 552 4141* Scott Brown

A freehouse with Belhaven 80/-, IPA, St Andrew's Ale, Sandy Hunter's Traditional Ale and Timothy Taylor Landlord always available. Five guests, changed weekly, may include Tomintoul brews or those from Aviemore and other small and micro-brewers.

T raditional, old-fashioned pub with one bar, overlooking the River Forth. Separate non-smoking dining area. Food at lunchtime and evenings. Children allowed.

OPEN *All day, every day.*

The Steading

118–20 Biggar Road, Edinburgh EH10 7DU
☎ *(0131) 445 1128* Ray Simpson

A freehouse with Caledonian Duchars IPA, Timothy Taylor Landlord and Orkney and Belhaven brews always available. Plus a guest, changed weekly. Brains Reverend James Original Ale is a favourite.

A country inn with two bars, one smoking, one non-smoking, plus a separate dining area. Food served all day. Children allowed.

OPEN *All day, every day.*

HADDINGTON

Waterside Bistro and Restaurant

1–5 Waterside, Nungate, Haddington, East Lothian EH41 4BE
☎ *(01620) 825674* James Findlay

Regular guests in this freehouse include Belhaven brews, Caledonian Duchars IPA, Marston's Pedigree and Timothy Taylor Landlord.

An old, restored cottage overlooking the River Tyne and the abbey. Separate dining area. Food at lunchtime and evenings. Children allowed.

OPEN *11am–2.30pm and 5–11pm.*

LINLITHGOW

The Four Marys

65 High Street, Linlithgow EH49 7ED
☎ *(01506) 842171* Mr Scott

Belhaven 80/- always available plus nine guest beers (400 per year) that may include Harviestoun Ptarmigan, Tomintoul Ginger Tom, Conciliation Ale, Cotleigh Harrier, Dent Bitter, Greene King IPA, Bateman Mild, RCH PG Steam and Caledonian ales.

A traditional pub with antique furniture and stone walls. The bar has masses of mementoes of Mary Queen of Scots, who was born at Linlithgow Palace. Bar food available at lunchtime and evenings (except Sunday evening). Parking. Children allowed. Opposite the entrance to Linlithgow Palace.

OPEN *12–2.30pm and 5–11pm Sun–Fri; 12–11.30pm Sat.*

MID-CALDER

Torpichen Arms

36 Bank Street, Mid-Calder, Livingston, West Lothian EH53 0AR
☎ *(01506) 880020* Helen Hill

Caledonian 80/- and Deuchars IPA always available, plus guests, changed weekly. Harviestoun, Nethergate, Robinson's, Tomintoul and Cains breweries are regularly featured.

Old village pub with weekend entertainment. Bed and breakfast. Lunches only. Children allowed until 8.30pm.

OPEN *All day, every day.*

NORTH BERWICK

Nether Abbey Hotel

20 Dirleton Avenue, North Berwick, East Lothian EH39 4BQ
☎ *(01620) 892802* Stirling Stewart

A freehouse with Belhaven brews always on the menu. Guests may include Caledonian Duchars IPA and 80/-, Orkney Dark Island and Marston's Pedigree.

A pub that has been family-run for the past 35 years, with one main bar and a brasserie. Food at lunchtime and evenings. Children allowed.

OPEN *All day, every day.*

SOUTH QUEENSFERRY

The Ferry Tap

36 High Street, South Queensferry, Nr Edinburgh EH30 9HN
☎ *(0131) 331 2000* Brian Inglis

A freehouse always offering Caledonian 80/- and Deuchars IPA plus Orkney Dark Island. Guests are changed weekly, one in winter, two in summer. Black Sheep Best Bitter is a favourite.

Old-fashioned real ale house with one bar and lounge. Food served at lunchtimes; snacks only in evenings. No children.

OPEN *All day, every day.*

Places Featured:

Arrochar
Ayr
Biggar
Castlecary
Cove
Darvel
Dumbarton
Dundonald
Furnace
Glasgow
Hamilton

Houston
Inverary
Inverkip
Johnstone
Kilmarnock
Largs
Lochwinnoch
Lugton
Paisley
Troon

THE PUBS

ARROCHAR

The Village Inn
Arrochar, Lochlong, Argyll and Bute
G83 7AX
☎ *(01301) 702279* Mrs Kenny

A pub managed by Maclay Brewery, with Maclay Wallace IPA always on the menu. Two guests are changed weekly and may include Orkney Dark Island.

Olde-worlde village pub with two bars and separate dining area. Food served all day. Children allowed.

OPEN All day, every day.

AYR

Burrowfields Café Bar
13 Beresford Terrace, Ayr KA7 2EU
☎ *(01292) 269152* Daniel Kelly

Real ale on three pumps in this freehouse. Regular guests, changed weekly, include brews from Caledonian, St Giles in the Wood, Greene King and Cains.

Live music once a week, TV and lounge bar. Food at lunchtime and evenings. Children allowed at lunchtime.

OPEN All day, every day.

Geordie's Byre
103 Main Street, Ayr KA8 88U
☎ *(01292) 264325*

Caledonian 80/- and Deuchars IPA always available plus three guest beers (450 per year) from Orkney (Skullsplitter) to Cornwall and Devon (Summerskill Whistle Belly Vengeance).

A friendly freehouse managed by the owners. Decorated with memorabilia and Victoriana. No food. Children not allowed. Located 50 yards from the police headquarters on King Street.

OPEN 11am–11pm (12am Thurs–Sat); 12.30–11pm Sun.

BIGGAR

The Crown Inn
109–11 High Street, Biggar, Lanarkshire
ML12 6DL
☎ *(01899) 220116* John Rolfe

A freehouse offering real ale on four pumps, two in each bar. Regular guests include Adnams Broadside, Morland Old Speckled Hen, Shepherd Neame Spitfire and Wadworth 6X.

A seventeenth-century pub with two bars. Food served at lunchtimes, plus evenings in summer. Children allowed.

OPEN All day, every day in summer; lunchtimes and evenings in winter.

CASTLECARY

Castlecary House Hotel
Main Street, Castlecary, Cumbernauld,
Lanarkshire G68 0HB
☎ *(01324) 840233* Mr McMillan

Freehouse with Caledonian Deuchars IPA among the brews always available. Two guests, changed fortnightly, might include brews from Harviestoun, Belhaven and Caledonian.

Traditional pub. Food at lunchtimes and evenings. Children allowed.

OPEN All day, every day.

COVE

Knockderry Hotel
204 Shore Road, Cove, Nr Helensburgh, Argyll
G84 0NX
☎ *(01436) 842283* Ian Johnston

A freehouse with real ale on three pumps. Regular guests, changed weekly, include brews from Orkney, Maclay Wallace IPA and Broadsword, Isle of Skye Red Cuillin and Black Cuillin.

A 12-bedroom, family-run hotel on the shores of Loch Long, built in 1851. Food served in separate restaurant. Children allowed.

OPEN All day, every day.

Loudounhill Inn
Darvel, Ayrshire KA17 0LY
☎ *(01560) 320275* Graham Wellby

Tied to the Belhaven Brewery. One guest, changed weekly, may be Orkney The Red MacGregor.

An old, one-bar coaching inn, with restaurant area. Lounge also used as a function room. Food at lunchtime and evenings. Children allowed. On the main A71, one mile east of Darvel.

OPEN *All day, every day (closed Tue night and Wed lunch).*

Cutty Sark
105 High Street, Dumbarton G82 1LF
☎ *(01389) 762509* Mr Fennell

Tied to Punch Taverns, with Belhaven St Andrew's Ale always available. A weekly guest beer might well be Orkney Dark Island.

A town-centre pub with lounge bar and a mixed clientele. Food at lunchtime only. Children allowed.

OPEN *All day, every day.*

Castle View
29 Main Street, Dundonald, Kilmarnock, Ayrshire KA2 9HH
☎ *(01563) 851112* Iain Fisher

Part of the Wilson Boyle development. Caledonian 80/- or Deuchars IPA are regularly featured. Alternatives from Orkney and Harviestoun.

Restaurant-dominated, with two bars. Food at lunchtime and evenings. Children allowed. Just off the B739.

OPEN *All day, every day.*

Furnace Inn
Furnace, Inverary, Argyll PA32 8XN
☎ *(01499) 500200* Gordon Pirie

A freehouse with four or five beers always available. Guests, changed weekly, often include brews from Orkney, St Giles in the Wood.

A country-style pub, with one bar, oak beams and fires. Food served all day. Children allowed.

OPEN *All day, every day.*

Athena Greek Taverna
780 Pollokshaws Road, Strathbungo, Glasgow Lanarkshire G42 2AE
☎ *(0141) 424 0858* Nicholas Geordiades

Six beers always available from a list of 200 guests that may include Otter Bright and beers from Rooster's, Yates, Belhaven, Caledonian and Shardlow breweries.

A café-style bar and adjacent Greek Cypriot restaurant serving Greek and European food. Children allowed. Situated beside Queen's Park railway station, not far from Shawlands Cross.

OPEN *11am–2.30pm and 5–11pm Mon–Sat; closed Sun.*

The Counting House
2 St Vincent Place, Glasgow, Lanarkshire G1 2DH
☎ *(0141) 248 9568* Phil Annet

This freehouse hosts a real ale festival in the spring, when there may be 50 brews on sale. The rest of the time, Tomintoul Wild Cat and Caledonian Deuchars IPA are among the beers always available. Guests change weekly, and Shepherd Neame Spitfire is a regular.

A converted Bank of Scotland building with original fixtures and fittings, including the safe. Ninety tables. Food available all day. No children.

OPEN *All day, every day.*

Station Bar
55 Port Dundas Road, Glasgow, Lanarkshire
☎ *(0141) 332 3117* Michael McHugh

A freehouse with Caledonian and Deuchars IPA always available plus a guest, which might be Caledonian Edinburgh Strong Ale or Fuller's ESB.

A traditional city-centre local with one bar. Snacks and rolls available. Children usually allowed until about 6pm.

OPEN *All day, every day.*

Tennents Bar

191 Byres Road, Hillhead, Glasgow G12
☎ *(0141) 339 0649* Alison O'Conner

Up to 12 beers available from a guest list (100 per year) that may include Fuller's London Pride, Morland Old Speckled Hen and Marston's Pedigree.

A large public bar with a friendly atmosphere and no music. Bar and restaurant food is available at lunchtime and evenings. A refurbishment has recently taken place. Adjacent to Glasgow University and Hillhead subway.

OPEN *11am–11pm Mon–Thurs; 11am–midnight Fri–Sat; 12.30–11.30pm Sun.*

The Three Judges

141 Dumbarton Road, Partick Cross, Glasgow G11 6PR
☎ *(0141) 337 3055* Helen McCarroll

Maclay 80/-, Broadsword and Wallace IPA always available plus five guest beers (250 per year) from independent and micro-breweries, old and new.

A lively West End pub. Bar food is served at lunchtime and evenings. Parking available. Near Kelvin Hall underground.

OPEN *11am–11pm Sun–Thurs; 11am–midnight Fri–Sat.*

The George Bar

18 Campbell Street, Hamilton, Lanarkshire ML3 6AS
☎ *(01698) 424225* Colin Adams

A freehouse with Hop Back Summer Lightning and Maclay 70/- always available plus three rotating guests. Regulars include Smiles Best and Heather Fraoch Ale.

A traditional-style, town-centre pub with small back room. Food at lunchtime. Children allowed. Can be tricky to find because of the one-way system!

OPEN *All day, every day.*

The Fox & Hounds

South Street, Houston, Johnstone, Renfrewshire PA6 7EN
☎ *(01505) 612991* Jonathan Wengel

A freehouse and brewpub. Home of the Houston Brewing Company, so home brews are always on the menu, plus guests, changed weekly, such as Isle of Skye Red Cuillin, Coniston Bluebird or Boddingtons Bitter.

A traditional coaching inn with three bars and a separate restaurant area. Food at lunchtime and evenings. Children allowed.

KILLELLAN 3.7% ABV
Golden, mellow ale.
BAROCHAN 4.0% ABV
Ruby-coloured and smooth.
ST PETER'S WELL 4.2% ABV
Fruity wheat beer made with continental hops.
FORMAKIN 4.3% ABV
Clean, tawny-coloured and nutty.

OPEN *All day, every day.*

The George Hotel

Main Street East, Inverary, Argyll PA32 8TT
☎ *(01499) 302111* Donald Clark

Real ale on up to three pumps in this freehouse. Guests are changed weekly, regulars include Broughton Greenmantle Ale and Belhaven St Andrew's Ale. Others might well come from the Houston Brewing Company.

An old-fashioned country house with two bars and a function room. Beer garden. Food served all day. Children allowed.

OPEN *All day, every day.*

Inverkip Hotel

Main Street, Inverkip, Greenock, Renfrewshire PA16 0AS
☎ *(01475) 521478* Mr Hardy and Mr Cushley

A freehouse with real ale on three pumps. Belhaven and Caledonian Breweries tend to supply much of the range.

A family-run pub with dining area and separate restaurant. TV in the public bar. Food at lunchtime and evenings. Children allowed.

OPEN *All day, every day.*

JOHNSTONE

Coanes

*26 High Street, Johnstone, Renfrewshire
PA5 8AH*
☎ *(01505) 321342* Michael Coane

A freehouse always offering Caledonian 80/- and Deuchars IPA and Orkney Dark Island. Guests, changed weekly, may include favourites such as Orkney The Red MacGregor, Greene King Abbot Ale, Adnams Broadside or Marston's Pedigree or other occasional features.

An olde-worlde pub with a bar and lounge. Food available at lunchtime and evenings from Wed to Sat. Children allowed up to 8pm if eating.

All day, every day.

KILMARNOCK

The Hunting Lodge

*14–16 Glencairn Square, Kilmarnock, Ayrshire
KA1 4AH*
☎ *(01563) 522920* Mr Little

A freehouse with real ale on up to seven pumps. Caledonian Deuchars IPA and Shepherd Neame Spitfire always available. Guests, changed weekly might include Timothy Taylor Landlord, Morland Old Speckled Hen, Greene King Abbot Ale and Fuller's London Pride.

Olde-worlde Georgian pub with three bars and a separate eating area. Food at lunchtime and evenings. Children allowed.

11am–3pm and 5–12pm Mon–Wed; all day Thurs–Sun.

LARGS

The Clachan Bar

14 Bath Street, Largs, Ayrshire KA30 8BL
☎ *(01475) 672224*

Tied to the Belhaven brewery, so IPA and others are always available.

An old-style, one-bar pub. Snacks available at lunchtime. Children allowed.

All day, every day.

LOCHWINNOCH

The Brown Bull

*33 Main Street, Lochwinnoch, Renfrewshire
PA12 4AJ*
☎ *(01505) 843250*

A freehouse with Orkney Dark Island always on offer plus four guest pumps with ales changed weekly. Heather Fraoch Ale, Harviestoun Schiehallion, Orkney The Red MacGregor and Raven Ale are all regularly featured.

Olde-worlde one-bar pub. No food at present but there are catering plans for the year 2000. Children allowed until 8pm.

All day, every day.

LUGTON

Lugton Inn

1 Lochlibo Road, Lugton, Ayrshire KA3 4DZ
☎ *(01505) 850267* Christopher Lynas

Home of the Lugton Brewery, so the full range of Lugton brews permanently available.

An old coaching inn in a village near Glasgow with open fires and copper wedge wire floor. Bar and restaurant food served at lunchtime and evenings. Car park, garden, children's room, accommodation. Children allowed.

LUGTON GOLD 5.0% ABV
A lager brewed in the traditional German fashion.

JOHN BARLEYCORN 5.0% ABV
Originally brewed for Burns's birthday using four types of barley, one hop and honey.

BLACK HEART 5.0% ABV
A traditional porter.

All day, every day.

PAISLEY

Gabriels

33 Gauze Street, Paisley, Renfrewshire PA1 1EX
☎ *(0141) 887 8204* Michael O'Hare

A freehouse with Caledonian Deuchars IPA and ales from the Houston Brewing Company always available. Guests change weekly and may include Fuller's London Pride, Cotleigh and Harviestoun ales.

An oval bar with traditional decor on the walls. Separate dining area and restaurant. Food all day. Children allowed.

All day, every day.

TROON

Dan McKay's Bar

69 Portland Street, Troon KA10 6QU
☎ *(01292) 311079* Dan McKay

A freehouse with Belhaven 80/-, Caledonian 80/- and Deuchars IPA always on offer. Plus a guest beer, changed once or twice a week, which might be Timothy Taylor Landlord, Wadworth 6X, Young's Special or Fuller's London Pride.

Traditional establishment, leaning towards a café bar, with TV, live music and jazz. Food at lunchtime and evenings. Children allowed during the day.

All day, every day.

Places Featured:

Abernethy	Inverkeilor
Blairgowrie	Kinross
Broughty Ferry	Kirkmichael
Carnoustie	Moulin
Clova	Perth
Dundee	Strathtummel

THE PUBS

ABERNETHY

Cree's Inn

Main Street, Abernethy, Perthshire PH2 9LA
☎ *(01738) 850714* Brian Johnston

A freehouse offering beers on four pumps. The range changes every week, but favourites include Belhaven 80/-, Marston's Pedigree, Greene King Abbot Ale and Caledonian Deuchars IPA and 80/-.

A one-bar country pub with food at lunchtime only. Children allowed.

⟨OPEN⟩ *11am–2.30pm and 5–11pm Mon–Fri; all day Sat–Sun.*

BLAIRGOWRIE

Rosemount Golf Hotel

Golf Course Road, Blairgowrie, Perthshire PH10 6LJ
☎ *(01250) 872604* Mr E Walker

A freehouse with McEwans 80/- and beers from Inveralmond Brewery always available, plus a guest, changed more frequently in summer. Caledonian Deuchars IPA is one favourite.

A family-run hotel, with one bar and a dining area with overspill for non-smokers. Food at lunchtime and evenings. Children allowed.

⟨OPEN⟩ *All day, every day.*

BROUGHTY FERRY

Fisherman's Tavern

12 Fore Street, Broughty Ferry, Dundee DD5 2AD
☎ *(01382) 775941* Mrs M Buntin

Belhaven 60/-, 80/- and St Andrew's Ale plus Maclay 80/- always available. Also three guest beers (600 per year) which include Traquair Bear Ale, Harviestoun Schiehallion, Buchan Gold, Belhaven Festival Gold and Sandy Hunter's, Maclay Wallace IPA, plus beers from every corner of England and Wales. Also Belgian and German bottled beers.

A 300-year-old listed building, formerly a fisherman's cottage. Bar and restaurant food available at lunchtime and evenings. Parking, secluded walled garden. Children welcome. Accommodation. Situated by the lifeboat station at Broughty Ferry.

⟨OPEN⟩ *11am–midnight Mon–Sat; 12.30pm–midnight Sun.*

CARNOUSTIE

The Stag's Head Inn

61 Dundee Street, Carnoustie, Angus DD7 7PN
☎ *(01241) 852265* Mr Duffy

A freehouse with real ale on five pumps. Guest beers are changed all the time. Regulars include Flowers Original, Timothy Taylor Landlord, Fuller's London Pride.

A locals' pub with two bars, disco on Friday, karaoke on Thursday and Sunday. Food served at lunchtime and evenings in the summertime. Children only allowed in the pool table area.

⟨OPEN⟩ *All day, every day.*

Clova Hotel

Glen Clova, Nr Kirriemuir, Angus DD8 4QS
☎ *(01575) 550222* Graham Davie

A freehouse with Broughton Greenmantle Ale among the brews always available. Guests, changed weekly, might include Caledonian Deuchars IPA.

A two-bar country hotel, with separate dining area. Food at lunchtime and evenings. Children allowed.

OPEN All day, every day.

Drouthy Neebors

142 Perth Road, Dundee, Angus DD1 4JW
☎ *(01382) 202187* Kirstin Wilson

A pub tied to the Belhaven Brewery, so their range is generally served, but Caledonian 80/- and others may be available as well.

Old, traditional Scottish pub. Food served at lunchtime and evenings. Children allowed from 12–3pm.

OPEN All day, every day.

The Phoenix Bar

103 Nethergate, Dundee, Angus DD1 4DH
☎ *(01382) 200014* Alan Bannerman

A freehouse always offering Orkney Dark Island, Caledonian Deuchars IPA and Timothy Taylor Landlord.

A traditional, one-bar pub with TV and music. Food served lunchtimes and evenings. No children.

OPEN All day, every day.

Speedwell Bar

165–7 Perth Road, Dundee, Tayside DD2 1AS
☎ *(01382) 667783* Jonathan Stewart

A freehouse with real ale on three pumps. Regulars include Timothy Taylor Landlord, Fuller's London Pride, Belhaven brews and Caledonian Deuchars IPA.

An Edwardian pub, unchanged since 1902. One bar, two rooms (one non-smoking). Bar snacks only. Children allowed until 6pm.

OPEN All day, every day.

The Chance Inn

Main Street, Inverkeilor, Arbroath, Angus DD11 5RN
☎ *(01241) 830308* Mrs Lee

A freehouse offering three real ales, with Wadworth 6X and a Robinson's brew always available. A guest beer, changed weekly, comes from a wide selection.

Two bars, plus accommodation and a recommended restaurant. Food served all day. Children allowed.

OPEN 12–3pm and 5–12pm Mon–Fri; all day Sat–Sun.

The Muirs Inn

49 Muirs, Kinross
☎ *(01577) 862270*
Mr Philip and Mr Westwood

Orkney Dark Island and Belhaven 80/- always available plus up to six guest beers (100 per year) perhaps from the Harviestoun or Border breweries. Also Scottish wines and whiskies.

A traditional Scottish country inn. Bar and restaurant food available at lunchtime and evenings. Car park and courtyard. Children allowed. Accommodation. M90 junction 6, then follow signs for the A922. At the T-junction, the inn is diagonally opposite to the right.

OPEN 12–2.30pm and 5–11pm Mon–Fri; all day Sat–Sun.

The Aldchlappie Hotel

Kirkmichael, Strath Ardle, Blairgowrie, Perthshire PH10 7NS
☎ *(01250) 881224* Mrs Mounsey

A brewpub serving own brews plus a couple of guests which are changed weekly.

A small country house hotel with two bars and separate restaurant. Food at lunchtime and evenings. Children allowed.

1707 4.2% ABV
A dark bitter beer.
1314 4.2% ABV
Slightly lighter and sweeter than 1707.

OPEN All day, every day

Moulin Hotel and Brewery

*11–13 Kirkmichael Road, Moulin, Nr Pitlochry,
Perthshire PH16 5EW*
☎ *(01796) 472196* Mr Tomlinson

 A freehouse and micro-brewery with
four own brews always on offer.

A popular 300-year-old village coaching
inn with log fires and low ceilings. Bar
and restaurant food served at lunchtime and
evenings. Car park, garden, accommodation.
Children allowed in the restaurant.

MOULIN LIGHT ALE 3.7% ABV
BRAVEHEART 4.0% ABV
ALE OF ATHOL 4.5% ABV
OLD REMEDIAL 5.2% ABV
All day, every day.

Greyfriars

15 South Street, Perth, Perthshire PH2 8PG
☎ *(01738) 633036* Jeanette Nicholson

A freehouse with Timothy Taylor
Landlord always available. Guests,
which change all the time, may include
Black Sheep Bitter or Orkney Raven Ale. The
emphasis is on independent breweries.

An old-fashioned pub with stone walls
and non-smoking dining room upstairs.
The clientele tends to be 25 and upwards.
Home-made food at lunchtime only.
Children allowed.
All day, every day.

Lovat Hotel

90–2 Glasgow Road, Perth, Tayside PH2 0LT
☎ *(01738) 636555* Mr Andrew Seal

A freehouse with real ale on four
pumps, one rotated each week. The
nearby Inveralmond brewery suppplies Lia
Fail, Ossian and others.

Two bars, accommodation, food at
lunchtime and evenings. Children
allowed. On the outskirts of Perth, a mile
from Broxton roundabout.
11am–2.30pm and 5pm–12am.

Loch Tummel Inn

*Strathtummel, Nr Pitlochry, Perthshire
PH16 5RP*
☎ *(01882) 634272* Michael Marsden

A freehouse with Moulin Braveheart
always available.

A coach house on the road to the Isles,
built by the Duke of Argyll. Food at
lunchtime and evenings. Children allowed.
All day, every day.

YOU TELL US

- ★ *Allan Ramsay Hotel,* Main Street, Carlops
- ★ *Archibald Simpson's,* 3 King Street, Aberdeen
- ★ *Buccleugh & Queensbury Hotel,* 112 Drumlanrig Street, Thornhill
- ★ *Blackfriar's,* Academy Street, Inverness
- ★ *Cairn Hotel,* Main Road, Carrbridge, Inverness-shire
- ★ *Ceres Inn,* The Cross, Ceres, Cupar, Fife
- ★ *The Cross Keys Inn,* The Green, Ancrum
- ★ *The Craw Inn,* Auchencrow
- ★ *The Cellar Bar,* 79 Stirling Street, Airdrie
- ★ *The Crow's Nest,* Tomintoul
- ★ *Carriages,* 101 Crown Street, Aberdeen
- ★ *Eglesbrech at Behind the Wall,* 14 Melville Street, Falkirk, Stirlingshire
- ★ *Green Tree Hotel,* 41 Eastgate, Peebles
- ★ *Goblin'ha Hotel,* Main Street, Gifford

- ★ *Golf Tavern,* Links Road, Earlsferry, Fife
- ★ *Hoolit's Nest,* Paxton
- ★ *The Mason's Arms,* 8 High Street, Belhaven, Lothians
- ★ *Mickey Coyle's,* 21–3 Old Hawkhill, Dundee
- ★ *The Old Coach House,* Moulin Inn, Moulin
- ★ *The Royal Hotel,* Melville Square, Comrie
- ★ *The Ship Inn,* 97 Michael Street, Dumfries, Dumfries and Galloway
- ★ *The Spinnaker Hotel,* 121 Albert Road, Gourock, Renfrewshire
- ★ *The Stormont Arms,* 101 Perth Street, Blairgowrie
- ★ *The Tap Bar & Coffee Huis,* 1055 Sauchiehall Street, Glasgow
- ★ *The Tap & Spile,* Aberdeen Airport
- ★ *Weston Tavern,* 27 Main Street, Kilmaurs
- ★ *Wynd Tower,* 57–63 High Street, Fraserburgh

stle Peel .Ramsey
Windermere . Kendal
.Douglas
Morecambe . .Lancaster
M6
LANCASHIRE
Blackpool. Burnley
Preston. H
Southport. **M6**
GREATER
MERSEYSIDE **MANCHESTER**
Liverpool . Manchest
Holyhead Llandudno . .Colwyn Bay **M53** **M56**
Llandudno . .Colwyn Bay
Denbigh . Flint **CHESHIRE**
Caernarvon **CLWYD** Wrexham . Chester **M6**
Portmadoc . Bala Llangollen Crewe S
GWYNEDD **STAFFORD**
Barmouth . .Dolgellau Llanfyllin Telford **M6**
.Dolgellau
Towyn **SHROPSHIRE**
Newtown Wolverhampton
Aberystwyth .Llanidloes Birn
POWYS Ludlow
Aberayron Knighton **HEREFORD**
New Quay . Kington **&**
Cardigan . Lampeter **WORCESTER**
Hereford . W
Fishguard **DYFED** Ross on Wye .
Llandovery Brecon **M50** Gl
Haverfordwest **WEST** Monmouth . GLO
GLAMORGAN **GWENT**
Pembroke **M4** **MID** Newport **AVON** Stroud
Swansea **GLAMORGAN**
Porthcawl . **SOUTH** .Cardiff Bristol
GLAMORGAN **M5** .Bath
Weston
Ilfracombe Minehead Super Mare
Barnstaple Warmi
Bideford . **SOMERSET**

THE BREWERIES

BULLMASTIFF BREWERY
14 Bessemer Close, Leckwith, Cardiff CF1 8DL
☎ *(01222) 665292*

CEREDIGION BREWERY
2 Brynderwen, Llangrannog, Llandysul
SA44 6AD
☎ *(012239) 654099*

 GWRACH DU 4.0% ABV
BARCUD COCH 4.3% ABV
YR DDRAIG AUR 5.0% ABV
HEN DARW DU 6.2% ABV

COTTAGE SPRING BREWERY
Gorse Cottage, Graig Road, Upper Cwmbran,
Gwent NP44 5AS
☎ *(01633) 482543*

 DRAYMAN'S BITTER 3.5% ABV
DRAYMAN'S GOLD 3.8% ABV
CROW VALLEY BITTER 4.2% ABV

FELINFOEL BREWERY CO. LTD
Farmers Row, Felinfoel, Llanelli SA14 8LB
☎ *(01554) 773357*

DRAGON BITTER 3.4% ABV
Light, refreshing and hoppy.
CAMBRIAN BEST 3.8% ABV
Easy-drinking, hoppy brew.
DOUBLE DRAGON 4.2% ABV
Rich, malty and smooth with balancing
hoppiness.

PEMBROKE BREWERY CO.
Eaton House, 108 Main Street, Pembroke
SA71 4HN
☎ *(01646) 682517 (Brewery tours)*

PLASSEY BREWERY
The Plassey, Eyton, Wrexham LL13 0SP
☎ *(01978) 780922 (Brewery tours)*

BITTER 4.0% ABV
BLACK DRAGON STOUT 4.5% ABV
FUSILIER 4.5% ABV
CWRW TUDNO 5.0% ABV
DRAGON'S BREATH 6.0% ABV

SA BRAIN AND CO. LTD
The Old Brewery, St Mary Street, Cardiff
CF1 1SP
☎ *(01222) 399022 (Brewery tours)*

 BUCKLEY'S DARK 3.4% ABV
A malty mild.
BRAINS DARK 3.5% ABV
Chocolate and nut flavours, with a dry finish.
BRAINS BITTER 3.7% ABV
Refreshing. Well-balanced with some sweetness.
BUCKLEY'S BEST BITTER 3.7% ABV
Smooth and nutty with balancing hoppiness.
BRAINS SA 4.2% ABV
Powerful malt flavour with bittersweet finish.
BUCKLEY'S REVEREND JAMES 4.5% ABV
Full-flavoured and complex.

TOMOS WATKIN AND SONS LTD
The Castle Brewery, 113 Rhosmaen Street,
Llandeilo SA19 6EN
☎ *(01558) 824140 (Brewery tours)*

 WATKINS' WHOOSH 3.7% ABV
Dark amber beer with light bitterness.
WATKINS BB 4.0% ABV
Malty, with moderate bitter flavour and floral
hoppiness.
MERLIN'S STOUT 4.2% ABV
Dark, with powerful liquorice flavour.
WATKINS OSB 4.5% ABV
Award-winning, malty with delicate hoppiness.
Plus seasonal ales.

WARCOP COUNTRY ALES
Warcop Brewery, St Brides, Wentloog NP1 9SE
☎ *(01633) 680058*

PIT SHAFT 3.4% ABV
Dark mild.
ARC 3.5% ABV
Light, hoppy session beer.
PITSIDE 3.7% ABV
Delicate and malty.
PIT PROP 3.8% ABV
Dark mild.
BLACK AND AMBER 4.0% ABV
Dark, full-flavoured with balancing hoppiness.
CASNEWYDD 4.0% ABV
Light, quaffer.
HILSTON PREMIER 4.0% ABV
Dry and refreshing.
STEELER'S 4.2% ABV
Red and malty.
FURNACE 4.5% ABV
Ruby, malty beer with dry finish.
DOCKER'S 5.0% ABV
Golden, fruity and full-bodied.

WHITE HART INN
Llanddarog SA32 8NT
☎ *(01267) 275395*

 CWRW BLASUS 4.5% ABV

Places Featured:

Aberedw
Aberystwyth
Cwmann
Goginan
Howey
Llanbadarn Fynydd
Llangynwyd
Llanidloes

Machynlleth
Montgomery
Pengenffordd
Pisgah
Rhayader
Rhydowen
Tregaron

THE PUBS

ABEREDW

The Seven Stars Inn

Aberedw, Builth Wells, Powys LD2 3UW
☎ *(01982) 560494* Deena Jones

A freehouse with three pumps and two guests from a range that has included Shepherd Neame Early Bird, Everards Tiger, Wood Shropshire Lad, Wye Valley brews and many others from micro- and small breweries.

A traditional, two-bar olde-worlde pub with log fires, darts and quoits, no fruit machines or juke box. Food available at lunchtime and evenings in the restaurant. Children allowed.

12–3pm and 7.30–11pm (10.30pm Sun).

ABERYSTWYTH

The Coopers Arms

Northgate Street, Aberystwyth, Ceredigion SY23 2JT
☎ *(01970) 624050* Mrs Somers

A Felinfoel Brewery tied house with two pumps serving Felinfoel ales and occasional guests.

Live music, no juke box or fruit machines. Well-mixed clientele of locals and students. No food. Children allowed.

11am–11pm Mon–Sat and 12–10.30pm Sun.

Flannery's Brewery Tap

High Street, Aberystwyth, Dyfed SY23 1JG
☎ *(01970) 612334* Miss Flannery

A freehouse and micro-brewery serving own beers plus two guests such as Hancock's HB and Fuller's London Pride. The guests change monthly.

An old one-bar pub with food available at lunchtime and evenings. Children allowed.

11am–11pm Mon–Sat; 12–10.30pm Sun.

CWMANN

The Ram Inn

Cwmann, Lampeter, Carmarthenshire SA48 8ES
☎ *(01570) 422556* Wynne and Mary Davies

A freehouse offering Archers Golden Bitter plus one or two guest beers changed frequently, from national and smaller breweries.

An old drover's pub one mile outside Lampeter on the Llandovery Road, dating from around 1560, with a dining room, bar and garden. Food available at lunchtime and evenings. Children allowed.

All day, every day.

GOGINAN

The Druid Inn

Goginan, Aberystwyth, Ceredigion SY23 3NT
☎ *01970 880650* William John Howell

A freehouse with three real ales always available. Hancock's HB, Banks's Bitter and Brains brews are regulars, while other guests changed monthly might include Cottage Champflower Ale.

The building dates back to 1730, when it was used by the local mining community. Bar, pool room, function room. A beer garden under construction. No juke box or games machines. Food available all day in a separate dining room. Children allowed. On the A44 heading into Aberystwyth.

11am–11pm Mon–Sat; 12–10.30pm Sun.

HOWEY

The Drovers Arms

Howey, Llandrindod Wells, Powys LD1 5PT
☎ *(01597) 822508* Mr Day

A freehouse with one guest ale changed weekly. Always from a Welsh brewery.

A traditional village inn with lounge and public bar. Food available at lunchtime and evenings. No children.

12–2.30pm and 7–11pm (10.30pm Sun); closed Tues lunchtime.

The New Inn
Llanbadarn Fynydd, Llandrindod Wells, Powys LD1 6YA
☎ *(01597) 840378* Robert Barton

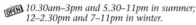 A freehouse with two real ale pumps changed at least monthly. Wood Shropshire Lad and brews from Eccleshall (Slaters) and Wye Valley are among those usually stocked.

A traditional ale and food house with log fires. Food available lunchtimes and evenings in a separate restaurant. Children allowed. Located on main A483 between Newton and Llandrindod Wells.

OPEN *10.30am–3pm and 5.30–11pm in summer; 12–2.30pm and 7–11pm in winter.*

The Coach & Horses Inn
12–13 Smithfield Street, Llanidloes, Powys SY18 6EJ
☎ *(01686) 412266* Tony Cox

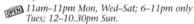 A freehouse servings Brains brews plus two guests changed weekly. These might include Robinson's Best, Everards Tiger, Shepherd Neame Early Bird and Spitfire or Tomintoul Grand Slam.

An edge-of-town, family-orientated pub with children's room, patio and aviary. Live entertainment every second Saturday. Food available all day, every day except Tuesday.

OPEN *11am–11pm Mon, Wed–Sat; 6–11pm only Tues; 12–10.30pm Sun.*

The Red Lion
8 Longbridge Street, Llanidloes, Powys SY18 6EE
☎ *(01686) 412270* Mandy James

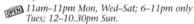 A Banks's Brewery tied house serving Banks's brews and others on up to eight pumps.

A modernised, ten-bedroom hotel with a friendly atmosphere. Food available lunchtimes and evenings. Children allowed in the restaurant only.

OPEN *11.30am–3pm and 7–11pm (10.30pm Sun).*

Wynnstay Arms Hotel
Maengwyn Street, Machynlleth, Powys SY20 8AE
☎ *(01654) 702941* Charles Dark

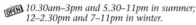 Brains beers permanently available, plus two weekly changing guests such as Greene King Abbot, Wadworth 6X and Flannery's Brewery seasonals.

A one-bar hotel and coaching inn. Accommodation and yard. Restaurant area serving food at lunchtimes and evenings. Children allowed.

OPEN *All day, every day.*

The Dragon Hotel
1 Market Square, Montgomery, Powys SY15 6PA
☎ *(01686) 668359* Mrs Michaels

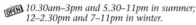 A freehouse serving guest beers on one pump. Brains brews and Fuller's London Pride are regular favourites.

A hotel bar with food available at lunchtime and evenings. Children allowed.

OPEN *11am–11pm Mon–Sat; 12–10.30pm Sun.*

The Castle Inn
Pengenffordd, Talgarth, Powys LD3 0EP
☎ *(01874) 711353* Paul Mountjoy

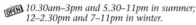 A freehouse with three pumps serving alternating guest ales. Brains Rev James Original, Shepherd Neame Spitfire and Bateman XXXB are often, plus others from breweries such as SP Sporting Ales, Cottage and others.

A rural country inn with separate dining area. B&B, plus barn-style dormitory accommodation in the middle of the hills: a good walking area at 1,000 feet. Food available at lunchtimes and evenings. Children allowed.

OPEN *11am–3pm and 7–11pm (10.30pm Sun).*

The Halfway Inn

Devil's Bridge Road, Pisgah, Aberystwyth, Dyfed SY23 4NE
☎ *(01970) 880631*

Three beers always available (30 per year) including Felinfoel brews plus Wadworth 6X, Bateman XXX, Hook Norton Old Hooky, Shepherd Neame Spitfire, Fuller's London Pride and Ringwood Old Thumper.

A traditional olde-worlde hostelry 700 feet up with magnificent views of the Cambrian mountains. Bar and restaurant food available at lunchtime and evenings. Car park and garden. Children allowed. Accommodation. Halfway along the A4120 Aberystwyth to Devil's Bridge road. Note, this is not the Pisgah near Cardigan.

OPEN *11.30am–2.30pm and 6.30pm–11pm Mon–Sat; 12–3pm and 7–10.30pm Sun.*

The Cornhill Inn

West Street, Rhayader, Powys LD6 5AB
☎ *(01597) 810869* Barbara Fraser

Marston's Pedigree and Wye Valley Hereford Bitter are always available plus two guests (100 per year) which may include Hop Back Summer Lightning, Titanic Brews, Dent T'owd Tup, Ringwood Fortyniner, Wye Valley brew 97, NYBC Fool's Gold and Moorhouse's Pendle Witches Brew.

A sixteenth-century freehouse with olde-worlde charm. Low beams and open fires. Bar food available at lunchtimes and evenings. Parking. Children allowed. Accommodation. On the road to Elan Valley.

OPEN *11am–3pm and 7–11pm (10.30pm Sun).*

The Alltyrodyn Arms

Rhydowen, Llandysul, Ceredigion SA44 4QB
☎ *(01545) 590319* Derrick and Jean Deakin

A freehouse serving three or four real ales. Archers Golden and Everards Tiger are regularly available plus hundreds of others constantly changing.

A 16th-century pub with a restaurant serving food all day, a pool room, beer garden with fish pond and waterfall. B&B and self-catering accommodation available. Children allowed in the bar until 9pm.

OPEN *11am–11pm Mon–Sat; 12–4pm Sun.*

The Talbot Hotel

Main Square, Tregaron, Ceredigion SY25 6HY
☎ *(01974) 298208* Graham Williams

A freehouse with three handpumps serving a wide range of real ales.

A n old, traditional pub offering a friendly welcome. Beer garden. Food available at lunchtime and evenings. Children allowed.

OPEN *12–2pm and 6.30–11pm (10.30pm Sun).*

THE PUBS

BANGOR

The Castle (Hogshead)

Glanrafon, off High Street, Bangor, Gwynedd LL57 1LH
☎ *(01248) 355866* Mark Fisher

A Whitbread tied house with up to ten hand pumps plus four beers served straight from the barrel. Regular guests include Timothy Taylor Landlord, Fuller's London Pride, Caledonian 80/- and Marston's Pedigree. Has served more than 500 beers in the past three years.

A roomy pub with a large open single floor, dark wood floors, background music. Non-smoking area, wheelchair access. Food available 12–7pm. Children allowed. Opposite the Cathedral, close to the railway station.

OPEN *11am–11pm Mon–Sat; 12–10.30pm Sun.*

The Tap & Spile

Garth Road, Bangor, Gwynedd LL57 2SW
☎ *(01248) 370835* Dean Ibbitson

Greene King Triumph, Otter Ale and a Tap & Spile own brew usually available on eight guest pumps. No permanent beers. Beers changed daily.

A suburban pub with B&B. Food lunchtimes and evenings. No children. Located by the pier.

OPEN *All day, every day..*

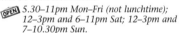

BRYNFORD

The Llyn y Mawn Inn

Brynford Hill, Brynford, Holywell, Flintshire CH8 8AD
☎ *(01352) 714367* Martin Jackson

A freehouse serving up to six brews every week. Welsh ales are favoured, plus others from small breweries. The owner is co-ordinator for the Pub Watch scheme in North Wales.

CAMRA Welsh pub of the year 1995 and 1997. Typical Welsh long house with restaurant and gardens. Real fires, no music. Food available Saturday and Sunday lunchtime only. Well-behaved children allowed. Adjacent to the A55 expressway, and can be seen from there.

OPEN *5.30–11pm Mon–Fri (not lunchtime); 12–3pm and 6–11pm Sat; 12–3pm and 7–10.30pm Sun.*

CAERNARFON

The Alexandra Hotel

North Road, Caernarfon, Gwynedd LL55 1BA
☎ *(01286) 672871* Ken Moulton

A Whitbread tied house serving a range of guests as well as the Whitbread brews. Regulars include Wadworth 6X, Morland Old Speckled Hen and Marston's Pedigree. The guest list changes fortnightly.

A local pub with B&B accommodation. Tables outside. No food. Children allowed in the afternoons only.

OPEN *11am–11pm Mon–Sat; 12–10.30pm Sun.*

Y Goron Fach

Hole in the Wall Street, Caernarfon, Gwynedd LL55 1RF
☎ *(01286) 673338* Mr Williams

A freehouse permanently serving Flannery's Celtic Ale, plus Fuller's London Pride, St Davids Ale and Adnams bitters as regular guests on two pumps.

A town pub with two bars and a garden. Food served at lunchtimes and evenings in the summer, lunchtime only in winter. Children allowed.

All day, every day.

The Travellers' Inn

Pen y Cefn, Caerwys, Mold, Clwyd CH7 5BL
☎ *(01352) 720251* Kevin Jones

A freehouse and brewpub with Marston's Pedigree regularly available plus various other guests rotated on the two remaining pumps.

A family pub and restaurant with food available all day. Children allowed. Located on the A55

ROY MORGAN'S ORIGINAL 3.8–3.9% ABV
OLD ELIAS 5.2% ABV

11am–11pm Mon–Sat; 12–10.30pm Sun.

The White Horse

The Square, Cilcain, Mold, Flintshire CH7 5NN
☎ *(01352) 740142* Mr Jeory

A freehouse with two hand pumps serving a wide range of beers on rotation. Exmoor Gold, Greene King Abbot, Marston's Pedigree and Fuller's London Pride are regularly featured. Others might include beers from Wood or Cottage breweries. The range changes every other day.

A small, cosy village pub, unspoilt for 150 years, spread over four rooms with real fires and beams. No juke box or pool table. Food available at lunchtime and evenings. No children.

12–3pm and 6.30–11pm Mon–Fri; 11am–11pm Sat; 12–3.30pm and 7–10.30pm Sun.

The White Lion Inn

Llanelian-Yn-Rhos, Colwyn Bay, Conwy LL29 8YA
☎ *(01492) 515807* Jack Cole

A freehouse with three real ales usually available from a wide range that changes fortnightly.

A traditional stone-built Welsh country inn with slate floor, log fires and beams. B&B accommodation and non-smoking dining area. Food available at lunchtime and evenings. Children allowed.

11am–3pm and 6–11pm Mon–Sat; 12–3pm and 7–10.30pm Sun.

The Eagle Inn

Back Row, Denbigh, Denbighshire LL16 3TE
☎ *(01745) 813203* Mr Evans

A freehouse serving up to eight real ales. Ward's Waggle Dance and Morland Old Speckled Hen are both popular but all real ales considered.

A large pub with a snooker room, pool, darts etc. The pub runs quiz nights and a cricket team. Food currently available at lunchtime only although expansion is planned. Children allowed if eating.

11am–11pm Mon–Sat; 12–10.30pm Sun.

The Druid Inn

Gorsedd, Holywell, Flintshire CH8 8QZ
☎ *(01352) 710944* Ken Doherty

A freehouse usually serving Marston's Pedigree plus four or five others from an extensive range that favours the smaller and micro-breweries rather than nationals.

A listed twelfth-century long house, with oak beams and log fires. The separate restaurant serves food every evening and Sunday lunchtime. Children allowed. Located off the A5026, two miles west of Holywell.

7–11pm Mon–Sat (closed lunchtimes except Sun); 12–3pm and 7–10.30 Sun.

LLANDUDNO

The Olde Victoria
Church Walks, Llandudno, Conwy LL30 2HL
☎ *(01492) 860949* Mr J Vaughan-Williams

A freehouse serving Banks's brews and up to five others.

A Victorian pub, comfortable, family-orientated. Food is a speciality, served in a separate restaurant and available at lunchtime and evenings. Children allowed. Situated near the pier.

OPEN *11am–11pm Mon–Sat; 12–10.30pm Sun.*

LLANGOLLEN

The Sun Inn
49 Regent Street, Llangollen, Denbighshire LL20 8HN
☎ *(01978) 860233*
Alan Adams and Paul Lamb

A freehouse offering six real ales that could well include Weetwood Old Dog and Wye Valley brews. Four Belgian beers and two real ciders also available.

A friendly, old, beer-drinker's pub with a good atmosphere. Food available at lunchtime and early evening. Take the A5 towards Llangollen.

OPEN *11am–11pm Mon–Sat; 12–10.30pm Sun.*

MOCHDRE

The Mountain View
7 Old Conwy Road, Mochdre, Colwyn Bay, Conwy LL28 5AT
☎ *(01492) 544724* Malcolm Gray

A Burtonwood Brewery tied house serving Burton Best and Top Hat permanently plus regular rotating guests including, perhaps, Everards Tiger, Bateman XXX, Gales HSB and Caledonian brews. Also a 'Brewery Choice' of a seasonal brew like Black Parrot.

A village pub with restaurant and large garden. Food available at lunchtimes and evenings. Children allowed.

OPEN *All day, every day.*

MOLD

Y Pentan
New Street, Mold, Flintshire CH7 1NY
☎ *(01352) 758884* Tim Hughes

A tied pub serving beers from the Marston's range. Plus one guest rotated fortnightly.

A pub in the town centre, with public bar and L-shaped lounge. Food available Mon-Sat lunchtime (not Sun). Children allowed.

OPEN *6.30–11pm Mon, Tues, Thurs; 11am–11pm Wed, Fri, Sat; 12–10.30pm Sun.*

MORFA NEFYN

Cliffs Inn
Beach Road, Morfa Nefyn, Gwynedd LL53 6BY
☎ *(01758) 720356* Glynne Roberts

A freehouse with two pumps usually serving one English and one Welsh ale, the Welsh brew usually from Brains.

A food-orientated pub with good beer. Outside patio. Food available at lunchtime and evenings in a separate dining area. Children allowed.

OPEN *12–3pm and 6–11pm; (10.30pm Sun).*

NORTHOP

Stables Bar at Soughton Hall
Soughton Hall Country House Hotel and Restaurant, Northop, Flintshire CH7 6AB
☎ *(01352) 840577* Mr Rodenhurst (owner); Alexander John (bar manager)

A freehouse serving real ales from Flannery's and Hanby Breweries. There are three dedicated Flannery pumps and three others serving brews rotated weekly. Small and micro-breweries preferred.

An unusual location, set in the old stable block of the hotel complex. The hayloft has been converted into a restaurant. Beer garden and wine shop. Food available at lunchtime and evenings. Children allowed. Located off the A55 Flint/Northop junction

OPEN *11am–11pm Mon–Sat; 12–10.30pm Sun.*

OLD COLWYN

The Red Lion

385 Abergele Road, Old Colwyn, Colwyn Bay, Conwy LL29 9PL
☎ *(01492) 515042* Wayne Hankie

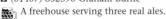 A freehouse serving seven cask ales, four of which are constantly rotated. Brains SA, Charles Wells Bombardier, Greene King Abbot Ale and Morland Old Speckled Hen usually available plus many, many more. Some 400 brews have been served over the past two years.

A village pub on the main road with a double lounge bar, open fires and no music in lounge. The public bar has a pool table, TV and juke box. No food. Children not allowed. A regional pub of the year.

5–11pm Mon–Fri; 11am–11pm Sat; 12–10.30pm Sun.

PENYSARN

Y Bedol

Penysarn, Anglesey, Gwynedd LL69 9YR
☎ *(01407) 832590* Graham Burne

A freehouse serving three real ales.

Warm, friendly pub with beer garden, pool room, karaoke and quiz nights and occasional local Welsh entertainment. No food. Children allowed.

11am–11pm Mon–Sat; 12–10.30pm Sun.

RHEWL

The Drovers Arms

Rhewl, Ruthin, Denbighshire LL15 2UD
☎ *(01824) 703163* Charles Gale-Hasleham

A freehouse serving three real ales. Tries to specialise in Welsh beers from small and micro-breweries. Coach House Honeypot and brews from Vale and Flannery's Breweries are often featured.

A 300-year-old pub and an old meeting place for drovers. An English Civil War skirmish took place on the bridge outside the pub. Large garden with tables, barbecues in nice weather. Food available at lunchtime and evenings. Well-behaved children allowed. The landlord used to own the Vale and Clwyd (now Flannery's) Breweries.

12–3pm (not Mon) and 7–11pm; 12–10.30pm Sun.

RHYD DDU

The Cwellyn Arms

Rhyd Ddu, Gwynedd LL54 6TL
☎ *(01766) 890321* Graham Bander

A freehouse serving nine real ales, perhaps Dorothy Goodbody's Warming Wintertime Ale (Wye Valley), Cottage Great Western Ale, Young's Special, Fuller's London Pride, Thwaites Bitter, Wadworth 6X and Old Timer, Gales HSB, Charles Wells Bombardier, Adnams Broadside, Coach House Gunpowder Strong Mild or McGuinness Feather Plucker Mild.

A country inn with B&B accommodation and cottages to let. Restaurant, beer garden, children's adventure playground. Food available all day every day. At the foot of Mount Snowdon, on the Caernarfon/ Beddgelert road.

11am–11pm Mon–Sat; 12–10.30pm Sun.

ST ASAPH

The Kentigern Arms

High Street, St Asaph, Clwyd LL17 0RG
☎ *(01745) 584157* Mrs Redgrave

A freehouse offering up to seven real ales. Popular brews come from Marston's, Cottage and other smaller breweries. The varied and unusual range changes every two weeks.

A seventeenth-century coaching inn with beams and open fires. A separate small room can be used for children or as a dining room. Four bedrooms available. Food available at lunchtimes only. Children allowed.

12–3pm and 7–11pm (10.30pm Sun).

WAUNFAWR

The Snowdonia Parc Hotel

Beddgelert Road, Waunfawr, Gwynedd LL55 4AQ
☎ *(01286) 650218* Karen Humphries

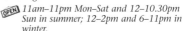 A brewpub in which the landlady's son Gareth provides the beer, usually to around 5% ABV. Passageway beers and other local brews are also often available. Up to four beers in total in summer.

A village pub in beautiful surroundings. Campsite, family room. Food available at lunchtime and evenings. Children allowed. On the A4085 Roman road from Caernarfon to Beddgelert

11am–11pm Mon–Sat and 12–10.30pm Sun in summer; 12–2pm and 6–11pm in winter.

Places Featured:

Abercrave
Bassaleg
Bettws Newydd
Bishopston
Blackmill
Blaenavon
Bridgend
Chepstow
Clytha
Gilwern
Glan-y-Llyn
Heol y Plas
Kenfig
Llanbedr
Llandogo
Llandovery
Llangorse
Llangynwyd

Llanrhidian Gower
Llantilio Crossenny
Machen
Mumbles
Newport
Pant
Penallt
Pontardawe
Raglan
Rassau
Sebastopol
Swansea
Talybont-on-Usk
Tredunnock
Trellech
Upper Llanover
Usk

THE PUBS

ABERCRAVE

The Copper Beech Inn
133 Heol Tawe, Abercrave, Swansea, West Glamorgan SA9 1XS
☎ *(01639) 730269* Philip and Paul Colman

A family-run freehouse. Young's Special and Brains brews usually available, plus guests served on one pump (changed weekly) from breweries such as Wye Valley and Cottage.

A local's pub, with function room and beer garden. Families welcome. Food available at lunchtimes and evenings.

11am–11pm Mon–Sat; 12–10.30pm Sun.

BASSALEG

The Tredegar Arms
4 Caerphilly Road, Bassaleg, Newport, Gwent NP1 9LE
☎ *(01633) 893247* David Hennah

A Whitbread tied house with up to nine hand pumps and six beers from the barrel. Up to 13 brews available, changing weekly. Regulars include Shepherd Neame Spitfire, Timothy Taylor Landlord and beers from Wychwood and Caledonian. Two beer festivals are held each year, in May and August.

A busy wayside inn; near junction 28 of the M4. Large beer garden, ample car parking. Food available lunchtime and evenings. Children allowed.

11am–11pm Mon–Sat; 12–10.30pm Sun.

BETTWS NEWYDD

The Black Bear
Bettws Newydd, Usk, Monmouthshire NP15 1JN
☎ *(01873) 880701* Gillian Molyneux

A freehouse with four real ales available at any one time, all straight from the barrel. The range changes every couple of weeks.

An old one-bar country pub with fine restaurant and beer garden. Families welcome. Food available at lunchtime and evenings except Sunday evening. Children allowed. Three miles outside of Usk

12–2pm and 6–11pm Mon–Sat (closed Mon lunch); 12–10.30pm Sun.

BISHOPSTON

The Joiners' Arms
50 Bishopston Road, Bishopston, Swansea, West Glamorgan SA3 3EJ
☎ *(01792) 232658* Ian Davies

Home of the Swansea Brewing Company. Up to eight pumps serve the full range of brews.

A traditional village pub with mixed clientele, no juke box. Food available at lunchtime and in the evenings. Children allowed.

11am–11pm Mon–Sat; 12–10.30pm Sun.

The Ogmore Junction Hotel

Blackmill, Mid Glamorgan CF35 6DR
☎ *(01656) 840371* John Nicholas

 Up to six pumps serving a range of beers that changes regularly.

A country pub with beams and log fires, beer garden and car park. Backs on to the River Ogmore. Food is available in the separate restaurant at lunchtime and evenings. Children allowed in a designated area. Situated not far from the M4 on the main road to the Rhondda Valley. A fortnightly sheep sale is held behind the pub from the end of July to the end of December.

OPEN *11am–11pm Mon–Sat; 12–10.30pm Sun.*

Cambrian Inn

Llanover Road, Blaenavon, Gwent NP4 9HR
☎ *(01495) 790327* J and P Morgans

Blaenavon Pride and Glory and Brains brews always available, plus a guest (50 per year) such as Morland Old Speckled Hen.

A typical Welsh mining village pub. Darts, pool, cards, etc. No food. Street parking opposite the pub. Children not allowed.

OPEN *6–11pm Mon–Thurs; 12–11pm Sat; 12–3pm and 7–10.30pm Sun.*

The Famous Pen y Bont Inn

Derwen Road, Bridgend, Mid Glamorgan CF31 1LH
☎ *(01656) 648452* Ruth and Jim Simpson

A Greenalls tied pub with five pumps, three of which serve a range of guest beers, rotated weekly. Regulars include Morland Old Speckled Hen, Greene King Abbot Ale, Wadworth 6X, Timothy Taylor Landlord, Charles Wells Bombardier and Badger Tanglefoot

A small, friendly, comfortable pub. Food is available at lunchtime and evenings. Children allowed at lunchtime only. Located near the railway station – formerly the Railway Hotel.

OPEN *11am–11pm Mon–Sat; 12–10.30pm Sun.*

The Coach & Horses

Welsh Street, Chepstow, Monmouthshire NP6 5LN
☎ *(01291) 622626* Ralph Thomas

A Brains tied pub, with the brewery's ales on three pumps and three guests. Regular visitors include Morland Old Speckled Hen.

A family pub with B&B accommodation and food available at lunchtime and evenings in a separate dining area. A beer festival is held every July to coincide with the Chepstow Carnival, when up to 20 different beers are available.

OPEN *11am–11pm Mon–Sat; 12–10.30pm Sun.*

Clytha Arms

Clytha, Gwent NP7 9BW
☎ *(01873) 840206* Mr and Mrs Canning

Hook Norton Best is among those beers permanently available, plus three guests (360 per year) from breweries such as Freeminer, Felinfoel, RCH, Wye Valley, Jennings, Fuller's, Harviestoun, Exmoor and Adnams. A mild is always available.

A large old dower house with restaurant and traditional bar. Bar and restaurant food available at lunchtime and evenings. Car park, garden, accommodation. Children allowed. Located on the old Abergavenny to Raglan road.

OPEN *6–11pm Mon; 11.30am–3pm and 6–11pm Tues–Fri and Sun; 11am–11pm Sat.*

Bridgend Inn

Main Road, Gilwern, Gwent
☎ *(01873) 830939* Mrs P D James

Up to four real ales always available including Felinfoel brews. Guests include Fuller's London Pride and ESB, also Wadworth 6X and IPA.

C analside, olde-worlde pub. Bar and restaurant food available at lunchtime and evenings. Car park, patio and garden. Children allowed for meals.

OPEN *12–2pm and 7–11pm Mon–Thurs; 12–11pm Fri–Sat; 12–10.30pm Sun.*

GLAN-Y-LLYN

Fagin's Ale & Chop House

Cardiff Road, Glan-y-Llyn, Mid Glamorgan
☎ *(0122) 811800* Jeff Butler

Five beers always available from a range that may include Shepherd Neame Bishop's Finger, Greene King Abbot, Morland Old Speckled Hen and many more.

A converted terraced house. Former CAMRA pub of the year. Bar and restaurant food available at lunchtime and evenings. Function room. Children allowed.

OPEN *12–11pm (10.30pm Sun).*

HEOL Y PLAS

Ye Olde Red Lion

Heol y Plas, Llannon, Carmarthenshire SA14 6AA
☎ *(01269) 841276*
Changed hands in June 1999

A Felinfoel Brewery tied house with two pumps serving Felinfoel ales.

A rural sixteenth-century pub with oak beams and log fires. Non-smoking and smoking dining areas. Food available every evening plus Saturday and Sunday lunchtimes. Children welcome.

OPEN *5–11pm Mon–Fri; 11am–11pm Sat; 12–10.30pm Sun.*

KENFIG

The Prince of Wales Inn

Kenfig, Mid Glamorgan CF33 4PR
☎ *(01656) 740356* Jeremy Evans

A freehouse serving up to four real ales at any one time. Tomas Watkin OSB and Fuller's London Pride are regularly available, plus a range of others, changing constantly, from a huge list that might include St Austell Tinners Ale or Morland Old Speckled Hen.

An olde-worlde pub with three open fires, a lounge, games room and function room (which houses the Sunday School). Food is available at lunchtime and evenings. Children allowed in the separate dining area.

OPEN *11am–4.30pm and 6–11pm Mon–Thurs; 11am–11pm Fri–Sun (10.30pm Sun).*

LLANBEDR

The Red Lion Inn

Llanbedr, Crickhowell, Powys NP8 1SR
☎ *(01873) 810754* Mr Sloan

A freehouse serving two real ales from breweries such as Wye Valley or Bateman.

A quiet 300-year-old pub with beams and real fires. Non-smoking room and garden. Nearby campsite situated in a very beautiful spot in the Black Mountains. Food available lunchtimes and evenings. Children allowed.

OPEN *7–11pm Mon–Fri; 12–2.30pm Wed–Fri; 11am–11pm Sat; 12–4pm and 7–10.30pm Sun.*

LLANDOGO

The Sloop Inn

Llandogo, Monmouthshire NP5 4TW
☎ *(01594) 530291* Eddie Grace

A freehouse with two real ales always on at any one time and more in summer. One session and one stronger ale always available.

Recently redecorated. Describes itself as more of an inn than a pub, family-orientated with accommodation and garden. Set in a beautiful village location in the Wye Valley. Food available every lunchtime and evening. On the A466.

OPEN *12–2.30pm and 5.30–11pm Mon–Fri, 11am–11pm Sat–Sun (10.30pm Sun); all day, every day in summer.*

LLANDOVERY

The White Swan

47 High Street, Llandovery, Carmarthenshire SA20 0DE
☎ *(01550) 720816* Ray Miller

A freehouse specialising in beers up to 4.2% ABV. Two always available, changed every two weeks.

A town pub offering darts, pool and a mixed local clientele. No juke box or fruit machines. No food. Children and dogs are welcome. The last pub on the way out of Llandovery, near the supermarket.

OPEN *12–3pm and 7–11pm (10.30pm Sun).*

The Castle Inn

Llangorse, Brecon, Powys LD3 7UB
☎ *(01874) 658225* Mr Williams

A freehouse with two pumps serving ales from a range including Bateman XB, Morland Old Speckled Hen and many more.

An olde-worlde village inn with a 27-seater restaurant. Food available at lunchtime and evenings. Children allowed under supervision.

OPEN *12–3pm and 6–11pm Mon–Fri;*
11am–11pm Sat; 12–10.30pm Sun.

The Old House

Llangynwyd, Maesteg, Mid Glamorgan CF34 9SB
☎ *(01656) 733310* Richard David

A freehouse with Brains SA permanently available plus guests from Marillwyd.

An old, traditional pub with three bars and a garden. Food available at lunchtimes and evenings. Children allowed.

OPEN *All day, every day.*

The Greyhound Inn

Old Walls, Llanrhidian Gower, Swansea, West Glamorgan SA3 1HA
☎ *(01792) 391027* Peter and Sally Green

A freehouse with six real ales available. Bullmastiff, Marston's, Morland and Wadworth brews are regular examples plus brews from the nearby Swansea Brewing Company.

An old, comfortable, family- and food-orientated pub, in the middle of nowhere, with coal fires. The beer garden has play equipment. Separate restaurant specialises in fish, fresh oysters, Indian and vegetarian food. Located in a ramblers walking area.

OPEN *11am–11pm Mon–Sat; 12–10.30pm Sun.*

The Hostry Inn

Llantilio Crossenny, Abergavenny, Gwent NP7 8SU
☎ *(01600) 780278* Pauline and Michael Parker

A freehouse offering up to three real ales. Bullmastiff and Cardiff brews regularly available plus one from Wye Valley or elsewhere.

A small, welcoming, country pub on Offa's Dyke ramblers path. Skittle alley, function room, non-smoking restaurant and non-smoking area in the bar. Food available lunchtime and evenings. Well-behaved children allowed. Located on the B4233, halfway between Monmouth and Abergavenny.

OPEN *11am–11pm Mon, Tues, Fri, Sat, Sun (10.30pm); closed lunchtime Oct–Mar.*

The White Hart Inn

Nant y Ceisiad, Machen, Newport, Gwent NP1 8QQ
☎ *(01633) 441005* Alan Carter

A freehouse which, over the last four years, reckons to have served 1,700 different beers on five handpumps. Small and micro-breweries from all over the British Isles have featured.

A very olde-worlde pub, designed as the interior of ship (the captain's cabin came from the Empress of France). Food available at lunchtime and evenings in a separate dining area which seats 100 people. Play area and beer garden. Children allowed. Located just off the main road (A448).

OPEN *11am–11pm Mon–Sat; 12–10.30pm Sun; closed 3.30–6pm in winter.*

The Park Inn

23 Park Street, Mumbles, Swansea, West Glamorgan SA3 4DA
☎ *(01792) 366738* Mr Francis

A freehouse with two guest pumps which change too frequently to list. Timothy Taylor Landlord and brews from Cottage are just two examples. Over 200 beers served over the past two years.

A small, traditional, one-bar local. No food. No children.

OPEN *12–3.30pm and 5.30–11pm Mon–Fri; 11am–11pm Sat; 12–10.30pm Sun.*

St Julian's Inn

Caerleon Road, Newport, Gwent NP6 1QA
☎ *(01633) 258663* Mr S J Williams

A Unique Brewing Company pub serving four beers with two guests changed twice-weekly. Wadworth 6X and Everards Tiger are regulars. Other brewers supported include Wye Valley, Cottage and B&T.

A pretty, family pub in a scenic location with balcony overlooking the River Usk. Food available Mon–Sat lunchtime and evenings. Children allowed.

OPEN *11am–11pm Mon–Sat; 12–10.30pm Sun.*

Wetherspoons

Cambrian Retail Centre, Cambrian Road, Newport, Gwent NP9 4AD
☎ *(01633) 251752* Paul McDonnell

Five handpumps serving a wide range of real ales that change on a weekly basis.

A busy pub with a wide-ranging clientele, old and young. Particularly lively in the evenings. Food available at lunchtime and evenings. No children. Next to the railway station.

OPEN *11am–11pm Mon–Sat; 12–10.30pm Sun.*

Pant Cad Ifor Inn

Pant, Merthyr Tydfil, Mid Glamorgan CF48 2DD
☎ *(01685) 7723688* Phillip Williams

Up to six real ales available, with regulars including Everards Tiger, Shepherd Neame Bishop's Finger and Young's brews.

A small country pub on the outskirts of town with a separate dining area. There is a steam railway 100 yards up the road. Coach parties are catered for. Food is available at lunchtime only. Children allowed.

OPEN *11am–11pm Mon–Sat; 12–10.30pm Sun.*

The Boat Inn

Lone Lane, Penallt, Monmouth, Gwent MP5 4AJ
☎ *(01600) 712615* Stephen Rowlands

Wadworth 6X and Oakhill Bitter are always available straight from the barrel, plus approximately six others, some from a rolling rota of about ten regulars and other occasionals.

A small riverside inn on the England–Wales border built into the hillside, with stone floors and simple decor. Jazz/blues and rock/folk nights twice weekly. Very cosy with no juke box or games machines. Bar food available at lunchtimes and evenings. Car park on the side of the river, terrace gardens with ponds, streams and waterfalls. Children allowed. The car park is in Redbrook (Gloucestershire) on the A466, next to a football field. Follow the footpath over an old railway bridge across the Wye.

OPEN *11am–3pm and 6–11pm Mon–Sat; 12–3pm and 7–10.30pm Sun.*

The Pontardawe Inn

Herbert Street, Pontardawe, Swansea, West Glamorgan SA8 4ED
☎ *(01792) 830791* Mr P Clayton

A freehouse serving 170 guest beers per year. Shepherd Neame Early Bird and Everards Tiger are often available, plus a constantly changing range on seven pumps plus one straight from the barrel.

An olde-worlde pub with no juke box and no pool table. Festival-orientated with music from all around the world. Four beer festivals and one music festival held every year. Food served at lunchtime and in the evenings in a separate 28-seater restaurant. Children allowed until 9pm.

OPEN *11am–11pm Mon–Sat; 12–10.30pm Sun.*

The Ship Inn

High Street, Raglan, Monmouthshire NP15 2DY
☎ *(01291) 690635* Jane Tucker

A freehouse serving up to four guest beers at any one time. Fuller's London Pride usually available, plus guests from Bath, Wye Valley, Eccleshall, SP Sporting and Morland changed weekly.

A sixteenth-century olde-worlde coaching inn with beams and log fires. There is a well in the cobblestoned forecourt. Food available in separate dining area at lunchtime and evenings. Children allowed. Located just off the High Street, opposite the supermarket.

OPEN *11am–11pm Mon–Sat; 12–10.30pm Sun.*

RASSAU

Rhyd u Blew

Rassau Road, Rassau, Ebbw Vale, Gwent NP23 5PW
☎ *(01495) 308935* Lyn Collins

 Up to four real ales available.

Out-of-town, open-plan, community pub with a beer garden. Food available at lunchtime only. No children. Located off the A465.

 12–3pm and 6–11pm Mon–Fri; 11.30am–4.30pm and 6–11pm Sat; 12–3pm and 7–10.30pm Sun.

SEBASTOPOL

The Open Hearth

Wern Road, Sebastopol, Pontypool, Torfaen NP4 5DR
☎ *(01495) 763752* Gwyn Philips

 A freehouse with five real ales always available. Wye Valley, Felinfoel and Burton Bridge brews regularly served, plus a range of guests from 65 different breweries. Over 500 barrels were served in 1998.

A busy pub on the canal side, with excellent food and beer reputation. Winner of two regional CAMRA awards. Food available in a separate non-smoking restaurant. No juke box or pool table. Mixed clientele of all ages. Children welcome, with children's room provided.

11.30am–3.30pm and 6–11pm Mon–Fri; 11am–11pm Sat; 12–4pm and 7–10.30pm Sun.

SWANSEA

The Glamorgan Hotel

88 Argyle Street, Swansea, West Glamorgan SA1 3TA
☎ *(01792) 455120* Vince Carr

Two real ales on the guest pumps including Camerons Strongarm, Marston's Bitter and Banks's Bitter.

A broad-based local, no juke box. Food available lunchtime and evenings. Children allowed in the afternoons only.

11am–11pm Mon–Sat; 12–10.30pm Sun.

The New Inn

The Lone, Swansea, West Glamorgan, SA6 5SU
☎ *(01792) 842839* Glynn Hopkin

A Whitbread-owned pub with up to seven real ales. Brains Dark, Morland Old Speckled Hen, Fuggles Imperial IPA and Fuller's London Pride are regularly available plus Greene King Abbot and others from time to time.

A village inn with a restaurant and function room. Food available at lunchtime and evenings. Children allowed.

11am–3pm and 6–11pm Mon–Thurs; 11am–11pm Fri–Sat; 12–4pm and 7–10.30pm Sun.

The Potters Wheel

85–6 The Kingsway, Swansea, West Glamorgan SA1 5JE
☎ *(01792) 465113* Nerys Jones

A JD Wetherspoon's pub with up to 16 real ales available.

A town-centre pub on the high street. No music, games or pool, non-smoking area. Food available all day. No children.

11am–11pm Mon–Sat; 12–10.30pm Sun.

TALYBONT-ON-USK

The Star Inn

Talybont-on-Usk, Brecon, Powys LD3 7YX
☎ *(01874) 676635* Mrs Coakham

A constantly changing range of 12 beers, including brews from Felinfoel, Freeminers, Bullmastiff, Wadworth and Crown Buckley.

A riverside and canalside site, with lovely garden. Bar and restaurant food is available at lunchtime and evenings. Parking, garden, live music on Wednesdays. Children allowed. Accommodation. Less than a mile off the A40 between Brecon and Abergavenny (Brecon six miles, Abergavenny 14 miles).

11am–11pm (10.30pm Sun) in summer; otherwise closed 3–6pm.

TREDUNNOCK

The Newbridge Inn

Tredunnock, Usk, Monmouthshire NP5 1LY
☎ *(01633) 450227* Robert Noone

A freehouse with four pumps and serving two guests from smaller breweries such as Wye Valley.

A recently totally refurbished pub on the banks of the River Usk. A traditional country pub atmosphere. Food available at lunchtime and evenings. Children allowed. Village signposted off the Caerlon–Usk road.

11am–11pm Mon–Sat; 12–10.30pm Sun.

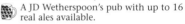

TRELLECH

The Lion Inn

Trellech, Nr Monmouth, Monmouthshire
NP25 4PA
☎ *(01600) 860322* Tom and Debbie Zsigo

 A freehouse with three guest pumps, changed weekly. Fuller's London Pride and Wadworth 6X are usually available plus another from a smaller brewery, such as Bath, Wychwood or Lees.

A stone-fronted, sixteenth-century typical country pub with open fire, no fruit machines or juke box. Favours traditional pub games such as bar billiards and bar skittles plus many social evenings. Prize-winning food available every lunchtime and all evenings except Sunday. Well-behaved children and dogs allowed, but no dogs in the lounge.

OPEN *12–3pm and 7–11pm Mon; 12–3pm and 6–11pm Tues–Fri; 6.30–11pm Sat; closed Sunday evenings.*

The Trekkers

The Narth, Nr Trellech, Monmouthshire
NP5 4QG
☎ *(01600) 860367* Mr and Mrs Flower

 A freehouse with two guest ales changed fortnightly. Greene King Abbot, Shepherd Neame Spitfire and Smiles Golden regularly available.

A local country pub, in the style of a log cabin, family-orientated with beer garden, swings and skittle alley. Traditional, home-made, British-bought food available in separate dining area lunchtimes and evenings. It is advisable to book for Sunday lunch.

OPEN *11am–2.30pm and 6–11pm Mon–Sat; 12–3pm and 7–10.30pm Sun.*

UPPER LLANOVER

The Goose & Cuckoo Inn

Upper Llanover, Abergavenny, Monmouthshire
NP7 9ER
☎ *(01873) 880277*
Ann and John McDonald Cullen

 A freehouse with three pumps, usually serving either a Brains ale or Wadworth 6X.

A small, isolated, picturesque country pub with a real fire. No juke box or games machines, traditional card games. Beer garden. Food available every lunchtime and all evenings except Thursday. Well-behaved children allowed.

OPEN *11.30–3pm and 7–11pm Tues–Sat; 12–3pm and 7–10.30pm Sun; closed Monday unless bank holiday.*

USK

The Greyhound Inn

1 Chepstow Road, Usk, Monmouthshire
NP5 1BL
☎ *(01291) 672074* Bob and Annette Burton

 A freehouse serving four beers including those from RCH, Brakspear, Greene King, Wye Valley, Shepherd Neame and Freeminer. The beers change fortnightly.

An early sixteenth-century pub on the edge of town. Bar, no juke box. Food available lunchtime and evenings. Children allowed.

OPEN *12–3pm and 6.30–11pm Mon–Sat; 12–3pm and 7–10.30pm Sun.*

The Kings Head Hotel

18 Old Market Street, Usk, Monmouthshire
NP5 1AL
☎ *(01291) 672963* S Musto

A freehouse with four pumps serving a wide range of guests.

A fifteenth-century pub with accommodation. Open fireplace, function room and restaurant serving food at lunchtime and evenings. Children allowed.

OPEN *All day, every day.*

Places Featured:

Felinfoel
Haverfordwest
Horeb
Llandeilo

Llansaint
Mynydd y Garreg
Narbeth
Pembroke

THE PUBS

FELINFOEL

The Royal Oak
Felinfoel Road, Felinfoel, Carmarthenshire
SA14 8LA
☎ *(01554) 751140* Mrs M Cleland

Tied to the nearby Felinfoel Brewery, with two handpumps serving the Felinfoel ales.

An old-fashioned local opposite the brewery, with food available at lunchtime and evenings. Children allowed.

All day, every day.

HAVERFORDWEST

King's Arms Hotel
23 Dew Street, Haverfordwest, Dyfed
☎ *(01437) 763726* Chris Hudd

Six beers always available from a list of approximately 150 brews per year.

An old, beamed and flagstoned pub in the town, just past the library. Street parking, function room. No children.

11am–3pm and 6–11pm Mon–Sat; 12–3pm and 7–10.30pm Sun.

HOREB

The Waunwyllt Inn
Horeb Road, Five Roads, Horeb, Llanelli, Carmarthenshire SA15 5AQ
☎ *(01269) 860209* Shaun Pawson

A freehouse with four pumps serving a constantly changing selection of real ales. Popular recent brews include Shepherd Neame Bishop's Finger, Everards Tiger and others from Cottage, Brecknock and Tomos Watkin.

A popular country inn in a quiet hamlet outside Llanelli. Close to the Celtic Trail cycle route. Large beer garden, non-smoking dining area, five en suite bedrooms. Food available at lunchtime and evenings. Children allowed. From Llanelli, take the B4309 towards Carmarthen.

11am–11pm Mon–Sat and 12–10.30pm Sun in summer; 12–3pm and 6.30–11pm in winter.

LLANDEILO

The Castle Hotel
113 Rhosmaen Street, Llandeilo, Dyfed
SA19 6EN
☎ *(01558) 823446* Mark Wilby

A Tomas Watkins tied house with Whoosh, Best, Old Special Brew and Merlin's Stout permanently available. Other seasonal guests rotated on one hand pump.

A town-centre pub with two bars serving five adjoining rooms, 65-seater restaurant, beer garden. Bar and restaurant food served lunchtimes and evenings. Children allowed. Tours of Tomas Watkins available.

All day, every day.

LLANSAINT

The King's Arms
13 Maes y Eglwys, Llansaint, Nr. Kidwelly, Carmarthenshire SA17 5JE
☎ *(01267) 267487* Mr Cairns

Shepherd Neame Bishop's Finger and Wadworth 6X permanently available, plus rotating guests.

A traditional country pub in a tucked-away location. Dining area and a cwtsh-cornel (a cosy corner in English!). Big on food which served at lunchtimes and evenings. Children allowed.

12-3pm and 6-11pm (10.30pm Sun).

MYNYDD Y GARREG

The Prince of Wales
Heol Meinciau, Mynydd y Garreg, Kidwelly, Carmarthenshire, SA17 4RP
☎ *(01554) 890522* Gail and Richard Pickett

Six beers always available from a list that includes brews from Wye Valley, Bullmastiff, Black Sheep, Cottage and various Welsh micro-breweries. Please phone ahead for details of beers currently on tap.

A 200-year-old cottage pub with a collection of cinema memorabilia and bric-à-brac. Bar and restaurant food available at lunchtime and evenings. Car park and garden. Take the Mynydd y Garreg turn from the Cydweli bypass, then just over a mile on the right.

5–11pm (10.30pm Sun).

NARBETH

The Kirkland Arms

East Gate, St James Street, Narbeth, Dyfed
SA67 7DB
☎ *(01834) 860423 Mr Edger*

🍺 A Felinfoel Brewery tied pub with guest beers rotated on one pump. These might include York Yorkshire Terrier, Swansea Bishopswood Bitter, Wadworth 6X and many others changed on a weekly basis.

A n old, traditional pub with pool table, games machines and beer garden. No food. Children allowed.

🍺 *11am–11pm Mon–Sat; 12–10.30pm Sun.*

PEMBROKE

The Castle Inn

17 Main Street, Pembroke, Pembrokeshire
SA71 4JS
☎ *(01646) 682883 Nigel Temple*

🍺 A freehouse usually serving Charles Wells Bombardier and Wadworth 6X plus up to two guests.

A very old pub with long and narrow stone walls and beams. No food. Children allowed.

🍺 *11am–11pm Mon–Sat; 12–10.30pm Sun.*

The First & Last

London Road, Pembroke Dock, Pembrokeshire
SA72 6TX
☎ *(01646) 682687 Richard Maynard*

🍺 A freehouse with Charles Wells Bombardier or Brains SA usually available plus one other.

A local community pub with beer garden. Light lunches only served. Children allowed at lunchtime only.

🍺 *11am–11pm Mon–Sat; 12–10.30pm Sun.*

YOU TELL US

★ *The Brittannia Inn,* Pentre Road, Halkyn, Holywell, Flintshire
★ *The Bull Hotel,* Chapel Street, Abergele, Conwy
★ *The Carpenter's Arms,* Usk Road, Shirenewton, Chepstow, Gwent
★ *The Castle Hotel,* 113 Rhosmaen Street, Llandeilo, Dyfed
★ *The Crown Hotel,* Church Street, Boderdern, Holyhead, Gwynedd
★ *Garrd Fon,* Beach Road, Felinheli, Gwynedd
★ *Gawain and the Green Knight,* Golftyn Lane, Connah's Quay, Deeside, Clwyd
★ *Llynfi Arms,* Maesteg Road, Tondu, Bridgend, Mid Glamorgan
★ *The Nag's Head,* Abercych, Pembrokeshire
★ *The New Inn,* Bedwellty, Blackwood, Gwent
★ *The Pilot Boat,* Dulas, Gwynedd
★ *Pont-Y-Pair Hotel,* Holyhead Road, Betwys-Y-Coed, Conwy
★ *The Red Lion,* Cyffylliog, Ruthin, Denbighshire
★ *The Rock Inn,* Llec, Holywell, Flintshire
★ *The Skirrid Mountain Inn,* Llanvihanfel Crucorney, Abergavenny, Gwent
★ *Stonecroft Inn,* Dolecoed Terrace, Llanwrtyd Wells, Powys
★ *The Wheatsheaf Inn,* Betws-Yn-Rhos, Abergele, Conwy
★ *The White Hart Inn,* Llanddarog (brewpub)
★ *Wynnstay Arms Hotel,* Maengwyn Street, Macgynlleth, Powys
★ *Ye Olde Talbot Inn,* Cymau Road, Cymau, Wrexham

Places Featured:
Bangor
Belfast

Hillsborough

THE BREWERIES

HILDEN BREWERY

Hilden House, Grand Street, Hilden, Lisburn BT27 4TY
☎ *(01846) 663863*

GREAT NORTHERN PORTER 4.0% ABV
HILDEN ALE 4.0% ABV
MOLLY MALONE 4.6% ABV
SPECIAL RESERVE 4.6% ABV
Plus occasional brews.

THE PUBS

BANGOR

Esplanade Bar

12 Ballyhome Esplanade, Bangor, Co Down BT20 5LZ
☎ *(01247) 270954* Maurice Smith

A freehouse with Cains Traditional always available plus one weekly rotating guest, perhaps a Caledonian or Tom Wood ale.

A public bar with TV and juke box, dining area and restaurant. Food available at lunchtime and evenings. Children allowed.

All day, every day.

BELFAST

Beaten Docket

48 Great Victoria Street, Belfast, Co Antrim BT2 7BB
☎ *(01232) 242986* Joseph McLarnon

Beers from Whitewater, Cains and Tom Wood breweries plus guests such as Wadworth Old Timer.

A designer-style pub with lots of mahogany and brass. Food served daily 10am–7pm. Children allowed. Opposite the railway station.

All day, every day.

HILLSBOROUGH

Hillside Restaurant & Bar

21 Main Street, Hillsborough, Co Down BT26 6AE
☎ *(01846) 382765* Ian Carmichael

Whitewater Solstice Pale Ale and Belfast Special always available, plus two guests guests such as Hop Back GFB.

A pub with bistro and à la carte restaurant serving food at lunchtime and evenings. Children allowed.

All day, every day.

YOU TELL US

★ *The Anchor Bar,* 9 Bryansford Road, Newcastle
★ *The Botanic Inn,* 23–7 Malone Road, Belfast
★ *The Burrendale Hotel,* Castlewellan Road, Newcastle
★ *The Dirty Duck,* 2 Kennegar Road, Holywood
★ *The Kitchen Bar,* 16 Victoria Square, Belfast
★ *Lavery's Gin Palace,* 12–16 Bradbury Place, Belfast
★ *Monico Bars,* 17 Lombard Street, Belfast
★ *Portside Inn,* 1 Dargan Road, Belfast
★ *The White Horse Inn,* 49–53 Main Street, Saintfield
★ *Woody's Cellars,* 607 Shore Road, Newtownabby, Co Antrim

Places Featured:

JERSEY
St Brelade
St Helier
St Laurence
St Ouen

St Peter's Village

GUERNSEY
St Peter Port

THE BREWERIES

THE GUERNSEY BREWERY CO. LTD

South Esplanade, St Peter Port, Guernsey GY1 1BJ
☎ *(01481) 720143*

 BRAYE MILD 3.7% ABV
Malty, toffee flavour. Balancing hops.
SUNBEAM BITTER 4.2% ABV
Smooth, well-balanced. Dry bitter finish.
Plus seasonal brews.

RW RANDALL LTD

PO Box 154, Vauxlaurens Brewery, St Julian's Avenue, St Peter Port, Guernsey GY1 3JG
☎ *(01481) 720134*

MILD 3.4% ABV
PATOIS ALE 5.0% ABV
Plus occasional brews.

THE PUBS

JERSEY

ST BRELADE

The Old Smugglers Inn

Ouaisne Bay, St Brelade, Jersey JE3 8AW
☎ *(01534) 41510* Nigel Godfrey

A freehouse usually serving ales from the Ringwood Brewery and occasional others from Brains, Randalls and elsewhere.

A very olde-worlde traditional country pub with no music or machines. Two bar areas and restaurant. Food served at lunchtime and evenings. Children allowed.

OPEN *All day, every day.*

ST HELIER

The Tipsy Toad Townhouse

57–9 New Street, St Helier, Jersey
☎ *(01534) 615000* Colin Manning

Mostly serves a selection of keg ales from The Jersey Brewery, but still worth a visit as Tipsy Toad Brewery's Jimmy's Bitter is also permanently available.

A pub in a converted warehouse with three function rooms for live music etc. Winner of CAMRA's Pub of the Year award. Bar and restaurant food available at lunchtime and evenings. Parking nearby. Children allowed.

OPEN *11am–11pm.*

ST LAWRENCE

The British Union

Main Road, St Lawrence, Jersey JE3 1NL
☎ *(01534) 861070* Alan Cheshire

Guernsey Bitter and other Guernsey brews always available.

An open-plan pub with two bars and games room. Small beer garden. Food available at lunchtime and evenings. Children allowed. Opposite St Lawrence Church

All day, every day.

ST OUEN

Le Moulin de Lecq

Greve de Lecq, St Ouen, Jersey JE3 2DT
☎ *(01534) 482818* Shaun Lynch

Guernsey Sunbeam and Tipsy Toad Jimmy's Bitter available plus occasional others from Tipsy Toad and Guernsey Breweries.

Built around a twelfth-century flour mill with working parts inside and outside the bar. One bar and small upstairs lounge, large outside seating area and adventure playground. Summer barbecues. Food served every lunchtime and Mon–Sat evenings. Children welcome. In the north-west of the island.

OPEN *All day, every day.*

The Star

La Grande Route de St Pierre, St Peter's Village,
Jersey JE3 7AA
☎ *(01534) 485556*

Home of The Tipsy Toad Brewery. One cask ale is permanently brewed on the premises, plus seasonal specials.

J ersey's first brewpub is situated in renovated and restored Victorian premises. The result is a cosy pub with a family atmosphere. The brewing process can be observed through a wall of windows. Bar food is available at lunchtime and evenings. Family room and conservatory, outdoor children's play area. Baby-changing facilities and disabled toilets.

JIMMY'S BITTER 4.2% ABV
DIXIES WHEAT BEER 4.1% ABV (Summer).
NAOMH PADRAIG'S PORTER 4.4% ABV (Autumn).
FESTIVE TOAD 8.0% ABV (Christmas).

10am–11.30pm.

★ *Anne Port Bay Hotel,* Anne Port Bay, St Martin, Jersey
★ *Cock & Bull,* 2 Lower Hautville, St Peter Port, Guernsey
★ *The Coronation Inn,* 36 High Street, St Anne, Alderney
★ *Fleur Du Jardin,* Kings Mills, Castel, Guernsey
★ *L'Auberge Divette,* Jerbourg, St Martins, Guernsey
★ *Lamplighter,* Mulcaster Street, St Helier, Jersey

The Drunken Duck

The Charroterie, St Peter Port, Guernsey
GY1 1EL
☎ *(01481) 725045 Marita Priaulx*

One of two freehouses bringing guest beers into Guernsey. A Ringwood brew is always available plus two guest beers (80 per year) which might include Hop Back Summer Lightning and Wheat Beer, Morland Old Speckled Hen, Hadrian Centurian and Shepherd Neame Spitfire.

A small, friendly pub for young and old. Live music each week. Food available all day from 12pm. Parking from 5pm. Bar billiards.

11am–11.45pm Mon–Sat; 12–3.30pm Sun.

★ *Le Friquet Hotel,* Castel, Guernsey
★ *Nellie's Garden Bistro,* Victoria Street, St Anne, Alderney
★ *The Prince of Wales,* Manor Place, St Peter Port, Guernsey
★ *The Prince of Wales Tavern,* Hilgrove Street, St Helier, Jersey
★ *The Royal Hotel,* Le Grande Route de Faldouet, St Martin, Jersey
★ *Seymour Inn,* La Rocque, Grouville, Jersey
★ *The Ship & Crown,* Pier Steps, Esplanade, St Peter Port, Guernsey
★ *The Venture Inn,* Rue de la Villiaze, Forest, Guernsey

The White House

2 Tynwald Road, Peel IM5 1LA
☎ *(01624) 842252 Jamie Keig*

A freehouse serving Arkells Mild and Bitter, Bushy's Bitter and Timothy Taylor Landlord plus regular guests often from Timothy Taylor.

A traditional pub with one main bar and four small adjoining rooms. Live local music every Saturday. TV. Light bar snacks served in the bar area. Children allowed until 9pm.

11am-11pm Mon-Fri; 11am-12am Sat.

★ *The Albert,* Chapel Row, Douglas
★ *The Old Market Inn,* Chapel Row, Douglas
★ *The Queen's Hotel,* Laxey
★ *The Raven,* Main Road, Ballaugh
★ *Saddle Inn,* Queen Street, Douglas
★ *Samuel Webb,* Marina Road, Douglas
★ *The Shore Hotel,* Shore Road, Laxey (brewpub)
★ *The Sidings,* Victoria Road, Castletown
★ *The Stanley Hotel,* West Quay, Ramsey
★ *The Trafalgar,* West Quay, Ramsey
★ *The Tramshunters Arms,* Sefton Hotel, Harris Promenade, Douglas

INDEX OF BREWERIES

READER RECOMMENDATIONS

Research for the next edition of the guide is already underway and, to ensure that it will be as comprehensive and up-to-date as possible, we should be grateful for your help.

We hope that you will agree that every pub included this year is in the book on merit, but ownership and operation can change both for better and for worse. Equally, there are bound to be hidden gems that have so far escaped our attention and that really ought to be included next time around.

So, if what you discover does not live up to expectations, or if you know of another pub that we cannot afford to be without, please let us know. Either fill in the forms below or send your views on a separate piece of paper to:

The Editor, The Real Ale Pub Guide
Foulsham, Bennetts Close, Slough, Berkshire, SL1 5AP.

Alternatively, you can visit our web site at www.foulsham.com and leave us your comments.

Please let us know if you would like additional forms. Every reply will be entered into a draw for one of five free copies of next year's guide. Thank you very much for your help.

Pub name: _____   Already in   Yes ☐
Address: _____   the guide?   No ☐

Comments: _____
_____
_____
_____

Your name: _____
Your address: _____
_____
_____ Tel: _____

Pub name: _____   Already in   Yes ☐
Address: _____   the guide?   No ☐

Comments: _____
_____
_____
_____

Your name: _____
Your address: _____
_____
_____ Tel: _____

Pub name: _____

Address: _____

Already in   Yes ☐
the guide?   No ☐

Comments: _____

_____

_____

Your name: _____

Your address: _____

_____ Tel: _____

Pub name: _____

Address: _____

Already in   Yes ☐
the guide?   No ☐

Comments: _____

_____

_____

Your name: _____

Your address: _____

_____ Tel: _____

Pub name: _____

Address: _____

Already in   Yes ☐
the guide?   No ☐

Comments: _____

_____

_____

Your name: _____

Your address: _____

_____ Tel: _____

Pub name: _____

Address: _____

Already in Yes ☐
the guide? No ☐

Comments: _____

_____

_____

Your name: _____

Your address: _____

_____ Tel: _____

Pub name: _____

Address: _____

Already in Yes ☐
the guide? No ☐

Comments: _____

_____

_____

Your name: _____

Your address: _____

_____ Tel: _____

Pub name: _____

Address: _____

Already in Yes ☐
the guide? No ☐

Comments: _____

_____

_____

Your name: _____

Your address: _____

_____ Tel: _____

QUESTIONNAIRE

Pub name: _____ Already in Yes ☐
Address: _____ the guide? No ☐

_____

Comments: _____
_____
_____
_____

Your name: _____
Your address: _____
_____
_____ Tel: _____

Pub name: _____ Already in Yes ☐
Address: _____ the guide? No ☐

_____

Comments: _____
_____
_____
_____

Your name: _____
Your address: _____
_____
_____ Tel: _____

Pub name: _____ Already in Yes ☐
Address: _____ the guide? No ☐

_____

Comments: _____
_____
_____
_____

Your name: _____
Your address: _____
_____
_____ Tel: _____

Pub name: _____

Address: _____

Already in Yes ☐
the guide? No ☐

Comments: _____

_____

_____

_____

Your name: _____

Your address: _____

_____

_____ Tel: _____

Pub name: _____

Address: _____

Already in Yes ☐
the guide? No ☐

Comments: _____

_____

_____

_____

Your name: _____

Your address: _____

_____

_____ Tel: _____

Pub name: _____

Address: _____

Already in Yes ☐
the guide? No ☐

Comments: _____

_____

_____

_____

Your name: _____

Your address: _____

_____

_____ Tel: _____

QUESTIONNAIRE

Pub name: _____   Already in   Yes ☐
Address: _____   the guide?   No ☐

Comments: _____
_____
_____
_____

Your name: _____
Your address: _____
_____
_____ Tel: _____

Pub name: _____   Already in   Yes ☐
Address: _____   the guide?   No ☐

Comments: _____
_____
_____
_____

Your name: _____
Your address: _____
_____
_____ Tel: _____

Pub name: _____   Already in   Yes ☐
Address: _____   the guide?   No ☐

Comments: _____
_____
_____
_____

Your name: _____
Your address: _____
_____
_____ Tel: _____

Pub name: _____

Address: _____

Already in Yes ☐
the guide? No ☐

Comments: _____
_____
_____
_____

Your name: _____

Your address: _____
_____

Tel: _____

Pub name: _____

Address: _____

Already in Yes ☐
the guide? No ☐

Comments: _____
_____
_____
_____

Your name: _____

Your address: _____
_____

Tel: _____

Pub name: _____

Address: _____

Already in Yes ☐
the guide? No ☐

Comments: _____
_____
_____
_____

Your name: _____

Your address: _____
_____

Tel: _____